Prentice Hall

Course 1 MATHEMATICS
Common Core

Charles
Illingworth
McNemar
Mills
Ramirez
Reeves

Taken from:

Prentice Hall Mathematics, Course 1, Global Edition
by Randall I. Charles, Mark Illingworth, Bonnie McNemar,
Darwin Mills, Alma Ramirez, and Andy Reeves

Prentice Hall Mathematics, Common Core, Course 1, Student Edition

PEARSON

Front Cover: Wolfgang Kaehler/CORBIS
Back Cover: Ian Cartwright/Getty Images.

Taken from:
Prentice Hall Mathematics Course 1, Global Edition
by Randall I. Charles, Mark Illingworth, Bonnie McNemar, Darwin Mills, Alma Ramirez and Andy Reeves

Published by Prentice Hall
Upper Saddle River, New Jersey 07458

Prentice Hall Mathematics Course 1, Common Core Edition
by Randall I. Charles, Mark Illingworth, Bonnie McNemar, Darwin Mills, Alma Ramirez and Andy Reeves

Published by Prentice Hall

Pearson Learning Solutions, 501 Boylston Street, Suite 900, Boston, MA 02116
A Pearson Education Company
www.pearsoned.com

Printed in the United States of America

10 17

000200010271649883

SD/TY

ISBN 10: 1-256-73716-X
ISBN 13: 978-1-256-73716-2

Authors

Series Author

Randall I. Charles, Ph.D., is Professor Emeritus in the Department of Mathematics and Computer Science at San Jose State University, San Jose, California. He began his career as a high school mathematics teacher, and he was a mathematics supervisor for five years. Dr. Charles has been a member of several NCTM committees and is the former Vice President of the National Council of Supervisors of Mathematics. Much of his writing and research has been in the area of problem solving. He has authored more than 75 mathematics textbooks for kindergarten through college.
Scott Foresman-Prentice Hall Mathematics Series Author Kindergarten through Algebra 2

Program Authors

Mark Illingworth has taught in both elementary and high school math programs for more than twenty years. During this time, he received the Christa McAuliffe sabbatical to develop problem solving materials and projects for middle grades math students, and he was granted the Presidential Award for Excellence in Mathematics Teaching. Mr. Illingworth's specialty is in teaching mathematics through applications and problem solving. He has written two books on these subjects and has contributed to math and science textbooks at Prentice Hall.

Bonnie McNemar is a mathematics educator with more than 30 years' experience in Texas schools as a teacher, administrator, and consultant. She began her career as a middle school mathematics teacher and served as a supervisor at the district, county, and state levels. Ms. McNemar was the director of the Texas Mathematics Staff Development Program, now known as TEXTEAMS, for five years, and she was the first director of the Teachers Teaching with Technology (T^3) Program. She remains active in both of these organizations as well as in several local, state, and national mathematics organizations, including NCTM.

Darwin Mills, an administrator for the public school system in Newport News, Virginia, has been involved in secondary level mathematics education for more than fourteen years. Mr. Mills has served as a high school teacher, a community college adjunct professor, a department chair, and a district level mathematics supervisor. He has received numerous teaching awards, including teacher of the year for 1999–2000, and an Excellence in Teaching award from the College of Wooster, Ohio, in 2002. He is a frequent presenter at workshops and conferences. He believes that all students can learn mathematics if given the proper instruction.

Alma Ramirez is co-director of the Mathematics Case Project at WestEd, a nonprofit educational institute in Oakland, California. A former bilingual elementary and middle school teacher, Ms. Ramirez has considerable expertise in mathematics teaching and learning, second language acquisition, and professional development. She has served as a consultant on a variety of projects and has extensive experience as an author for elementary and middle grades texts. In addition, her work has appeared in the 2004 NCTM Yearbook. Ms. Ramirez is a frequent presenter at professional meetings and conferences.

Andy Reeves, Ph.D., teaches at the University of South Florida in St. Petersburg. His career in education spans 30 years and includes seven years as a middle grades teacher. He subsequently served as Florida's K–12 mathematics supervisor, and more recently he supervised the publication of The Mathematics Teacher, Mathematics Teaching in the Middle School, and Teaching Children Mathematics for NCTM. Prior to entering education, he worked as an engineer for Douglas Aircraft.

Contributing Author

Denisse R. Thompson, Ph.D., is a Professor of Mathematics Education at the University of South Florida. She has particular interests in the connections between literature and mathematics and in the teaching and learning of mathematics in the middle grades. Dr. Thompson contributed to the Guided Problem Solving features.

Reviewers

Course 1 Reviewers

Donna Anderson
Math Supervisor, 7–12
West Hartford Public Schools
West Hartford, Connecticut

Nancy L. Borchers
West Clermont Local Schools
Cincinnati, Ohio

Kathleen Chandler
Walnut Creek Middle School
Erie, Pennsylvania

Jane E. Damaske
Lakeshore Public Schools
Stevensville, Michigan

Frank Greco
Parkway South Middle School
Manchester, Missouri

Rebecca L. Jones
Odyssey Middle School
Orlando, Florida

Marylee R. Liebowitz
H. C. Crittenden Middle School
Armonk, New York

Kathy Litz
K. O. Knudson Middle School
Las Vegas, Nevada

Don McGurrin
Wake County Public School System
Raleigh, North Carolina

Ron Mezzadri
K–12 Mathematics Supervisor
Fair Lawn School District
Fair Lawn, New Jersey

Sylvia O. Reeder-Tucker
Prince George's County Math Department
Upper Marlboro, Maryland

Julie A. White
Allison Traditional Magnet Middle School
Wichita, Kansas

Charles Yochim
Bronxville Middle School
Bronxville, New York

Course 2 Reviewers

Cami Craig
Prince William County Public Schools
Marsteller Middle School
Bristow, Virginia

Donald O. Cram
Lincoln Middle School
Rio Rancho, New Mexico

Pat A. Davidson
Jacksonville Junior High School
Jacksonville, Arkansas

Yvette Drew
DeKalb County School System
Open Campus High School
Atlanta, Georgia

Robert S. Fair
K–12 District Mathematics Coordinator
Cherry Creek School District
Greenwood Village, Colorado

Michael A. Landry
Glastonbury Public Schools
Glastonbury, Connecticut

Nancy Ochoa
Weeden Middle School
Florence, Alabama

Charlotte J. Phillips
Wichita USD 259
Wichita, Kansas

Mary Lynn Raith
Mathematics Curriculum Specialist
Pittsburgh Public Schools
Pittsburgh, Pennsylvania

Tammy Rush
Consultant, Middle School Mathematics
Hillsborough County Schools
Tampa, Florida

Judith R. Russ
Prince George's County Public Schools
Capitol Heights, Maryland

Tim Tate
Math/Science Supervisor
Lafayette Parish School System
Lafayette, Louisiana

Dondi J. Thompson
Alcott Middle School
Norman, Oklahoma

Candace Yamagata
Hyde Park Middle School
Las Vegas, Nevada

Course 3 Reviewers

Linda E. Addington
Andrew Lewis Middle School
Salem, Virginia

Jeanne Arnold
Mead Junior High School
Schaumburg, Illinois

Sheila S. Brookshire
A. C. Reynolds Middle School
Asheville, North Carolina

Jennifer Clark
Mayfield Middle School
Putnam City Public Schools
Oklahoma City, Oklahoma

Nicole Dial
Chase Middle School
Topeka, Kansas

Christine Ferrell
Lorin Andrews Middle School
Massillon, Ohio

Virginia G. Harrell
Education Consultant
Hillsborough County, Florida

Jonita P. Howard
Mathematics Curriculum Specialist
Lauderdale Lakes Middle School
Lauderdale Lakes, Florida

Patricia Lemons
Rio Rancho Middle School
Rio Rancho, New Mexico

Susan Noce
Robert Frost Junior High School
Schaumburg, Illinois

Carla A. Siler
South Bend Community School Corp.
South Bend, Indiana

Kathryn E. Smith-Lance
West Genesee Middle School
Camillus, New York

Kathleen D. Tuffy
South Middle School
Braintree, Massachusetts

Patricia R. Wilson
Central Middle School
Murfreesboro, Tennessee

Patricia Young
Northwood Middle School
Pulaski County Special School District
North Little Rock, Arkansas

Content Consultants

Ann Bell
Mathematics
Prentice Hall Consultant
Franklin, Tennessee

Blanche Brownley
Mathematics
Prentice Hall Consultant
Olney, Maryland

Joe Brumfield
Mathematics
Prentice Hall Consultant
Altadena, California

Linda Buckhalt
Mathematics
Prentice Hall Consultant
Derwood, Maryland

Andrea Gordon
Mathematics
Prentice Hall Consultant
Atlanta, Georgia

Eleanor Lopes
Mathematics
Prentice Hall Consultant
New Castle, Delaware

Sally Marsh
Mathematics
Prentice Hall Consultant
Baltimore, Maryland

Bob Pacyga
Mathematics
Prentice Hall Consultant
Darien, Illinois

Judy Porter
Mathematics
Prentice Hall Consultant
Raleigh, North Carolina

Rose Primiani
Mathematics
Prentice Hall Consultant
Harbor City, New Jersey

Jayne Radu
Mathematics
Prentice Hall Consultant
Scottsdale, Arizona

Pam Revels
Mathematics
Prentice Hall Consultant
Sarasota, Florida

Barbara Rogers
Mathematics
Prentice Hall Consultant
Raleigh, North Carolina

Michael Seals
Mathematics
Prentice Hall Consultant
Edmond, Oklahoma

Margaret Thomas
Mathematics
Prentice Hall Consultant
Indianapolis, Indiana

From the Authors

Dear Student,

We have designed this unique mathematics program with you in mind. We hope that Prentice Hall Mathematics will help you make sense of the mathematics you learn. We want to enable you to tap into the power of mathematics.

Examples in each lesson are broken into steps to help you understand how and why math works. Work the examples so that you understand the concepts and the methods presented. Then do your homework. Ask yourself how new concepts relate to old ones. Make connections! As you practice the concepts presented in this text, they will become part of your mathematical power.

The many real-world applications will let you see how you can use math in your daily life and give you the foundation for the math you will need in the future. The applications you will find in every lesson will help you see why it is important to learn mathematics. In addition, the Dorling Kindersley Real-World Snapshots will bring the world to your classroom.

This text will help you be successful on the tests you take in class and on high-stakes tests required by your state. The practice in each lesson will prepare you for the format as well as for the content of these tests.

Ask your teacher questions! Someone else in your class has the same question in mind and will be grateful that you decided to ask it.

We wish you the best as you use this text. The mathematics you learn this year will prepare you for your future as a student and your future in our technological society.

Sincerely,

Randy Charles. Andy Reeves
Darwin E. Mills Mark Illingworth
Bonnie McNemar Alma Beatriz Ramirez

Contents in Brief

About the Common Core State Standards

In 2009, members of the National Governors Association agreed to work together to develop standards for mathematics and English language arts that many states would adopt. Having the same standards from one state to the next would make it much easier when students and their families move to a new school in a different state. The governors agreed to work with the National Governors' Association Center for Best Practices and the Council for Chief State School Officers to develop these standards.

The **Common Core State Standards for Mathematics** (CCSSM) were released in June 2010. Over 40 states have already adopted them. Schools and school districts are now working on plans to implement these standards. Teachers and administrators are developing curricula that teach the concepts and skills required at each grade level.

The CCSSM consist of two sets of standards, the Standards for Mathematical Practice and the Standards for Mathematical Content. The **Standards for Mathematical Practice** describe the processes, practices, and dispositions of mathematicians. These eight Standards for Mathematical Practice are the same across all grade levels, K–12 to emphasize that students are developing these processes, practices, and dispositions throughout their school career.

The **Standards for Mathematical Practice** are shown below.

1. Make sense of mathematics and persevere in solving them.
2. Reason abstractly and quantitatively.
3. Construct viable arguments and critique the reasoning of others.
4. Model with mathematics.
5. Use appropriate tools strategically.
6. Attend to precision.
7. Look for and make use of structure.
8. Look for and express regularity in repeated reasoning.

The **Standards for Mathematical Content** outline the concepts and skills that are important at each grade level. At Grade 6, these standards focus on these areas:

- Ratios and Proportional Relationships
- The Number System
- Expressions and Equations
- Geometry
- Statistics and Probability

These are many of the same topics that middle grade students have been studying for many years. One big difference, however, is that the Standards for Mathematical Content contain fewer standards and fewer topics to study at each grade level. With fewer topics, you can spend more time on concepts and achieve greater mastery of these concepts.

Assessing the Common Core State Standards

Partnership for Assessment of Readiness for College and Careers (PARCC)

The PARCC assessment system will be made up of Performance-Based Assessments and an End-of-Year or End-of-Course Assessment.

The **Performance-Based Assessment** will be an extended, multi-session performance-based assessment. It will focus on assessing students' proficiency with applying math content and skills learned throughout the school year. Students will be expected to complete two different tasks.

- They will be administered in the third quarter of the school year.
- Students will submit their responses on computers or other digital devices.
- The scoring will be a combination of computer-scored and human-scored.

The **End-of-Year Assessment** will assess all of the standards at the grade level. It will measure students' conceptual understanding, procedural fluency, and problem solving.
- It will be taken online during the last 4 to 6 weeks of the school year.
- It will have 40 to 65 items, with a range of item types (i.e., selected-response, constructed-response, performance tasks) and cognitive demand.
- It will be entirely computer-scored.

A student's score will be based on his or her scores on the Performance-Based Assessment and the End-of-Year Assessment. This score will be used for the purposes of accountability. PARCC will also make available aligned formative assessments that teachers can use in the classroom throughout the school year.

SMARTER Balanced Assessment Consortium (SBAC)

The SBAC summative assessment system consists of performance tasks and one End-of-Year Adaptive Assessment.
- Performance tasks: You will complete up to two performance tasks during the last 12 weeks of the school year. These tasks will measure your ability to integrate knowledge and skills from the CCSSM. You will take these assessments primarily on computers or other digital devices.
- The End-of-Year Assessment will also be administered during the last 12 weeks of the school year. It will be made up of 40 to 65 items, with a range of item types (i.e., selected-response, constructed-response, performance tasks). Some items will be computer-scored while others will be human-scored.

Your summative score will be based on your scores on the Performance Tasks and the End-of-Year Adaptive Assessment.

Number Properties and Decimals

In this chapter, you will fluently add, subtract, multiply, and divide decimals using standard algorithms. You will also identify the parts of an expression using mathematical terms and evaluate numerical expressions using the order of operations.

Expressions & Equations
6.EE.2.b
6.EE.2.c
6.EE.3

The Number System
6.NS.2
6.NS.3

Assessment and Test Prep

Expressions and Equations

In this chapter, you will extend your understanding of arithmetic to algebraic expressions and equations. You will use letters as variables to represent unknown numerical values and write expressions and solve equations of the form $x + p = q$ and $px = q$.

Expressions & Equations

6.EE.2
6.EE.2.a
6.EE.2.b
6.EE.2.c
6.EE.5
6.EE.6
6.EE.7

Assessment and Test Prep

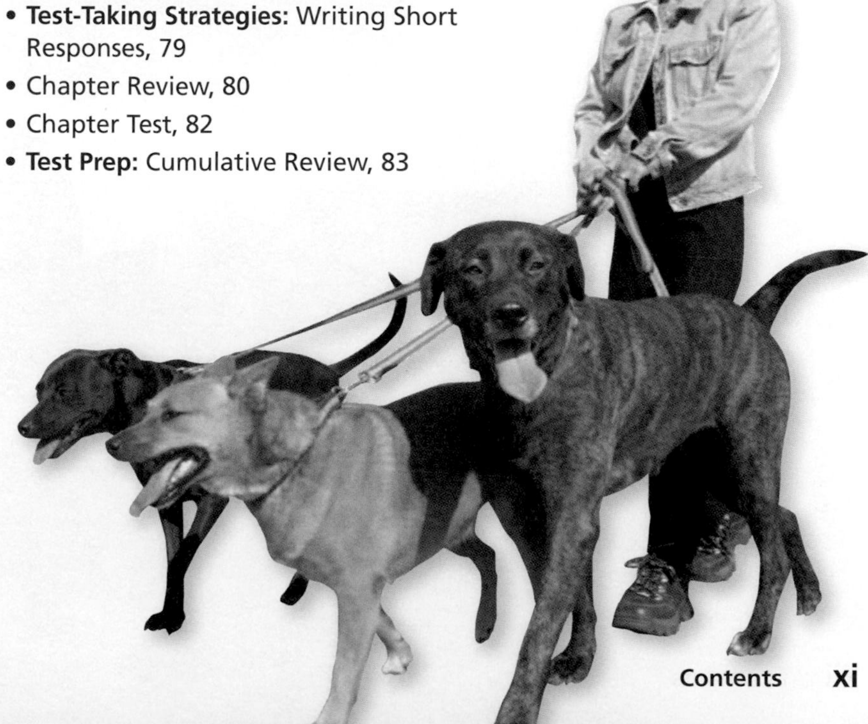

Number Theory

COMMON CORE STATE STANDARDS

In this chapter, you will apply your understanding of place value, operations, and inverse properties of operations to explore algebraic number theory. You will find the greatest common factor and least common multiple of two whole numbers. You will also use the distributive property and identify when two expressions are equivalent.

The Number System
6.NS.4

Expressions & Equations
6.EE.1
6.EE.2
6.EE.2.b
6.EE.2.c
6.EE.3
6.EE.4

Fraction Operations

Assessment and Test Prep

COMMON CORE STATE STANDARDS

In this chapter, you will apply and extend previous understandings of multiplication and division of fractions. You will draw on your knowledge of operations, fractions, multiples, and factors to multiply and divide fractions and mixed numbers. You will apply these skills as you write and solve equations involving multiplication and division of fractions.

The Number System
6.NS.1

Expressions & Equations
6.EE.6
6.EE.7

Ratios and Percents

COMMON CORE STATE STANDARDS

In this chapter, you will extend your knowledge of simplifying and computing with fractions as you explore the concept of ratios and unit rates. You will use ratios and rates to solve real-world and mathematical problems.

Ratios & Proportional Relationships

6.RP.1
6.RP.2
6.RP.3
6.RP.3.a
6.RP.3.b
6.RP.3.c
6.RP.3.d

Assessment and Test Prep

Integers and Rational Numbers

In this chapter, you will apply and extend previous understandings of numbers to the system of rational numbers. You will use number lines to order and compare integers and models to represent addition and subtraction of integers with same or different signs. You will also reason about and develop strategies for solving one-variable inequalities.

The Number System
- 6.NS.5
- 6.NS.6
- 6.NS.6.a
- 6.NS.6.c
- 6.NS.7.a
- 6.NS.7.b
- 6.NS.7.c
- 6.NS.7.d

Expressions & Equations
- 6.EE.5
- 6.EE.6
- 6.EE.8

The Coordinate Plane

In this chapter, you will extend your understanding of ordered pairs by graphing integers and functions containing integers on the coordinate plane. You will also represent and analyze quantitative relationships between dependent and independent variables. You will write functions with unknown variables to model and solve real-world problems.

The Number System

6.NS.6
6.NS.6.b
6.NS.6.c
6.NS.8

Expressions & Equations

6.EE.9

Geometry

6.G.3

Assessment and Test Prep

Geometry and Measurement

In this chapter, you will reason about the relationships among shapes as you use formulas to determine area, surface area, and volume of two- and three-dimensional shapes. You will find the area of triangles, special quadrilaterals, and polygons, and the volume of right rectangular prisms. You will also represent three-dimensional figures using nets made up of rectangles and triangles, and use the nets to find the surface area of these figures.

Geometry
- 6.G.1
- 6.G.2
- 6.G.4

Data and Graphs

In this chapter, you will develop an understanding of statistical variability and distributions. You will also display numerical data in plots and graphs, look for and use patterns in the data, and summarize numerical data sets based on their contexts.

Statistics & Probability

6.SP.1
6.SP.2
6.SP.3
6.SP.4
6.SP.5
6.SP.5.a
6.SP.5.b
6.SP.5.c
6.SP.5.d

Additional Features

Connect Your Learning

through problem solving, activities, and the Web

Applications: Real-World Applications

Applications: **Math at Work**

Applications: Interdisciplinary Connections

Activity Labs

Activity Labs: **Hands On**

Activity Labs: Technology

Activity Labs: Data Analysis

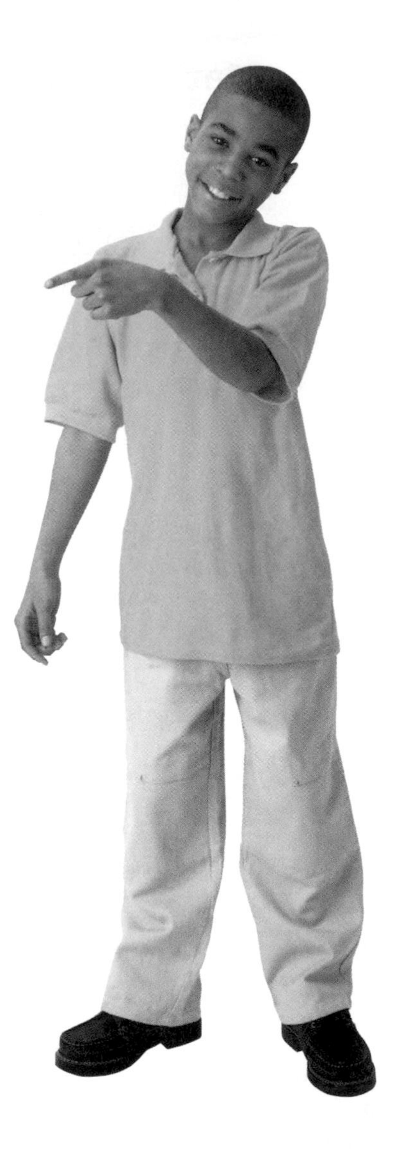

Activity Labs: Algebra Thinking

Activity Labs: Chapter Projects

Test-Taking Strategies

Guided Problem Solving Features

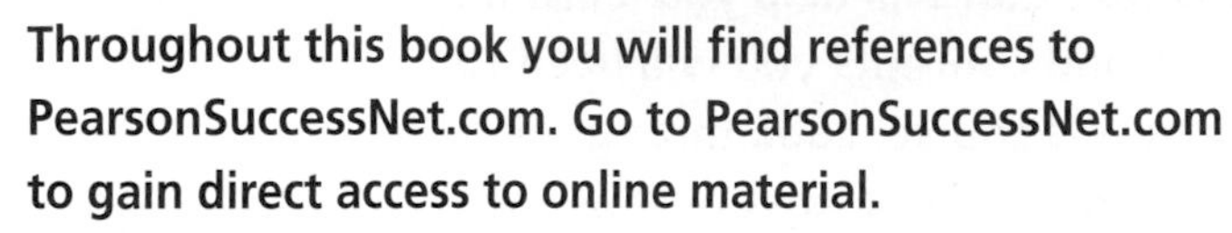

Throughout this book you will find references to PearsonSuccessNet.com. Go to PearsonSuccessNet.com to gain direct access to online material.

Lesson Features

Lesson Quizzes: There is an online quiz forevery lesson. Access these quizzes on PearsonSuccessNet.com.

Chapter Tests: For each chapter, a chapter test can be found online at PearsonSuccessNet.com.

Homework Video Tutor: For every lesson,there is additional support online to help studentscomplete their homework. Access the Homework VideoTutors on PearsonSuccessNet.com.

Additional Features

Video Tutor Help: Use PearsonSuccessNet.com to access engaging online instructional videos to help bring math concepts to life.

Data Updates: Use PearsonSuccessNet.com to get up-to-date government data for use in examples and exercises.

Math at Work: For information about each Math at Work feature, use PearsonSuccessNet.com.

Using Your Book for Success

Welcome to *Prentice Hall Course 1*.
There are many features built into the daily lessons of this text that will help you learn the important skills and concepts you will need to be successful in this course. Look through the following pages for some study tips that you will find useful as you complete each lesson.

Getting Ready to Learn

Check Your Readiness

Complete the *Check Your Readiness* exercises to see what topics you may need to review before you begin the chapter.

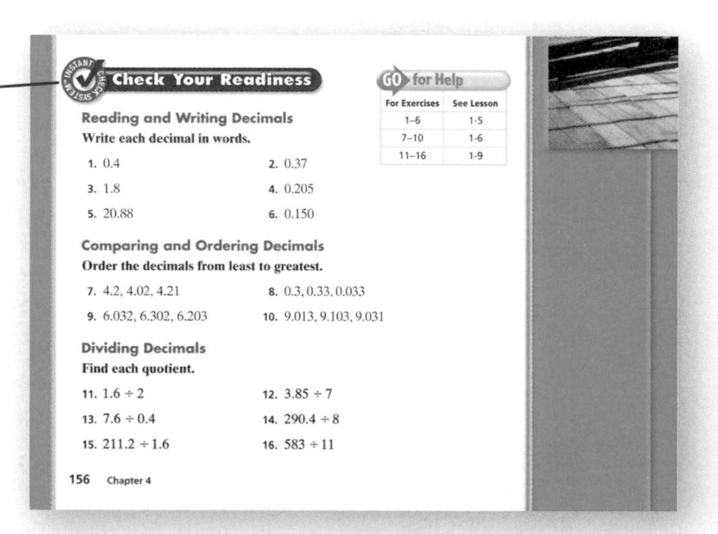

Check Your Readiness

GO for Help

For Exercises	See Lesson
1–6	1-5
7–10	1-6
11–16	1-9

Reading and Writing Decimals

Write each decimal in words.

1. 0.4
2. 0.37
3. 1.8
4. 0.205
5. 20.88
6. 0.150

Comparing and Ordering Decimals

Order the decimals from least to greatest.

7. 4.2, 4.02, 4.21
8. 0.3, 0.33, 0.033
9. 6.032, 6.302, 6.203
10. 9.013, 9.103, 9.031

Dividing Decimals

Find each quotient.

11. $1.6 \div 2$
12. $3.85 \div 7$
13. $7.6 \div 0.4$
14. $290.4 \div 8$
15. $211.2 \div 1.6$
16. $583 \div 11$

156 Chapter 4

Check Skills You'll Need

Complete the *Check Skills You'll Need* exercises to make sure you have the skills needed to successfully learn the concepts in the lesson.

New Vocabulary

New Vocabulary is listed for each lesson, so you can pre-read the text. As each term is introduced, it is highlighted in yellow.

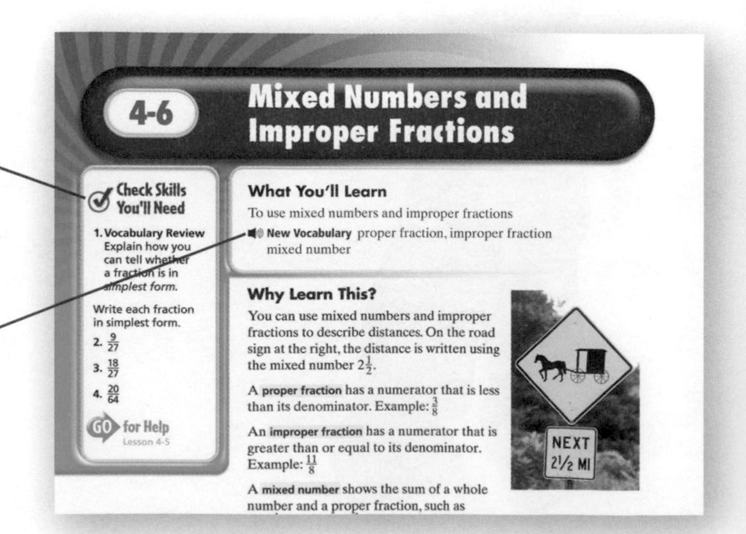

4-6 Mixed Numbers and Improper Fractions

Check Skills You'll Need

1. **Vocabulary Review** Explain how you can tell whether a fraction is in *simplest form*.

Write each fraction in simplest form.

2. $\frac{9}{27}$
3. $\frac{18}{27}$
4. $\frac{20}{64}$

GO for Help Lesson 4-5

What You'll Learn

To use mixed numbers and improper fractions

New Vocabulary proper fraction, improper fraction mixed number

Why Learn This?

You can use mixed numbers and improper fractions to describe distances. On the road sign at the right, the distance is written using the mixed number $2\frac{1}{2}$.

A **proper fraction** has a numerator that is less than its denominator. Example: $\frac{3}{8}$

An **improper fraction** has a numerator that is greater than or equal to its denominator. Example: $\frac{11}{8}$

A **mixed number** shows the sum of a whole number and a proper fraction, such as

Built-In Help

Go for Help

Look for the green labels throughout your book that tell you where to "Go" for help. You'll see this built-in help in the lessons and in the homework exercises.

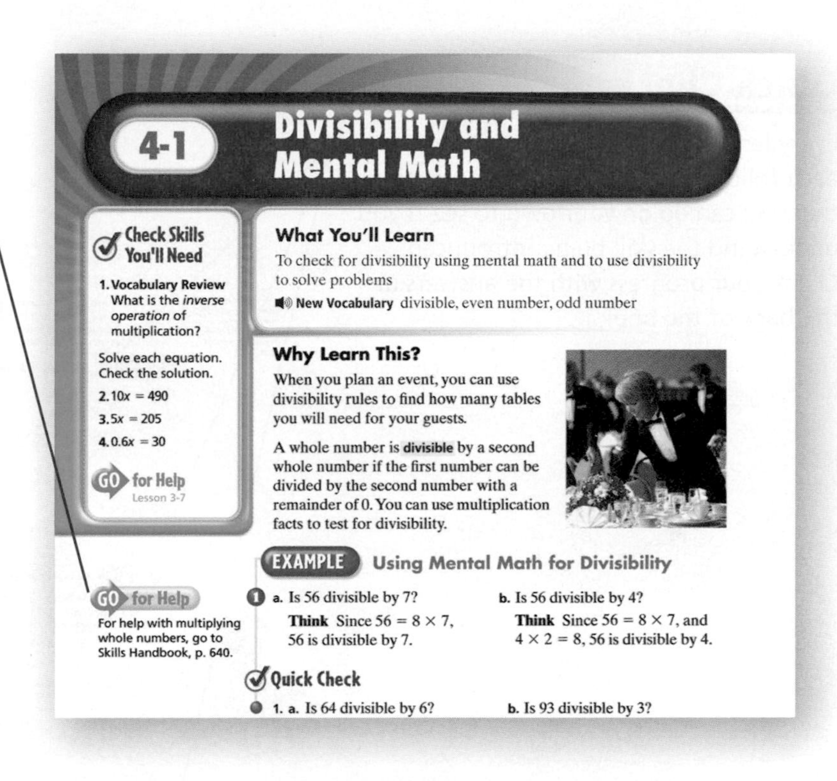
4-1 Divisibility and Mental Math

Check Skills You'll Need

1. Vocabulary Review What is the *inverse operation* of multiplication?

Solve each equation. Check the solution.

2. $10x = 490$

3. $5x = 205$

4. $0.6x = 30$

GO for Help Lesson 3-7

What You'll Learn

To check for divisibility using mental math and to use divisibility to solve problems

New Vocabulary divisible, even number, odd number

Why Learn This?

When you plan an event, you can use divisibility rules to find how many tables you will need for your guests.

A whole number is **divisible** by a second whole number if the first number can be divided by the second number with a remainder of 0. You can use multiplication facts to test for divisibility.

EXAMPLE Using Mental Math for Divisibility

GO for Help For help with multiplying whole numbers, go to Skills Handbook, p. 640.

1 a. Is 56 divisible by 7?

Think Since $56 = 8 \times 7$, 56 is divisible by 7.

b. Is 56 divisible by 4?

Think Since $56 = 8 \times 7$, and $4 \times 2 = 8$, 56 is divisible by 4.

Quick Check

1. a. Is 64 divisible by 6? b. Is 93 divisible by 3?

Video Tutor Help

Go online to see engaging videos to help you better understand important math concepts.

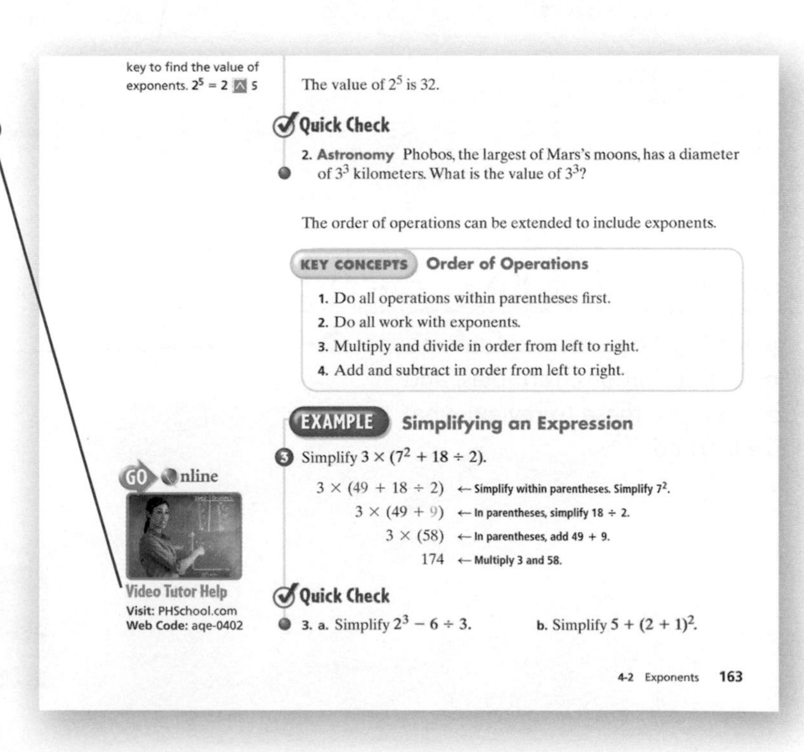
key to find the value of exponents. 2^5 = 2 ^ 5

The value of 2^5 is 32.

Quick Check

2. **Astronomy** Phobos, the largest of Mars's moons, has a diameter of 3^3 kilometers. What is the value of 3^3?

The order of operations can be extended to include exponents.

KEY CONCEPTS Order of Operations

1. Do all operations within parentheses first.
2. Do all work with exponents.
3. Multiply and divide in order from left to right.
4. Add and subtract in order from left to right.

EXAMPLE Simplifying an Expression

3 Simplify $3 \times (7^2 + 18 \div 2)$.

$3 \times (49 + 18 \div 2)$ ← Simplify within parentheses. Simplify 7^2.

$3 \times (49 + 9)$ ← In parentheses, simplify $18 \div 2$.

$3 \times (58)$ ← In parentheses, add 49 + 9.

174 ← Multiply 3 and 58.

GO Online

Video Tutor Help

Visit: PHSchool.com

Web Code: aqe-0402

Quick Check

3. a. Simplify $2^3 - 6 \div 3$. b. Simplify $5 + (2 + 1)^2$.

4-2 Exponents 163

Understanding the Mathematics

Quick Check

Every lesson includes numerous examples, each followed by a *Quick Check* question that you can do on your own to see if you understand the skill being introduced. Check your progress with the answers at the back of the book.

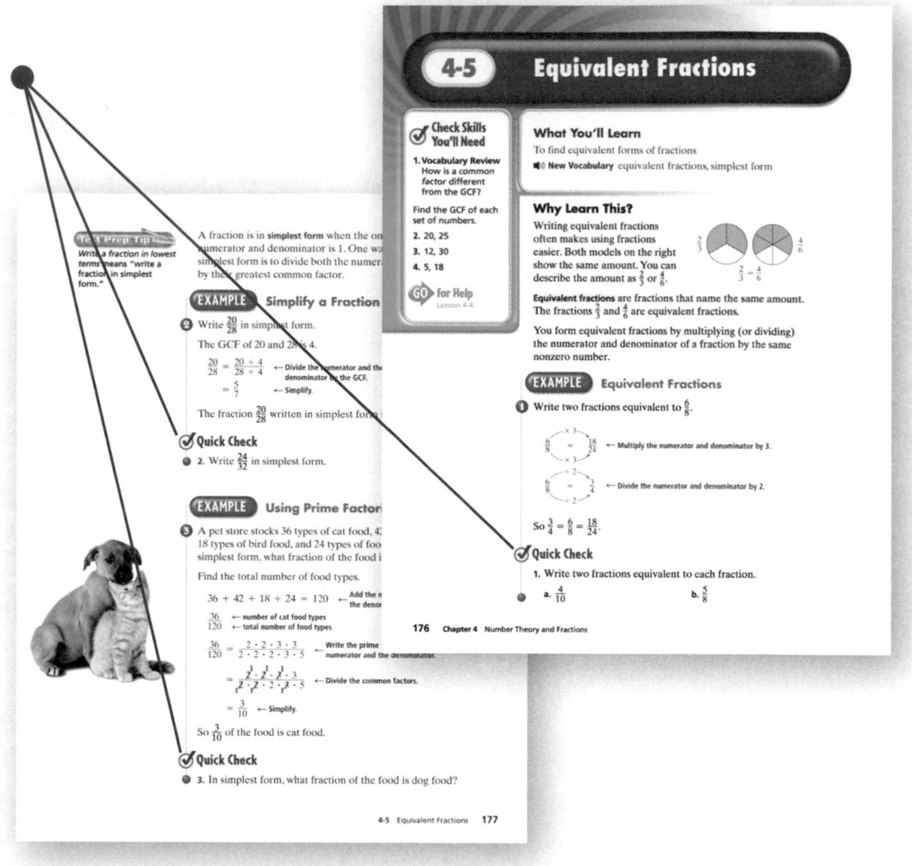
4-5 Equivalent Fractions

Check Skills You'll Need

1. Vocabulary Review How is a common factor different from the GCF?

Find the GCF of each set of numbers.

2. 20, 25

3. 12, 30

4. 5, 18

GO for Help Lesson 4-4

What You'll Learn

To find equivalent forms of fractions

New Vocabulary equivalent fractions, simplest form

Why Learn This?

Writing equivalent fractions often makes using fractions easier. Both models on the right show the same amount. You can describe the amount as $\frac{2}{3}$ or $\frac{4}{6}$.

$\frac{2}{3} = \frac{4}{6}$

Equivalent fractions are fractions that name the same amount. The fractions $\frac{2}{3}$ and $\frac{4}{6}$ are equivalent fractions.

You form equivalent fractions by multiplying (or dividing) the numerator and denominator of a fraction by the same nonzero number.

EXAMPLE Equivalent Fractions

1 Write two fractions equivalent to $\frac{6}{8}$.

$\frac{6}{8} = \frac{18}{24}$ ← Multiply the numerator and denominator by 3.

$\frac{6}{8} = \frac{3}{4}$ ← Divide the numerator and denominator by 2.

So $\frac{3}{4} = \frac{6}{8} = \frac{18}{24}$.

Quick Check

1. Write two fractions equivalent to each fraction.

a. $\frac{4}{10}$ b. $\frac{5}{8}$

176 Chapter 4 Number Theory and Fractions

Test Prep Tip: Write a fraction in lowest terms means "write a fraction in simplest form."

A fraction is in **simplest form** when the on… numerator and denominator is 1. One wa… simplest form is to divide both the numer… by their greatest common factor.

EXAMPLE Simplify a Fraction

2 Write $\frac{20}{28}$ in simplest form.

The GCF of 20 and 28 is 4.

$\frac{20}{28} = \frac{20 \div 4}{28 \div 4}$ ← Divide the numerator and the denominator by the GCF.

$= \frac{5}{7}$ ← Simplify.

The fraction $\frac{20}{28}$ written in simplest form…

Quick Check

2. Write $\frac{24}{32}$ in simplest form.

EXAMPLE Using Prime Factor…

3 A pet store stocks 36 types of cat food, 4… 18 types of bird food, and 24 types of foo… simplest form, what fraction of the food i…

Find the total number of food types.

$36 + 42 + 18 + 24 = 120$ ← Add the n… the denom…

$\frac{36}{120}$ ← number of cat food types / ← total number of food types

$\frac{36}{120} = \frac{2 \cdot 2 \cdot 3 \cdot 3}{2 \cdot 2 \cdot 2 \cdot 3 \cdot 5}$ ← Write the prime … numerator and the denominator.

$= \frac{\not{2} \cdot \not{2} \cdot \not{3} \cdot 3}{\not{2} \cdot \not{2} \cdot 2 \cdot \not{3} \cdot 5}$ ← Divide the common factors.

$= \frac{3}{10}$ ← Simplify.

So $\frac{3}{10}$ of the food is cat food.

Quick Check

3. In simplest form, what fraction of the food is dog food?

4-5 Equivalent Fractions 177

Understanding Key Concepts

Frequent *Key Concept* boxes summarize important definitions, formulas, and properties. Use these to review what you've learned.

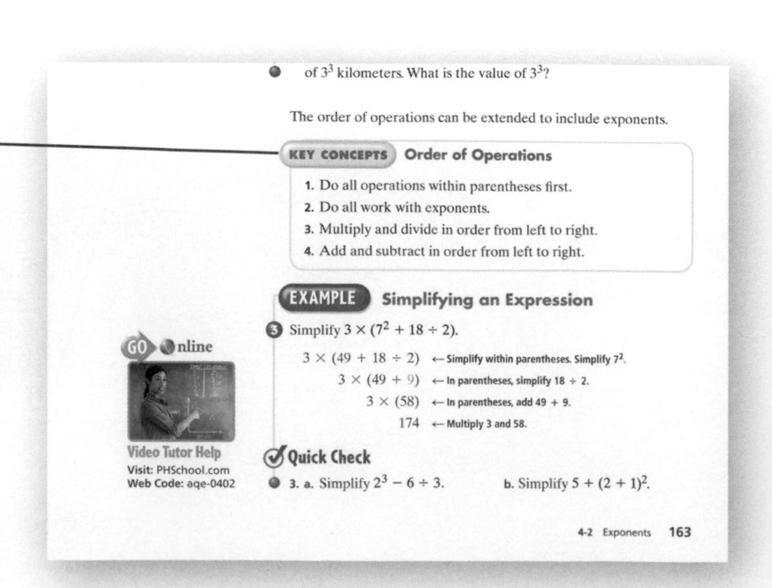
of 3^3 kilometers. What is the value of 3^3?

The order of operations can be extended to include exponents.

KEY CONCEPTS Order of Operations

1. Do all operations within parentheses first.
2. Do all work with exponents.
3. Multiply and divide in order from left to right.
4. Add and subtract in order from left to right.

EXAMPLE Simplifying an Expression

3 Simplify $3 \times (7^2 + 18 \div 2)$.

$3 \times (49 + 18 \div 2)$ ← Simplify within parentheses. Simplify 7^2.

$3 \times (49 + 9)$ ← In parentheses, simplify $18 \div 2$.

$3 \times (58)$ ← In parentheses, add 49 + 9.

174 ← Multiply 3 and 58.

GO Online

Video Tutor Help

Visit: PHSchool.com

Web Code: aqe-0402

Quick Check

3. a. Simplify $2^3 - 6 \div 3$. b. Simplify $5 + (2 + 1)^2$.

4-2 Exponents 163

Online Active Math

Make math come alive with these online activities. Review and practice important math concepts with these engaging online tutorials.

can use a division ladder or a factor tree to find the prime factorization of a number.

EXAMPLE **Prime Factorization**

3 Write the prime factorization of 84 using exponents.

Method 1 Use a division ladder.

$2\overline{)84}$ ← Divide 84 by the prime number 2. Work down.
$2\overline{)42}$ ← The result is 42. Since 42 is even, divide by 2 again.
$3\overline{)21}$ ← The result is 21. Divide by the prime number 3.
7 ← The prime factorization is 2 × 2 × 3 × 7.

Method 2 Use a factor tree.

84 ← Since the sum of the digits of 84 is 12, 84 is divisible by 3.
84 = 3 × 28 → ③ 28
28 = 4 × 7 → 4 ⑦ ← Circle the prime numbers as you find them.
4 = 2 × 2 → ② ②

The prime factorization of 84 is 2 × 2 × 3 × 7, or $2^2 \times 3 \times 7$.

Online active math
For: Prime Factorization Activity
Use: Interactive Textbook, 4-3

Quick Check

3. Find the prime factorization of 27.

4-3 Prime Numbers and Prime Factorization 167

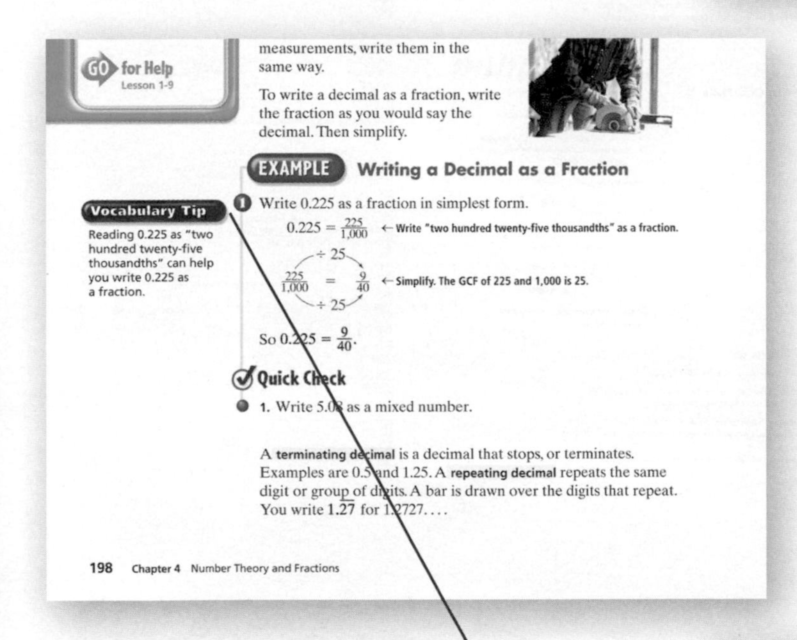

GO for Help Lesson 1-9

measurements, write them in the same way.

To write a decimal as a fraction, write the fraction as you would say the decimal. Then simplify.

EXAMPLE **Writing a Decimal as a Fraction**

1 Write 0.225 as a fraction in simplest form.

$0.225 = \frac{225}{1,000}$ ← Write "two hundred twenty-five thousandths" as a fraction.

$\frac{225}{1,000} = \frac{9}{40}$ (÷ 25) ← Simplify. The GCF of 225 and 1,000 is 25.

So $0.225 = \frac{9}{40}$.

Vocabulary Tip
Reading 0.225 as "two hundred twenty-five thousandths" can help you write 0.225 as a fraction.

Quick Check

1. Write 5.08 as a mixed number.

A **terminating decimal** is a decimal that stops, or terminates. Examples are 0.5 and 1.25. A **repeating decimal** repeats the same digit or group of digits. A bar is drawn over the digits that repeat. You write $1.\overline{27}$ for 1.2727....

198 Chapter 4 Number Theory and Fractions

Vocabulary Support

Understanding mathematical vocabulary is an important part of studying mathematics. *Vocabulary Tips* and *Vocabulary Builders* throughout the book help focus on the language of math.

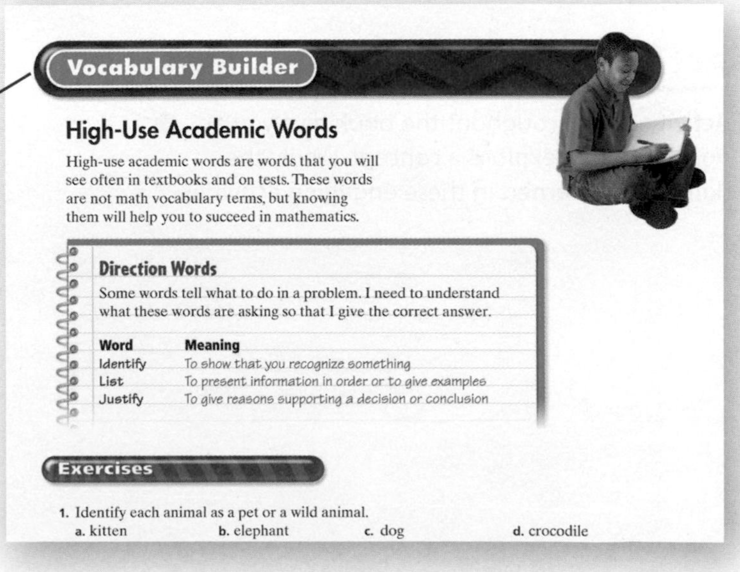

Vocabulary Builder

High-Use Academic Words

High-use academic words are words that you will see often in textbooks and on tests. These words are not math vocabulary terms, but knowing them will help you to succeed in mathematics.

Direction Words

Some words tell what to do in a problem. I need to understand what these words are asking so that I give the correct answer.

Word	Meaning
Identify	To show that you recognize something
List	To present information in order or to give examples
Justify	To give reasons supporting a decision or conclusion

Exercises

1. Identify each animal as a pet or a wild animal.
a. kitten b. elephant c. dog d. crocodile

Understanding the Mathematics

Guided Problem Solving

These features throughout your Student Edition provide practice in problem solving. Solved from a student's point of view, this feature focuses on the thinking and reasoning that goes into solving a problem.

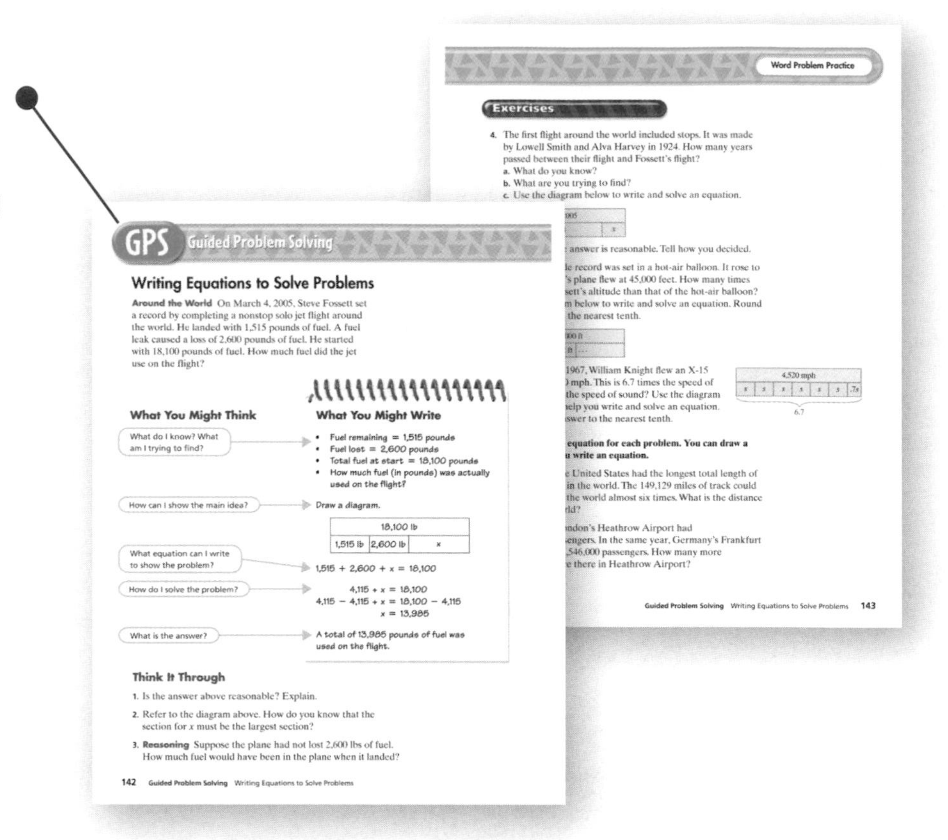

Word Problem Practice

Exercises

4. The first flight around the world included stops. It was made by Lowell Smith and Alva Harvey in 1924. How many years passed between their flight and Fossett's flight?
   a. What do you know?
   b. What are you trying to find?
   c. Use the diagram below to write and solve an equation.

answer is reasonable. Tell how you decided.

le record was set in a hot-air balloon. It rose to 's plane flew at 45,000 feet. How many times sett's altitude than that of the hot-air balloon? m below to write and solve an equation. Round the nearest tenth.

1967, William Knight flew an X-15 mph. This is 6.7 times the speed of the speed of sound? Use the diagram help you write and solve an equation. swer to the nearest tenth.

equation for each problem. You can draw a u write an equation.

e United States had the longest total length of in the world. The 149,129 miles of track could the world almost six times. What is the distance rld?

ndon's Heathrow Airport had engers. In the same year, Germany's Frankfurt ,546,000 passengers. How many more e there in Heathrow Airport?

Guided Problem Solving Writing Equations to Solve Problems 143

GPS Guided Problem Solving

Writing Equations to Solve Problems

Around the World On March 4, 2005, Steve Fossett set a record by completing a nonstop solo jet flight around the world. He landed with 1,515 pounds of fuel. A fuel leak caused a loss of 2,600 pounds of fuel. He started with 18,100 pounds of fuel. How much fuel did the jet use on the flight?

What You Might Think	What You Might Write
What do I know? What am I trying to find?	• Fuel remaining = 1,515 pounds • Fuel lost = 2,600 pounds • Total fuel at start = 18,100 pounds • How much fuel (in pounds) was actually used on the flight?
How can I show the main idea?	Draw a diagram. 18,100 lb: 1,515 lb, 2,600 lb, x
What equation can I write to show the problem?	$1,515 + 2,600 + x = 18,100$
How do I solve the problem?	$4,115 + x = 18,100$ $4,115 - 4,115 + x = 18,100 - 4,115$ $x = 13,985$
What is the answer?	A total of 13,985 pounds of fuel was used on the flight.

Think It Through

1. Is the answer above reasonable? Explain.
2. Refer to the diagram above. How do you know that the section for x must be the largest section?
3. **Reasoning** Suppose the plane had not lost 2,600 lbs of fuel. How much fuel would have been in the plane when it landed?

142 Guided Problem Solving Writing Equations to Solve Problems

Activity Labs

Activity Labs throughout the book give you an opportunity to explore a concept. Apply the skills you've learned in these engaging activities.

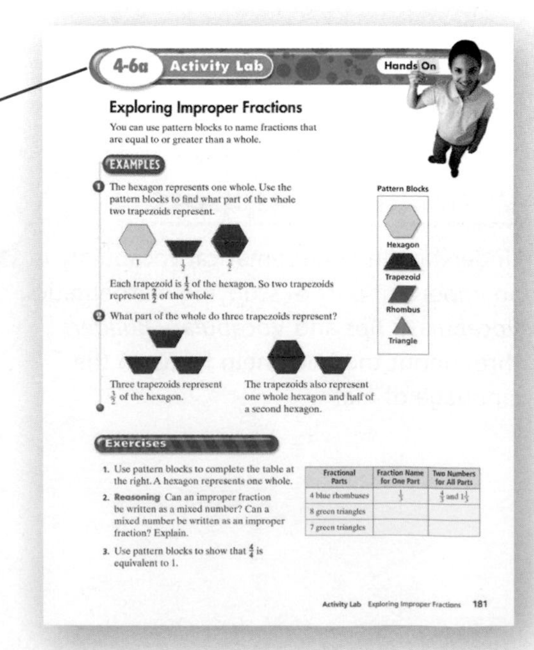

4-6a Activity Lab Hands On

Exploring Improper Fractions

You can use pattern blocks to name fractions that are equal to or greater than a whole.

EXAMPLES

1. The hexagon represents one whole. Use the pattern blocks to find what part of the whole two trapezoids represent.

   Each trapezoid is $\frac{1}{2}$ of the hexagon. So two trapezoids represent $\frac{2}{2}$ of the whole.

2. What part of the whole do three trapezoids represent?

   Three trapezoids represent $\frac{3}{2}$ of the hexagon. The trapezoids also represent one whole hexagon and half of a second hexagon.

Exercises

1. Use pattern blocks to complete the table at the right. A hexagon represents one whole.
2. **Reasoning** Can an improper fraction be written as a mixed number? Can a mixed number be written as an improper fraction? Explain.
3. Use pattern blocks to show that $\frac{4}{4}$ is equivalent to 1.

Fractional Parts	Fraction Name for One Part	Two Numbers for All Parts
4 blue rhombuses	$\frac{1}{3}$	$\frac{4}{3}$ and $1\frac{1}{3}$
8 green triangles		
7 green triangles		

Activity Lab Exploring Improper Fractions 181

Practice What You've Learned

There are numerous exercises in each lesson that give you the practice you need to master the concepts in the lesson. The following exercises are included in each lesson.

Check Your Understanding

These exercises help you prepare for the Homework Exercises.

Practice by example

These exercises refer you back to the Examples in the lesson, in case you need help with completing these exercises.

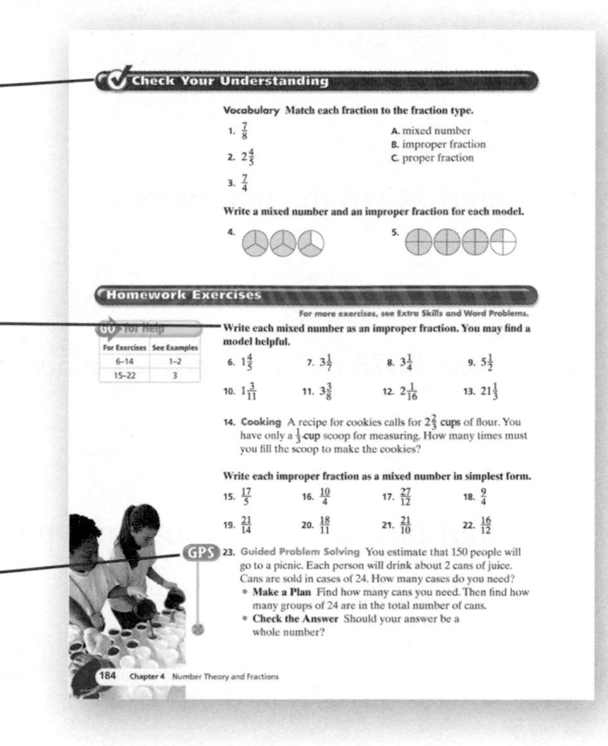

Check Your Understanding

Vocabulary Match each fraction to the fraction type.

1. $\frac{7}{8}$
2. $2\frac{4}{5}$
3. $\frac{7}{4}$

A. mixed number
B. improper fraction
C. proper fraction

Write a mixed number and an improper fraction for each model.

4. 5.

Homework Exercises

For more exercises, see Extra Skills and Word Problems.

GO for Help

For Exercises	See Examples
6–14	1–2
15–22	3

Write each mixed number as an improper fraction. You may find a model helpful.

6. $1\frac{4}{5}$ 7. $3\frac{1}{7}$ 8. $3\frac{1}{4}$ 9. $5\frac{1}{2}$

10. $1\frac{3}{11}$ 11. $3\frac{3}{8}$ 12. $2\frac{1}{16}$ 13. $21\frac{1}{3}$

14. **Cooking** A recipe for cookies calls for $2\frac{2}{3}$ cups of flour. You have only a $\frac{1}{3}$-cup scoop for measuring. How many times must you fill the scoop to make the cookies?

Write each improper fraction as a mixed number in simplest form.

15. $\frac{17}{5}$ 16. $\frac{10}{4}$ 17. $\frac{27}{12}$ 18. $\frac{9}{4}$

19. $\frac{21}{14}$ 20. $\frac{18}{11}$ 21. $\frac{21}{10}$ 22. $\frac{16}{12}$

GPS 23. **Guided Problem Solving** You estimate that 150 people will go to a picnic. Each person will drink about 2 cans of juice. Cans are sold in cases of 24. How many cases do you need?
- **Make a Plan** Find how many cans you need. Then find how many groups of 24 are in the total number of cans.
- **Check the Answer** Should your answer be a whole number?

184 Chapter 4 Number Theory and Fractions

Apply your skills

These exercises combine skills from earlier lessons to offer you richer skill exercises and multi-step application problems.

Homework Video Tutor

These interactive tutorials provide you with homework help for *every lesson*.

Challenge

This exercise gives you an opportunity to extend and stretch your thinking.

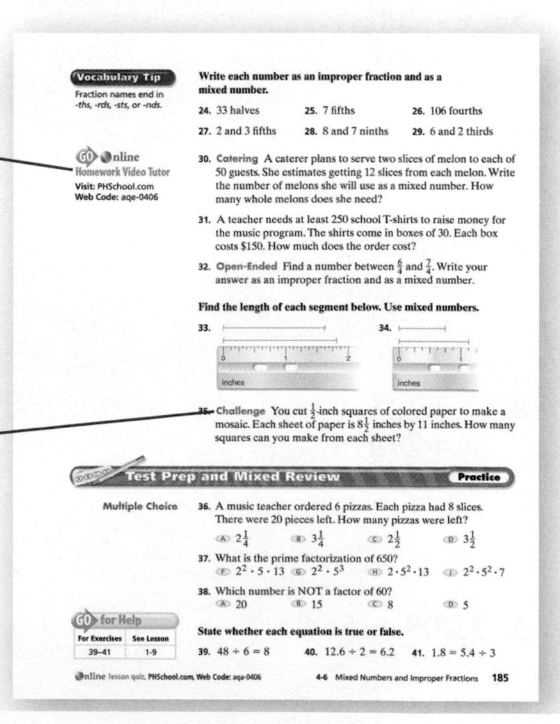

Vocabulary Tip
Fraction names end in *-ths, -rds, -sts,* or *-nds.*

Write each number as an improper fraction and as a mixed number.

24. 33 halves 25. 7 fifths 26. 106 fourths

27. 2 and 3 fifths 28. 8 and 7 ninths 29. 6 and 2 thirds

Online Homework Video Tutor
Visit: PHSchool.com
Web Code: aqe-0406

30. **Catering** A caterer plans to serve two slices of melon to each of 50 guests. She estimates getting 12 slices from each melon. Write the number of melons she will use as a mixed number. How many whole melons does she need?

31. A teacher needs at least 250 school T-shirts to raise money for the music program. The shirts come in boxes of 30. Each box costs $150. How much does the order cost?

32. **Open-Ended** Find a number between $\frac{6}{4}$ and $\frac{7}{4}$. Write your answer as an improper fraction and as a mixed number.

Find the length of each segment below. Use mixed numbers.

33. 34.

35. **Challenge** You cut $\frac{1}{2}$-inch squares of colored paper to make a mosaic. Each sheet of paper is $8\frac{1}{2}$ inches by 11 inches. How many squares can you make from each sheet?

Test Prep and Mixed Review Practice

Multiple Choice

36. A music teacher ordered 6 pizzas. Each pizza had 8 slices. There were 20 pieces left. How many pizzas were left?
A $2\frac{1}{4}$ B $3\frac{1}{4}$ C $2\frac{1}{2}$ D $3\frac{1}{2}$

37. What is the prime factorization of 650?
F $2^2 \cdot 5 \cdot 13$ G $2^2 \cdot 5^3$ H $2 \cdot 5^2 \cdot 13$ J $2^2 \cdot 5^2 \cdot 7$

38. Which number is NOT a factor of 60?
A 20 B 15 C 8 D 5

GO for Help

For Exercises	See Lesson
39–41	1-9

State whether each equation is true or false.

39. $48 \div 6 = 8$ 40. $12.6 \div 2 = 6.2$ 41. $1.8 = 5.4 \div 3$

Online lesson quiz, PHSchool.com, Web Code: aqa-0406

4-6 Mixed Numbers and Improper Fractions 185

Beginning-of-Course Diagnostic Test

1. Write the place value of the underlined digit in $5\underline{2}3{,}411{,}396$.

2. Write the place value of the underlined digit in $40\underline{2}{,}659$.

3. Round 742 to the tens place.

4. Round 4,078 to the hundreds place.

5. Round 116,830 to the thousands place.

Add.

6. $\begin{array}{r} 4{,}208 \\ +\ 6{,}967 \\ \hline \end{array}$

7. $591 + 79$

8. $\begin{array}{r} 7{,}223 \\ +\ 4{,}279 \\ \hline \end{array}$

9. $3{,}208 + 564$

10. four thousand sixty-two plus nine hundred eighteen

Subtract.

11. $\begin{array}{r} 57 \\ -\ 42 \\ \hline \end{array}$

12. $79 - 31$

13. $\begin{array}{r} 8{,}841 \\ -\ 3{,}194 \\ \hline \end{array}$

14. $\begin{array}{r} 116{,}493 \\ -\ 90{,}287 \\ \hline \end{array}$

15. $2{,}051 - 988$

16. nine thousand minus five hundred thirty eight

Multiply.

17. 594×8

18. $1{,}174 \times 6$

19. six thousand eighty-one times seven

20. 54×917

21. 806×255

22. one thousand sixty-nine times forty-eight

23. one hundred thirty-three times four thousand, two hundred eighty-six

Divide.

24. $6\overline{)822}$

25. $964 \div 6$

26. one thousand, two hundred eighty-seven divided by nine

27. $6{,}432 \div 24$

28. $504 \div 24$

29. $1{,}756 \div 29$

30. $5\overline{)1{,}016}$

Multiply using mental math.

31. $4{,}729 \times 10$

32. $462 \times 10{,}000$

33. $706{,}215 \times 100$

Divide using mental math.

34. $120 \div 10$

35. $17{,}000 \div 1{,}000$

36. $8{,}203{,}000 \div 100$

USING THE Problem Solving Plan

One of the most important skills you can have is the ability to solve problems. An integral part of learning mathematics is how adept you become at unraveling problems and looking back to see how you found the solution. Maybe you don't realize it, but you solve problems every day—some problems are easy to solve, and others are challenging and require a good plan of action. In this Problem Solving Handbook, you will learn how to work though mathematical problems using a simple four-step plan:

1. **Understand** **Understand the problem.**
   Read the problem. Ask yourself, "What information is given? What is missing? What am I being asked to find or to do?"

2. **Plan** **Make a plan to solve the problem.**
   Choose a strategy. As you use problem solving strategies throughout this book, you will decide which one is best for the problem you are trying to solve.

3. **Carry Out** **Carry out the plan.**
   Solve the problem using your plan. Organize your work.

4. **Check** **Check the answer to be sure it is reasonable.**
   Look back at your work and compare it against the information and question(s) in the problem. Ask yourself, "Is my answer reasonable? Did I check my work?"

Problem Solving Strategies

Creating a good plan to solve a problem means that you will need to choose a strategy. What is the best way to solve that challenging problem? Perhaps drawing a diagram or making a table will lead to a solution. A problem may seem to have too many steps. Maybe working a simpler problem is the key. There are a number of strategies to choose from. You will decide which strategy is most effective.

As you work through this book, you will encounter many opportunities to improve your problem solving and reasoning skills. Working through mathematical problems using this four-step process will help you to organize your thoughts, develop your reasoning skills, and explain how you arrived at a particular solution.

Putting this problem solving plan to use will allow you to work through mathematical problems with confidence. Getting in the habit of planning and strategizing for problem solving will result in success in future math courses and high scores on those really important tests!

THE STRATEGIES

Here are some examples of problem solving strategies. Which one will work best for the problem you are trying to solve?

- **Draw a Picture**
- **Look for a Pattern**
- **Systematic Guess and Check**
- **Act It Out**
- **Make a Table**
- **Work a Simpler Problem**
- **Work Backward**
- **Write an Equation**

Good Luck!

Draw a Picture

When to Use This Strategy Drawing a picture can help you visualize and understand a word problem.

Volleyball A volleyball tournament will be held on a soccer field that is 110 yards long and 80 yards wide. Each volleyball court is 25 yd long by 15 yd wide. How many courts will fit on the field?

Understand

The field is 110 yd by 80 yd. Each volleyball court is 25 yd by 15 yd. You are asked to find how many courts will fit on the field.

Plan

To help decide, first *draw a picture* of the field. Then show how many courts will fit on the field.

Carry Out

Mark off 7 courts along the length of the field and 3 courts along the width of the field. Since $3 \times 7 = 21$, you can fit 21 courts in the field.

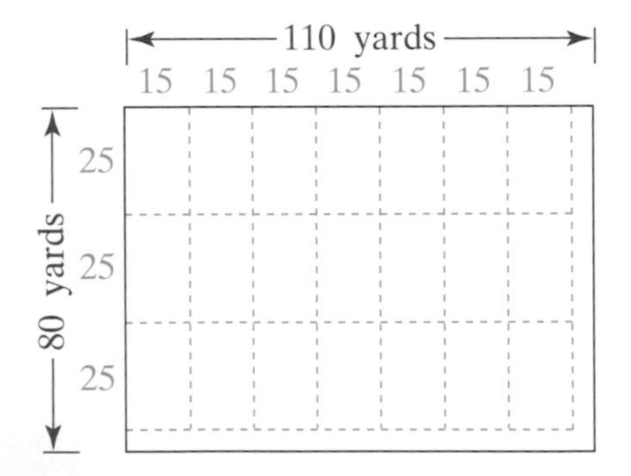

Check

Check the answer by dividing the area of the field by the area of a court. Use the formula area = length × width.

$$\frac{\text{soccer field}}{\text{volleyball court}} \rightarrow \frac{110 \text{ yards} \times 80 \text{ yards}}{25 \text{ yards} \times 15 \text{ yards}} \rightarrow \frac{8{,}800 \text{ square yards}}{375 \text{ square yards}} \approx 23$$

So 21 courts is a reasonable answer.

Practice

1. A bookcase is made from wood that is 3 in. thick. The bookcase has four shelves, including the top. The space between shelves is 20 inches. Find the height of the bookcase.

2. Lights are placed every 2 feet along both sides of a 14-foot driveway. How many lights are needed?

3. A rectangular garden is 4 feet by 3 feet. A landscaper plants flowers 1 ft apart along the edges and corners. How many plants does the landscaper need?

4. A bricklayer is finishing a section of a patio that is 60 in. wide by 60 in. long. Each brick is 10 in. wide by 12 in. long. How many bricks will it take to complete the patio?

5. Look at the figures below.

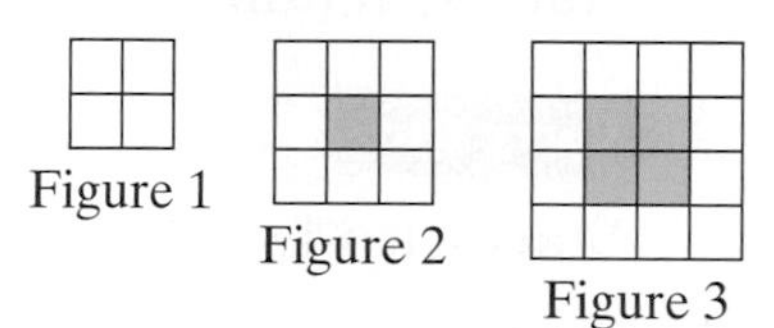

How many white squares will Figure 7 have?

6. A dartboard manufacturer makes dartboards with a black center. How many different dartboards can be made using the colors blue, yellow, and orange for the different rings? Each color can only be used once. *Hint: One combination is shown below.*

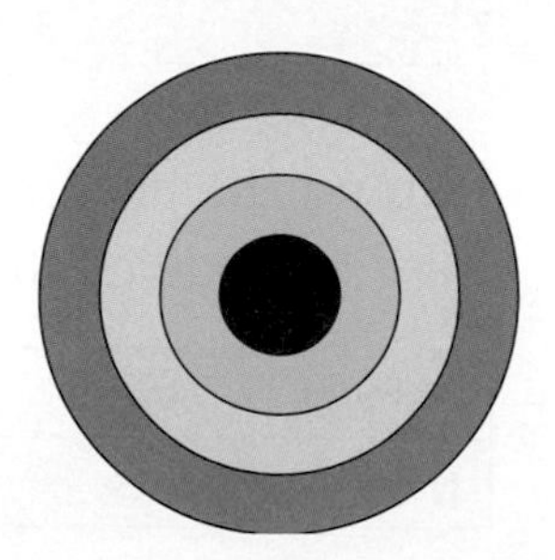

Look for a Pattern

When to Use This Strategy In problems where more objects are added, you can *look for a pattern* to solve the problem.

Seating A rectangular table seats two people on each end and three on each side. How many seats are available if you push the ends of five tables together?

Understand

There are five rectangular tables. Each table seats two people on each end and three on a side.

Plan

To find the number of seats when five tables are pushed together, start by finding the number of seats when there are fewer tables.

Carry Out

Start with 1, 2, and 3 tables.

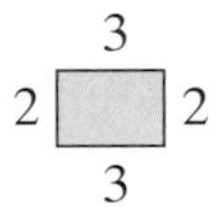

1 table $\rightarrow$ 10 seats

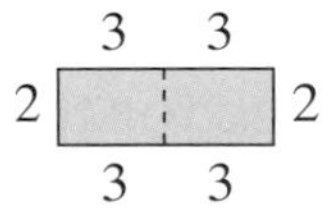

2 tables $\rightarrow$ 16 seats

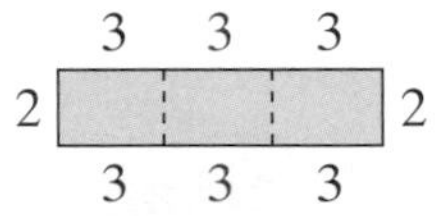

3 tables $\rightarrow$ 22 seats

Extend the pattern by adding six seats for each new table, three for each side of the new table.

Number of Tables	1	2	3	4	5
Number of Seats	10	16	22	28	34

Check

Five tables pushed together seat 5×6, or 30, people on the sides and 2 people on each end, or $30 + 2 + 2 = 34$.

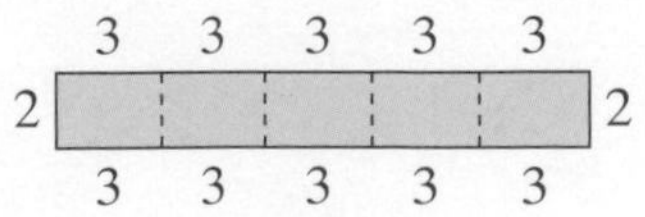

Practice

1. **Multiple Choice** A high school student has started a new job. He plans to save $1 in the first week, $2 in the second week, $4 in the third week, and $8 in the fourth week. If this pattern of savings could continue, how much would he save in the tenth week?

   A. $10
   B. $128
   C. $256
   D. $512

2. A rectangular table seats four people on each side and three on each end. How many seats are available if the ends of seven tables are pushed together?

3. Your younger brother is pulling a sled up a hill. Each minute he moves forward 20 feet but also slides back 3 feet. How long will it take him to pull his sled 130 feet up the hill?

4. Look at the figures below. How many squares will be in Figure 8?

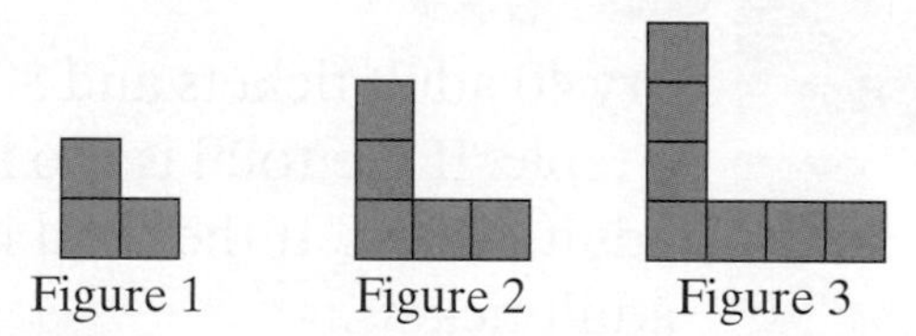

5. **Multiple Choice** Continue the pattern 1, 4, 16, 64…

   A. 256, 1004, 4016
   B. 256, 924, 3696
   C. 256, 1024, 4086
   D. 256, 1024, 4096

6. Draw the next 2 figures in the pattern below.

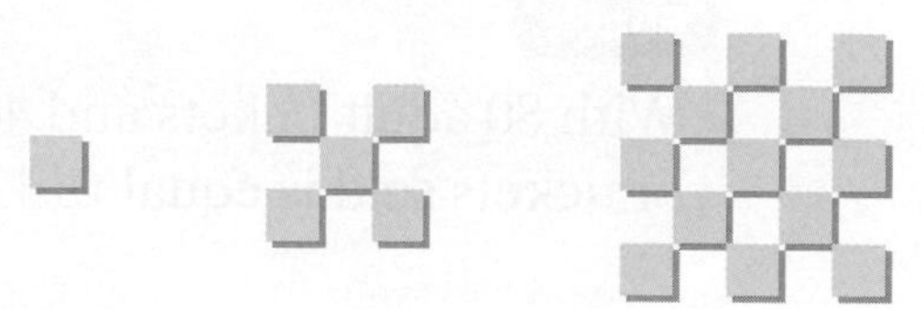

Systematic Guess and Check

When to Use This Strategy Sometimes problems have a limited number of possible answers. Sometimes the solution to a problem involves several related numbers. Using *systematic guess and check* can get you closer to the right answer.

Movie tickets cost $10 for adults and $8 for children. On Friday the total sales from 120 tickets was $1,120. How many adult tickets were sold?

Understand

Adult tickets cost $10. Children's tickets cost $8. The theater collected $1,120 by selling 120 tickets. You need to find how many adult tickets were sold.

Plan

To find how many adult tickets were sold, make an initial guess, check the results, and then revise your guess.

Carry Out

Try 40 adult tickets and 80 children's tickets. Organize the data in a table. If the total is too low, increase the number of expensive, adult, tickets. If the total is too high, decrease the number of adult tickets.

Adult Tickets	Children's Tickets	Total Sales
$40 \times \$10 = \$400$	$80 \times \$8 = \$640$	$\$400 + \$640 = \$1,040$
$50 \times \$10 = \$500$	$70 \times \$8 = \$560$	$1,060
$90 \times \$10 = \$900$	$30 \times \$8 = \$240$	$1,140
$80 \times \$10 = \$800$	$40 \times \$8 = \$320$	$1,120

Check

With 80 adult tickets and 40 children's tickets, the number of tickets sold is equal to 120, and the total sales are $1,120.

Practice

1. A vendor sells salads and juices. A salad costs $3.00 and a juice costs $2.50. The vendor earned $216 by selling 80 items. How many juices were sold?

2. **Multiple Choice** A rectangular turtle cage is made with 40 feet of wire fence. The length is 6 feet greater than the width. What are the length and width of the turtle cage?

   A. length 7 feet; width 1 foot
   B. length 10 feet; width 4 feet
   C. length 13 feet; width 6 feet
   D. length 13 feet; width 7 feet

3. A gardener is attempting to put a fence around a rectangular garden. The total length of the fence is 30 feet. The width of the garden is 3 feet longer than the length. What are the length and width of the garden?

4. A petting zoo charges $14 for adults and $8 for children. One morning, the zoo collected a total of $416 from selling 40 tickets in total. How many children entered the zoo during the morning?

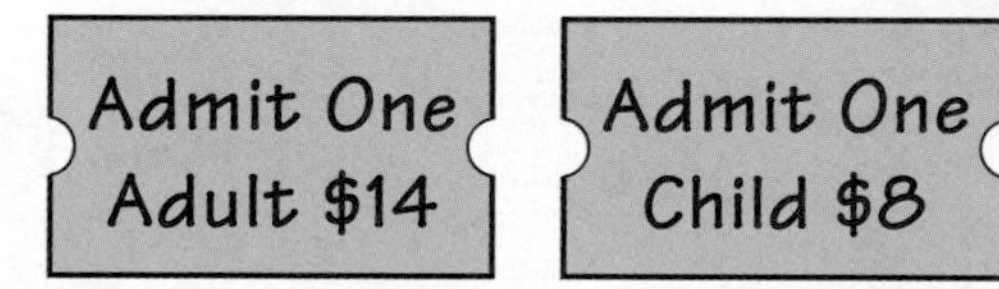

5. A school cafeteria sells sandwiches for $4.50 each, cartons of milk for $1 and bananas for $.50 each. One table of students spent $36.00 total. They bought 2 more milks than sandwiches and they bought three times more sandwiches than bananas. How many bananas did the students buy?

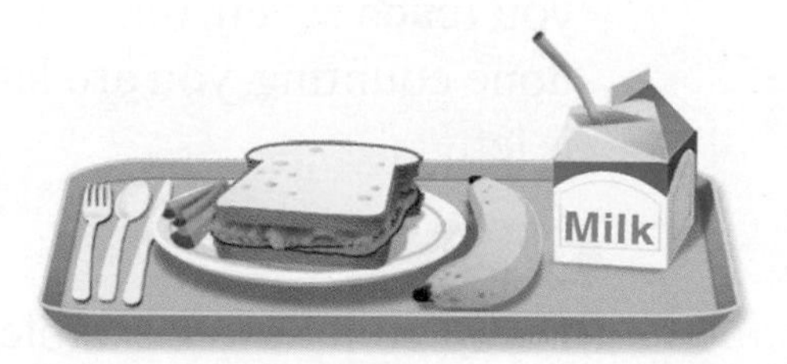

Act It Out

When to Use This Strategy Sometimes the best way to solve a problem is to imitate the actions described in the problem.

Ten students stand in a circle. Starting with the first student, the teacher begins counting as follows: "One, two, three, four, five, six, out!" When a student is called out, he or she has to leave the circle. The teacher then continues until only one student is left. Which student is it?

Understand

The teacher is counting out every seventh student as she goes around in a circle. The students are numbered 1 to 10. You need to find the number of the last student left in.

Plan

Using 10 pennies you can *act out* the steps and see who wins.

Carry Out

Arrange the pennies in a circle.

Start counting, pointing at the pennies one at a time. Every time you reach seven, remove the penny you point to. When you are done counting, you are left with the ninth penny. The ninth student is left.

Check

If you complete the table, you get the same result.

Student #

1	2	3	4	5	6	7	8	9	10
1	2	3	4	5	6	✗	1	2	3
4	5	6	✗	1	2	✗	3	4	5
6	✗		✗			✗			
	✗		✗			✗			
	✗		✗			✗			

Practice

1. If the teacher has 12 students and counts out every ninth student, which student will be left?

2. An uncle is giving some baseball cards away to five nieces and nephews. He decides the fairest way to do this is to give just one card to the first child, then two to the second, and so on. If everybody gets three turns, how many cards will each niece or nephew have?

3. Four robots stand in the corners of a four-by-four grid. All four robots are facing in the same direction. They move at the same time. If a robot sees another robot directly ahead, it takes one step forward, and if not, it stays in place but turns right. Where are the robots after three moves?

4. Janelle, Ciara, and Macario start with the following baskets.

Janelle takes 3 apples from Macario and 1 from Ciara. Macario takes 5 apples from Ciara and 2 apples from Janelle. Ciara takes half of Janelle's apples and 4 from Macario. Janelle takes 6 more from Macario and half as many from Ciara. Who has the most apples?

5. At the start of a bus route, 30 people get on the bus. At the second stop, 14 people get off and 2 people get on the bus. At the third stop, 8 people get off and no people get on. At the fourth stop, 10 people get off the bus and 6 people get on. How many people are left on the bus after the fourth stop?

6. A board game is played by rolling a standard number cube. The board has 25 spaces that must be passed before winning the game. The rules state that if an odd number is rolled, the player moves that many spaces backward. If an even number is rolled, the player moves that many spaces forward. Three turns of 4 players are shown. Which player is in the lead?

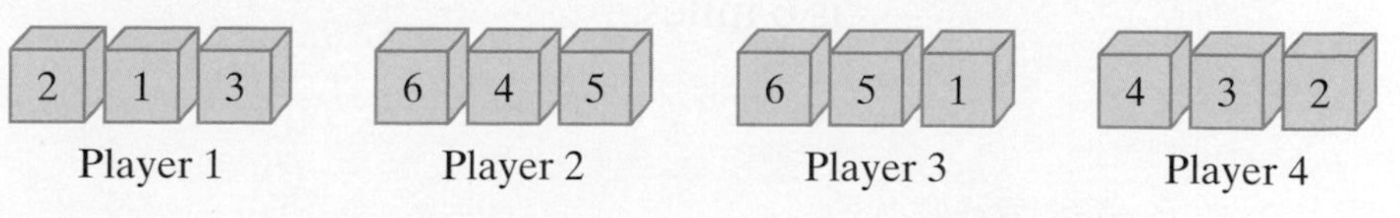

Make a Table

When to Use This Strategy Organizing data in a table can help you see connections.

Exercise Tara wants to walk in a charity event. In her first week of training, she walks three miles each day. Each week after that, she adds $\frac{3}{4}$ mile to her daily distance. In which week of training does Tara walk six miles per day?

Understand

During the first week, Tara walks three miles each day. Each week, she walks an additional $\frac{3}{4}$ mile. You need to find the week in which her daily walk is six miles.

Make a table that shows weeks and distance. Add rows until the distance reaches six miles.

Carry Out

Label the first column Week and the second column Distance. Fill in the values for each week.

Week	Distance (miles/day)
1	3
2	$3 + \frac{3}{4} = 3\frac{3}{4}$
3	$3\frac{3}{4} + \frac{3}{4} = 4\frac{1}{2}$
4	$4\frac{1}{2} + \frac{3}{4} = 5\frac{1}{4}$
5	$5\frac{1}{4} + \frac{3}{4} = 6$

Tara walks 6 miles during her fifth week of training.

Check

You can check by working backward. In five weeks there were 4 increases of $\frac{3}{4}$ mile. $\frac{3}{4} + \frac{3}{4} + \frac{3}{4} + \frac{3}{4} = 3$. So the total increase was 3 miles. The 3 miles plus the original 3 miles per day is 6 miles.

Practice

1. In how many ways can you make 25 cents using pennies, nickels, and dimes?

2. Find the smallest number that meets both of these conditions.
   - When you divide the number by 7, the remainder is 1.
   - When you divide the number by 9, the remainder is 7.

3. A certain farm has both chickens and goats. Each chicken has 2 legs. Each goat has 4 legs. There are 35 animals on the farm. All together the chickens and goats have 100 legs. How many chickens and how many goats does the farm have?

4. A family is taking a vacation. They travel 248 miles on the first day. Each day after that, they travel 45 additional miles. On which day will they have traveled 563 total miles?

5. A bag full of 10 red and blue marbles spills out on the floor as shown.

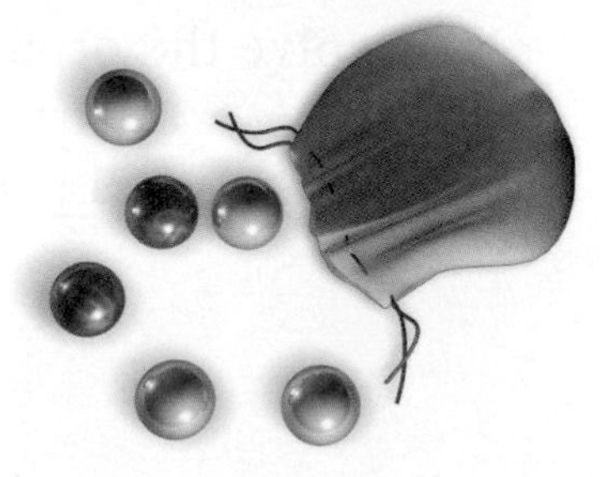

How many different groups can you make with the marbles that are still in the bag?

Work a Simpler Problem

When to Use This Strategy Using simpler numbers can sometimes help you solve a difficult problem.

Floor Tiles You tile a rectangular floor $17\frac{1}{2}$ ft by $13\frac{3}{4}$ ft. You are using square tiles that are $1\frac{1}{4}$ ft on each side. How many tiles do you need?

Understand

The rectangular floor is $17\frac{1}{2}$ feet long and $13\frac{3}{4}$ feet wide. Each tile is a square with sides $1\frac{1}{4}$ feet long. You must find how many tiles are needed to cover the floor.

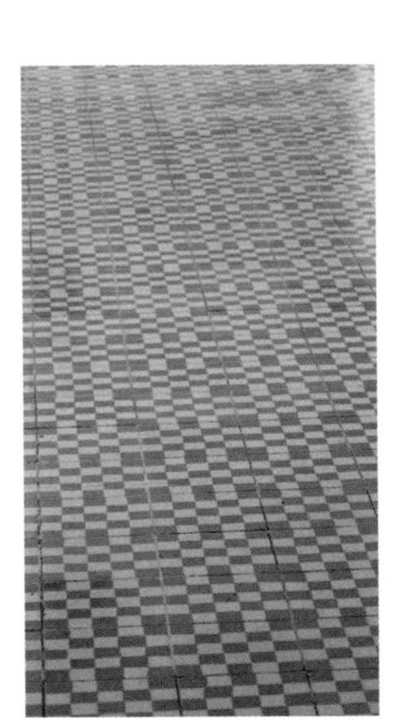

Plan

First, *work a simpler problem.* Then use the same approach to solve the harder problem. Multiply each number by 4 to remove the fractions. Replace $17\frac{1}{2}$ with $17\frac{1}{2} \times 4 = 70$. Replace $13\frac{3}{4}$ with $13\frac{3}{4} \times 4 = 55$, and $1\frac{1}{4}$ with $1\frac{1}{4} \times 4 = 5$.

Simpler Problem A rectangular floor is 70 feet by 55 feet. How many 5 ft-by-5 ft tiles do you need to cover the floor?

Carry Out

For one row of tiles to cover the length of the room, you need $70 \div 5$, or 14, tiles. For enough rows to cover the width of the room, you need $55 \div 5$, or 11, rows. So you need 14×11, or 154, tiles.

Now solve the original problem. For one row of tiles, you need $17\frac{1}{2} \div 1\frac{1}{4}$, or 14, tiles. For enough rows to cover the width, you need $13\frac{3}{4} \div 1\frac{1}{4}$, or 11, rows. So you need 14×11, or 154, tiles.

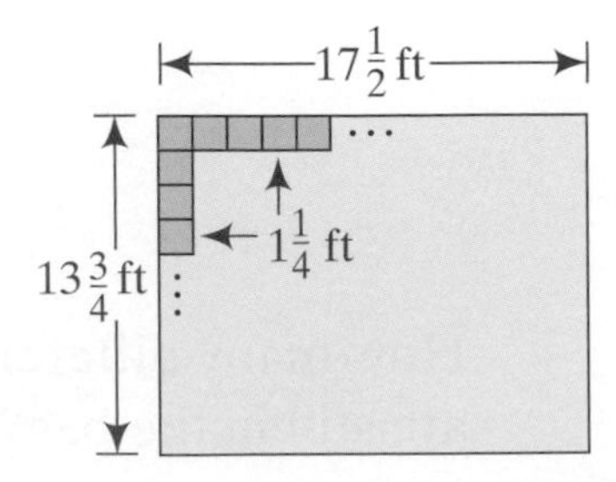

Check

Because all the lengths in the simpler problem are four times as long, the answers to both problems should be the same. They are, so the answer checks.

Practice

1. On a school day, José spends $5\frac{1}{4}$ hours in classes. Each class lasts $\frac{3}{4}$ hour. How many classes does José have?

2. **Multiple Choice** A tailor has a section of material that is $28\frac{1}{2}$ feet long. He wants to cut it into pieces, each one $1\frac{1}{2}$ feet long. How many cuts will he have to make?

   A. 5 cuts
   B. 11 cuts
   C. 15 cuts
   D. 18 cuts

3. An employee is at work for $8\frac{3}{4}$ hours per day. Every day she takes two 15 minute breaks and one $\frac{1}{2}$ hour lunch. Not counting breaks and lunch, how many hours will she work in 5 days?

4. What is the sum of all odd numbers from 1–1000? *Hint: What is the sum of odd numbers between 1–10? Between 1–20?*

5. **Shopping** A club needs to order 37 XL Adult Sweatshirts and 37 Child's t-shirts. How much money will they need?

T-Shirts and Sweatshirts For Sale

Adult T-shirt
(M-XL) \$15.00
(XXL) \$17.95

Adult Sweatshirt
(M-XL) \$27.50
(XXL) \$27.95

Child's T-shirt
\$12.50

Child's Sweatshirt
\$16.95

Work Backward

When to Use This Strategy Some problems involve a series of steps that lead to a final result. If you are asked to find the initial amount, you can *work backward* from the final result by using inverse operations.

Zoo Luis went to the zoo for a school trip. He paid \$5 for admission. He spent \$14 at the souvenir shop. When he got home, he had \$18 left. How much money did he start with?

Understand

You know how much money Luis had when he got home. You know how much he spent. You want to know how much money he started with.

Plan

To find the amount Luis started with, begin with the amount he had at the end. Then *work backward.* To undo each operation, use its inverse.

Carry Out

To undo the amounts Luis spent, add.

$\$18$ ← **Luis had \$18 left at the end.**

$\$18 + \$14 = \$32$ ← **He spent \$14 at the souvenir shop. Add.**

$\$32 + \$5 = \$37$ ← **He spent \$5 on admission. Add.**

Luis started with \$37.

Check

Read the problem again. Subtract the amounts as Luis spends money in the problem.

$\$37$ ← **Luis started with \$37.**

$\$37 - \$5 = \$32$ ← **He paid \$5 for admission.**

$\$32 - \$14 = \$18$ ← **He spent \$14 at the souvenir shop.**

He has \$18 left. The answer checks.

Practice

1. You divide a number by 2, add 7, and then multiply by 5. The result is 50. What is the number?

2. Brenda spent half her money at a store in a mall. At another store, she spent half her remaining money and $6 more. She had $2 left. How much did Brenda have when she arrived at the mall?

3. Kai sold half his baseball cards to Ana, half of the remaining cards to Joe, and the last 10 to Chip. How many cards did Kai sell in all?

4. A rental car gets 30 miles per gallon of gas. A full tank holds 16 gallons of gas. A woman drives the car 60 miles to the beach and back. She uses $\frac{1}{2}$ of the remaining amount of gas to visit her family. She adds 8 gallons to the tank and then drives 30 miles to return the rental car. Her final gas reading is shown below.

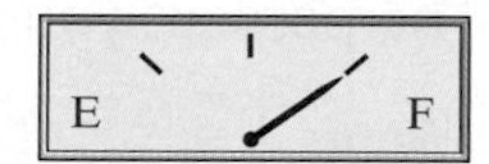

How does the final gas reading compare to the amount of gas in the car when she rented it?

5. You left your house and walked 35 minutes to the library.

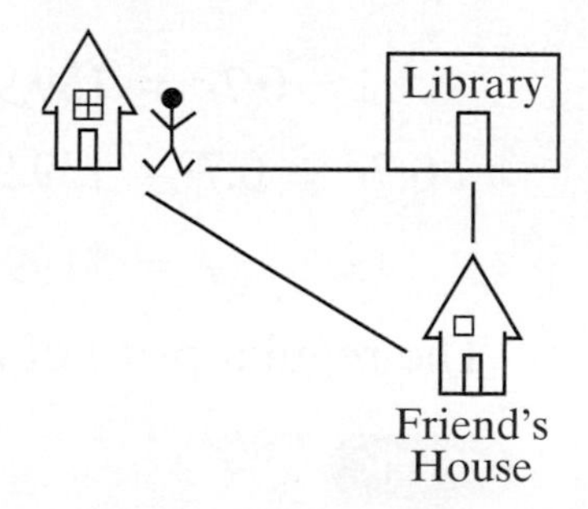

After $2\frac{1}{2}$ hours, you left the library to walk for 15 minutes to a friend's house. After $1\frac{3}{4}$ hours, you walked for 30 minutes to arrive home at 7:30. What time did you leave your house?

Write an Equation

When to Use This Strategy To *write an equation* is one way of organizing the information needed to solve a problem.

Discount A bicycle is on sale for \$139.93. This is 30% off the regular price. What is the regular price of the bicycle?

Understand

The sale price of the bicycle, \$139.93, is 30% off the regular price. You need to find the regular price.

Plan

Translate the words into an equation. You will pay $100\% - 30\% = 70\%$ of the regular price.

Carry Out

The percent you pay times the regular price equals the sale price.

Words percent you pay times regular price equals sale price

Let r = the regular price.

Equation

$$70\% \times r = \$139.93$$

$0.7r = 139.93$ ← Write 70% as a decimal: 0.7.

$0.7r \div 0.7 = 139.93 \div 0.7$ ← Divide each side by 0.7 to find r.

$r = \$199.90$ ← Simplify.

The regular price of the bicycle is \$199.90.

Check

The regular price is about \$200. The sale price is about 70% of \$200, or \$140. This is close to the sale price.

Practice

1. A magazine has 5,580,000 subscribers this year. This number is down 7% from last year. How many subscribers were there last year?

2. A "light" popcorn has 120 Calories per serving. This is 25% fewer Calories than a serving of regular popcorn. How many Calories does each serving of regular popcorn have?

3. The sign at the entrance of a store reads, "30% off all winter apparel! Discount given at the register." The price tag of a coat is missing. The register rings up a price before tax of $55.93. What is the regular price of the coat?

4. You earned $13 doing yard work for your neighbor. You now have $91 dollars. Write an equation to find how much money you had before doing the yard work. How much money did you have to begin with?

5. A local newspaper writes that math test scores have gone up 12% from last year. The average test score is now 560. What was the average test score last year?

6. A store is selling a hat and scarf set for 15% off the marked price. How much will you pay for the set?

CHAPTER 1 Number Properties and Decimals

What You've Learned

- In a previous course, you compared and ordered whole numbers.
- You used addition, subtraction, multiplication, and division to solve problems involving whole numbers.
- You used rounding to estimate reasonable results for problems involving whole numbers.

GO for Help

For Exercises	See Skills Handbook
1–6	p. 381
7–12	pp. 382–383
13–16	p. 384
17–20	p. 386

Rounding to the Nearest Ten

Round each number to the nearest ten.

1. 312 **2.** 7,525 **3.** 38

4. 55 **5.** 699 **6.** 1,989

Adding and Subtracting Whole Numbers

Add or subtract.

7. $59 + 116$ **8.** $182 - 37$ **9.** $8{,}745 + 5{,}447$

10. $4{,}823 - 1{,}796$ **11.** $9{,}004 + 996$ **12.** $2{,}049 - 657$

Multiplying Whole Numbers

Multiply.

13. 9×83 **14.** 64×71 **15.** 437×100 **16.** 33×14

Dividing Whole Numbers

Divide.

17. $50 \div 10$ **18.** $85 \div 5$ **19.** $256 \div 8$ **20.** $1{,}944 \div 27$

What You'll Learn Next

- In this chapter, you will learn how to compare and order decimals.
- You will use addition, subtraction, multiplication, and division to solve problems involving decimals.
- You will use rounding and front-end estimation to estimate reasonable results.
- You will use the order of operations to simplify numerical expressions.

Key Vocabulary

- associative properties (pp. 4–5)
- commutative properties (pp. 4–5)
- expanded form (p. 15)
- expression (p. 8)
- front-end estimation (p. 19)
- identity properties (pp. 4–5)
- order of operations (p. 8)

1-1 Properties of Operations

Check Skills You'll Need

1. **Vocabulary Review** *Multiplication* of whole numbers can be described as repeated _?_.

Find each product.

2. 5×30
3. 6×15
4. 50×7

for Help
Skills Handbook p. 384

CONTENT STANDARDS
6.EE.2.b, 6.EE.3

What You'll Learn

To understand and use the properties of operations

New Vocabulary commutative properties, associative properties, identity properties

Why Learn This?

The properties of operations can help you do mental math.

KEY CONCEPTS Properties of Addition

Commutative Property of Addition Changing the order of addends does not change the sum.

$9 + 5 = 5 + 9$

Associative Property of Addition Changing the grouping of addends does not change the sum.

$(9 + 5) + 4 = 9 + (5 + 4)$

Identity Property of Addition The sum of 0 and any number is that number.

$0 + 9 = 9$

You can simplify a mathematical phrase by replacing it with the simplest name for the value of the phrase. So to simplify $4 + 5$, you write 9 for its value.

EXAMPLE Using the Properties of Addition

1 **Field Trips** The table shows two groups of students who went on a field trip. Use mental math to find the total number of students.

Room	Number of Students
101	32
102	28

What you think

First I will think of 28 as $20 + 8$. Next, I will add $8 + 32$ to get 40. $40 + 20$ is 60. So $32 + 28 = 60$.

Vocabulary Tip

Parentheses ( ) indicate operations that you should do first.

Why it works

$32 + 28 = 32 + (20 + 8)$ ← Rewrite 28 as 20 + 8.

$= 32 + (8 + 20)$ ← Use the Commutative Property of Addition.

$= (32 + 8) + 20$ ← Use the Associative Property of Addition.

$= 40 + 20$ ← Add inside the parentheses first.

$= 60$ ← Simplify.

The total number of students is 60.

Quick Check

1. **Mental Math** Find the sum $36 + 25 + 34$.

KEY CONCEPTS **Properties of Multiplication**

Commutative Property of Multiplication Changing the order of factors does not change the product.

$4 \times 6 = 6 \times 4$

Associative Property of Multiplication Changing the grouping of factors does not change the product.

$(4 \times 6) \times 2 = 4 \times (6 \times 2)$

Identity Property of Multiplication The product of 1 and any number is that number.

$4 \times 1 = 4$

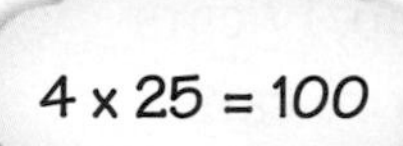

EXAMPLE Using the Properties of Multiplication

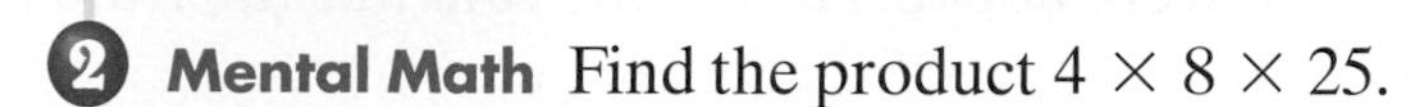

2 **Mental Math** Find the product $4 \times 8 \times 25$.

What you think

First I will multiply 4 and 25. $4 \times 25 = 100$, and $8 \times 100 = 800$.

Why it works

$4 \times 8 \times 25 = 4 \times 25 \times 8$ ← Commutative Property of Multiplication

$= (4 \times 25) \times 8$ ← Associative Property of Multiplication

$= 100 \times 8$ ← Multiply inside the parentheses.

$= 800$ ← Simplify.

Quick Check

2. **Mental Math** Find $20 \times (6 \times 5)$.

Check Your Understanding

1. **Vocabulary** Name the property used in this statement: $25 + 27 + 15 = 25 + 15 + 27$.

2. Give a reason to justify each step.

$$
\begin{aligned}
(4 \times 9) \times 5 &= (9 \times 4) \times 5 && \underline{\ ?\ } \\
&= 9 \times (4 \times 5) && \underline{\ ?\ } \\
&= 9 \times 20 && \underline{\ ?\ } \\
&= 180 && \underline{\ ?\ }
\end{aligned}
$$

3. **Writing in Math** Use mental math to find $(25 \times 9) \times 8$. Describe the steps you used.

Use mental math to find each sum or product.

4. $4 + 26$
5. $33 + 0 + 17$
6. $50 \times 7 \times 2$

Homework Exercises

For more exercises, see Extra Skills and Word Problems.

GO for Help

For Exercises	See Example
7–16	1
17–25	2

Use mental math to find each sum.

7. $0 + 57 + 4$
8. $32 + 48$
9. $18 + 6 + 42$
10. $(8 + 17) + 13$
11. $81 + 23 + 19$
12. $(17 + 24) + 183$
13. $837 + 14 + 26$
14. $24 + 33 + 167$
15. $160 + 0 + 2{,}740$

16. A train started a trip pulling 9 cars. At the first stop, 17 cars were added to the train. At the second stop, 11 more cars were added. How many cars was the train pulling then?

Use mental math to find each product.

17. $5 \times 47 \times 2$
18. $70 \times 1 \times 4$
19. $25 \times 13 \times 4$
20. $20 \times (19 \times 50)$
21. $40 \times (33 \times 25)$
22. $5 \times 683 \times 20$
23. $65 \times (100 \times 2)$
24. $4 \times 20 \times 1{,}000$
25. $5 \times 8 \times 25$

26. **Guided Problem Solving** Four running clubs raised money in a 24-hour relay race. Club A ran 183 miles, Club B ran 144 miles, Club C ran 117 miles, and Club D ran 146 miles. What was the total number of miles that all four clubs ran?
    - Which pairs of numbers can you add using mental math?
    - What is the sum of each of those pairs?

Name the property that is used to find each answer.

27. $41 + 29 = 41 + (9 + 20) = (41 + 9) + 20 = 50 + 20 = 70$

28. $4 \times 11 \times 25 = 4 \times 25 \times 11 = 100 \times 11 = 1{,}100$

29. Modeling Draw a model to show the statement is true: $8 + 6 + 2 = (8 + 2) + 6$.

30. Error Analysis Below is a friend's solution to a problem. Is your friend correct? Explain.

$100 \times (5 + 9) = (100 \times 5) + 9 = 500 + 9 = 509$

31. Choose a Method You plan to earn $15 per week for a charity. Will you use estimation, mental math, paper and pencil, or a calculator to determine how many weeks it will take you to earn $1,000? Explain why.

32. Art Class In a student art contest, there are 14 drawings, 22 sculptures, and some paintings. There are 18 more paintings than sculptures. What is the total number of art pieces?

33. The monthly rate for a 3-year subscription to an online music service is $10. What is the total cost for 3 years?

34. Challenge Is subtraction commutative? Is division? Is either operation associative? Explain using examples.

Test Prep and Mixed Review — Practice

Multiple Choice

35. Gary is asked to find two whole numbers that have a sum of 9 and a product that is double the sum. He writes 7 and 2. Why is Gary's answer incorrect?

- (A) The sum of 7 and 2 is not 9.
- (B) The product of 7 and 2 is not double the sum.
- (C) The sum of 7 and 2 is 9.
- (D) The product of 7 and 2 is double the sum.

36. Last night Martha spent 29 minutes on social studies homework, 13 minutes on English, and 22 minutes on science. About how much time did she spend on all three subjects?

- (F) 40 minutes
- (G) 50 minutes
- (H) 1 hour
- (J) 1 hour and 10 minutes

GO for Help

For Exercises	See Skills Handbook
37–39	p. 382

Find each sum.

37. $407 + 89$ **38.** $728 + 647$ **39.** $1{,}312 + 3{,}905$

1-2 Order of Operations

1. **Vocabulary Review** Name the property that lets you write $35 + 5 = 5 + 35$.

Use mental math to find each sum.

2. $35 + 17 + 5$
3. $22 + 0 + 8$
4. $124 + (25 + 26)$

Lesson 1-1

CONTENT STANDARDS
6.EE.2.b, 6.EE.2.c

What You'll Learn

To use the order of operations to simplify expressions and solve problems

New Vocabulary order of operations, expression

Why Learn This?

A problem such as $18 + 11 \times 6$ requires you to do more than one operation. To find the correct answer, you need to know which operation to do first. Should you add first, or multiply?

Diane's Work (addition first)

$$18 + 11 \times 6 \stackrel{?}{=} (18 + 11) \times 6$$
$$\stackrel{?}{=} 29 \times 6$$
$$\stackrel{?}{=} 174$$

Dana's Work (multiplication first)

$$18 + 11 \times 6 \stackrel{?}{=} 18 + (11 \times 6)$$
$$\stackrel{?}{=} 18 + 66$$
$$\stackrel{?}{=} 84$$

Only one answer is correct. To make sure everyone gets the same value, you use the **order of operations.**

KEY CONCEPTS **Order of Operations**

1. Do all operations within parentheses first.
2. Multiply and divide in order from left to right.
3. Add and subtract in order from left to right.

Based on the order of operations, you multiply before you add.

$$18 + 11 \times 6 = 18 + 66 = 84$$

So Dana's answer is correct.

An **expression** is a mathematical phrase that contains numbers and operation symbols. In the work above, $18 + 11 \times 6$ is an expression.

Players must put on soccer equipment—socks, shoes with cleats, and shin guards—in a certain order.

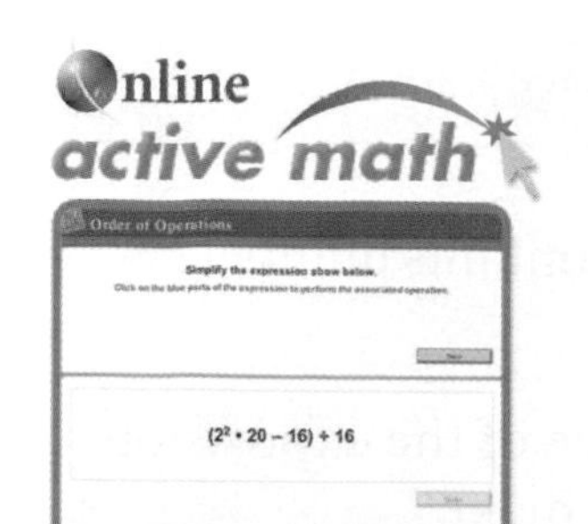

For: Order of Operations Activity
Use: Interactive Textbook, 1-2

EXAMPLE Finding the Value of Expressions

1 Find the value of each expression.

a. $6 + 96 \div 3 = 6 + 32$ ← **Divide 96 by 3.**

$= 38$ ← **Add.**

b. $30 - (6 + 2) \times 3 = 30 - 8 \times 3$ ← **Add 6 and 2 within the parentheses.**

$= 30 - 24$ ← **Multiply 8 and 3.**

$= 6$ ← **Subtract 24 from 30.**

Quick Check

1. Find the value of each expression.

a. $34 + 5 \times 2 - 17$ **b.** $(6 + 18) \div 3 \times 2$

EXAMPLE Using Expressions to Solve Problems

2 **Multiple Choice** Suppose you buy the items shown on the store receipt. What is the total cost of the items, including the tax?

Ⓐ $160 Ⓒ $190
Ⓑ $170 Ⓓ $1,570

CRAWFORD'S
ITEMS ORDERED
JEANS 3@ $35.00 EACH
DISCOUNT -$5.00
SHIRTS 4@ $15.00 EACH
TAX $10.00
TOTAL

Test Prep Tip
You can model a problem using words that describe the quantities in the problem.

You can write an expression to help you find the total cost.

Words	cost of jeans	−	discount	+	cost of shirts	+	tax
Expression	$3 \times \$35$	−	$5	+	$4 \times \$15$	+	$10

$105 − $5 + $60 + $10 ← **Multiply.**

$100 + $60 + $10 ← **Subtract.**

$170 ← **Add.**

The total cost is $170. The correct answer is choice B.

Quick Check

2. You are paid $7 per hour to rake leaves. Your brother is paid $5 per hour. You worked 4 hours and your brother worked 3 hours. How much did the two of you earn together?

Check Your Understanding

1. **Vocabulary** A mathematical phrase that contains numbers and operation symbols is a(n) __?__.

2. **Error Analysis** A student says that the value of the expression $5 + 25 \div 5$ is 6. What error did the student make?

Which operation should you do first?

3. $6 - 2 \times 2$ 4. $33 - (4 + 6)$ 5. $6 \times (2 - 5)$ 6. $7 + 4 \times 3$

Find the value of each expression.

7. $(1 + 2) \times 2$ 8. $3 \times (4 - 2)$ 9. $3 \times 4 - 2$ 10. $2 + 15 \div 3$

Homework Exercises

For more exercises, see Extra Skills and Word Problems.

GO for Help

For Exercises	See Example
11–19	1
20–28	2

Find the value of each expression.

11. $450 \div 45 + 5$ 12. $29 - 4 \times 7$ 13. $16 + 36 \div 12$

14. $14 - (7 + 5) \div 2$ 15. $(13 + 21) \times 2$ 16. $400 \div (44 - 24)$

17. $16 - (2 + 4) \times 2$ 18. $26 + 5 - 4 \times 3$ 19. $13 + 5 \times 12 - 4$

20. $4 \times \$40 - \$5$ 21. $\$50 + \$20 \div 2$

22. $\$100 - 2 \times \$30$ 23. $\$35 \times 2 + \$42 \div 2$

24. $3(\$28 + \$32) - \$10$ 25. $\$15 \times 10 + \$30 \times 2$

26. $(\$45 \times 4 + \$125 \times 3) \div 5$ 27. $(\$75 \times 5) + (\$25 \times 6) - \$10$

28. **Marbles** You buy 2 red rainbow marbles for 50¢ each, 3 bumblebee marbles for 90¢ each, and 2 tricolor marbles for 65¢ each. Find the total cost of the marbles.

GPS 29. **Guided Problem Solving** A group of 25 students and 3 adults goes to an art museum. Admission costs \$6 per student and \$9 per adult. There is a \$15 discount for groups of 20 or more. Find the total cost for the trip.
- **Make a Plan** Write an expression for the cost of both the students and the adults. Next, find the total cost of the trip.
- **Carry Out the Plan** An expression for the total cost for students and adults is $25 \times \$\blacksquare + 3 \times \$\blacksquare - \blacksquare$.

PearsonSuccessNet.com

Careers Nutritionists help people plan their diets.

Reasoning **Insert parentheses to make each statement true.**

30. $11 - 7 \div 2 = 2$

31. $1 + 2 \times 15 - 4 = 33$

Nutrition **Use the table to answer Exercises 32 and 33.**

32. How many grams of protein are in 6 oz of chicken and 2 c of vegetables?

33. How many grams of protein are in 9 oz of chicken, 2 c of vegetables, and 1 c of rice?

Food	Serving Size	Protein
Chicken	3 oz	21 g
Vegetables	1 c	2 g
Rice	1 c	9 g

34. **Coins** There are 300 coins of the same type in two stacks. One stack is 380 millimeters tall. The other is 220 millimeters tall. Find the thickness of one coin.

35. **Writing in Math** Explain the steps you would use to find the value of the expression $8 \div 4 \times 6 + (7 - 5)$.

36. **Challenge** Copy the statement: 14 ■ 7 ■ 2 ■ 3 = 7. Insert operations symbols to make the statement true.

Test Prep and Mixed Review

Practice

Multiple Choice

37. A group of 11 boys and 9 girls goes to a movie. Admission costs \$7 per person. Which expression does NOT show the total amount the group will pay?
    - Ⓐ \$7 × (11 + 9)
    - Ⓑ \$7 × 11 × 9
    - Ⓒ (\$7 × 11) + (\$7 × 9)
    - Ⓓ \$7 × 20

38. There are 6 bike racks at a park. Each bike rack can hold 14 bikes. If there are 11 bikes, which method can be used to find the number of empty spaces in the bike racks?
    - Ⓕ Add 6 to the product of 11 and 14.
    - Ⓖ Subtract 6 from the product of 11 and 14.
    - Ⓗ Add 11 to the product of 6 and 14.
    - Ⓙ Subtract 11 from the product of 6 and 14.

39. For which sum is 2,200 a reasonable estimate?
    - Ⓐ 422 + 1,085 + 897
    - Ⓑ 280 + 1,375 + 466
    - Ⓒ 605 + 786 + 1,022
    - Ⓓ 1,532 + 963 + 45

GO for Help

For Exercises	See Skills Handbook
40–42	p. 392

Estimate using compatible numbers.

40. $57 \div 6$

41. 14×4

42. $627 \div 23$

Checkpoint Quiz 1

Lessons 1-1 through 1-2

Use mental math to find each answer.

1. $19 + 7 + 31$
2. $(6 + 18) + 14$
3. $25 \times 10 \times 4$
4. $33 + 28 + 7$
5. $8 \times 7 \times 25$
6. $(43 \times 5) \times 20$
7. A bus has 4 passengers. After the second stop, the number of passengers had doubled. After the third stop, the number of passengers had doubled again. How many passengers were on the bus after the third stop?

Find the value of each expression.

8. $30 - 6 \times 5$
9. $(12 + 23) \times 2$
10. $\$60 + \$30 \div 3$
11. $(17 + 3) \div 2 - 1$
12. $3 \times (18 \div 6) + 2$
13. $51 + 5 \times 3 - 2$
14. List the operations in the order you will perform them to simplify $12 + (60 - 2) \div 7$.

MATH AT WORK

Accountant

Accountants usually work in some area of finance. They must enjoy working with numbers and know how to budget money well.

They use mathematics to prepare and analyze financial reports, tax returns, and budgets. Accountants also help individuals and companies track financial history and plan for future growth.

Accountants' reports help people make good business decisions.

For information on accounting
PearsonSuccessNet.com

1-3a Activity Lab

Exploring Decimal Models

You can use grid models or base-ten pieces to represent decimals. For both types of models, the large square represents the whole.

Grid Models

Tenths model

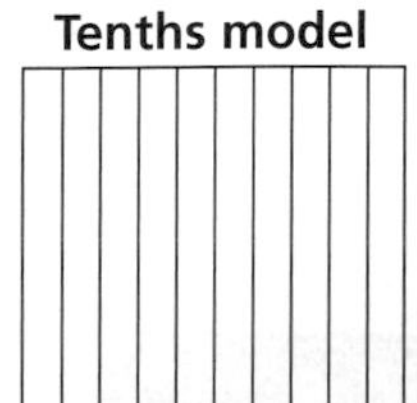

Hundredths model

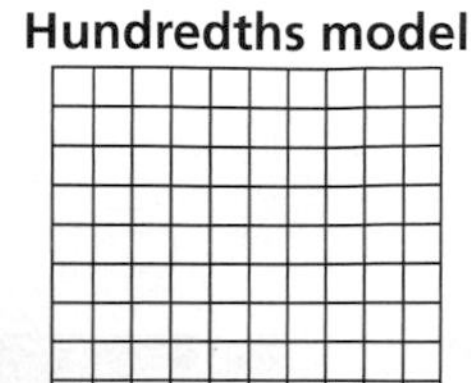

Base-Ten Pieces

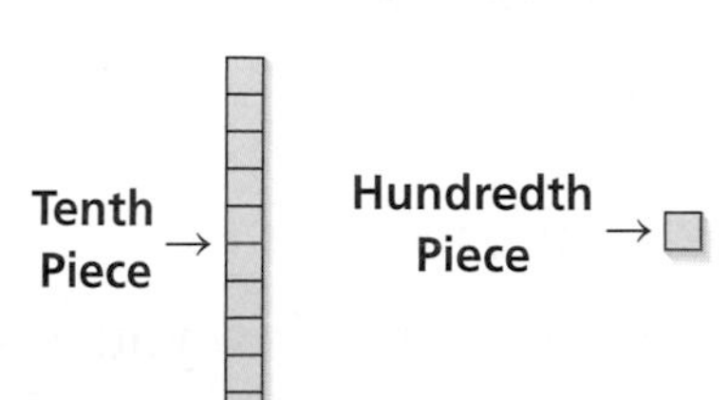

EXAMPLE Modeling Decimals

Write the decimal for the model below, in words and in numerals.

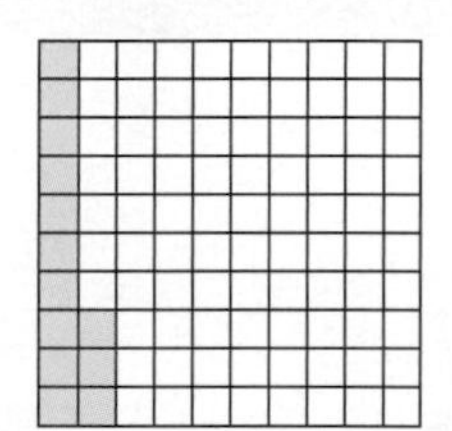

There are 100 squares. Thirteen squares are shaded.

Words thirteen hundredths

Numerals 0.13

Exercises

Write a decimal for each model.

1\.

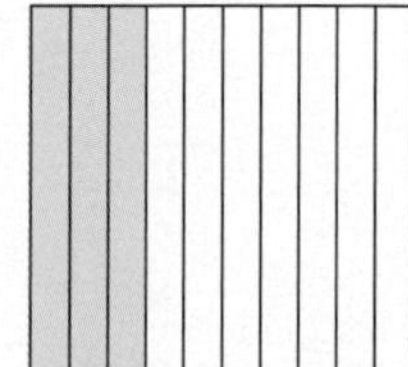

2\.

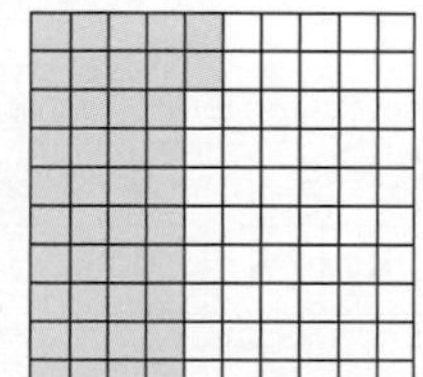

3\.

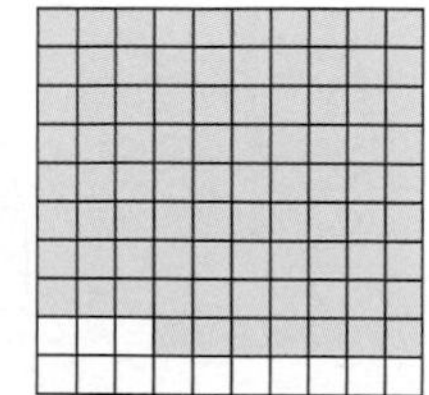

Model each decimal using a grid model or base-ten pieces.

4\. two tenths

5\. forty hundredths

6\. eighty-five hundredths

7\. a. Draw models for five tenths and for fifty hundredths.

b. **Number Sense** Show that the decimals are equal.

1-3 Understanding Decimals

1. Vocabulary Review Write one thousand, three hundred twenty-one in *standard form.*

Write each whole number in words.

2. 28 **3.** 8,672

4. 612,980 **5.** 58,026

for Help
Skills Handbook
p. 380

CONTENT STANDARD
Essential for understanding 6.NS.3

What You'll Learn

To read, write, and round decimals

New Vocabulary expanded form

Why Learn This?

Decimal numbers allow you to write very precise values. In sports, the difference between first place and second place sometimes depends on decimal places.

You can extend the place value chart to include values for decimal places. When you read a decimal that is greater than 1, read the decimal point as "and."

EXAMPLE Writing a Decimal in Words

1 **Fuel** The price of a gallon of gasoline is \$2.459. Write 2.459 in words.

Begin by writing 2.459 in a place value chart.

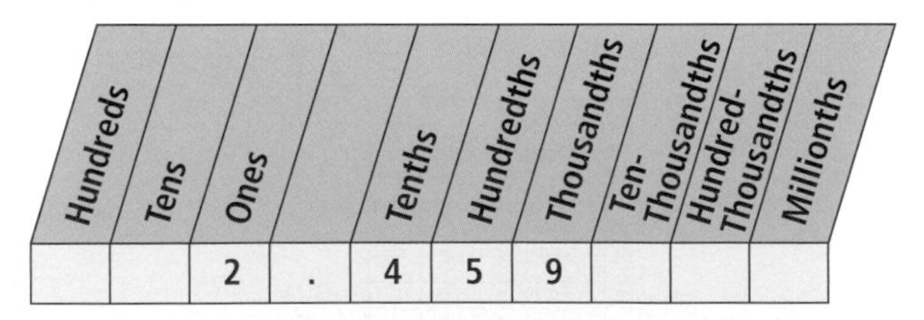

Hundreds	Tens	Ones		Tenths	Hundredths	Thousandths	Ten-Thousandths	Hundred-Thousandths	Millionths
		2	.	4	5	9			

2.459 ← **Three decimal places indicate thousandths.**

two and four hundred fifty-nine thousandths

Quick Check

1. Write each decimal in words.

a. 67.3 **b.** 6.734 **c.** 0.67

You can write decimals in both standard form and expanded form. **Expanded form** is a sum that shows the place and value of each digit of a number.

Standard Form		Expanded Form		
0.75	=	0.7	+	0.05
↑		↑		↑
seventy-five hundredths		seven tenths	+	five hundredths

EXAMPLE Standard Form and Expanded Form

2 **Sports** At a gymnastics meet, the best score on the pommel horse was nine and forty-two thousandths. Write the score in standard form and in expanded form.

9. ← Write the whole number part. Place the decimal point.

9.▢▢▢ ← Thousandths is three places to the right of the decimal point.

9.▢42 ← Place 42 to the far right.

9.042 ← Insert a zero for tenths.

Standard form: 9.042 Expanded form: $9 + 0.04 + 0.002$

Quick Check

2. The winning car in a race won by fifteen hundredths of a second. Write the decimal in standard and expanded forms.

Rounding decimals is similar to rounding whole numbers.

The value to the right of 3 is < 5, so round down to nearest tenth. → 0.32 ↓ 0.3

0.36 ↓ 0.4 ← The value to the right of 3 is ≥ 5. So round up.

EXAMPLE Rounding Decimals

3 Round 0.426 to the nearest hundredth.

0.426 ← Look at the digit to the right of the hundredths place.
↑
6 is ≥ 5, so round up.

So 0.426 rounded to the nearest hundredth is 0.43.

Quick Check

3. Round each decimal to the underlined place.

a. 2.3<u>4</u>28 b. 0.173<u>4</u>7 c. 9.<u>0</u>53

Check Your Understanding

1. **Number Sense** In the number 12.057, which digit has the greater value, the 5 or the 7? Explain.

2. **Open-Ended** Write a decimal with 4 decimal places in words and in standard form. Then round the decimal to the nearest hundredth.

Find the value of the digit 3 in each number.

3. 0.3 4. 0.237 5. 7.553 6. 8.2103

Write each decimal in expanded form.

7. 1.2 8. 8.4 9. 7.52 10. 0.239

Homework Exercises

For more exercises, see Extra Skills and Word Problems.

GO for Help

For Exercises	See Example
11–20	1
21–25	2
26–33	3

Write each decimal in words.

11. 2.3 12. 6.02 13. 0.006 14. 2.061 15. 3.08

16. 0.40 17. 50.603 18. 1.28 19. 3.004 20. 0.23

Write each decimal in standard form and in expanded form.

21. forty and nine thousandths
22. sixty-four hundredths
23. seven hundred thousandths
24. nine and twenty hundredths

25. **Running** A marathon is twenty-six and two tenths miles long. Write the number in standard form and in expanded form.

Round each decimal to the underlined place.

26. $0.6\underline{8}3$ 27. $2.\underline{7}248$ 28. $3.414\underline{6}9$ 29. $10.9\underline{5}6$

30. $6.2\underline{4}7$ 31. $0.\underline{5}54$ 32. $4.\underline{0}625$ 33. $4.8\underline{9}6$

34. **Guided Problem Solving** The diameter of a white blood cell is twelve ten-thousandths of a centimeter. Round the diameter to the nearest thousandth of a centimeter.
    - What is twelve ten-thousandths in standard form?
    - Is the digit to the right of the thousandths place *less than, greater than,* or *equal to* 5?

35. According to the bar graph, sales for Company A were 0.7 million dollars. As a whole number, this is written $700,000. Write the annual sales for each company as a decimal and as a whole number.

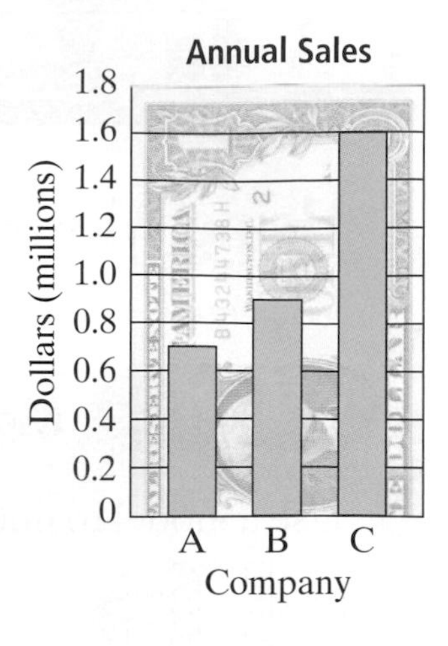

36. **Money** A mill is a unit of money sometimes used by state governments. One mill is equal to one thousandth of a dollar ($0.001). Write each amount as a decimal part of a dollar.

a. 6 mills **b.** 207 mills **c.** 53 mills

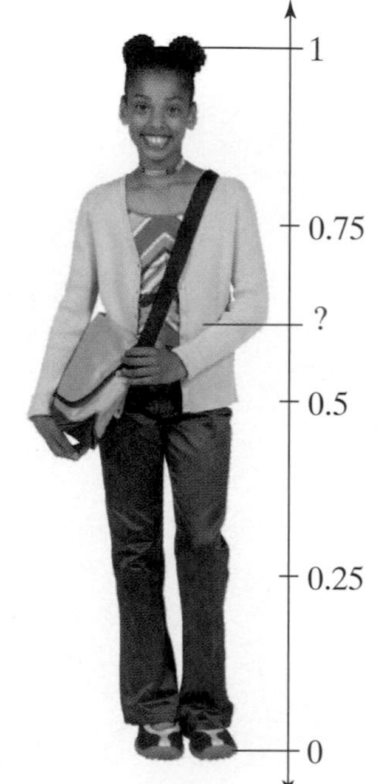

Find the value of the digit 4 in each number.

37. 0.4 **38.** 42.3926 **39.** 17.55643

40. 1.2468 **41.** 121.004 **42.** 425.209

43. Artists use a ratio called the Golden Mean to describe a person's height. Your height from the floor to your waist is usually six hundred eighteen thousandths of your total height. Round this number to the nearest hundredth.

44. **Writing in Math** Describe how the values of the digit 2 in the number 22.222 change as you move from right to left.

45. **Challenge** Extend the place value chart to write 0.0000001 in words.

Test Prep and Mixed Review — Practice

Multiple Choice

46. At a sale, shirts were marked down $5 each. Lisa bought 3 shirts for $39. Find the price of each shirt before the sale.

Ⓐ $7 Ⓑ $13 Ⓒ $18 Ⓓ $24

47. You and three friends bought a large pizza for $13.00. Each of you paid an equal share of the cost. Which method can be used to find the amount each person paid?

Ⓕ Divide 13.00 by 3. Ⓗ Divide 13.00 by 4.
Ⓖ Multiply 13.00 by 4. Ⓙ Multiply 13.00 by 3.

GO for Help

For Exercises	See Lesson
48–50	1-1

Mental Math Use mental math to find each sum or product.

48. $(20 \times 3) \times 5$ **49.** $70 + 0$ **50.** $2 \times (42 \times 5)$

1-4a Activity Lab

Hands On

Using Models

You can use models to add or subtract two decimals.

EXAMPLE Modeling Decimal Sums

1 Use a model to find $0.4 + 0.03$.

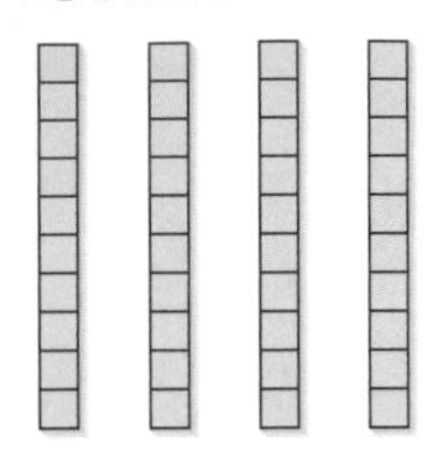

$+$

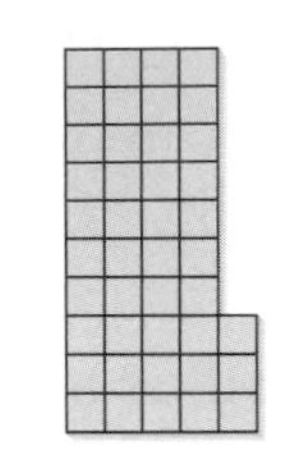

$=$

Start with four tenth pieces. **Add three hundredth pieces.** **Count the total number of hundredth pieces.**

There are a total of 43 hundredths pieces, so $0.4 + 0.03 = 0.43$.

EXAMPLE Modeling Decimal Differences

2 Use a model to find $1.4 - 0.6$.

Use two tenths grids. Shade ten tenths in one grid and four tenths in the other grid.

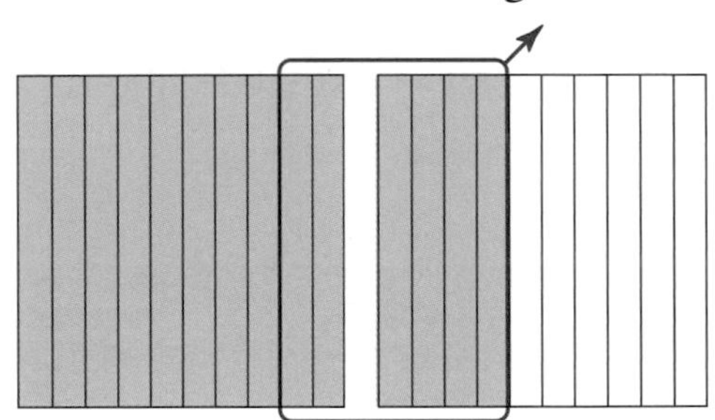

← **Remove six tenths from fourteen tenths.**

There are eight tenths left, so $1.4 - 0.6 = 0.8$.

Exercises

Use a model to find each sum or difference.

1. $0.1 + 0.8$ **2.** $1.5 - 1.2$ **3.** $0.06 + 0.55$ **4.** $1.54 - 0.72$

5. a. Use a model to find $0.41 + 0.59$.
b. Number Sense Explain why there are no hundredths in the answer.

1-4 Adding and Subtracting Decimals

Check Skills You'll Need

1. Vocabulary Review
__?__ is a method of estimation that compares a digit's value to 5.

Round each number to the underlined place.

2. 72 **3.** 108

4. 149 **5.** 3,196

for Help
Skills Handbook p. 381

CONTENT STANDARD
6.NS.3

Video Tutor Help
PearsonSuccessNet.com

What You'll Learn

To add and subtract decimals and to solve problems involving decimals

New Vocabulary front-end estimation

Why Learn This?

To find the sum or difference of two amounts of money, you need to add or subtract decimals.

If you estimate before you add or subtract, you can tell whether your answer is reasonable. One way to estimate is to round.

EXAMPLE Finding Decimal Sums

1 Find $3.026 + 14.7 + 1.38$.

Step 1 Estimate. $3.026 + 14.7 + 1.38$
$\approx 3 + 15 + 1$, or 19

Step 2 Add.

$$\begin{array}{r} 3.026 \\ 14.700 \\ +\ 1.380 \\ \hline 19.106 \end{array}$$

Line up the decimal points.

Write zeros so that all of the decimals have the same number of digits to the right of the decimal point.

Check for Reasonableness The sum 19.106 is reasonable, since it is close to 19.

Quick Check

1. Find $0.84 + 2.0 + 3.32$. Estimate first.

In **front-end estimation,** you estimate by first adding the "front-end digits." Then you estimate the sum of the remaining digits. You adjust the sum of the front-end digits as necessary.

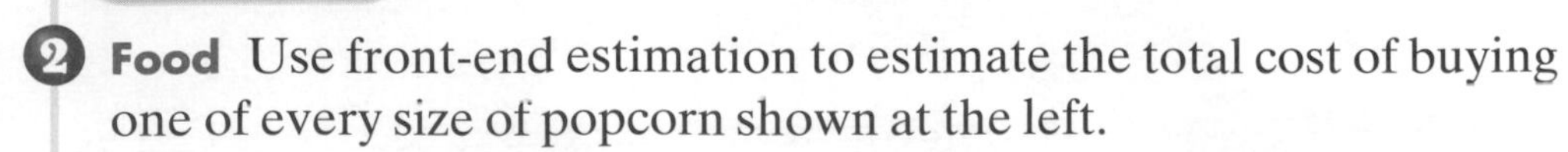

EXAMPLE Using Front-End Estimation

Popcorn
Small $3.98
Medium $6.49
Large $9.08
Junior $3.47

2 **Food** Use front-end estimation to estimate the total cost of buying one of every size of popcorn shown at the left.

Step 1 Add the front-end digits. These are the dollar amounts.

$$\begin{array}{r} \$3.98 \\ \$6.49 \\ \$9.08 \\ +\ \$3.47 \\ \hline \$21 \end{array}$$

Step 2 Estimate the total cents. Then adjust the dollar amounts.

$$\begin{array}{rl} \$3.98 & \rightarrow \text{about } \$1 \\ \$6.49 & \\ \$9.08 & \text{about } \$1 \\ +\ \$3.47 & \\ \hline \$21 & \text{about } \$2 \end{array}$$

The total cost is about $21 + $2, or $23.

Quick Check

2. Use front-end estimation to estimate the total cost of one small popcorn and two large popcorns.

EXAMPLE Finding a Difference

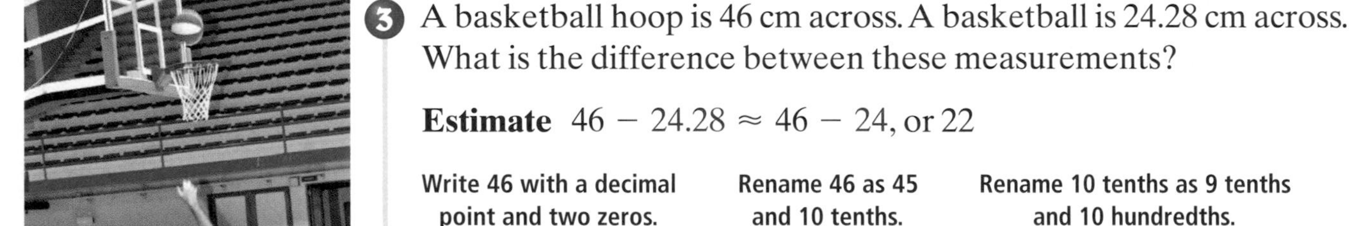

3 A basketball hoop is 46 cm across. A basketball is 24.28 cm across. What is the difference between these measurements?

Estimate $46 - 24.28 \approx 46 - 24$, or 22

Write 46 with a decimal point and two zeros.	Rename 46 as 45 and 10 tenths.	Rename 10 tenths as 9 tenths and 10 hundredths.
46.00 − 24.28	45 10 ~~46.0~~0 − 24.28	9 45 ~~10~~ 10 ~~46.00~~ − 24.28 21.72

The difference is 21.72 cm.

Check for Reasonableness 21.72 is close to 22, so the answer is reasonable.

Quick Check

3. Use the graph at the right. How much greater is the women's record discus throw than the men's throw?

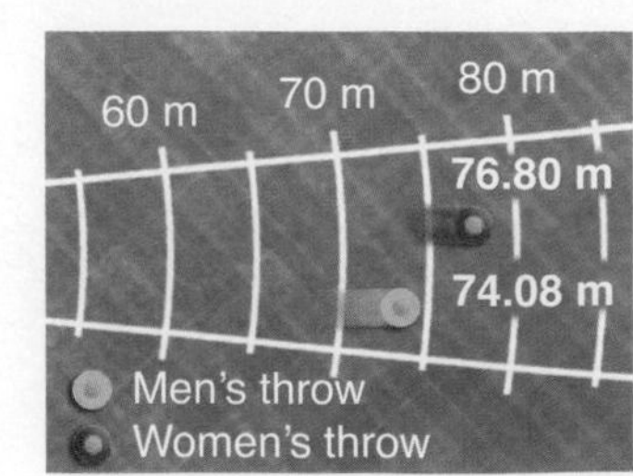

Check Your Understanding

1. **Error Analysis** Explain and correct the error in the work at the right.

$$\begin{array}{r} 5.8 \\ -\ 2 \\ \hline 5.6 \end{array}$$

Find each sum or difference.

2. 6.37 + 2.45

$$\begin{array}{r} 6.37 \\ +\ ■.■■ \\ \hline \end{array}$$

3. 8.9 − 7.52

$$\begin{array}{r} ■.■■ \\ -\ 7.52 \\ \hline \end{array}$$

4. 7.3 + 4

$$\begin{array}{r} 7.3 \\ +\ ■.■ \\ \hline \end{array}$$

Use front-end estimation to estimate each sum.

5. \$6.70 + \$2.40
6. \$8.92 + \$7.10
7. \$7.10 + \$4

Homework Exercises

For more exercises, see Extra Skills and Word Problems.

GO for Help

For Exercises	See Example
8–13	1
14–17	2
18–27	3

First estimate. Then find each sum.

8. 0.6 + 3.4
9. 6.2 + 0.444
10. 8.001 + 0.77
11. 7 + 11.436 + 3.08
12. 0.445 + 8.99 + 3
13. 0.33 + 1.11 + 3.2

Use front-end estimation to estimate each sum.

14. \$4.89 + \$3.97
15. \$6.15 + \$8.86
16. \$14.65 + \$27.29 + \$63.85
17. \$16.81 + \$19.94 + \$11.49

First estimate. Then find each difference.

18. 22.2 − 4.3
19. 8.91 − 6.08
20. 9.45 − 3.76
21. 9.1 − 6.05
22. 0.8 − 0.126
23. 4 − 1.29
24. 60 − 2.037
25. 9 − 0.45
26. 6.72 − 2.45
27. A digital camera costs \$174.99 online. At a local store, the same camera costs \$222.98. What is the difference in prices?

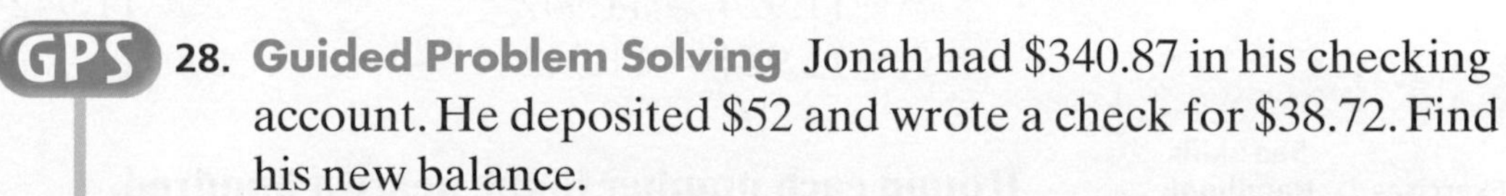

GPS

28. **Guided Problem Solving** Jonah had \$340.87 in his checking account. He deposited \$52 and wrote a check for \$38.72. Find his new balance.
    - How did Jonah's balance change after he deposited \$52?
    - How did the balance change after he wrote the check?

PearsonSuccessNet.com

Use $<$, $=$, or $>$ to complete each statement.

29. 0.041 + 0.009 ■ 0.5

30. 0.315 + 0.14 + 0.05 ■ 0.5

31. 669.583 + 204.222 ■ 873.8

32. 665.5 − 281.7 ■ 373.8

33. Population In 2000, the New England states had a total population of about 13.92 million. Find the population of Maine.

State	Population
Connecticut	3.41 million
Maine	■
Massachusetts	6.35 million
New Hampshire	1.24 million
Rhode Island	1.05 million
Vermont	0.61 million

SOURCE: U.S. Census Bureau.
Go to **www.PHSchool.com** for a data update.
Web Code: aqg-9041

T-Shirts and Sweatshirts For Sale

Adult T-shirt
(M-XL) $15.00
(XXL) $17.95

Adult Sweatshirt
(M-XL) $29.50
(XXL) $29.95

Child's T-shirt
$12.50

Child's Sweatshirt
$16.95

34. A series of orders was placed with a clothing company. Using the prices at the left, estimate the total cost of each order.

a. 2 XXL adult T-shirts and 1 child sweatshirt

b. 3 XL adult sweatshirts and 4 child sweatshirts

c. 3 child T-shirts, 2 XL adult T-shirts and 2 XXL adult T-shirts

35. Choose a Method A hot dog vendor receives a $20 bill for a $5.25 purchase. Is the vendor most likely to use estimation, mental math, or a calculator to find the amount of change? Explain.

36. Challenge Find the missing numbers.

a. 1.2 × ■ = 18

b. 2.5 × ■ = 11.25

Test Prep and Mixed Review

Practice

Multiple Choice

37. At a baseball game, Ben ordered peanuts for $3.25. He paid with a $5 bill. How much change did Ben get?

Ⓐ $1.25 Ⓑ $1.75 Ⓒ $2.25 Ⓓ $2.75

38. Patrick spent $22 on a taxi ride, $48 on a theater ticket, and $31 on snacks. Which is closest to the total amount he spent?

Ⓕ $90 Ⓖ $100 Ⓗ $110 Ⓙ $120

39. Which statement about 11.924 and 11.942 is true?

Ⓐ 11.924 $>$ 11.942 Ⓒ 11.942 $>$ 11.924
Ⓑ 11.924 = 11.942 Ⓓ 11.942 $<$ 11.924

GO for Help

For Exercises	See Skills Handbook
40–44	p. 381

Round each number to the nearest hundred.

40. 287 **41.** 812 **42.** 86 **43.** 1,413 **44.** 6,546

Vocabulary Builder

High-Use Academic Words

High-use academic words are words that you will see often in textbooks and on tests. These words are not math vocabulary terms, but knowing them will help you to succeed in mathematics.

Direction Words

Some words tell what to do in a problem. I need to understand what these words are asking so that I give the correct answer.

Word	Meaning
Explain	To give facts and details that make an idea easier to understand
Compare	To tell or show how two things are alike and different
Name	To identify something by stating its name

Exercises

1. Explain how to make a peanut butter and jelly sandwich.
2. Compare a peanut butter and jelly sandwich to a ham and cheese sandwich.
3. Name the ingredients in a peanut butter and jelly sandwich.
4. Explain how to round a decimal to the nearest tenth.
5. Compare 0.8 and 0.85.
6. Name the place and value of each digit in 10.92.
7. a. **Word Knowledge** Think about the word *reasonable.* Choose the letter that shows how well you know the word.
   - A. I know its meaning.
   - B. I have seen it, but I don't know its meaning.
   - C. I don't know it.

   b. **Research** Look up and write the definition of *reasonable.*

   c. Use the word in a sentence involving mathematics.

1-5a Activity Lab

Modeling Decimal Multiplication

A model can help you to multiply decimals.

EXAMPLES Multiplying Decimals

1 **Coin Collecting** A collector buys two 1942 Mercury dimes. Each coin costs \$.92. Draw a model to find the total cost.

Miss Liberty's winged cap makes her look like the Roman god Mercury, so the coin was called the "Mercury" dime.

You want to find $0.92 + 0.92$, or 2×0.92.

Shade 92 squares in each of two grids.

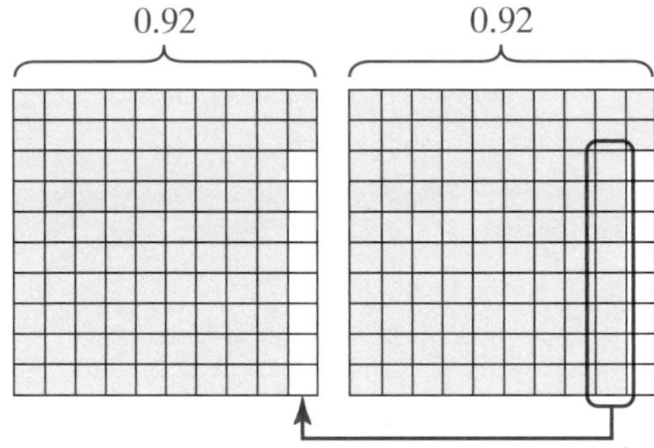

Count the shaded squares in the grids.

Move 8 hundredths to fill the first grid.

The shaded area is 1 whole and 84 hundredths, or 1.84. The total cost is \$1.84.

2 Draw a model to find the product 0.5×0.4.

Shade 4 *columns* → of a grid to represent 0.4.

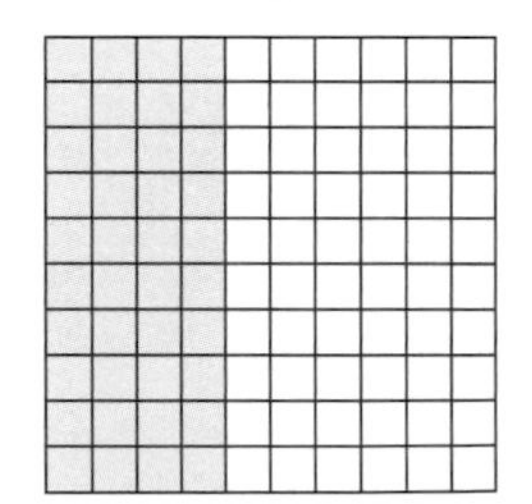

Shade 5 *rows* to → represent 0.5. Use a different color or style.

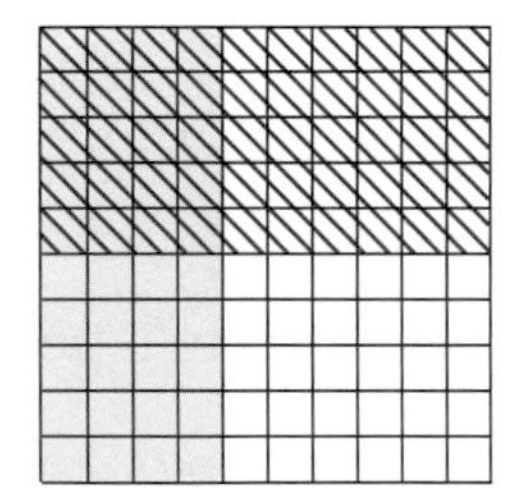

The shadings overlap in 20 squares, representing 20 hundredths, or 0.20. So $0.5 \times 0.4 = 0.20$.

Exercises

Draw a model to find each product.

1. 3×0.9 **2.** 2×0.61 **3.** 0.8×0.5 **4.** 0.7×0.2 **5.** 0.1×0.6

6. **Writing in Math** Explain how to use models to find 2.6×0.2.

1-5 Multiplying Decimals

Check Skills You'll Need

1. Vocabulary Review Are 130 and 5 *compatible* numbers when dividing 130 by 5? Explain.

Estimate using compatible numbers.

2. 21×29 **3.** 59×3

4. $498 \div 5$ **5.** $71 \div 7$

GO for Help Skills Handbook p. 392

CONTENT STANDARDS
6.NS.3, 6.EE.2.b

What You'll Learn

To multiply decimals and to solve problems involving decimals

Why Learn This?

Understanding how much a plant will grow over time is important in gardening. You can multiply decimals to estimate how tall a flower or tree will grow.

The model below shows how to find 0.5×1.5. You are finding half of 1.5.

Shade 15 columns to represent 1.5.

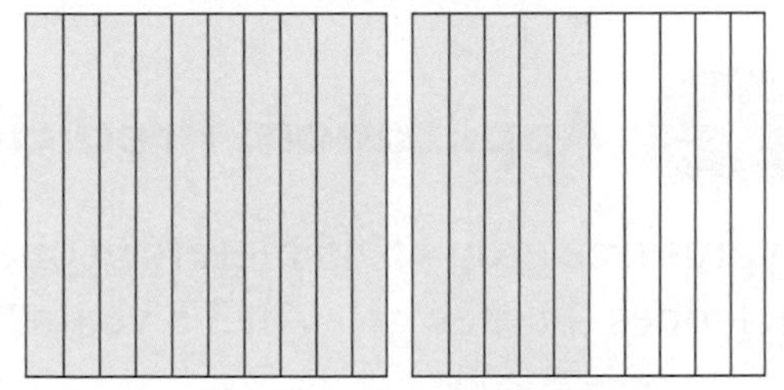

Shade 5 rows of each grid to represent 0.5.

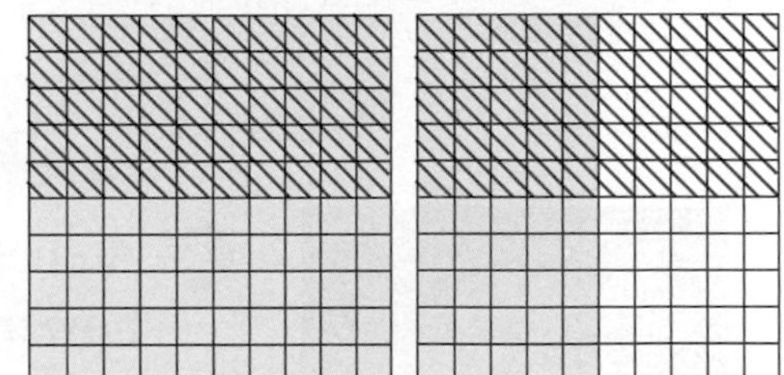

The shadings overlap in 75 squares, or 0.75. So $0.5 \times 1.5 = 0.75$.

To find the number of decimal places in a product, add the number of decimal places in the factors.

EXAMPLE Multiplying by a Decimal

1 Find the product 0.47×8.

0.47	←	2 decimal places
× 8	←	+ 0 decimal places
3.76	←	2 decimal places

Quick Check

1. a. Find 6×0.13. **b.** Find 4.37×5.

You can show multiplication in these three ways:

$0.5 \times 1.5 \qquad 0.5 \cdot 1.5 \qquad 0.5(1.5)$

Video Tutor Help

PearsonSuccessNet.com

EXAMPLE Multiplying Decimals

2 Find the product $1.31 \cdot 2.4$.

$$\begin{array}{r l} 1.31 & \leftarrow \text{ 2 decimal places} \\ \times\ 2.4 & \leftarrow \underline{+\text{ 1 decimal place}} \\ \hline 524 & \\ +\ 262 & \\ \hline 3.144 & \leftarrow \text{ 3 decimal places} \end{array}$$

Check for Reasonableness It makes sense that a number slightly greater than 1 times a number slightly greater than 2 equals a product of about 3.

Quick Check

2. Find each product.
   a. $0.3(0.2)$ b. $1.9 \cdot 5.32$ c. 0.9×0.14

You can estimate the product before you multiply decimals.

EXAMPLE Application: Predicting Growth

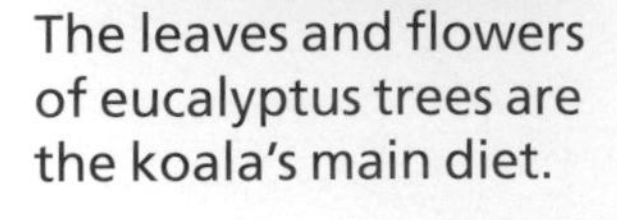

The leaves and flowers of eucalyptus trees are the koala's main diet.

3 A eucalyptus tree grows 5.45 meters in one year. At that rate, how much does the tree grow in 3.5 years?

Estimate $3.5 \times 5.45 \approx 4 \times 5$, or 20 ← 4 and 5 are rounded numbers.

$$\begin{array}{r l} 5.45 & \leftarrow \text{ 2 decimal places} \\ \times\ 3.5 & \leftarrow \text{ 1 decimal place} \\ \hline 2725 & \\ +\ 1635 & \\ \hline 19.075 & \leftarrow \text{ 3 decimal places} \end{array}$$

At that rate, the tree grows about 19.075 meters in 3.5 years.

Check for Reasonableness 19.075 is close to 20, so the answer is reasonable.

3. One pound of tomatoes costs $1.29. To the nearest cent, how much do 2.75 pounds of tomatoes cost?

Check Your Understanding

1. **Reasoning** You are multiplying 9.876×5.4321. How many decimal places does the answer have? Explain.

2. **Error Analysis** A student says $19.8 \times 3.1 = 612.8$. Is this answer correct? Explain how you know.

Number Sense Is the product *greater than, equal to,* or *less than* 1? Explain your reasoning.

3. 2×0.2
4. 2.2×0.7
5. 2×0.5

Copy each problem. Place the decimal point in the product.

6. $0.403 \times 5 = 2015$
7. $524 \times 0.5 = 2620$
8. $0.15 \times 0.31 = 465$
9. $8.42 \times 6.7 = 56414$

Homework Exercises

For more exercises, see Extra Skills and Word Problems.

GO for Help

For Exercises	See Example
10–17	1
18–34	2–3

Find each product.

10. 0.018×4
11. 1.9×9
12. 35×5.6
13. 39×0.06
14. 358×0.7
15. 0.12×47
16. 53×0.04
17. 0.25×92
18. 0.2×0.7
19. 0.8×0.4
20. 0.3×0.5
21. 0.7×0.9
22. $0.12(0.96)$
23. $0.06(0.18)$
24. $0.486 \cdot 0.9$
25. $0.03 \cdot 0.574$
26. $4.5(230)$
27. 1.7×3.702
28. $3.2 \cdot 4.5$
29. $8.1 \cdot 1.3$
30. $3.3(420)$
31. $3.2 \cdot 15.5$
32. $4.25 \cdot 6.18$
33. 1.2×2.065

34. A year on Mars is 1.88 times as long as a year on Earth. An Earth year lasts 365.3 days. Find the length of a year on Mars.

35. **Guided Problem Solving** Ham costs \$8.79 per pound and turkey costs \$9.48 per pound. What is the total cost of 2 pounds of ham and 1.5 pounds of turkey?
    - What is the cost of 2 pounds of ham? 1.5 pounds of turkey?

36. **Nutrition** There is 0.2 gram of calcium in 1 serving of cheddar cheese. How much calcium is in 3.25 servings of cheddar cheese?

Choose a Method Find each product. Tell whether you use mental math, paper and pencil, or a calculator.

37. 16×2.5 38. $60(0.5)$ 39. 56.37×5.29

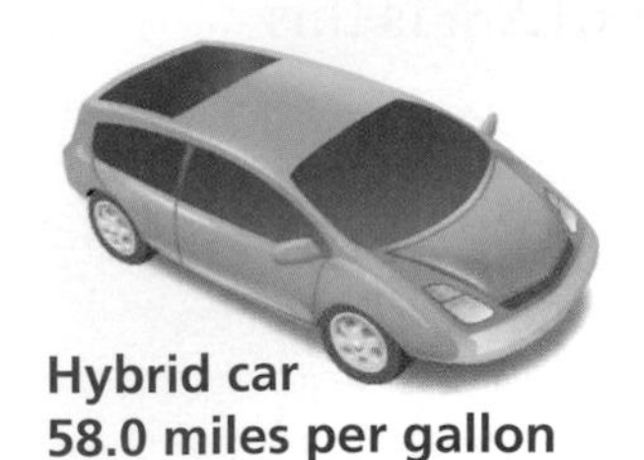

Hybrid car
58.0 miles per gallon

Sport utility vehicle (SUV)
13.5 miles per gallon

40. The average fuel rates for a hybrid car and an SUV are shown at the left. How much farther than the SUV can the hybrid car travel using 13 gallons of gas?

41. **Astronomy** Mercury is about 36 million miles from the sun. Jupiter is about 13.43 times that distance. About how far is Jupiter from the sun?

42. **Writing in Math** Explain how multiplying 0.3×0.4 is like multiplying 3×4. How are the two problems different?

43. **Challenge** Find the value that makes each statement true.
a. ■ $\div 0.2 = 0.7$ b. ■ $\div 0.03 = 0.5$

Test Prep and Mixed Review

Practice

Multiple Choice

44. Abby's mother and father take Abby and three of her friends to a water park. Admission is $14 for adults and $11 for children. The steps for finding the total cost are below.

Step K: Multiply $11 by 4.
Step L: Add the products.
Step M: Count two adults and four children.
Step N: Multiply $14 by 2.

Which list shows the correct order of steps?
(A) L, M, K, N (C) K, N, L, M
(B) M, K, N, L (D) M, L, N, K

45. Which is a reasonable estimate of the sum $214 + 92 + 56$?
(F) 300 (G) 350 (H) 400 (J) 450

46. Which statement about 2.315 is NOT true?
(A) $2.315 > 2.13$ (C) $2.15 < 2.315$
(B) $2.31 < 2.315$ (D) $2.315 > 2.51$

GO for Help

For Exercises	See Lesson
47–49	1-4

Find each sum or difference.

47. $7.32 + 4.29$ 48. $11.07 - 1.2$ 49. $6.5 - 0.32$

1-5b Activity Lab — Technology

Multiplying and Dividing Decimals by 10, 100, and 1,000

There are shortcuts for multiplying and dividing decimals by 10, 100, and 1,000. You can use these shortcuts to multiply mentally.

ACTIVITY

1. Use a calculator to multiply.
   a. $2.6 \times 10 = ■$
      $2.6 \times 100 = ■$
      $2.6 \times 1{,}000 = ■$
   b. $0.45 \times 10 = ■$
      $0.45 \times 100 = ■$
      $0.45 \times 1{,}000 = ■$
2. a. **Patterns** What do you notice about the movement of the decimal point in your answer when you multiply by 10? By 100? By 1,000?
   b. Write a rule for multiplying a decimal by 10, 100, and 1,000.
3. Use a calculator to divide.
   a. $2.6 \div 10 = ■$
      $2.6 \div 100 = ■$
      $2.6 \div 1{,}000 = ■$
   b. $0.45 \div 10 = ■$
      $0.45 \div 100 = ■$
      $0.45 \div 1{,}000 = ■$
4. a. **Patterns** What do you notice about the movement of the decimal point when you divide by 10? By 100? By 1,000?
   b. Write a shortcut for dividing a decimal by 10, 100, and 1,000.

Exercises

Use mental math to find each answer.

1. 6.2×10
2. $122.9 \div 10$
3. $161.7 \div 100$
4. $1{,}000(4.3)$
5. $1.5 \div 100$
6. $1{,}000 \cdot 0.89$
7. Use a calculator to multiply.
   a. 527×0.1
   b. 527×0.01
   c. 527×0.001
   d. 527×0.0001
   e. **Patterns** What do you notice about the movement of the decimal point in your answers for parts (a)–(d)?

Checkpoint Quiz 2

Lessons 1-3 through 1-5

1. Write 12.035 in words.

Find each sum or difference.

2. $1.25 + 6.07$
3. $9.06 - 0.8$
4. $\$8.00 - \$2.76$
5. $1.7 - 0.28$

Find each product.

6. 2.2×6.3
7. 4.9×7
8. 1.23×0.8
9. 5.03×1.04

10. Jo made 7 pounds of cookies. She gave 3.25 pounds to her friends and 0.7 pound to each of her three brothers. How many pounds did she have left?

MATH GAMES

Slide and Score

What You'll Need

- Six note cards with $\times$ *10,* $\times$ *100,* $\times$ *1,000,* $\div$ *10,* $\div$ *100,* and $\div$ *1,000* written on them
- Two chips to use as decimal points
- Two strips of paper with 4 1 2 3 5 and 5 3 1 4 2 written on them

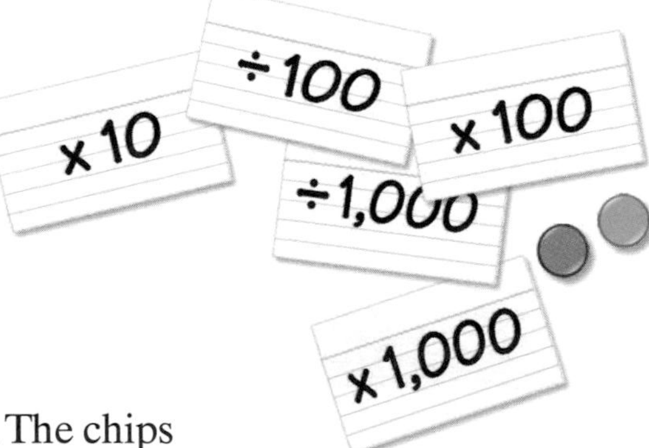

How To Play

- Place the chips after the first digit in each number. The chips are used as decimal points. Line up the decimal points.
- A player draws a card and performs the operation on one of the numbers. Then the player lines up the decimal points again. The player receives points for any two numbers in a column. In the game below, the player will receive 3 points when the decimal is moved to the left.
- Replace the operation card and shuffle. A player's turn continues until the operation cannot be performed on either number. The winner is the first person to score 11 points.

4 1 2 3 5

5 3 1 4 2

1-6 Dividing Decimals

Check Skills You'll Need

1. Vocabulary Review How is a *dividend* different from a *divisor*?

Simplify.

2. $935 \div 5$

3. $296 \div 8$

4. $636 \div 12$

for Help
Skills Handbook p. 386

CONTENT STANDARDS

6.NS.2, 6.NS.3, 6.EE.2.b

What You'll Learn

To divide decimals and to solve problems involving decimals

Why Learn This?

Sometimes you want to share costs with your friends. You can divide decimals to find the amount each person should pay.

Dividing decimals is similar to dividing whole numbers.

Vocabulary Tip

You can indicate division three ways:

$15 \div 3$

$3\overline{)15}$

$\frac{15}{3}$ ← dividend ← divisor

EXAMPLE Dividing Whole Numbers

1 **Rides** A roller coaster at the amusement park has 8 cars. Each car holds 4 riders. How many times will the ride have to run so that 384 people can ride?

Each time the ride runs, it takes one group of $8 \times 4 = 32$ riders.

You need to divide: 384 divided into equal groups of 32.

$$\begin{array}{r} 12 \\ 32\overline{)384} \\ -32\downarrow \\ 64 \\ -64 \\ 0 \end{array}$$

← Multiply. $1 \times 32 = 32$
← Subtract. Bring down the 4.
← Multiply. $2 \times 32 = 64$
← Subtract. The remainder is 0.

Check $12 \times 32 = 384$. The solution checks.

Quick Check

1. a. $3{,}348 \div 9$ **b.** $27\overline{)837}$

EXAMPLE Dividing a Decimal by a Whole Number

2 Transportation and tickets for 12 friends to an amusement park cost \$364.20. How much will each person pay?

You are looking for the size of equal groups, so divide.

Estimate $364.20 \div 12 \approx 360 \div 12$, or 30

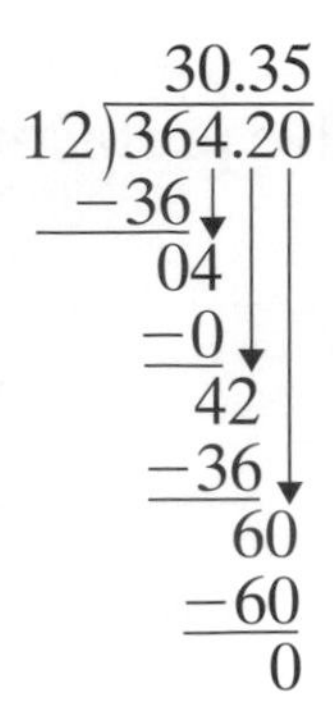

← Divide as with whole numbers. Place the decimal point in the quotient above the decimal point in the dividend.

Each person will pay \$30.35 for transportation and a ticket.

Check for Reasonableness 30.35 is close to 30.

Quick Check

2. a. Find $8\overline{)385.6}$. **b.** Find $9.12 \div 6$.

One way to think about dividing decimals is to break the dividend into equal groups. The model below shows $0.8 \div 0.2$, or how many groups of 0.2 are in 0.8.

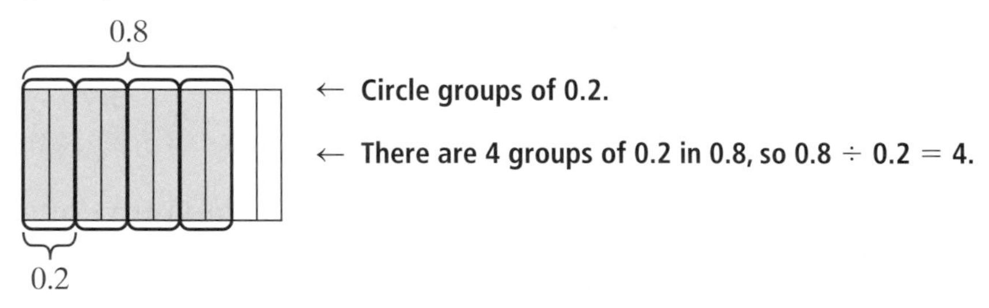

Study the pattern of quotients below.

	Dividend	÷	Divisor	=	Quotient
	0.8	÷	0.2	=	4
Multiply dividend and divisor by 10. →	8	÷	2	=	4
Multiply dividend and divisor by 100. →	80	÷	20	=	4

The pattern shows that when you multiply both the dividend and the divisor by the same number, the quotient remains the same.

KEY CONCEPTS Dividing Decimals

To divide a decimal by a decimal, multiply both the dividend and the divisor by 10, 100, or 1,000 so that the divisor is a whole number.

EXAMPLE Dividing a Decimal by a Decimal

3 **Recipes** You use 0.5 pound of berries to make one smoothie. How many smoothies can you make with 2.25 pounds of berries?

Multiply 0.5 by 10 to make the divisor a whole number.

$0.5\overline{)2.25}$

Also multiply 2.25 by 10.

$$\begin{array}{r} 4.5 \\ 5\overline{)22.5} \\ -20 \\ 25 \\ -25 \\ 0 \end{array}$$

← Divide as with whole numbers. Place the decimal point in the quotient above the decimal point in the dividend.

You can make 4.5 smoothies.

Quick Check

3. You have \$2.75. You want to buy trading cards that cost \$.25 each. How many can you buy?

Check Your Understanding

1. **Vocabulary** When you divide both the dividend and the divisor by the same number, the (dividend, divisor, quotient) remains the same.

2. **Number Sense** Is the quotient of 3.05 ÷ 1.25 *greater than*, *less than*, or *equal to* 3? Explain your reasoning.

3. Draw a model to find 0.6 ÷ 0.2.

Estimate each quotient.

4. 18 ÷ 1.01

5. 106.7 ÷ 11

6. 299 ÷ 0.9

Complete each division.

7. 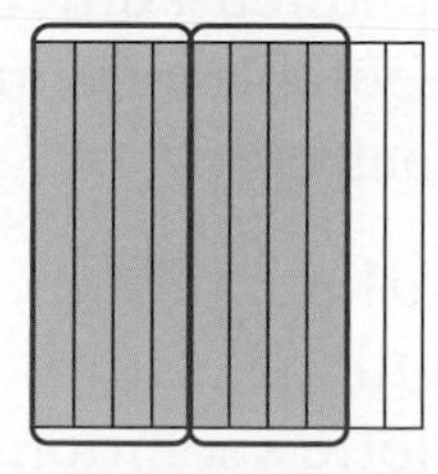

0.8 ÷ 0.4 = ■
8 ÷ 4 = ■

8. 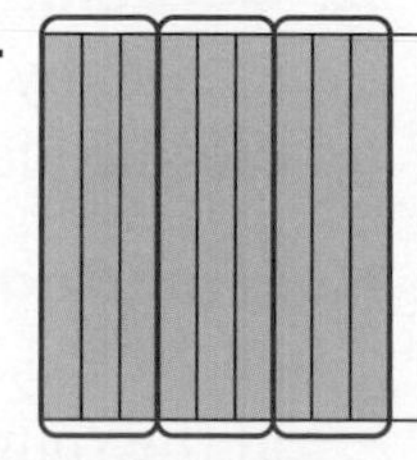

0.9 ÷ 0.3 = ■
9 ÷ 3 = ■

9. 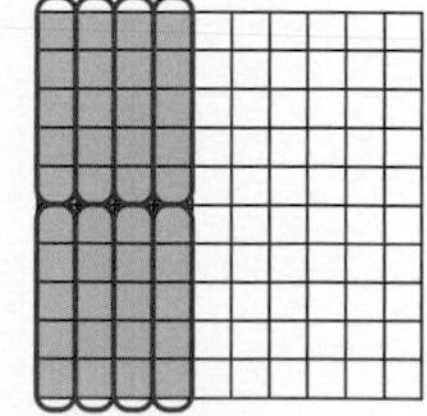

0.40 ÷ 0.05 = ■
40 ÷ 5 = ■

Homework Exercises

For more exercises, see Extra Skills and Word Problems.

GO for Help

For Exercises	See Example
10–12	1
13–21	2
22–27	3

Find each quotient.

10. $534 \div 6$
11. $990 \div 45$
12. $1{,}683 \div 3$
13. $328.25 \div 13$
14. $7\overline{)255.5}$
15. $237.6 \div 33$
16. $32\overline{)258.24}$
17. $84\overline{)26.46}$
18. $144.54 \div 6$
19. $27\overline{)99.36}$
20. $38.27 \div 43$
21. $29.5 \div 0.4$
22. $8.9\overline{)6.497}$
23. $3.1\overline{)10.261}$
24. $16.8 \div 2.4$
25. $0.96\overline{)0.144}$
26. $10.54 \div 0.17$
27. $5.9\overline{)0.649}$

28. **Guided Problem Solving** Seventeen customers bought two movie tickets each. The total cost was $263.50. What was the price per ticket?
    - What was the total number of tickets purchased?
    - What operation should you use to find the price per ticket?

29. **School Supplies** A stack of paper measures 0.9 centimeter thick. Each piece of paper is 0.01 centimeter thick.
    a. How many pieces of paper are in the stack?
    b. Could each of 25 students get three pieces of paper?

30. Students made 7 art posters that were hung along a hallway that is 4.4 m long. The posters are 0.2 m apart and the first and last posters are 0.2 m from the ends of the hallway. How many meters wide was each poster?

31. **Monthly Payments** Suppose you can buy Car 1 for $17,194.56 for 48 equal monthly payments. You can buy Car 2 for $21,851.40 for 60 equal monthly payments. What is the difference in the monthly payments you would make?

32. **Gardening** Jackie planted 4 different crops equally in her 24.8-m by 15.2-m vegetable garden. How many square meters did she plant with each crop?

33. **Error Analysis** Charlotte solved $13.28 \div 3.2$. Her solution is shown at the right. Is Charlotte's solution correct? Explain.

$3.2\overline{)13.28}$

$$\begin{array}{r} 4.125 \\ 32\overline{)132.8} \\ -128 \\ \hline 40 \\ -32 \\ \hline 80 \\ -64 \\ \hline 160 \\ -160 \\ \hline 0 \end{array}$$

34. **Bridges** The Great Seto Bridge in Japan is 9,368 meters long. A bicyclist riding across the bridge can travel 500 meters in 1 minute. A person walking can travel 100 meters in 1 minute. How many minutes shorter is the bicycle trip than the walk?

35. Five friends share three pizzas that cost $12.75 each. How much does each friend pay?

Find each quotient. Round to the nearest hundredth.

36. $64.97 \div 3.2$
37. $10.126 \div 2.3$
38. $3.3\overline{)26.81}$
39. $5.637 \div 0.17$
40. $6.24\overline{)78.28}$
41. $0.12\overline{)1.2542}$

42. A utility company charges $.12 for each kilowatt-hour of electricity you use. Your electric bill was $125.10. How many kilowatt-hours did you use?

43. **Reasoning** Which quotient is greater, $127.34 \div 0.673$ or $127.34 \div 0.671$? Explain your reasoning.

44. **Challenge** You and a friend are paid $38.25 for doing yard work. You work 2.5 hours and your friend works 2 hours. How much should you get for your share of the work? Explain.

Test Prep and Mixed Review

Practice

Multiple Choice

45. Four friends line up from shortest to tallest. Mac is shorter than Nate and taller than Ben. Charlie is taller than Mac and not on either end of the line. Which friend is first in line?
    - (A) Ben
    - (B) Charlie
    - (C) Mac
    - (D) Nate

46. Kelly bought a pair of jeans, a pair of sneakers, and four shirts. What missing piece of information is needed to find the total amount Kelly spent?
    - (F) the price of a shirt
    - (G) the amount of money Kelly has
    - (H) the original prices before the discount
    - (J) the number of shirts Kelly bought

Sale!
Jeans $24.99
Sneakers $34.99
Shirts 2 for the price of 1

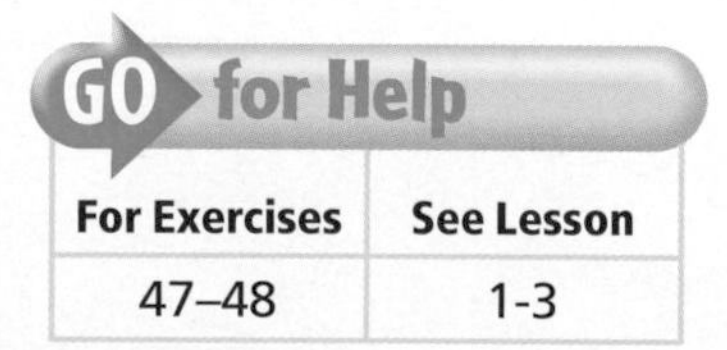

GO for Help

For Exercises	See Lesson
47–48	1-3

Order each set of decimals from least to greatest.

47. 8.3, 8.03, 8.308, 8.035
48. 1.8, 1.18, 1.801, 1.081

Using Decimals

Archaeologists are detectives who solve mysteries. The items they unearth provide clues about the people who once lived in a region. For example, archaeologists can measure the length of bones to determine the approximate heights of people.

ACTIVITY

1. The table at the right shows the length of the humerus, or arm bone, for five skeletons from an archaeological dig. Estimate the height of Male 1 in inches. Use the steps below.

Skeleton	Length of Humerus (cm)
Male 1	35
Female 1	32.5
Male 2	31.5
Female 2	■
■	24.5

Male	Female
Step 1 Multiply the length of the humerus by 2.9.	**Step 1** Multiply the length of the humerus by 2.8.
Step 2 Add 70.6 to the result.	**Step 2** Add 74.8 to the result.
Step 3 Divide by 2.54 to find the height in inches.	**Step 3** Divide by 2.54 to find the height in inches.

2. Find the height in inches of Female 1 and Male 2.
3. Measure the length of your own humerus in centimeters. To do this, measure from your elbow to the edge of your shoulder. Use this value to estimate your height in inches. How accurate is this estimate?
4. Suppose that the height of Female 2 is 148 cm. Work backward to estimate the length of her humerus.
5. The person listed in the bottom row of the chart was 140 cm tall. Is it more likely that this person was a male or a female? Support your answer with data and calculations.
6. **Writing in Math** Write a short paragraph explaining how this technique for estimating a person's height might have been developed. How accurate is it?

Choosing the Right Operation

Rubber Band Ball John Bain made the largest rubber-band ball in the world. The ball was 5 feet tall. It took 550,000 rubber bands, and 4 years, 2 months to put together. About how many rubber bands did Mr. Bain add each month?

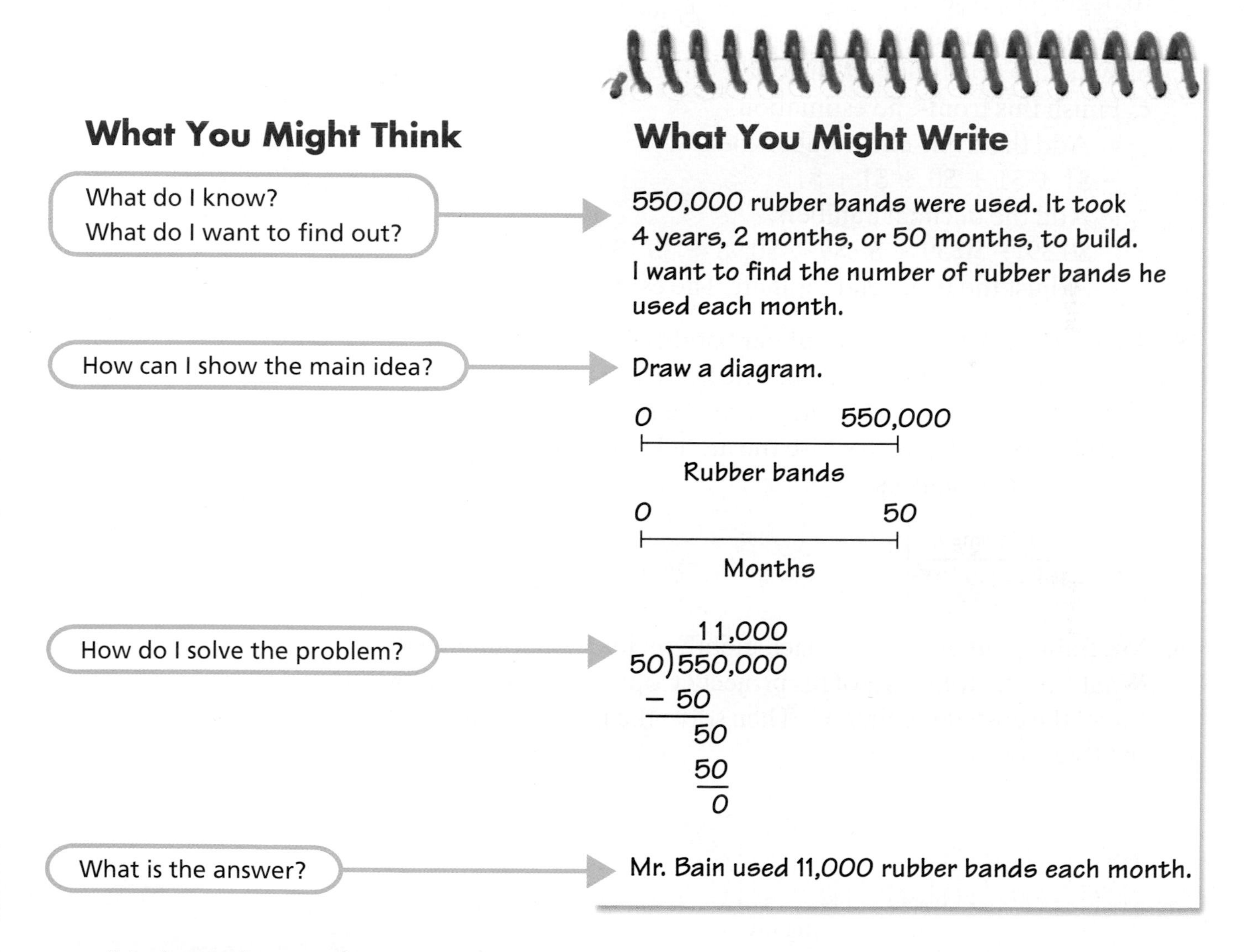

What You Might Think
What You Might Write
What do I know?
What do I want to find out?
550,000 rubber bands were used. It took 4 years, 2 months, or 50 months, to build.
I want to find the number of rubber bands he used each month.
How can I show the main idea?
Draw a diagram.
0
550,000
Rubber bands
0
50
Months
How do I solve the problem?
11,000
50)550,000
− 50
50
50
0
What is the answer?
Mr. Bain used 11,000 rubber bands each month.

Think It Through

1. Why does the diagram show 0–550,000 rubber bands on a line the same length as the line for 0–50 months?
2. Explain why 4 years, 2 months is the same as $4 \times 12 + 2$ months.
3. **Estimation** Use estimation to show that the answer is reasonable.

Exercises

4. Suppose Mr. Bain started with 5 packages of rubber bands. The packages cost $1.39, $1.59, $0.89, $1.98, and $1.13. Use front-end estimation to determine about how much he spent to begin his project.
   a. What do you know?
   b. What are you trying to find out?
   c. Finish this front-end estimation.
      - Add the front-end numbers below.
        $1 + $1 + $0 + $1 + $1
      - Add the decimal numbers.
        $0.39 + $0.59 + $0.89 + $0.98 + $0.13 is about $■.
      - Adjust the front-end estimate. The estimate is then $■.

5. To test the elasticity of the rubber bands, Mr. Bain stretched each rubber band in a package. The farthest a rubber band stretched was 38.5 inches. The shortest a rubber band stretched was 34.8 inches. Use the model below to find the difference in distances.

38.5 inches	
34.8 inches	?

6. Mr. Bain spent about $240 each month on his rubber-band ball. What was the total cost of his project? Copy the drawing below. Label the cost at the first ■. Then solve the problem and label the total cost at the second ■.

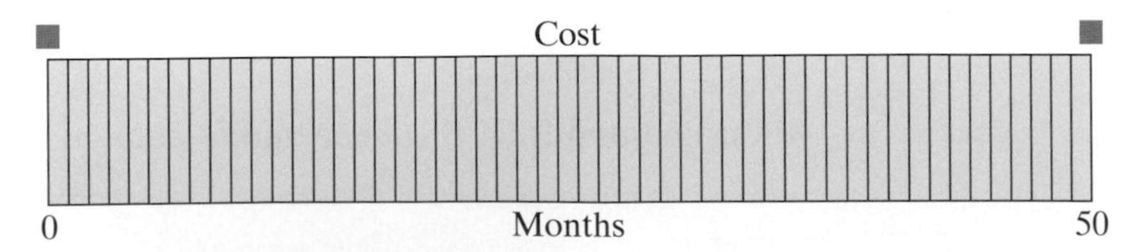

7. You can make a chain 1 mile long using 63,360 paper clips. The world record is a chain 19.62 miles long. How many paper clips were used to make this chain?

8. A teacher made a paper-clip chain using 60,650 paper clips. It took the teacher about 26.75 hours to make the chain. About how many seconds did the teacher spend adding each paper clip?

Writing Gridded Responses

Some tests include gridded responses. When you find an answer, write the answer at the top of the grid. Then fill in the matching bubbles.

EXAMPLE Using the Answer Grid

A fitness trail is 3.4 miles long. You walk 2.7 miles of the trail. How many more miles must you walk to reach the end of the trail?

$3.4 \text{ miles} - 2.7 \text{ miles} = 0.7 \text{ mile}$

You can write the answer as 0.7 or .7. Here are the two ways to enter these answers. You do not include labels in the grid.

Start to grid your answer at the right side of the grid. ↓

Add the 0 to the left of the decimal point. →

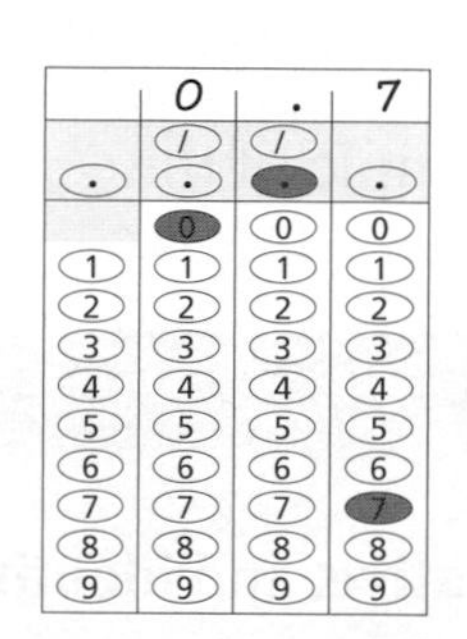

← Add the decimal point in the correct place. →

. 7

Exercises

Find each answer. If you have a grid, record your answer and fill in the bubbles.

1. A diver received scores of 6.5, 5.5, 6.0, 6.5, and 6.0 in a diving competition. What was his total score?
2. Nadia has a pitcher with 22.5 ounces of fruit punch. How many 4.5-ounce portions of punch can she pour?
3. Duane bought 3.8 pounds of bananas for $.55 per pound. How much did he spend in dollars?
4. Lisa bought 32.4 ounces of glue. She used 6.8 ounces to put together a model. How many ounces of glue did Lisa have left?

Chapter 1 Review

Vocabulary Review

Associative Property of Addition (p. 4)
Associative Property of Multiplication (p. 5)
Commutative Property of Addition (p. 4)
Commutative Property of Multiplication (p. 5)
expanded form (p. 15)
expression (p. 8)
front-end estimation (p. 19)
Identity Property of Addition (p. 4)
Identity Property of Multiplication (p. 5)
order of operations (p. 8)

Choose the correct vocabulary term to complete each sentence.

1. An example of the __?__ is $5 + 0 = 5$.
2. A sum that shows the place and value of each digit of a number is called __?__.
3. To simplify the expression $2 \times (10 + 1)$, add 10 and 1 first because of the __?__.
4. $7 + 4 \times 2$ is a(n) __?__.
5. $5 + (6 + 8) = (5 + 6) + 8$ is an example of the __?__.

Go Online

For vocabulary quiz
PearsonSuccessNet.com

Skills and Concepts

Lesson 1–1

- To understand and use the properties of operations

You can use the **commutative, associative,** and **identity properties** to help you add and multiply mentally.

Use mental math to find each sum.

6. $1 + 250 + 99$
7. $6 + 3 + 4 + 7$
8. $22 + 11 + 0 + 68$

Use mental math to find each product.

9. $2 \times 13 \times 5$
10. $3 \times 23 \times 1 \times 10$
11. $4 \times 43 \times 25$

Lesson 1-2

- To use the order of operations to simplify expressions and solve problems

An **expression** is a mathematical phrase that contains numbers and operation symbols. You can use the **order of operations** to find the value of an expression.

Find the value of each expression.

12. $30 - 5 + 4 \times 3$
13. $6 - (27 - 9) \div 3$
14. $5 \times 8 + 4 \div 2$

Lesson 1-3

- To read, write, and round decimals

You can write decimals in words, in standard form, and in **expanded form**.

Write each decimal in words.

15. 525.5 **16.** 0.5255 **17.** 5.025 **18.** 50.0025

Round each decimal to the underlined place.

19. $45.\underline{1}6$ **20.** $98.\underline{6}45$ **21.** $5.1\underline{2}5$ **22.** $1.2\underline{4}6$

Write each decimal in standard form and expanded form.

23. twenty-seven hundredths **24.** forty-two and six tenths

Lesson 1-4

- To add and subtract decimals and to solve problems involving decimals

You can use estimation to tell whether your answer is reasonable. You can use **front-end estimation** to estimate a sum.

First estimate. Then find each sum or difference.

25. $337.4 + 20.08$ **26.** $1.741 - 0.81$ **27.** $1.6 + 1.8$

28. $9.6 - 7.9$ **29.** $4.12 - 0.253$ **30.** $2.01 + 5.39$

Lesson 1-5

- To multiply decimals and to solve problems involving decimals

When multiplying decimals, add the decimal places in the factors to place the decimal point in the product.

Find each product.

31. 1.2×29.5 **32.** 0.54×17 **33.** 3.21×9.8 **34.** 13×0.8

35. John earns $10.26 an hour. How much will he earn if he works for 6.5 hours?

Lesson 1-6

- To divide decimals and to solve problems involving decimals

When dividing decimals, multiply both the dividend and the divisor by the same number so that the divisor is a whole number.

Find each quotient.

36. $12.12 \div 6$ **37.** $38.4 \div 0.08$ **38.** $27.76 \div 4$ **39.** $8.5 \div 0.05$

40. Maria has 0.8 loaf of raisin bread. What part the loaf will each person get if she divides it into 5 equal parts?

Chapter 1 Test

For online chapter test
PearsonSuccessNet.com

Use mental math to find each answer.

1. $829 + 71$
2. $24 + (72 + 64)$
3. $25 \times 6 \times 4$
4. $10 \times 7 \times 20$
5. $132 + 15 + 68$
6. $50 \times 16 \times 4$

Find the value of each expression.

7. $16 \div (4 \times 4)$
8. $8 - 4 \div 2$
9. $5 + (32 - 16)$
10. $(9 - 1 \times 3) \div 2$
11. $72 \div (3 + 6) + 2$
12. $6 + 4 \div 2 \times 6$

Write each number in words.

13. 623.7
14. 2,086,374
15. 89.123
16. 35,743,620,000
17. 172,254
18. 3.024

19. **Estimation** Suppose your savings account has a balance of \$238.52. You deposit \$42.56. Then you withdraw \$92.35. About how much is left in your savings account?

Use rounding or front-end estimation to estimate each answer.

20. $37 + 42 + 142$
21. 50.32×22.1
22. 4.63×50.491
23. $98 \div 24$
24. $1.01 + 2.89$
25. $62.85 - 24.12$

26. **DVDs** Five DVDs cost a total of \$75. Explain whether the best estimate for the cost of one DVD is greater than or less than \$14.

27. You buy movie tickets for yourself and three friends. Each ticket costs \$7. You pay with two \$20 bills. How much change do you get back?

First estimate. Then find each sum or difference.

28. $3.89 + 15.3$
29. $4.6 - 2.07$
30. $41.2 - 19.8$
31. $53.7 + 28.6$

Find each product or quotient.

32. 9.063×24
33. $0.36(15)$
34. $21.6 \div 0.06$
35. $7 \div 0.14$
36. 4.7×63.1
37. $97.2 \div 1.2$

38. **Pet Food** Zelda spent \$6.24 on pet food. The food costs \$.24 per cup. How many cups of pet food did Zelda purchase?

39. **Money** There are 40 quarters in a roll of quarters. What is the value of 9 rolls of quarters?

40. **Track** Two schools competed in a 4-person relay race. The times for each runner are shown in the table below.

	Riverside Middle School	Lakeside Middle School
Runner	Time (in sec)	Time (in sec)
1	26.8	24.3
2	27.2	28.4
3	25.6	23.2
4	23.7	26.1

a. Which school won the race by having the total fastest time?

b. What is the difference between the total times of the two schools?

Test Prep **Practice**

Reading Comprehension

Read each passage below. Then answer the questions based on what you have read.

Rainfall Hilo, Hawaii, usually receives 129.19 inches of rain each year. Compare that to Phoenix, Arizona, which receives 7.66 inches of rain a year. In Hilo, the wettest month is April, with 15.26 inches of rain, while the driest month is June, with 6.2 inches of rain. Phoenix's wettest month is December, with 1 inch, and its driest is May, with 0.12 inch.

1. In Hilo, how many more inches of rain typically fall in April than in June?

Ⓐ 0.88 inch Ⓒ 9.06 inches
Ⓑ 15.26 inches Ⓓ 21.46 inches

2. In July, Phoenix typically gets 0.83 inch of rain. About how many times as much rain falls in July as in May?

Ⓕ 6 Ⓖ 7 Ⓗ 8 Ⓙ 9

3. How many inches of rain does Hilo receive in a typical ten-year period?

Ⓐ 1,291.9 inches Ⓒ 76.60 inches
Ⓑ 12.919 inches Ⓓ 0.766 inches

4. Hilo's yearly rainfall is about how many times the yearly rainfall of Phoenix?

Ⓕ 1,040 times Ⓗ 138 times
Ⓖ 122 times Ⓙ 17 times

Coins Did you know that some coins contain more pure metal than others? American Gold Eagle coins are 0.9166 gold and Canadian Maple Leaf coins are 0.9999 gold. American Silver Eagle coins are 0.999 silver while American Platinum Eagle coins are 0.9995 platinum.

5. How might you write the purity of the American Silver Eagle coin in order to compare it with the other coins?

Ⓐ 0.99 Ⓒ 0.0999
Ⓑ 0.9990 Ⓓ 0.9999

6. What portion of the American Gold Eagle coin is NOT gold?

Ⓕ 0.0004 Ⓗ 0.0034
Ⓖ 0.0834 Ⓙ 0.0934

7. How much gold is in an American Gold Eagle coin that weighs 0.1 ounce?

Ⓐ 9.166 ounces
Ⓑ 0.91660 ounce
Ⓒ 0.9166 ounce
Ⓓ 0.09166 ounce

CHAPTER 2 Expressions and Equations

What You've Learned

- In Chapter 1, you learned to add, subtract, multiply, and divide decimals.
- You used rounding and front-end estimation to estimate with decimals.
- You used the order of operations to simplify espressions.

Check Your Readiness

GO for Help

For Exercises	See Lesson
1–4	1-2
5–10	1-4
11–13	1-5
14–16	1-6

Using the Order of Operations

Find the value of each expression.

1. $3 \times 8 + 5$
2. $36 + 6 \div 2$
3. $48 - 6 \times 5$
4. $(23 - 18) \times 6$

Adding and Subtracting Decimals

First estimate. Then find each sum or difference.

5. $36.05 + 6.1$
6. $36 - 26.5$
7. $0.05 + 5.05$
8. $5.2 - 3.04$
9. $5.12 - 2.85$
10. $9.8 + 4.56$

Multiplying Decimals

Find each product.

11. 3.79×5
12. 6.4×3.04
13. 43.7×7.1

Dividing Decimals

Find each quotient.

14. $13.2 \div 4$
15. $85 \div 0.5$
16. $1.917 \div 2.7$

What You'll Learn Next

- In this chapter, you will learn to use algebraic expressions to describe relationships.
- You will use mental math to estimate solutions to equations.
- You will use addition, subtraction, multiplication, and division to solve equations.
- You will write equations to solve problems.

Key Vocabulary

- Addition Property of Equality (p. 68)
- algebraic expression (p. 47)
- Division Property of Equality (p. 72)
- equation (p. 58)
- evaluate (p. 48)
- inverse operations (p. 64)
- Multiplication Property of Equality (p. 73)
- numerical expression (p. 47)
- open sentence (p. 59)
- Subtraction Property of Equality (p. 65)
- solution (p. 59)
- variable (p. 47)

2-1a Activity Lab

Patterns and Expressions

You can use a table to record data as you explore a pattern. A table can help you represent the pattern using symbols.

ACTIVITY

1. The first three designs in a pattern are shown at the right. Continue the pattern. Sketch the fourth and fifth designs on grid paper.

2. How many squares are in the fourth design? In the fifth design?

3. Copy and complete the table.

Design Number	1	2	3	4	5	6	7
Number of Squares	1	5	■	■	■	■	■

4. **Writing in Math** Describe how you will find the number of squares in the nth design of the pattern.

ACTIVITY

5. In each diagram, segments already join point A to the points on the circle. Copy each diagram. Join point A directly to the other points on the circle.

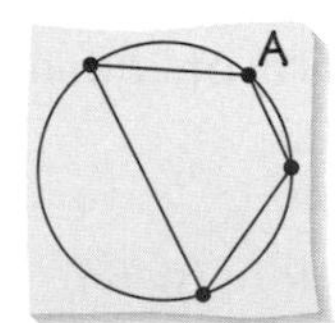

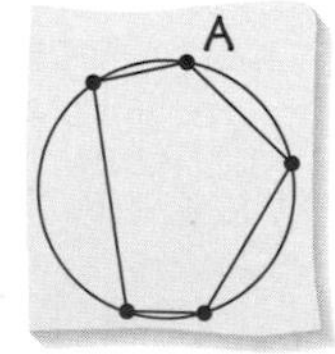

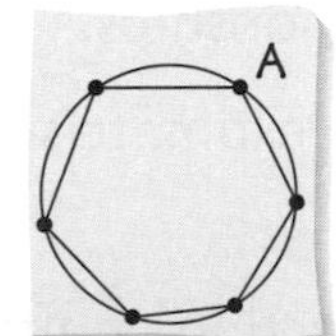

6. Copy and complete the table at the right.

Number of points on circle	4	5	6
Number of segments added to each diagram	■	■	■

7. Extend your table to include 7 and 8 points on a circle.

8. **(Algebra)** How many segments would you draw for n points on a circle?

Algebra

2-1 Variables and Expressions

Check Skills You'll Need

1. **Vocabulary Review** What is a mathematical *expression*?

Find the value of each expression.

2. $40 - 16 \div 2$
3. $3 \times 5 + 12 \div 3$
4. $7 \times (95 - 32)$

Lesson 1-2

CONTENT STANDARDS
6.EE.2, 6.EE.2.c, 6.EE.6

What You'll Learn

To evaluate algebraic expressions

New Vocabulary numerical expression, variable, algebraic expression, evaluate

Why Learn This?

You do not know how many people will attend a school fair. You can use a variable to represent the number of people.

A **numerical expression** is a mathematical phrase with only numbers and operation symbols $(+, -, \times, \div)$. An example of a numerical expression is $8 + 5 - 2$.

In the expressions below, n, d, b, and x are variables. A **variable** is a symbol that can represent one or more numbers. A mathematical expression with one or more variables is an **algebraic expression.**

$n + 2$ $\quad 5d \quad$ $7b - 2$ $\quad 12x \div 3$

Test Prep Tip

The expression $5d$ means "5 times a number d." It can also be written as $5 \times d$ and $5 \cdot d$.

You can use algebra tiles to model algebraic expressions.

A yellow tile represents 1.

A green tile represents a variable.

EXAMPLE Modeling With Algebra Tiles

1 Model the expression $5x + 3$ with algebra tiles.

← **5 green tiles represent 5*x*. 3 yellow tiles represent 3.**

Quick Check

1. Draw algebra tiles to model the expression $x + 2$.

The title screen of a video game usually asks, "How many players?" The number of players is a variable. The game software uses your entry to set up the game.

To **evaluate** an algebraic expression, you replace each variable with a number. Then you use the order of operations to simplify the expression.

EXAMPLE Evaluating an Algebraic Expression

2 Evaluate $2x - 8$ for $x = 11$.

$2x - 8 = 2(11) - 8$ ← Replace x with 11.

$= 22 - 8$ ← Multiply 2 and 11.

$= 14$ ← Subtract.

Quick Check

2. Evaluate each expression for $x = 7$.

a. $3x + 15$ **b.** $5x \div 7$ **c.** $56 - 4x$

You can evaluate an expression using more than one value. Make a table to organize the different values.

EXAMPLE Application: Fundraising

3 You earn $3 for each person who plays the game at your booth at the school fair. The expression $3p$ represents the amount of money you earn, where p is the number of people who play your game. Copy and complete the table for the given number of people.

School Fair Booth Earnings

Number of People	Process	Amount Earned	
p	$3 \times p$	$3p$	← Substitute each number of people for p.
15	$3 \times$ ■	■	← $3 \times 15 = 45$
40	$3 \times$ ■	■	← $3 \times 40 = 120$
65	$3 \times$ ■	■	← $3 \times 65 = 195$

Quick Check

3. How much will you earn from 85 people coming to your booth?

Check Your Understanding

1. **Vocabulary** How are numerical and algebraic expressions different? Give examples.

2. **Number Sense** Will the expression $50 - x$ get *larger*, *smaller*, or *stay the same* as the value of x increases?

Evaluate each expression for $x = 8$.

3. $x + 12$ 4. $80 \div x$ 5. $2x$ 6. $x - 3$

Homework Exercises

For more exercises, see Extra Skills and Word Problems.

GO for Help

For Exercises	See Example
7–14	1
15–19	2
20–23	3

Draw algebra tiles to model each expression.

7. $3x + 5$ 8. $c + 3$ 9. 8 10. $z + 4$

11. $4 + 2x$ 12. $a + 6$ 13. $c + c + c$ 14. $3m + 2$

Evaluate each expression.

15. $24 \div d$ for $d = 3$ 16. $p + 8$ for $p = 6$ 17. $3r - 2$ for $r = 65$

18. $8b - 12$ for $b = 2.1$ 19. $18 - 3y$ for $y = 2.5$

20. **Biking** The rental fee for a bicycle is \$5, plus \$2 for each hour h the bike is rented. The expression for the total cost is $5 + 2h$. Copy and complete the table for the given number of hours.

Hour	Rental Fee
h	$5 + 2h$
1	■
2	■
3	■

Copy and complete each table.

21.

x	$x + 6$
1	7
4	■
7	■

22.

x	$7x$
2	■
4	■
6	■

23.

x	$100 - x$
20	■
35	■
50	■

24. **Guided Problem Solving** The formula $P = 2\ell + 2w$ gives the distance around a rectangle with length ℓ and width w. Find P for a rectangle with length 7 cm and width 4 cm.
   - Replace each variable in the formula with the given values.

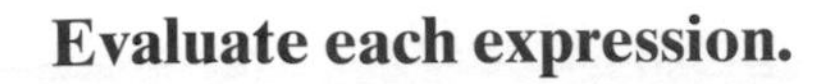

Evaluate each expression.

25. $11t - 6v$ for $t = 9$ and $v = 4$

26. $2ab$ for $a = 35$ and $b = 3$

27. The formula $N = 7 \times \ell \times h$ gives the number of bricks needed for a wall of length ℓ feet and height h feet. How many bricks are needed for a wall with length 22 feet and height 30 feet?

28. Dogs A dog walker charges \$10 to walk a large dog and \$6 to walk a small dog. She uses $10d + 6s$ to calculate her earnings, where d is the number of large dogs and s is the number of small dogs. How much does she earn for walking each group?

a. 4 large and 2 small dogs **b.** 6 small dogs

29. Challenge Bob plays a game at the school fair. He starts with 0 points. He gets 25 throws. He wins 12 points for hitting the target and loses 8 points for each miss. Bob ends with a score of 0. How many hits and misses does Bob have?

Test Prep and Mixed Review

Practice

Multiple Choice

30. Mr. Vasquez can seat 200 people in his restaurant. He has booths that seat 6 people and tables that seat 4 people. So far tonight, Mr. Vasquez has seated 8 full booths. Which method can he use to figure out how many more people he can seat?

Ⓐ Add the product of 6 and 8 to 4.
Ⓑ Subtract the product of 6 and 8 from 200.
Ⓒ Multiply 4 by the sum of 6 and 8.
Ⓓ Divide 200 by the sum of 6 and 4.

31. Each number in the pattern has the same relationship to the number immediately before it.

1; 20; 400; 8,000; ...

How can the next number in the pattern be found?

Ⓕ Add 20. Ⓗ Multiply by 20.
Ⓖ Subtract 20. Ⓙ Divide by 20.

32. Jenice rides her bike 3.4 miles to school. She takes a different route home. The route home is 3.7 miles. How many miles does Jenice ride each day?

Ⓐ 0.3 mile Ⓑ 3.5 miles Ⓒ 6.8 miles Ⓓ 7.1 miles

GO for Help

For Exercises	See Lesson
33–35	1-5

Find each product.

33. 2.43×12

34. 4.05×1.5

35. 37.4×0.001

Modeling Expressions

You can draw a diagram to help understand a word phrase.

Operation	Word Phrase	Diagram 1	Diagram 2
addition	a number m plus 3.2 the sum of a number m and 3.2 3.2 more than a number m	m 3.2	m 3.2
subtraction	a number p minus 6 the difference of a number p and 6 6 subtracted from a number p	p ? 6	p ? 6
multiplication	4 times a number k the product of 4 and a number k	k k k k	k k k k
division	the quotient of a number z and 5 a number z divided by 5	z ? ? ? ? ?	z ? ? ? ? ?

EXAMPLE

1 Draw a diagram for each word phrase.

a. 2.5 more than x

x 2.5 or x 2.5

b. the product of 3 and w

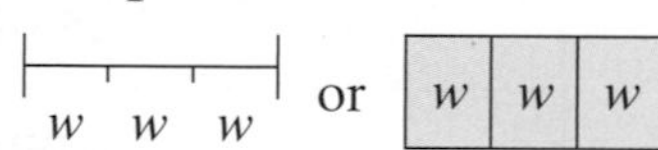

Exercises

Copy and complete the table below. Each line is missing two parts.

Word Phrase	Diagram 1	Diagram 2
1. Height h divided by 6		
2.		q 8
3.	r r r r r r r	
4. 6.3 smaller than t		

Algebra

2-2 Writing Algebraic Expressions

Check Skills You'll Need

1. **Vocabulary Review** What does it mean to *evaluate* an expression?

Evaluate each expression for $a = 7$.

2. $a + 3$
3. $7a - 19$
4. $6 \cdot (a + 1)$
5. $2 + (2a - 5)$

GO for Help Lesson 2-1

CONTENT STANDARDS
6.EE.2, 6.EE.2.a, 6.EE.2.b, 6.EE.6

What You'll Learn

To write algebraic expressions and use them to solve problems

Why Learn This?

Sometimes you need to find a quantity, cost, or amount. You can use an algebraic expression to model the cost of a night out with your family.

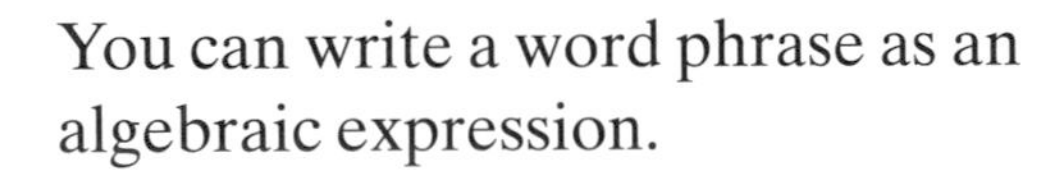

You can write a word phrase as an algebraic expression.

Operation	Word Phrase	Algebraic Expression
addition	a number m plus 45 the sum of a number m and 45 45 more than a number m	$m + 45$
subtraction	a number p minus 6 the difference of a number p and 6 6 subtracted from a number p	$p - 6$
multiplication	4 times a number k the product of 4 and a number k	$4k$
division	the quotient of a number z and 25 a number z divided by 25	$z \div 25, \frac{z}{25}$

Online active math

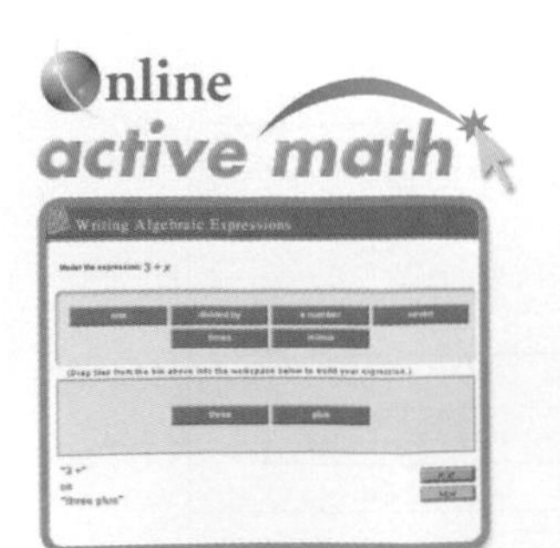

For: Algebraic Expressions Activity
Use: Interactive Textbook, 2-2

EXAMPLE From Words to Expressions

1 Write an expression for "the product of 7 and k."

$7 \cdot k$, or $7k$ ← ***Product*** **means multiplication.**

Quick Check

1. Write an expression for "2 more than x."

Drawing a diagram can help you write an expression for a real-world situation. Remember to state what the variable represents.

EXAMPLE Application: Bowling

2 You go bowling and bowl three games. Shoe rental for the day was \$1.75. Write an algebraic expression for the total amount you pay.

Test Prep Tip

When you choose a variable, use a letter that reminds you of what the variable stands for.

Let g = the cost of the game. ← Choose a variable to represent the cost of one game.

Total Cost			
g	g	g	1.75

Each g represents the cost of one game.

The total cost is $3g + 1.75$.

Quick Check

2. Brandon is 28 years younger than his father. Write an expression using Brandon's age to describe his father's age.

You can see the relationship between numbers when they are organized in a table. You can use an algebraic expression to describe this relationship.

EXAMPLE From a Pattern to an Expression

Perimeter of Squares

Side Length	Perimeter
2 cm	8 cm
3 cm	12 cm
5 cm	20 cm

3 **Multiple Choice** The table at the left shows the length of the sides of three squares and their perimeters. Which expression can you use to find the perimeter of a square with a side s units long?

Ⓐ $s + 4$ Ⓑ $s - 4$ Ⓒ $4s$ Ⓓ $s \div 4$

Side Length	Process	Perimeter
2 cm	$4 \times 2 = 8$	8 cm
3 cm	$4 \times 3 = 12$	12 cm
5 cm	$4 \times 5 = 20$	20 cm
s cm	$4 \times s = 4s$	$4s$ cm

Look for a relationship between side length and perimeter. It might be "multiply by 4."

Check the rule for the other pairs of numbers.

The expression $4s$ describes the pattern. The correct answer is C.

Quick Check

3. Write an algebraic expression to describe the relationship in the table.

n	■
2	6
5	9
7	11

More Than One Way

A long-distance call costs 10 cents, plus 4.5 cents for each minute. How much will an 8-minute call cost?

Jessica's Method

I can let m represent the number of minutes. To find the cost of the call, I can use the algebraic expression $10 + 4.5m$. Then I will evaluate the expression for $m = 8$.

$$\begin{aligned} 10 + 4.5m &= 10 + 4.5(8) && \leftarrow \text{Replace } m \text{ with 8.} \\ &= 10 + 36 && \leftarrow \text{Multiply 4.5 and 8.} \\ &= 46 && \leftarrow \text{Add 10 to 36.} \end{aligned}$$

The telephone call will cost 46 cents.

Luis's Method

If one minute costs 4.5 cents, then a two-minute call will cost 9 cents. A four-minute call will cost 18 cents, and an eight-minute call will cost 36 cents. I need to add the 10 cents. So the total cost is 36 cents + 10 cents, or 46 cents.

Choose a Method

Another long-distance plan charges 5 cents per call, plus 4 cents for each minute. Find how much a 10-minute call costs with this plan. Explain why you chose the method you used.

Check Your Understanding

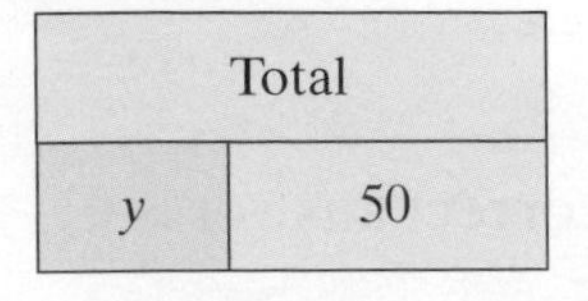

Total	
y	50

1. **Open-Ended** Write a problem that can be represented using the model at the left.

2. **Boating** Renting a paddle boat costs \$8 per hour. Write an expression for the cost to rent a paddle boat for h hours.

Write an expression for each word phrase.

3. m increased by 4: ■ + ■

4. y divided by five: ■ ÷ ■

5. six times z: ■ × ■

6. 4 subtracted from m: ■ − ■

Homework Exercises

For more exercises, see Extra Skills and Word Problems.

GO for Help

For Exercises	See Example
7–16	1–2
17–22	3

Write an expression for each word phrase.

7. 34 less than k **8.** 4 plus e **9.** d more than 50

10. 23 times q **11.** 7 decreased by b **12.** b divided by 3

13. 13 minus d **14.** a times 32 **15.** n less than 19

16. Jobs Three brothers earn money by doing yardwork. The brothers split the money equally. Write an expression that describes how much money each brother earns.

Write an expression to describe the relationship in each table.

17.

n	■
10	7
12	9
15	12

18.

n	■
1	7
2	14
3	21

19.

n	■
3	5
4.5	6.5
7	9

20.

n	■
42	7
54	9
72	12

21.

n	■
1	11
2	22
3	33

22.

n	■
30	23
45	38
52	45

GPS **23. Guided Problem Solving** The largest pan of lasagna weighed 3,477 pounds. The length of the pan was ten times its width. The lasagna pan was 7 feet wide. Find the length.

- You can use the strategy *Draw a Picture* to help you solve the problem.

Lasagna

width = ■

length = ■ · width

- The expression is ■. The length is ■.

24. Zoos Admission to the zoo costs \$3 per person. A family has a coupon for a discount of \$5. There are p people in the family. Write an expression to represent how much the family pays.

GO Online
Homework Video Tutor
PearsonSuccessNet.com

Write an expression for each word phrase.

25. 5 less than the quotient of m and n

26. 12 greater than the product of 3 and j

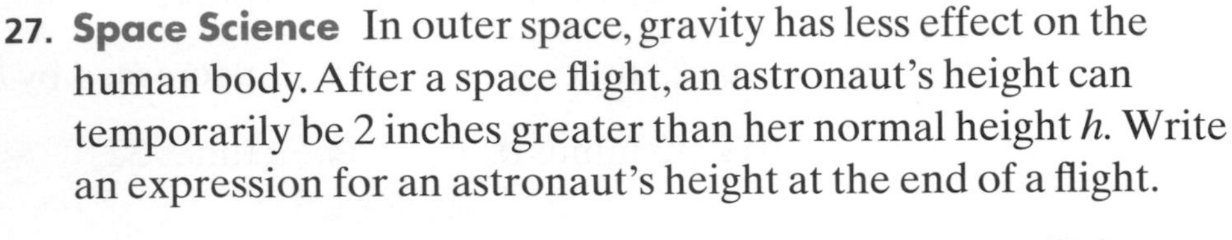

27. **Space Science** In outer space, gravity has less effect on the human body. After a space flight, an astronaut's height can temporarily be 2 inches greater than her normal height h. Write an expression for an astronaut's height at the end of a flight.

Careers Astronaut researchers conduct scientific experiments in space.

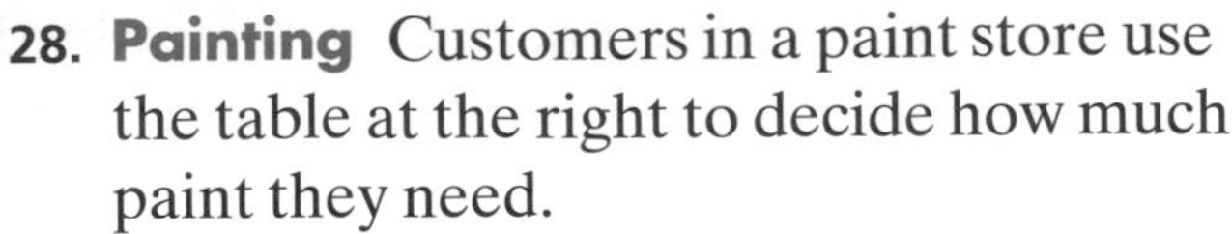

28. **Painting** Customers in a paint store use the table at the right to decide how much paint they need.

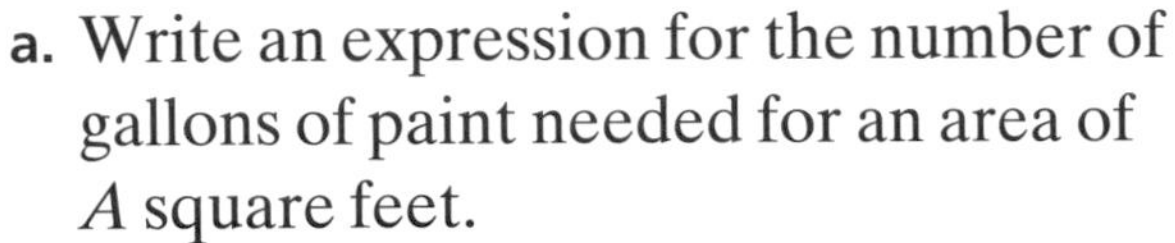

a. Write an expression for the number of gallons of paint needed for an area of A square feet.

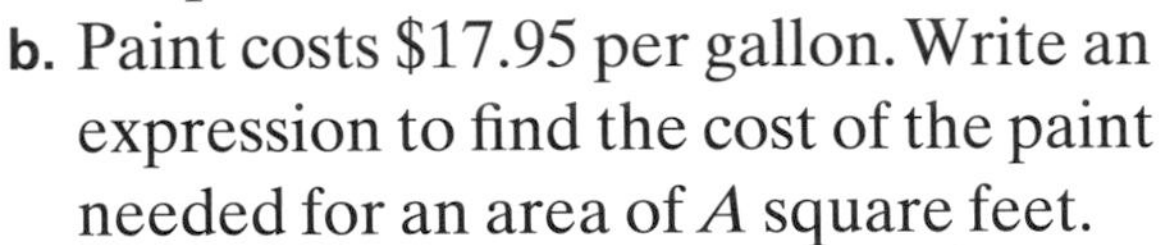

b. Paint costs $17.95 per gallon. Write an expression to find the cost of the paint needed for an area of A square feet.

Area sq. ft.	Gallons
400	1
800	2
2,000	5
3,200	8

29. **Challenge** A store that personalizes shirts charges $20 for a shirt plus $.75 for each letter. Write an algebraic expression for the cost of t shirts using n letters each.

Test Prep and Mixed Review

Practice

Multiple Choice

30. Maria has a box of 20 cookies. She gives 2 cookies to each friend. Which expression shows the number of cookies Maria has left after giving cookies to m friends?

Ⓐ $2m - 20$ Ⓑ $20 - 2m$ Ⓒ $20m - 2$ Ⓓ $20 + 2m$

31. The first four figures in a pattern are shown below.

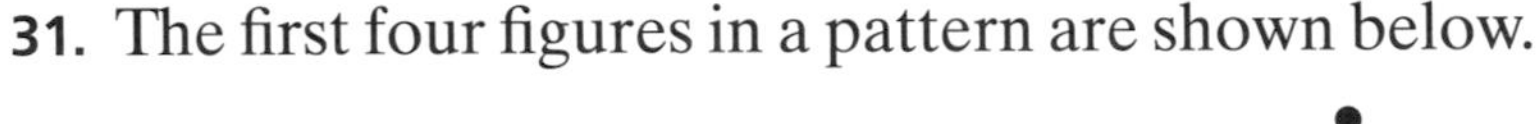

Which statement best describes the tenth figure in the pattern?

Ⓕ The tenth figure has 10 dots in the bottom row.

Ⓖ The tenth figure has 12 rows of dots.

Ⓗ The tenth figure is 7 cm tall.

Ⓙ The tenth figure has more than 100 dots.

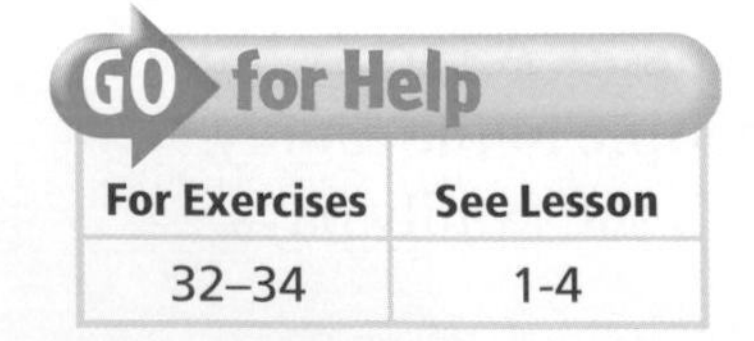

GO for Help

For Exercises	See Lesson
32–34	1-4

Find each sum.

32. $4.432 + 1.009$ 33. $2.005 + 12.5$ 34. $2.449 + 0.7$

Checkpoint Quiz 1

Lessons 2-1 through 2-2

Draw algebra tiles to model each expression.

1. $2x + 6$
2. $3x + 4$
3. $x + 10$

Algebra **Evaluate each expression for $x = 7$.**

4. $8x$
5. $3 \cdot (x - 4)$
6. $x \cdot (x + 3)$

Copy and complete the table.

7.

x	$\frac{x}{5}$
15	■
70	■
125	■

8.

x	$3x + 1$
4	■
10	■
22	■

Write an expression for each word phrase.

9. d less than 17
10. a times e
11. 14 divided by q

Write an expression to describe the relationship in each table.

12.

n	■
3	18
12	72
100	600

13.

n	■
16	20
51	55
129	133

MATH AT WORK

Coach

What is your favorite sport? Do you like playing or watching it better? If you know the sport well, you may choose to be a coach someday. Coaches use mathematics to keep track of their players' and teams' statistics. In soccer, they track shots on goal, average number of goals per game, a goalkeeper's saves per game, and each player's minutes played.

Go Online For information on coaching PearsonSuccessNet.com

Algebra

2-3 Using Number Sense to Solve One-Step Equations

Check Skills You'll Need

1. Vocabulary Review How can you use front-end estimation to add $3.46 + $6.54?

First estimate. Then find each sum or difference.

2. $5.3 + 1.07$

3. $6.1 - 2.4$

4. $8 - 6.3$

GO for Help Lesson 1-4

CONTENT STANDARDS
6.EE.5, 6.EE.6, 6.EE.7

What You'll Learn

To use mental math to estimate and solve problems

New Vocabulary equation, open sentence, solution

Why Learn This?

Part of the fun of collecting is completing your collection. You can use an equation to find the number of items you still need.

An **equation** is a mathematical sentence that has an equal sign, =. An equation is like a balanced scale.

To be in balance, a scale must have weights with the same total on each side.

$8 + 4 = 3 \times 4$ ← A true equation has equal values on each side of the equal sign.

If each side of the equation does not have the same value, the equation is false. Use ≠ to indicate that an equation is false.

EXAMPLE 1 True Equations and False Equations

Is the equation $6 + 13 = 18$ true or false?

$6 + 13 \stackrel{?}{=} 18$ ← Write the equation.

19 ← Add 6 + 13.

$19 \neq 18$ ← Compare.

The equation is false.

Vocabulary Tip

Read "$1 \stackrel{?}{=} 2$" as "Does 1 equal 2?" Read "$1 \neq 2$" as "1 does not equal 2."

Quick Check

1. Tell whether each equation is true or false.

   a. $7 \times 9 = 63$ b. $4 + 5 = 45$ c. $70 - 39 = 41$

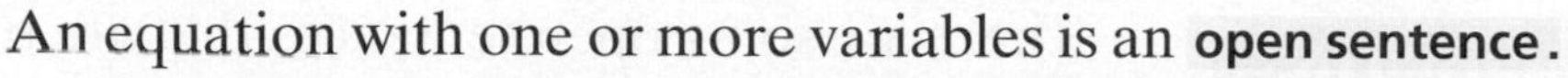

An equation with one or more variables is an **open sentence**. A **solution** of an equation is the value of the variable that makes the equation true. For example, $x - 15 = 12$ is an open sentence. Since $27 - 15 = 12$, the value 27 is the solution to $x - 15 = 12$.

You can use mental math to find the solution of some equations.

EXAMPLE Using Mental Math

2 **Baseball Cards** How many baseball cards do you need to add to the 14 cards you already own to have a total of 25 cards? Solve the equation $n + 14 = 25$, which models this situation.

What you think

I need to find a number that I can add to 14 and get 25. Since $11 + 14 = 25$, the solution is 11.

I need 11 more cards.

Quick Check

2. **Mental Math** Solve each equation.
   a. $17 - x = 8$ b. $w \div 4 = 20$ c. $4.7 + c = 5.9$

EXAMPLE Guess, Check, and Revise

GO for Help

For help with problem solving strategies, go to the Problem Solving Handbook.

3 Use the strategy *Guess, Check, and Revise* to solve $n - 43 = 19$.

Estimate Round the numbers to get a good starting point.

$$\begin{array}{ccccc} n & - & 43 & = & 19 \\ \downarrow & & \downarrow & & \downarrow \\ n & - & 40 & = & 20 \end{array}$$

What you think

Using mental math, I know $60 - 40 = 20$, so n is close to 60.

I can try substituting 60 for n in the equation: $60 - 43 = 17$. The number 17 is too low. I will try $n = 65$: $65 - 43 = 22$. The number 22 is too high. I will try $n = 62$: $62 - 43 = 19$.

Since $62 - 43 = 19$ is true, the solution to $n - 43 = 19$ is 62.

Quick Check

3. Use the strategy *Guess, Check, and Revise* to solve $k + 39 = 82$.

Vocabulary Tip

Algebraic is pronounced "al juh BRAY ik."

There are some open sentences that are true for every value you use for the variable. The algebraic equations that illustrate the number properties are true for all values of a, b, and c.

KEY CONCEPTS **Number Properties**

Identity Properties

The sum of 0 and any number is that number.

Arithmetic $0 + 9 = 9$
Algebra $0 + a = a$

The product of 1 and any number is that number.

$1 \times 9 = 9$
$1 \times a = a$

Commutative Properties Changing the order of addends or factors does not change the sum or the product.

Arithmetic $9 + 6 = 6 + 9$ $\quad 9 \times 6 = 6 \times 9$
Algebra $a + b = b + a$ $\quad a \times b = b \times a$

Associative Properties Changing the grouping of numbers does not change the sum or the product.

Arithmetic
$9 + (6 + 4) = (9 + 6) + 4$ $\quad 9 \cdot (6 \times 4) = (9 \cdot 6) \times 4$
Algebra
$a + (b + c) = (a + b) + c$ $\quad a(bc) = (ab)c$

1. **Vocabulary** Why is an equation with one or more variables called an open sentence?
2. **Writing in Math** Explain how to use the strategy *Guess, Check, and Revise* to solve $y + 19 = 42$.
3. **Number Sense** Use the balance scale at the left. What value for n will make the equation $n + 3 = 18$ a true equation?

Find the missing number that makes the equation true.

4. $\blacksquare + 3 = 5$
5. $\blacksquare \times 4 = 12$

Tell whether each equation is true or false.

6. $5 + 14 = 14 + 5$
7. $0 \times 9 = 9$
8. $2 \times 5 = 5 + 2$
9. $0 + 3 = 3$
10. $1 \cdot y = y$
11. $x + 1 = x$

Homework Exercises

For more exercises, see Extra Skills and Word Problems.

GO for Help

For Exercises	See Example
12–14	1
15–20	2
21–26	3

Tell whether each equation is true or false.

12. $3 + 50 = 80$ **13.** $3 + 4 + 2 = 3 + 6$ **14.** $0 \times 5.7 = 5.7$

Solve each equation. Use either mental math or the strategy *Guess, Check, and Revise.*

15. $x + 5 = 7$ **16.** $4x = 32$ **17.** $x + 2 = 6.3$

18. $g \div 4 = 2$ **19.** $p - 6 = 25$ **20.** $r + 14 = 23$

21. $6d = 612$ **22.** $k + 9 = 28$ **23.** $p \times 4 = 792$

24. $588 = 3n$ **25.** $b - 23 = 68$ **26.** $w + 13 = 71$

GPS **27. Guided Problem Solving** Suppose you spent \$74.95 for a shirt and a jacket. The shirt cost \$20.25. Solve the equation $20.25 + j = 74.95$ to find how much you spent on the jacket.
- You can work a simpler problem to estimate an answer. Use number sense to solve $20 + j = 75$.

28. Pollution When burned, 18 gallons of gasoline produce about 360 pounds of carbon dioxide. Solve the equation $18n = 360$ to find how much carbon dioxide 1 gallon of gasoline produces.

GO Online
Homework Video Tutor
PearsonSuccessNet.com

29. You have c pounds of cashews and 2.7 pounds of peanuts. You have 6 pounds of nuts altogether. Solve the equation $c + 2.7 = 6$ to find how many pounds of cashews you have.

30. Challenge Use estimation to check whether 59.4 is a reasonable solution to $x + 27.6 = 31.8$. Explain your answer.

Test Prep and Mixed Review

Practice

Multiple Choice

31. Sue was 30 years old when her daughter Amy was born. If s represents Sue's age, which expression describes Amy's age?

Ⓐ $s + 30$ Ⓑ $s - 30$ Ⓒ $30 - s$ Ⓓ $30s$

32. A bus has 25 passengers at the beginning of its route. At each stop, 5 people get off the bus and one person gets on. After how many stops will there be one passenger on the bus?

Ⓕ 4 Ⓖ 5 Ⓗ 6 Ⓙ 10

GO for Help

For Exercises	See Lesson
33–34	2-1

Evaluate each expression.

33. $53 - 6y$ for $y = 7$ **34.** $17m + 4n$ for $m = 5$ and $n = 16$

Online lesson quiz, PearsonSuccessNet.com

Vocabulary Builder

High-Use Academic Words

High-use academic words are words that you will see often in textbooks and on tests. These words are not math vocabulary terms, but knowing them will help you to succeed in mathematics.

Direction Words

Some words tell what to do in a problem. I need to understand what these words are asking so that I give the correct answer.

Word	Meaning
Identify	To show that you recognize something
List	To present information in order or to give examples
Justify	To give reasons supporting a decision or conclusion

Exercises

1. Identify each animal as a pet or a wild animal.
   a. kitten   b. elephant   c. dog   d. crocodile
2. List five animals you could keep as a pet.
3. Justify your answer to Exercise 2.
4. Identify each expression as numerical or algebraic.
   a. $n \div 10$ b. $5 + (6 - 2) \div 3$ c. $5x - y$ d. $(1 + 3) \cdot (10 - 3)$
5. List 3 different examples of an algebraic expression.
6. Is $10x$ a numerical expression? Justify your answer.
7. **Word Knowledge** Think about the word *pattern.*
   a. Choose the letter for how well you know the word.
      A. I know its meaning.
      B. I've seen it, but I don't know its meaning.
      C. I don't know it.
   b. **Research** Look up and write a definition for *pattern.*
   c. Write a sentence involving mathematics and using the word *pattern.*

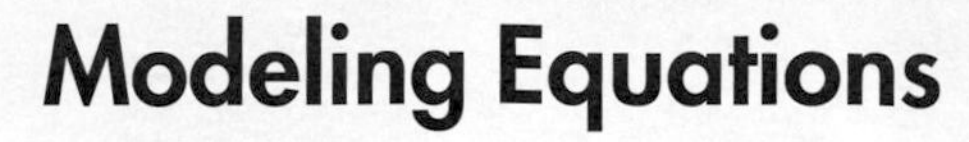

Hands On

Modeling Equations

To solve an equation using models, get the variable by itself on one side.

EXAMPLE Addition Equations

Solve $x + 7 = 15$.

$x + 7 = 15$

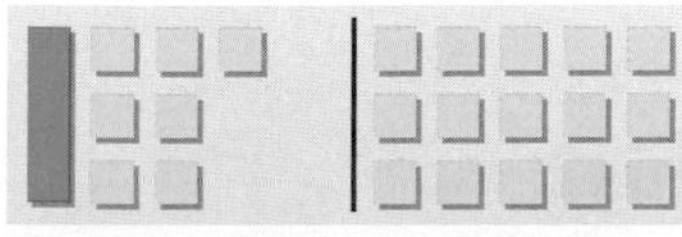

← Model the equation.

$x + 7 - 7 = 15 - 7$

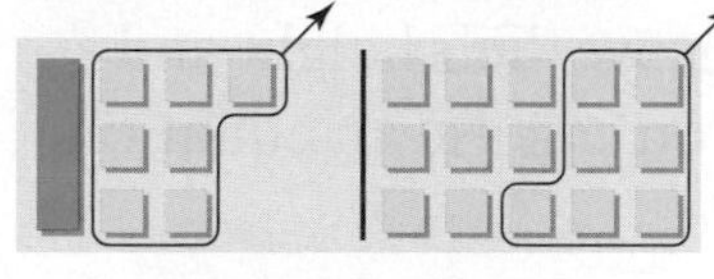

← Remove 7 tiles from each side. This will keep the equation balanced.

$x = 8$

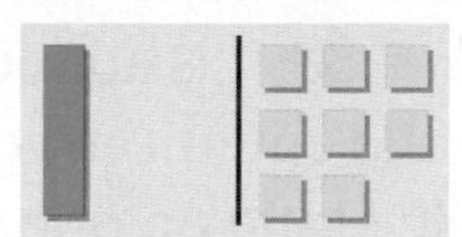

← Find the solution.

Exercises

Write the equation represented by the model.

1. 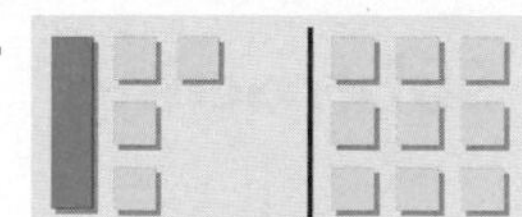

2. 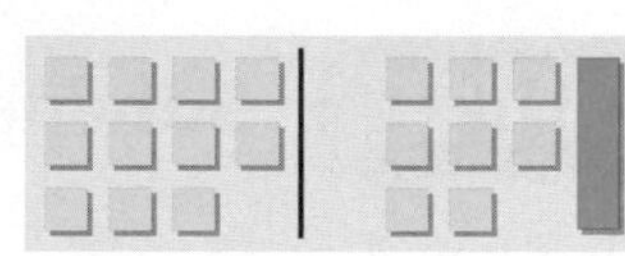

3. 

4. 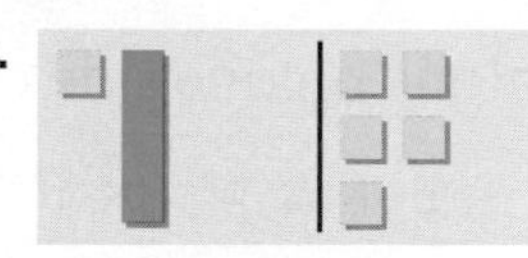

Solve each equation by drawing models or using tiles.

5. $x + 2 = 7$
6. $5 + c = 35$
7. $7 + m = 21$
8. $8 = n + 5$
9. $h + 9 = 16$
10. $12 = g + 6$
11. $15 = 7 + r$
12. $15 + q = 18$
13. $13 = 4 + a$
14. $b + 20 = 33$

Algebra

2-4 Solving Addition Equations

Check Skills You'll Need

1. **Vocabulary Review** How can you tell that an equation is an *open sentence*?

Use mental math to solve each equation.

2. $5 = 4 + t$
3. $x + 4 = 74$
4. $7 + x = 21$

Lesson 2-3

What You'll Learn

To use subtraction to solve equations

New Vocabulary inverse operations, Subtraction Property of Equality

Why Learn This?

As living things grow, their height and weight change. You can use an equation to find the change.

In the equation $x + 4 = 38$, 4 is added to a variable. To solve the equation, you need to get the variable alone on one side of the equal sign.

To get the variable alone, you *undo* the operation. You undo adding 4 by subtracting 4. Operations that undo each other are **inverse operations**.

CONTENT STANDARDS
6.EE.5, 6.EE.6, 6.EE.7

EXAMPLE Solving Equations by Subtracting

1 Solve $x + 4 = 38$.

Get x alone on one side of the equation.

$x + 4 = 38$

$x + 4 - 4 = 38 - 4$ ← Subtract 4 from each side to undo the addition and get x by itself.

$x = 34$ ← Simplify.

Check $x + 4 = 38$ ← Check your solution in the original equation.

$34 + 4 \stackrel{?}{=} 38$ ← Substitute 34 for x.

$38 = 38$ ✔

For help with evaluating expressions, go to Lesson 2-1, Example 2.

Quick Check

1. Solve $w + 4.3 = 9.1$. Check the solution.

When you solve problems using equations, drawing a diagram may help. The model indicates that the whole = part + part.

Whole	
Part	Part

EXAMPLE Application: Cats

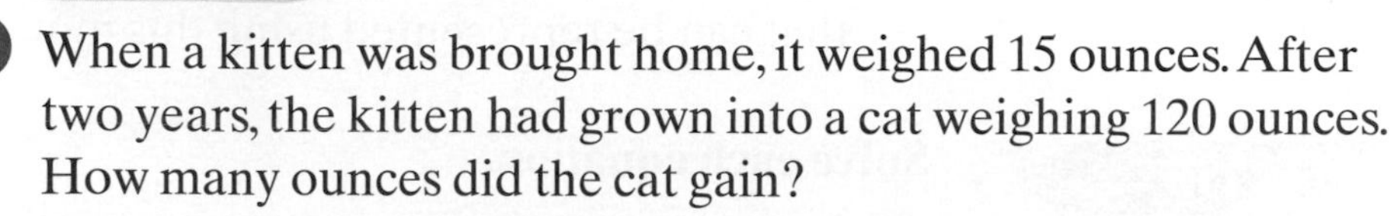

2 When a kitten was brought home, it weighed 15 ounces. After two years, the kitten had grown into a cat weighing 120 ounces. How many ounces did the cat gain?

Weight after 2 years	
Original weight	Ounces gained

Let g = the number of ounces gained.

120	
15	g

The equation $15 + g = 120$ models this situation.

$$15 + g = 120$$

$$15 + g - 15 = 120 - 15 \quad \leftarrow \text{Subtract 15 from each side to undo the addition.}$$

$$g = 105 \quad \leftarrow \text{Simplify.}$$

The cat gained 105 ounces.

Quick Check

2. A cat has gained 1.8 pounds in a year. It now weighs 11.6 pounds. Write and solve an equation to find how much it weighed one year ago. Check the solution.

GO Online

Video Tutor Help

PearsonSuccessNet.com

When you use inverse operations to solve equations, you are using a mathematical property. The property you use in this lesson is called the **Subtraction Property of Equality**.

KEY CONCEPTS Subtraction Property of Equality

If you subtract the same value from each side of an equation, the two sides remain equal.

Arithmetic $2 \cdot 3 = 6$, so $2 \cdot 3 - 4 = 6 - 4$.

Algebra If $a = b$, then $a - c = b - c$.

Check Your Understanding

1. **Vocabulary** What is the inverse operation of adding 6?

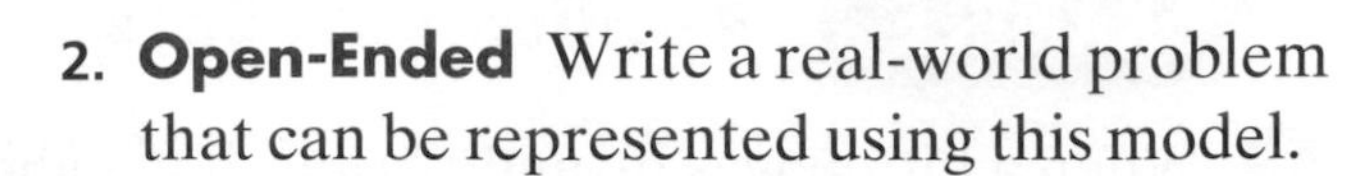

2. **Open-Ended** Write a real-world problem that can be represented using this model.

8	
n	3

Test Prep Tip

Drawing a diagram can help you model a real-world situation.

Solve each equation.

3. $d + 3 = 21$

21	
d	3

4. $k + 5.1 = 7.4$

7.4	
k	5.1

5. $x + 4.3 = 7$

7	
x	4.3

Homework Exercises

For more exercises, see Extra Skills and Word Problems.

GO for Help

For Exercises	See Example
6–17	1
18–19	2

Solve each equation. Check the solution. Remember, you can draw a diagram to help you solve an equation.

6. $x + 46 = 72$
7. $d + 5 = 53$
8. $y + 12 = 64$
9. $n + 17 = 56$
10. $m + 1.3 = 2.8$
11. $n + 4.5 = 10.8$
12. $14.7 = 5 + f$
13. $31 + y = 82$
14. $28 + g = 72$
15. $15 = k + 8.2$
16. $2.7 + g = 8.2$
17. $2.6 = 1.9 + g$

Write and solve an equation. Then check the solution.

18. You build 7 model airplanes during the summer. At the end of the summer, you have 25 model airplanes. How many model airplanes did you have before the summer?

19. **Music History** Wolfgang Amadeus Mozart wrote his first piano sonata in 1762, when he was 6 years old. In what year was Mozart born?

20. **Guided Problem Solving** Jeans that were on sale last week now cost \$29.97. The savings were \$4.99. Write and solve an equation to find the sale price of the jeans.
    - You can draw a diagram to help you write an equation.

Full price of jeans	
Sale price p	Savings \$4.99

Homework Video Tutor

PearsonSuccessNet.com

21. **Music** You add a 4-minute song to your digital music player. The player now has 2 hours of music. Use an equation to find how much music was on the player before you added the song.

22. In a number square, the sum of the numbers in each row, column, and main diagonal is the same.
    a. Find the sum for the number square at the right.
    b. Use the sum to write and solve equations to find the values of a, b, and c.

a	7	2
1	5	b
8	c	4

23. **Biology** A hippopotamus can hold its breath for about 15 minutes. It can hold its breath 5 minutes longer than a sea otter. Use an equation to find how long a sea otter can hold its breath.

Solve each equation. Then check the solution.

24. $y + 13.82 = 24$ 25. $1.5 + x = 9.7$ 26. $0.4 + g = 1.9$

27. $6.2 = j + 5.91$ 28. $b + 0.87 = 1$ 29. $11.4 = h + 5.9$

30. **Challenge** A large stepping stone weighs five times as much as a brick. Together, one brick and one stepping stone weigh 30 pounds. Find the weight of the stepping stone.

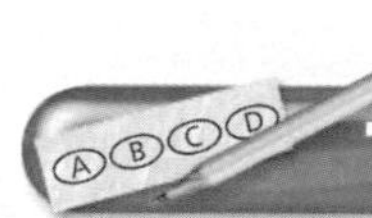

Test Prep and Mixed Review

Practice

Multiple Choice

31. The table shows the length and perimeter of different rectangles with a width of 3 cm. Which expression can be used to find the perimeter of a rectangle with a length of n units?

Side Length	Perimeter
5 cm	16 cm
10 cm	26 cm
15 cm	36 cm

(A) $n + 5$ (B) $n + 10$ (C) $n + 11$ (D) $2n + 6$

32. Which of the following is NOT an example of the Associative Property?
    (F) $(3 \times 4) \times 5 = 3 \times (4 \times 5)$
    (G) $2 + (10 + 3) = 2 + (3 + 10)$
    (H) $6 \times (4 \times 9) = (6 \times 4) \times 9$
    (J) $(5 + 8) + 2 = 5 + (8 + 2)$

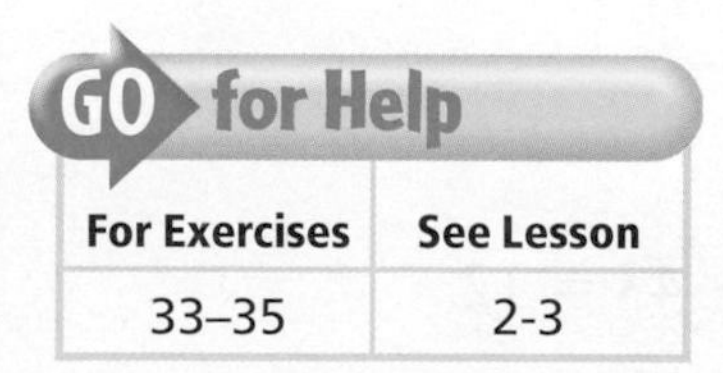

For Exercises	See Lesson
33–35	2-3

Solve each equation. Use either mental math or the strategy *Guess, Check, and Revise.*

33. $33x = 528$ 34. $127 - r = 62$ 35. $108 \div b = 12$

Algebra

2-5 Solving Subtraction Equations

Check Skills You'll Need

1. **Vocabulary Review** Explain why the number 4 is a *solution* to $x + 2 = 6$.

Use mental math to solve each equation.

2. $t - 4 = 10$
3. $x - 6 = 5$
4. $p - 7 = 3$

GO for Help Lesson 2-3

CONTENT STANDARDS
6.EE.5, 6.EE.6, 6.EE.7

What You'll Learn

To use addition to solve equations

New Vocabulary Addition Property of Equality

Why Learn This?

Nutritional information on products can help you decide what you should eat. You can use an equation to find the nutritional contents of foods.

You learned to solve equations by subtracting the same amount from each side of an equation. You can also solve equations by using addition.

KEY CONCEPTS **Addition Property of Equality**

If you add the same value to each side of an equation, the two sides remain equal.

Arithmetic $2 \cdot 3 = 6$, so $2 \cdot 3 + 4 = 6 + 4$.
Algebra If $a = b$, then $a + c = b + c$.

Some equations have a number subtracted on one side. To get the variable by itself, add the same number to each side of the equation.

EXAMPLE **Solving an Equation by Adding**

1 Solve $c - 12 = 43$.

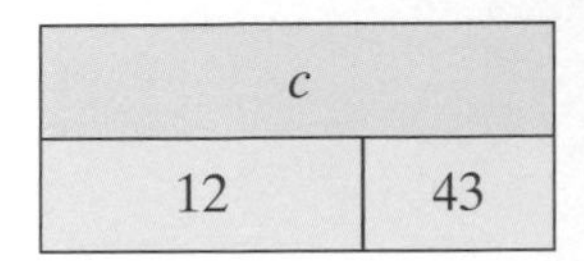

$c - 12 + 12 = 43 + 12$ ← Add 12 to each side to undo the subtraction.

$c = 55$ ← Simplify.

Quick Check

1. **a.** Solve $n - 53 = 28$. **b.** Solve $x - 43 = 12$.

Another way to model a real-world situation is to state the problem as simply as you can. Then use your statement to write an equation.

EXAMPLE Application: Nutrition

Test Prep Tip

Verbs such as *is, are, has,* and *was* show you where to place the = sign.

5	.	4	5

2 **Gridded Response** A serving of wheat flakes contains 3.7 mg of zinc. The amount of zinc in wheat flakes is 1.75 mg less than the amount in a breakfast bar. How much zinc is in a breakfast bar?

Words amount in flakes is 1.75 less than amount in bar

Let b = the amount of zinc in a breakfast bar.

Equation $3.7 \quad = \quad b \quad - \quad 1.75$

$b - 1.75 = 3.7$ ← **Write the equation.**

$b - 1.75 + 1.75 = 3.7 + 1.75$ ← **Add 1.75 to each side to undo the subtraction.**

$b = 5.45$ ← **Simplify.**

The breakfast bar contains 5.45 mg of zinc.

Quick Check

2. **Temperature** The temperature dropped 9°F between 7 P.M. and midnight. It was 54°F at midnight. Use an equation to find the temperature at 7 P.M.

Check Your Understanding

1. **Error Analysis** Your friend says the solution to $y - 4 = 24$ is 20. What did your friend do wrong?

2. Sheila is 2 years younger than Javon. Sheila is 10 years old. Write and solve an equation to find Javon's age.

   Words: Sheila is 2 years younger than Javon.

   Let j = Javon's age in years.

   Equation: $\blacksquare = j - \blacksquare$

Match each equation with the correct solution.

3. $x - 3 = 7$ **A.** 15

4. $x - 4 = 11$ **B.** 11

5. $x - 5 = 6$ **C.** 10

Homework Exercises

For more exercises, see Extra Skills and Word Problems.

GO for Help

For Exercises	See Example
6–17	1
18	2

Solve each equation. You may find a model helpful.

6. $x - 16 = 72$
7. $q - 2.4 = 1.8$
8. $n - 297 = 18$
9. $d - 68 = 40$
10. $y - 12 = 23$
11. $k - 56 = 107$
12. $5.8 = n - 0.35$
13. $0.6 = h - 2.9$
14. $q - 8.2 = 154$
15. $p - 1.23 = 8.77$
16. $n - 10.5 = 11.7$
17. $x - 5.7 = 5.7$

18. **Geography** The area of Cape Canaveral National Seashore in Florida is about 57,662 acres. That is about 72,772 acres less than the area of Padre Island National Seashore in Texas. Use an equation to find the area of Padre Island National Seashore.

19. **Guided Problem Solving** A healthy person has a normal temperature of about 98.6°F. Suppose a sick person needs to decrease his temperature by 3.7°F to return to normal. Use an equation to find the sick person's temperature.
    - What equation will you use to model this problem?
    - What operation will you use to solve the equation?

GO Online
Homework Video Tutor
PearsonSuccessNet.com

20. You buy several posters. The total cost is \$18.95. You have \$7.05 left after you pay. Write and solve an equation to find how much money you had before this purchase.

21. **Challenge** Sue is 2 years older than Mary. Mary is 3 years younger than Bob. Sue is 11 years old. How old is Bob?

Test Prep and Mixed Review

Practice

Gridded Response

22. A store rents DVDs for \$2 each, after you pay a membership fee of \$10. Jeremy has spent a total of \$26. How many DVDs has he rented?

23. The gas tank in the Rivera family car can hold a maximum of 18.2 gallons. After a trip, they filled the tank with 9.6 gallons of gas. How much gas was in the tank before it was filled?

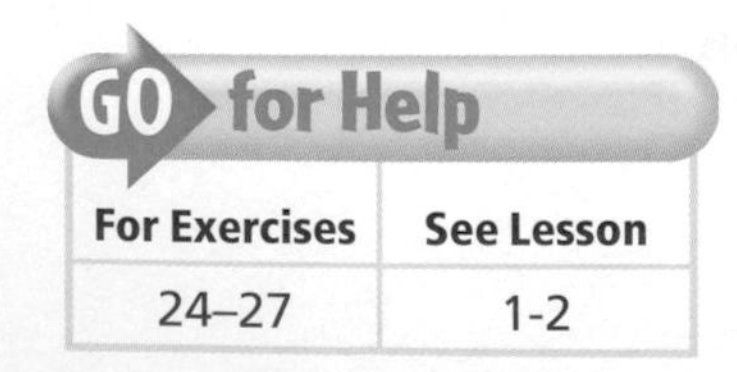
GO for Help

For Exercises	See Lesson
24–27	1-2

Find the value of each expression.

24. $24 \div 4 - 2 \times 3$
25. $24 \div 3 - 2 \times 4$
26. $24 \div (3 - 2) \times 4$
27. $(24 \div 3 - 2) \times 4$

Checkpoint Quiz 2

Lessons 2-3 through 2-5

Solve each equation.

1. $5 + x = 65$
2. $n - 3.2 = 15$
3. $z + 6 = 8.2$
4. $k - 4 = 3.6$
5. $14 = 3.2 + y$
6. $28 = 1.4 + a$
7. $23 = 16 + y$
8. $48 = 9.6 + a$
9. You pay for the refreshments at a movie theater with a $10 bill. The refreshments cost $5.73. Write an equation to find how much change you should receive. Solve the equation.

2-6a Activity Lab

Hands On

Modeling Division Equations

Models can help you understand the steps you need to follow to solve an equation.

EXAMPLE **Solving Equations by Dividing**

Solve $4x = 12$.

$4x = 12$

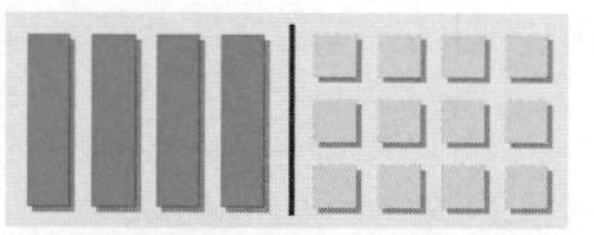

← Model the equation.

$4x \div 4 = 12 \div 4$

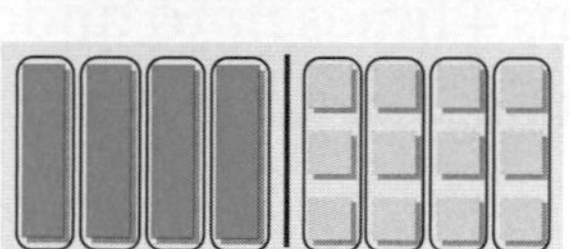

← Divide each side of the equation into 4 equal parts.

$x = 3$

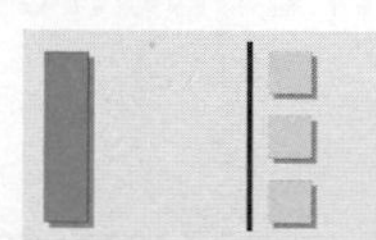

← Find the solution.

Exercises

Solve each equation by drawing a model or using tiles.

1. $2x = 20$
2. $5c = 35$
3. $3g = 12$
4. $7m = 21$
5. **Reasoning** Explain how you could use a model to solve $6y = 1.8$.

Algebra

2-6 Solving Multiplication and Division Equations

Check Skills You'll Need

1. **Vocabulary Review** How are *equations* different from *expressions*?

Use mental math to solve each equation.

2. $3x = 27$
3. $6 \div y = 3$
4. $p \div 3 = 3$
5. $7x = 21$

Lesson 2-3

CONTENT STANDARDS
6.EE.5, 6.EE.6, 6.EE.7

Calculator Tip

Remember that you can never divide by zero. Your calculator will give you an error message if you try.

What You'll Learn

To use multiplication and division to solve equations

New Vocabulary Division Property of Equality, Multiplication Property of Equality

Why Learn This?

Many products are sold in groups—cartons, cases, boxes, and bags. You can use an equation to find the cost of a single item.

You can use the **Division Property of Equality** to solve equations involving multiplication.

KEY CONCEPTS Division Property of Equality

If you divide each side of an equation by the same nonzero number, the two sides remain equal.

Arithmetic $4 \times 2 = 8$, so $4 \times 2 \div 2 = 8 \div 2$.

Algebra If $a = b$ and $c \neq 0$, then $a \div c = b \div c$.

You recall that $4n$ means 4 times n. To undo multiplication, you divide by the same number. So $4n \div 4 = n$.

EXAMPLE Solving an Equation by Dividing

1 Solve $4n = 68$.

$4n \div 4 = 68 \div 4$ ← **Divide each side by 4 to undo the multiplication and get *n* alone.**

$n = 17$ ← **Simplify.**

Check $4(17) \stackrel{?}{=} 68$ ← **Check your solution in the original equation. Replace *n* with 17.**

$68 = 68$ ✔

Quick Check

1. Solve $0.8p = 32$. Then check the solution.

EXAMPLE Application: Photography

2 You buy a package containing six rolls of film for your camera. The total cost is \$38.88. Use an equation to find the cost of one roll of film.

Test Prep Tip

A model can help you understand what operation is needed for the equation.

Use a diagram to model the situation.

\$38.88					
c	c	c	c	c	c

Let c = the cost of one roll of film. The equation $6c = \$38.88$ models this situation.

$6c = 38.88$ ← Write the equation.

$6c \div 6 = 38.88 \div 6$ ← Divide each side by 6 to undo the multiplication and get c alone.

$c = 6.48$ ← Simplify.

The cost of one roll of film is \$6.48.

Check for Reasonableness

You spend about \$39.

\$6.48 is between \$6 and \$7.

6 rolls × \$6 = \$36

6 rolls × \$7 = \$42

This answer makes sense because \$36 < \$39 < \$42.

Quick Check

2. A club sells greeting cards for a fundraiser. The profit for each card sold is \$.35. The club's total profit is \$302.75. Use an equation to find the total number of cards the club sells.

You can use the **Multiplication Property of Equality** to solve equations involving division.

KEY CONCEPTS Multiplication Property of Equality

If you multiply each side of an equation by the same number, the two sides remain equal.

Arithmetic $6 \div 2 = 3$, so $(6 \div 2) \times 2 = 3 \times 2$.

Algebra If $a = b$, then $a \cdot c = b \cdot c$.

EXAMPLE Solving an Equation by Multiplying

3 Solve $y \div 6.4 = 8$.

$$y \div 6.4 \times 6.4 = 8 \times 6.4$$ ← Multiply by 6.4 to undo the division and get y alone.

$$y = 51.2$$ ← Simplify.

Check $y \div 6.4 = 8$ ← Check your solution in the original equation. Replace y with 51.2.

$$51.2 \div 6.4 \stackrel{?}{=} 8$$

$$8 = 8$$

Quick Check

3. Solve $w \div 1.5 = 10$. Then check the solution.

You can use equations involving division to help you solve real-world problems.

EXAMPLE Application: Sharing Profits

4 **Business** You and 3 of your friends have a business where you make T-shirts for different clubs at school. In December, you share the profits equally, giving each of you a $127 paycheck. What was the total profit for the business in December?

Let p = profit.

$$p \div 4 = 127$$ ← Write the equation.

$$p \div 4 \times 4 = 127 \times 4$$ ← Multiply by 4 to undo the division and get p alone.

$$p = 508$$ ← Simplify.

The total profit was $508.

Quick Check

4. You are giving away your entire collection of mystery books. You give 4 friends the same number of books to read. Each friend gets 12 books. Use an equation to find the total number of books that are in your collection.

Check Your Understanding

1. **Vocabulary** How are the Multiplication Property of Equality and the Division Property of Equality different?

Match each equation with the correct model below.

2. $4x = 20$
3. $x \div 4 = 5$
4. $5x = 20$
5. $x \div 5 = 4$

A.

x				
4	4	4	4	4

B.

x			
5	5	5	5

C.

20			
x	x	x	x

D.

20				
x	x	x	x	x

Solve each equation.

6. $3x = 12.6$
   $3x \div \blacksquare = 12.6 \div \blacksquare$
7. $v \div 2 = 7$
   $v \div 2 \cdot \blacksquare = 7 \cdot \blacksquare$

Homework Exercises

For more exercises, see Extra Skills and Word Problems.

GO for Help

For Exercises	See Example
8–17	1-2
18–26	3-4

Solve each equation. Check the solution. You may find a model helpful.

8. $5a = 100$
9. $8k = 76$
10. $7n = 11.9$
11. $25h = 450$
12. $0.4x = 1$
13. $75 = 15c$
14. $16j = 80$
15. $2.5g = 17.5$
16. $10y = 5$

17. **Farming** An egg carton holds 12 eggs. One day a farmer gathers 8,616 eggs. Write and solve an equation to find how many cartons are needed for the eggs.

Solve each equation. Then check the solution.

18. $q \div 6 = 4$
19. $a \div 7 = 63$
20. $n \div 2.5 = 3$
21. $y \div 43 = 1{,}204$
22. $10 = k \div 20$
23. $12 = r \div 9$
24. $n \div 4 = 0.6$
25. $t \div 0.3 = 1.4$
26. $b \div 11 = 87$

GPS 27. **Guided Problem Solving** Each volleyball team in a league needs 6 players, 2 alternates, and a coach. How many teams can be formed with 288 people?
- How many people are needed for each team?
- Draw a diagram to model this situation.

28. **Videos** A video store charges the same price to rent each movie. The store collected a total of \$80.73 for the rentals shown in the table. Use an equation to find the cost to rent one movie.

Day	Number of Movie Rentals
Monday	6
Tuesday	4
Wednesday	3
Thursday	6
Friday	8

29. **Biology** An elephant's height is about 5.5 times the length of her hind footprint. Use an equation to find the approximate height of an elephant whose hind footprint is 1.5 feet long.

Solve each equation. Check the solution.

30. $y \div 1.6 = 0.256$
31. $13 = 65x$
32. $30 = p \div 30$
33. $5.6k = 19.152$
34. $0.02g = 6$
35. $h \div 2.4 = 15$

36. **Challenge** One of the world's largest oil tankers, the *Jahre Viking*, is so long that if 3.5 identical tankers were placed end to end, they would measure about 1 mile long. Estimate the length, in feet, of the *Jahre Viking*. (*Hint*: 1 mile = 5,280 feet)

Test Prep and Mixed Review

Practice

Multiple Choice

37. Tickets to an event cost \$25 each. Which equation can you use to find the number of tickets t that you can buy with \$100?
    - (A) $4t = 100$
    - (B) $25t = 100$
    - (C) $4 + t = 100$
    - (D) $25 + t = 100$

38. Ashley bought a book for \$15.99. She now has \$32.12. How much money did Ashley have before she bought the book?
    - (F) \$16.13
    - (G) \$17.13
    - (H) \$47.11
    - (J) \$48.11

39. The table shows a sequence of terms. Which expression can be used to find the value of the term in position n?
    - (A) $n + 2$
    - (B) $2n$
    - (C) $n + 3$
    - (D) $3n$

Position, n	Value of Term
1	3
2	6
3	9
n	■

GO for Help

For Exercises	See Lesson
40–42	1-3

Write each decimal in words.

40. 6.07
41. 4.903
42. 5.8

Writing Equations to Solve Problems

Around the World On March 4, 2005, Steve Fossett set a record by completing a nonstop solo jet flight around the world. He landed with 1,515 pounds of fuel. A fuel leak caused a loss of 2,600 pounds of fuel. He started with 18,100 pounds of fuel. How much fuel did the jet use on the flight?

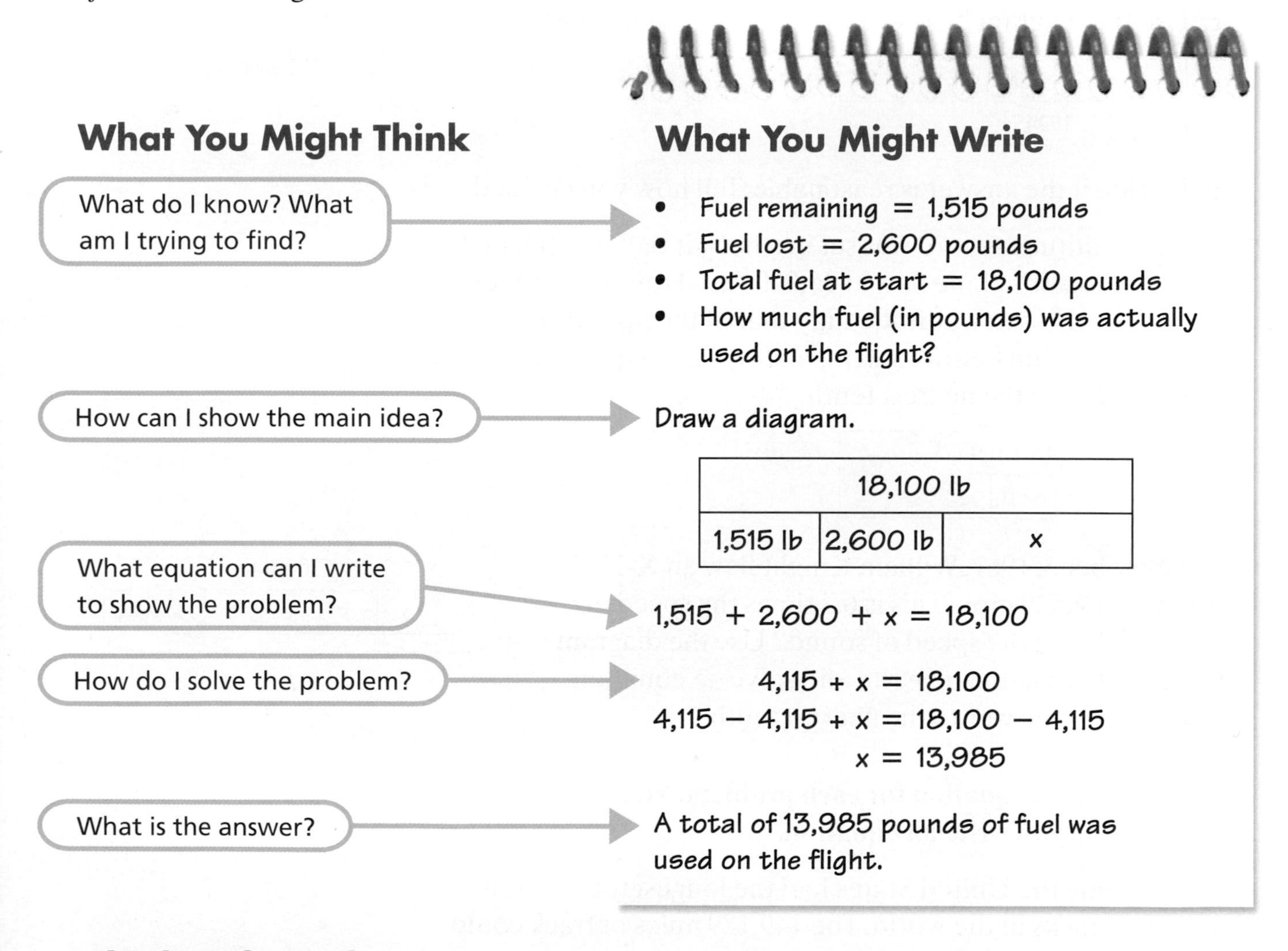

Think It Through

1. Is the answer above reasonable? Explain.
2. Refer to the diagram above. How do you know that the section for x must be the largest section?
3. **Reasoning** Suppose the plane had not lost 2,600 lbs of fuel. How much fuel would have been in the plane when it landed?

Exercises

4. The first flight around the world included stops. It was made by Lowell Smith and Alva Harvey in 1924. How many years passed between their flight and Fossett's flight?
   a. What do you know?
   b. What are you trying to find?
   c. Use the diagram below to write and solve an equation.

2005	
1924	x

   d. Decide if the answer is reasonable. Tell how you decided.

5. The first altitude record was set in a hot-air balloon. It rose to 82 feet. Fossett's plane flew at 45,000 feet. How many times higher was Fossett's altitude than that of the hot-air balloon? Use the diagram below to write and solve an equation. Round your answer to the nearest tenth.

45,000 ft			
82 ft	82 ft	82 ft	. . .

6. On October 3, 1967, William Knight flew an X-15 aircraft at 4,520 mph. This is 6.7 times the speed of sound. What is the speed of sound? Use the diagram at the right to help you write and solve an equation. Round your answer to the nearest tenth.

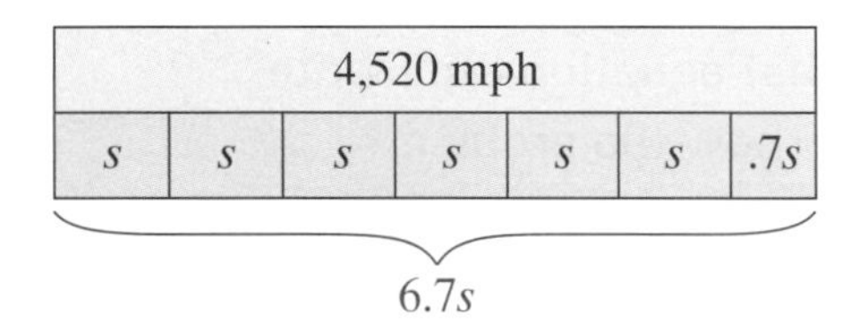

Write and solve an equation for each problem. You can draw a diagram to help you write an equation.

7. At one time the United States had the longest total length of railroad tracks in the world. The 149,129 miles of track could stretch around the world almost six times. What is the distance around the world?

8. In one year, London's Heathrow Airport had 44,262,000 passengers. In the same year, Germany's Frankfurt Airport had 27,546,000 passengers. How many more passengers were there in Heathrow Airport?

Writing Short Responses

Short-response questions in this textbook are worth 2 points. To receive full credit, you must give the correct answer with units, if needed, and show your work or explain your reasoning.

EXAMPLE

Measurement Jenny stands on a scale. She weighs 104 pounds. Then she steps on the scale while holding her dog. Now the scale reads 121 pounds. Define a variable. Write and solve an equation to find the weight of the dog.

The problem asks you to define a variable, set up an equation, and solve the equation to find the weight of the dog. Below is a scoring guide that shows the number of points awarded for different answers.

Scoring

[2] The equation and solution are correct and all work is shown. The dog weighs 17 pounds.

[1] There is no equation, but there is a method to show that the dog weighs 17 pounds, OR an equation is written and solved. The response may contain minor errors.

[0] There is no response, no work shown, OR the response is completely incorrect.

Three responses are shown below, with the points each received.

2 points	1 point	0 points
Let d = weight of dog. $104 + d = 121$ $104 + d - 104 = 121 - 104$ $d = 17$ The dog weighs 17 pounds.	$121 - 104 = 17$ 17 pounds	27 pounds

Exercises

Use Example 1 to answer each question.

1. Why did each response receive the indicated number of points?
2. Write a 2-point response for solving the equation $121 - d = 104$.

Chapter 2 Review

Vocabulary Review

Addition Property of Equality (p. 68)
algebraic expression (p. 47)
Division Property of Equality (p. 72)
equation (p. 58)
evaluate (p. 48)
inverse operations (p. 64)
Multiplication Property of Equality (p. 73)
numerical expression (p. 47)
open sentence (p. 59)
solution (p. 59)
Subtraction Property of Equality (p. 65)
variable (p. 47)

Fill in the blank.

1. To __?__ an expression, replace each variable with a number and then simplify it.
2. A(n) __?__ contains one or more variables.
3. The value of the variable that makes an equation true is a(n) __?__.
4. A(n) __?__ is a symbol that stands for a number.
5. A(n) __?__ is a mathematical sentence with an equal sign.

Go Online
For vocabulary quiz
PearsonSuccessNet.com

Skills and Concepts

Lesson 2-1

- To evaluate algebraic expressions

A **numerical expression** contains only numbers and operation symbols. An **algebraic expression** contains at least one **variable.**

Evaluate each expression.

6. $48 \div x$ for $x = 6$
7. $c - 7$ for $c = 56$
8. $14b$ for $b = 3$

Lesson 2-2

- To write algebraic expressions and use them to solve problems

Write an expression for each word phrase.

9. x divided by 12
10. 2 times b
11. h plus k

Write an expression to describe the relationship in each table.

12.

n	■
5	13
8	16
11	19

13.

n	■
2	14
4	28
9	63

14.

n	■
3	1
9	3
18	6

Lesson 2-3

- To use mental math to estimate and solve problems

An **equation** is a mathematical sentence that contains an equal sign. An **open sentence** is an equation that contains one or more variables. A value of the variable that makes an equation true is a **solution.**

Tell whether each equation is true or false.

15. $15 + 25 = 30$ **16.** $21 \div 3 = 7$ **17.** $6 \times 4 = 28$

Mental Math Solve each equation.

18. $x + 7 = 12$ **19.** $m + 13 = 21$ **20.** $4t = 32$

Lessons 2-4 and 2-5

- To use addition and subtraction to solve equations

You can use the **Addition Property of Equality** and the **Subtraction Property of Equality** to solve equations. Operations that undo each other are **inverse operations.**

Solve each equation.

21. $r - 1{,}078 = 4{,}562$ **22.** $m + 8 = 15$

23. $5.6 + x = 7$ **24.** $d - 2.16 = 3.9$

25. Paul is 2.7 pounds heavier than Elizabeth. Paul weighs 132.4 pounds. How much does Elizabeth weigh?

26. Caroline is 12 years younger than Kevin. Caroline is 28 years old. How old is Kevin?

Lesson 2-6

- To use multiplication and division to solve equations

You can use the **Multiplication Property of Equality** and the **Division Property of Equality** to solve equations.

Solve each equation.

27. $78x = 4{,}368$ **28.** $t \div 4 = 32$ **29.** $1.2h = 3$

30. $7.2 = u \div 1.5$ **31.** $v \div 3.2 = 19$ **32.** $4.5 = 5n$

33. John has five times as much money as Stuart. John has \$83.40. How much money does Stuart have?

34. Kali decides to give away all of the comic books in her collection. She gives each of her 6 friends the same number of comic books. If each friend gets 17 comic books, how many did Kali have in her collection?

Chapter 2 Test

Go Online For online chapter test PearsonSuccessNet.com

Copy and complete each table.

1.

x	$40 - x$
13	■
24	■
38	■

2.

x	$2x$
28	■
56	■
101	■

Evaluate each expression for $y = 20$.

3. $2y + 9$
4. $60 - (y + 14)$
5. $28 - y \div 5$
6. $y + 4y$

Evaluate each expression for $x = 12$.

7. $500 + (x - 8)$
8. $2x - 3$
9. $8 + x \div 2$

Write an algebraic expression for each model.

10. 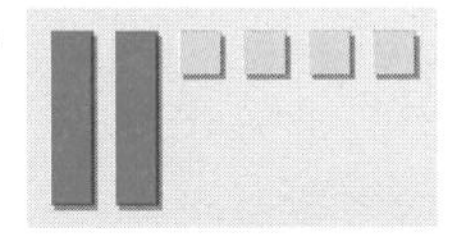

11. 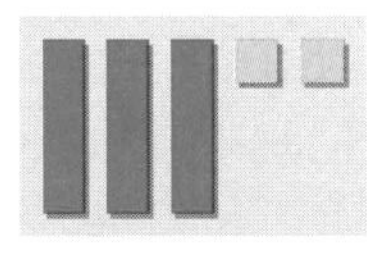

Use algebra tiles or a drawing to model each equation. Then solve.

12. $v + 3 = 8$
13. $3g = 15$

Write an expression for each word phrase.

14. c more than 4
15. 8 less than $3d$

16. Gus is 8 years younger than his brother, Alex. Alex is x years old. Write an algebraic expression that describes how old Gus is.

17. **Writing in Math** Write a word problem that could be described by the expression $d + 4$.

Tell whether each equation is true or false.

18. $6 + 7 \times 3 = 39$
19. $1.5 \times (6 - 4) = 3$

Tell whether the given number is a solution to the equation.

20. $x + 1.5 = 32$; 17
21. $h - 8 = 2$; 28

Solve each equation.

22. $n - 4 = 8.4$
23. $25 + b = 138$
24. $k \div 12 = 3$
25. $11t = 99$

26. **Fundraising** A baseball team sold greeting cards to raise money for uniforms. The team received \$.40 profit for each card sold. The total profit was \$302. How many cards did the team sell?

27. The profits from a business are shared equally among four business owners. If each owner receives \$810, what were the total profits for the business?

28. Ned scored 14 more points than Bob on a video game. If Ned scored 78 points, how many points did Bob score?

29. The library is 3 miles closer to home than the middle school. If the library is 7 miles from home, how far is the middle school from home?

Test Prep **Practice**

Cumulative Review

Multiple Choice

Read each question. Then write the letter of the correct answer on your paper.

1. Which decimal is fifty-four hundredths?
   (A) 0.054 (B) 0.54 (C) 5.40 (D) 54.00

2. What is 5.092 rounded to the nearest hundredth?
   (F) 6 (G) 5.1 (H) 5.09 (J) 5

3. Which sentence represents the Commutative Property of Multiplication?
   (A) $5 \times 2 = 10$
   (B) $5 \times (6 + 3) = 5 \times 9$
   (C) $5 \times 9 = 9 \times 5$
   (D) $(5 \times 6) \times 2 = 5 \times (6 \times 2)$

4. Akiko used the expression $\ell \div 4$ to determine the number of miles she ran during practice, where ℓ represents the number of laps she ran. If $\ell = 24$, how many miles has Akiko run?
   (F) 4 (G) 6 (H) 20 (J) 24

5. Which word phrase does NOT describe the algebraic expression $b - 10$?
   (A) ten less than b
   (B) b less ten
   (C) b less than 10
   (D) b minus ten

6. Which expression has a value of 13?
   (F) $2 \times (3 + 2)$
   (G) $14 - 6 \div 2$
   (H) $1 + 6 \times 2$
   (J) $15 \div 3 + 7$

7. Which operation would you use to get the variable in $x - 15 = 40$ alone on one side of the equation?
   (A) Subtract 15 from each side.
   (B) Subtract x from each side.
   (C) Add 15 to each side.
   (D) Add 40 to each side.

8. What is the value of $2.5c + 2$ when $c = 6$?
   (F) 2.56 (G) 17 (H) 20 (J) 256

9. Which expression is NOT equal to 12 when $p = 4$?
   (A) $2p + p$
   (B) $24 \div p \times 2$
   (C) $50 - p \times 11 + 6$
   (D) $12 + 36 \div p$

10. Apples cost $.38 each. You have $4.00. What is the greatest number of apples you can buy?
    (F) 5 (G) 9 (H) 10 (J) 11

Gridded Response

Record your answer in a grid.

11. What is the solution of $x \div 0.15 = 1.2$?

12. Cod sells for $4.86 per pound. You buy two pieces, which cost a total of $12.15. How many pounds of fish do you buy?

13. A sheet of metal has a thickness of 0.004 inches. How many inches thick is a stack of 100 sheets?

Short Response

14. Jake cleans his room in 17.1 minutes. This was 4.8 minutes longer than Leo.
    a. Write an equation to find how long it takes Leo to clean his room.
    b. How long did it take Leo to clean his room?

15. Frank spent the following amounts at three different stores: $4.31, $2.35, and $6.89. He said he spent a total of $34.70. Is Frank correct? Explain your answer.

CHAPTER 3 Number Theory

What You've Learned

- In Chapter 1, you used the order of operations to solve problems.
- In Chapter 2, you wrote and evaluated expressions using variables.
- You solved addition and subtraction equations.

Check Your Readiness

GO for Help

For Exercises	See Lesson
1–6	1-2
7–10	2-1
11–16	2-4, 2-5

Using Order of Operations

Find the value of each expression.

1. $350 \div 10 + 15$

2. $42 - 3 \times 8$

3. $12 + 45 \div 15$

4. $16 - (5 + 7) \div 3$

5. $(14 + 25) \times 3$

6. $200 \div (65 - 25)$

Evaluating Expressions

Evaluate each expression.

7. $27 \div j$ for $j = 3$

8. $q + 7$ for $q = 5$

9. $4d - 2$ for $d = 22$

10. $14 - 2w$ for $w = 3$

Solving Equations

Solve each equation.

11. $y + 45 = 88$

12. $27 + g = 65$

13. $21 = m + 8$

14. $x - 18 = 75$

15. $d - 88 = 30$

16. $y - 14 = 34$

What You'll Learn Next

- In this chapter, you will use divisibility rules, prime numbers, multiples, and factors to solve problems.
- You will write and simplify expressions using exponents.
- You will simplify and factor expressions using the Distributive Property.
- You will also use properties to simplify expressions.

Key Vocabulary

- base (p. 90)
- coefficient (p. 113)
- common factor (p. 99)
- common multiple (p. 103)
- composite number (p. 94)
- Distributive Property (p. 107)
- divisible (p. 86)
- equivalent expressions (p. 108)
- even number (p. 87)
- exponent (p. 90)
- factor (p. 94)
- greatest common factor (GCF) (p. 99)
- least common multiple (LCM) (p. 103)
- multiple (p. 103)
- odd number (p. 87)
- power (p. 90)
- prime factorization (p. 95)
- prime number (p. 94)
- term (p. 113)

3-1 Divisibility and Mental Math

Check Skills You'll Need

1. **Vocabulary Review** What is the *inverse operation* of multiplication?

Solve each equation. Check the solution.

2. $10x = 490$

3. $5x = 205$

4. $0.6x = 30$

Lesson 2-6

What You'll Learn

To check for divisibility using mental math and to use divisibility to solve problems

New Vocabulary divisible, even number, odd number

Why Learn This?

When you plan an event, you can use divisibility rules to find how many tables you will need for your guests.

A whole number is **divisible** by a second whole number if the first number can be divided by the second number with a remainder of 0. You can use multiplication facts to test for divisibility.

CONTENT STANDARD
Essential for understanding 6.NS.4

For help with multiplying whole numbers, go to Skills Handbook, p. 384.

EXAMPLE Using Mental Math for Divisibility

1. a. Is 56 divisible by 7?

Think Since $56 = 8 \times 7$, 56 is divisible by 7.

b. Is 56 divisible by 4?

Think Since $56 = 8 \times 7$, and $4 \times 2 = 8$, 56 is divisible by 4.

Quick Check

1. a. Is 64 divisible by 6?

b. Is 93 divisible by 3?

You can test for divisibility using the rules below.

KEY CONCEPTS Divisibility of Whole Numbers

A whole number is divisible by

- 2, if the number ends in 0, 2, 4, 6, or 8.
- 3, if the sum of the number's digits is divisible by 3.
- 5, if the number ends in 0 or 5.
- 9, if the sum of the number's digits is divisible by 9.
- 10, if the number ends in 0.

GO Online

Video Tutor Help
PearsonSuccessNet.com

An **even number** is a whole number that ends with a 0, 2, 4, 6, or 8. An **odd number** is a whole number that ends with a 1, 3, 5, 7, or 9.

EXAMPLE Divisibility by 2, 3, 5, and 10

2 Test 715 for divisibility by 2, 3, 5, and 10.

2: 715 is not an even number. So 715 is not divisible by 2.

3: Find the sum of the digits in 715.

$7 + 1 + 5 = 13$ ← **Add the digits.**

The sum of the digits of 715 is 13, which is not divisible by 3. So 715 is not divisible by 3.

5: 715 ends in a 5. So 715 is divisible by 5.

10: 715 does not end in 0. So 715 is not divisible by 10.

So 715 is divisible by 5, but not by 2, 3, or 10.

Quick Check

2. Test each number for divisibility by 2, 3, 5, and 10.
a. 150 **b.** 1,021 **c.** 2,112

To test a number for divisibility by 9, you start by finding the sum of the number's digits—just as you did with divisibility by 3.

EXAMPLE Divisibility by 9

3 **Planning** There are 163 people signed up to play softball. Each team will have exactly 9 players. Will everyone who has signed up have a spot on one of the 9-person teams?

If 163 is divisible by 9, then everyone will have a spot on a team.

$1 + 6 + 3 = 10$ ← **Find the sum of the digits in 163.**

$10 \div 9$ has a remainder of 1. ← **The sum is not divisible by 9.**

163 is not divisible by 9. Not everyone will have a spot on a team.

Quick Check

3. Music A high school marching band has 126 members. Each row in the band formation on the field has 9 musicians. Will everyone in the band fit in a nine-person row?

Check Your Understanding

1. **Vocabulary** How can you tell whether a number is odd or even?

2. **Number Sense** Since 54 is divisible by 6, 54 is also divisible by 2 and 3. Explain.

Match each number with its divisibility numbers.

3. 60 — A. 3, 9

4. 48 — B. 2, 3

5. 81 — C. 2, 3, 5, 10

Homework Exercises

For more exercises, see Extra Skills and Word Problems.

GO for Help

For Exercises	See Examples
6–9	1
10–22	2
23–25	3

Is the first number divisible by the second? Use mental math.

6. 48 by 4
7. 46 by 4
8. 63 by 7
9. 122 by 6

Test each number for divisibility by 2, 3, 5, and 10.

10. 48,960
11. 2,385
12. 928
13. 672
14. 202,470
15. 53,559
16. 57
17. 92
18. 171
19. 962
20. 1,956
21. 11,160

22. A total of 114 people have signed up to play in a basketball tournament. There are 3 people on each team. Will everyone who has signed up have a spot on a 3-person team? Explain.

Test each number for divisibility by 9.

23. 1,187
24. 2,187
25. 17,595

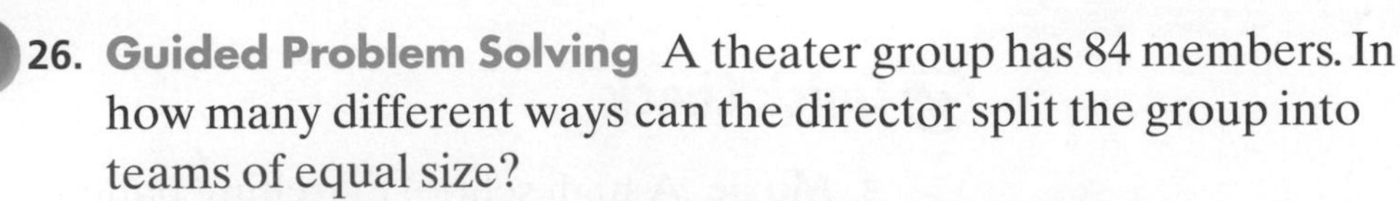

GPS 26. **Guided Problem Solving** A theater group has 84 members. In how many different ways can the director split the group into teams of equal size?
- Is there more than one way to divide the group?
- How can you use divisibility rules to solve this problem?

What digit makes each number divisible by 9?

27. 9,0■5 **28.** ■7,302 **29.** 2■6,555

30. Time The number 60 is convenient for timekeeping because it can be easily divided by many numbers. Is 60 divisible by 2, 3, 4, 5, 6, 7, 8, 9, or 10?

31. Money Elissa and eight friends have lunch at a restaurant. The bill is $56.61. Can the friends split the bill into nine equal shares? Use the divisibility rule for 9 to explain your answer.

32. Patterns A number pattern begins 6, 12, 18, 24, . . .
 a. Write the next four numbers in the pattern.
 b. Which of the eight numbers are divisible by both 2 and 3?
 c. **Writing in Math** Write a rule for divisibility by 6.

33. You have $17 to spend on rides that cost $2 each. If you go on as many rides as you can afford, how much money will you have left?

34. Challenge Write all the three-digit numbers containing a 1, 2, and 3. Which of these numbers are divisible by 4? Explain.

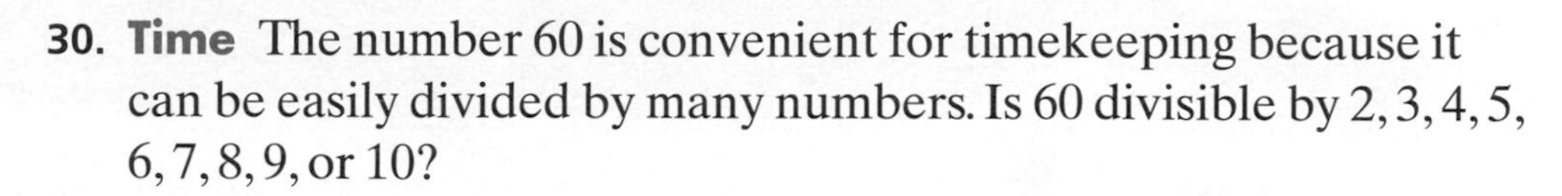

Test Prep and Mixed Review — Practice

Multiple Choice

35. Rosa plants rows of flowers with exactly the same number in each row. Each row has more than one flower. She has 28 flowers. What is the greatest number of rows she can make?
Ⓐ 4 Ⓑ 7 Ⓒ 12 Ⓓ 14

36. Ben must buy all the equipment on the list. He estimates the total cost by rounding each price. Which is the closest to the amount Ben will spend?
Ⓕ $77 Ⓗ $79
Ⓖ $78 Ⓙ $80

Soccer Equipment

Item	Price($)
Ball	14.98
Cleats	18.99
Shin guards	11.75
Team socks	6.25
Team jersey	28.50

37. A centimeter is one hundredth of a meter. Which measurement is equal to a centimeter?
Ⓐ 0.1 m Ⓑ 0.01 m Ⓒ 0.001 m Ⓓ 0.0001 m

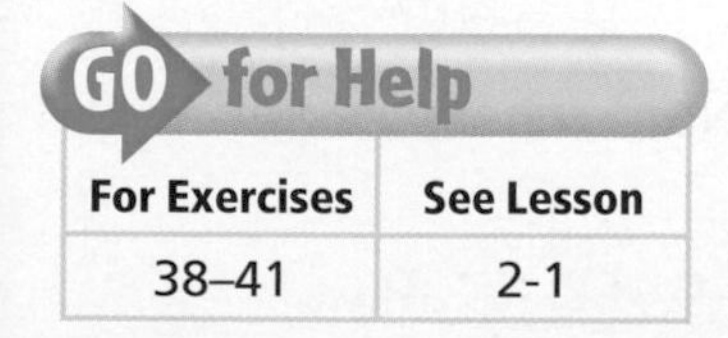

GO for Help

For Exercises	See Lesson
38–41	2-1

Evaluate each expression.

38. $2(a - 1)$ for $a = 2$ **39.** $1 + 7a$ for $a = 5$

40. $6(b + 2)$ for $b = 3$ **41.** $3b - 2$ for $b = 3$

Online lesson quiz, PearsonSuccessNet.com

3-2 Exponents

1. **Vocabulary Review** A mathematical phrase containing numbers and symbols is an __?__.

Find the value of each expression.

2. $3 \times 3 + 4 \times 4$
3. $1 \times 3 - 1 \times 3$
4. $1 + 1 \times 2 - 1$

Lesson 1-2

CONTENT STANDARDS

6.EE.1, 6.EE.2, 6.EE.2.c

What You'll Learn

To use exponents and to simplify expressions with exponents

New Vocabulary exponent, base, power

Why Learn This?

Exponents are used to represent numbers. You need exponents to write large numbers like the number of stars in a galaxy.

You can write 625 as a product of factors.

$$625 = \underbrace{5 \times 5 \times 5 \times 5}_{\text{factors}}$$

The number 5 is used as a factor four times. An **exponent** tells you how many times a number, or **base,** is used as a factor.

$$5 \times 5 \times 5 \times 5 = 5^4$$

← exponent (4); ↑ base (5)

5^4 is a power. A **power** is a number that can be expressed using an exponent.

Vocabulary Tip

You read 5^4 as "5 to the fourth power."

EXAMPLE Using an Exponent

1 Write $3 \times 3 \times 3 \times 3$ using an exponent. Name the base and the exponent.

$$3 \times 3 \times 3 \times 3 = 3^4$$ ← 3^4 means that 3 is used as a factor 4 times.

The base is 3, and the exponent is 4.

Quick Check

1. Write each expression using an exponent. Name the base and the exponent.
   a. 3.94×3.94 b. $7 \times 7 \times 7 \times 7$ c. $x \cdot x \cdot x$

EXAMPLE Simplifying a Power

Calculator Tip

You can use the exponent key to find the value of exponents. $2^5 = 2$ [^] 5

2 **Anatomy** You have 2^5 bones in your hand and arm. What is the value of 2^5?

$2^5 = 2 \times 2 \times 2 \times 2 \times 2 = 32$ ← The base 2 is used as a factor 5 times.

The value of 2^5 is 32.

Quick Check

2. **Astronomy** Phobos, the largest of Mars's moons, has a diameter of 3^3 kilometers. What is the value of 3^3?

The order of operations can be extended to include exponents.

KEY CONCEPTS Order of Operations

1. Do all operations within parentheses first.
2. Do all work with exponents.
3. Multiply and divide in order from left to right.
4. Add and subtract in order from left to right.

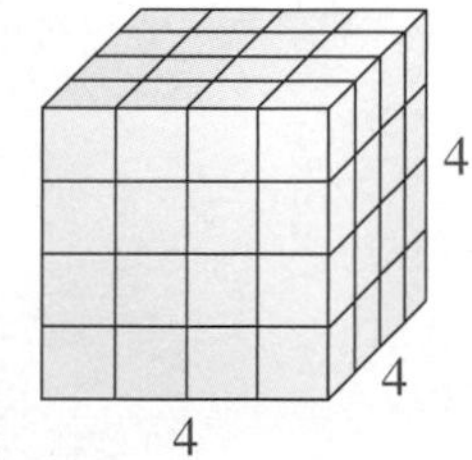

The volume of the cube is $V = s^3$. You read s^3 as "s cubed." The diagram shows that $s = 4$, so $V = 4^3$ or 64 cubic units.

The surface area of the cube is $A = 6s^2$. You read $6s^2$ as "six times s squared." Since $s = 4, A = 6 \times 4^2$. Using order of operations, simplify the exponent first.

$A = 6 \times 4^2 = 6 \times 16 = 96$ square units.

EXAMPLE Simplifying an Expression

3 Simplify $3 \times (7^2 + 18 \div 2)$.

$3 \times (49 + 18 \div 2)$ ← Simplify within parentheses. Simplify 7^2.

$3 \times (49 + 9)$ ← In parentheses, simplify $18 \div 2$.

$3 \times (58)$ ← In parentheses, add $49 + 9$.

174 ← Multiply 3 and 58.

GO Online

Video Tutor Help

PearsonSuccessNet.com

Quick Check

3. a. Simplify $2^3 - 6 \div 3$. b. Simplify $5 + (2 + 1)^2$.

Check Your Understanding

1. **Vocabulary** How are exponents used to represent factors?

2. **Number Sense** Does 5^4 have the same value as 5×4? Explain.

Write each expression below using an exponent.

3. $3 \times 3 = 3^{\blacksquare}$

4. $2 \times 2 \times 2 = \blacksquare^3$

5. $9 \times 9 \times 9 = 9^{\blacksquare}$

Fill in each blank.

6. $4^2 = 4 \times 4 = \blacksquare$

7. $2^3 = \blacksquare \times \blacksquare \times \blacksquare = 8$

Homework Exercises

For more exercises, see Extra Skills and Word Problems.

GO for Help

For Exercises	See Examples
8–16	1
17–20	2
21–26	3

Write each expression using an exponent. Name the base and the exponent.

8. $1 \times 1 \times 1 \times 1$

9. 29

10. $3 \times 3 \times 3 \times 3$

11. $25 \times 25 \times 25$

12. $2.5 \times 2.5 \times 2.5$

13. $100 \times 100 \times 100$

14. $r \cdot r$

15. $b \cdot b \cdot b \cdot b \cdot b$

16. $25 \cdot n \cdot n \cdot n \cdot n$

17. A small plane needs 5^3 meters to take off or land. What is the value of 5^3?

Simplify each expression.

18. 5^2

19. 4^3

20. 2.5^2

21. $(2 + 3)^2$

22. $(3^2 - 1)^2$

23. $(9 - 7)^3 \times 6$

24. $(9 + 1)^2 - 1^3$

25. $15^2 - (1 + 13^2)$

26. $(10 - 8)^4 \times 3.5$

GPS 27. **Guided Problem Solving** A band of cumulus clouds is located at 10^4 feet. A commercial jet is traveling at 38,000 feet. What is the difference between the altitude of the clouds and the altitude of the jet?
- How many feet is 10^4 feet?

28. **Geography** The population of Australia is more than 20,000,000 people. You can write 20,000,000 as $2 \times 10,000,000$. Write 10,000,000 using exponents.

Evaluate each expression for $j = 2$ and $g = 4$.

29. j^6

30. $(j + g)^3$

31. $(j + g)^2 + 4$

32. Patterns Copy the table.

a. Fill in the missing values.

b. **Writing in Math** Explain how the number of zeros in the standard form of a power of 10 relates to the exponent.

c. Extend the table to 10^8.

d. Write a rule for the number pattern.

Power	Standard Form
10^1	10
10^2	100
10^3	1,000
10^4	■
■	■

33. Biology A single-celled organism splits in two after one hour. Each new cell also splits in two after one hour. How many cells will there be after eight hours? Write your answer using an exponent.

34. Reasoning Does the expression $2^2 \cdot 3^2 - 2^3 - 1$ have the same value as $2^2 \cdot (3^2 - 2^3) - 1$? Explain.

35. Challenge In the equation $d = s^2$, d equals 32. Between what two whole numbers is the value of s?

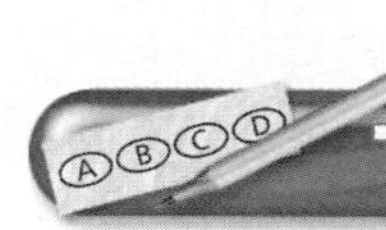

Test Prep and Mixed Review

Practice

Multiple Choice

36. Yoel has 3 fewer coins than Selena. Selena has 15 coins. Which equation can be used to find k, the number of coins Yoel has?

Ⓐ $k = 3 \cdot 5$

Ⓑ $k = 15 \div 3$

Ⓒ $k = 15 - 3$

Ⓓ $k = 15 + 3$

37. Karen and her son share 30 grapes. Karen eats twice as many grapes as her son. How many grapes does Karen eat?

Ⓕ 10 Ⓖ 15 Ⓗ 20 Ⓙ 30

38. The table shows the relationship between side length and volume of a cube. If the side length is n, what is the volume of the cube?

Ⓐ $2n$

Ⓑ n^2

Ⓒ $3n$

Ⓓ n^3

Side Length, n	Volume
1	1
2	8
3	27
n	■

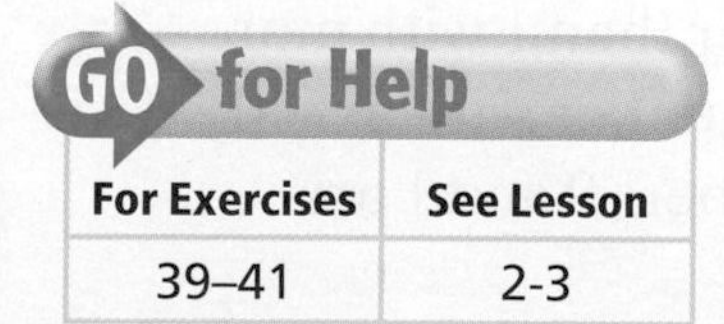

For Exercises	See Lesson
39–41	2-3

Tell whether each equation is true or false.

39. $0.80 \times 5 = 4.00$

40. $72 \div 8 = 8$

41. $16.43 - 3.82 = 13.41$

Online lesson quiz, PearsonSuccessNet.com

3-3 Prime Numbers and Prime Factorization

Check Skills You'll Need

1. **Vocabulary Review** Is a number *divisible* by 5 always divisible by 10?

Test each number for divisibility by 2, 3, 5, 9, and 10.

2. 990 **3.** 901

4. 800 **5.** 2,080

for Help
Lesson 3-1

CONTENT STANDARD
Essential for understanding 6.EE.1

What You'll Learn

To factor numbers and to find the prime factorization of numbers

New Vocabulary factor, composite number, prime number, prime factorization

Why Learn This?

Using factors, you can organize items or people in rows.

Divisibility rules can help you find factors. A **factor** is a whole number that divides a nonzero whole number with remainder 0.

EXAMPLE 1 Finding Factors

An instructor plans a dance routine for 20 dancers in rows. Each row has the same number of dancers. What are the arrangements the instructor can use?

Look for pairs of factors for 20 to find the possible arrangements.

1×20 ← Write each pair of factors. Start with 1.

$2 \times 10,\ 4 \times 5$ ← 2 and 4 are factors. Skip 3, since 20 is not divisible by 3.

5×4 ← Stop when you repeat factors.

The arrangements are 1×20, 2×10, and 4×5.

Quick Check

1. A gift box must hold the same number of pears in each row. You have 24 pears. What arrangements can you use?

A **composite number** is a whole number greater than 1 with more than two factors. A **prime number** is a whole number with exactly two factors, 1 and the number itself. The numbers 0 and 1 are neither prime nor composite.

EXAMPLE Prime or Composite?

2 Is the number prime or composite? Explain.

a. 51
Composite: 51 is divisible by 3. So 51 has more than two factors.

b. 53
Prime: 53 has only two factors, 1 and 53.

Quick Check

2. Is the number prime or composite? Explain.

a. 39 **b.** 47 **c.** 63

To write the **prime factorization** of a composite number, you write the number as a product of prime numbers. Each composite number has only one prime factorization.

When a factor repeats, use exponents to write your answer. You can use a division ladder or a factor tree to find the prime factorization of a number.

EXAMPLE Prime Factorization

3 Write the prime factorization of 84 using exponents.

Method 1 Use a division ladder.

For: Prime Factorization Activity
Use: Interactive Textbook, 3-3

2)84 ← **Divide 84 by the prime number 2. Work down.**
2)42 ← **The result is 42. Since 42 is even, divide by 2 again.**
3)21 ← **The result is 21. Divide by the prime number 3.**
7 ← **The prime factorization is 2 × 2 × 3 × 7.**

Method 2 Use a factor tree.

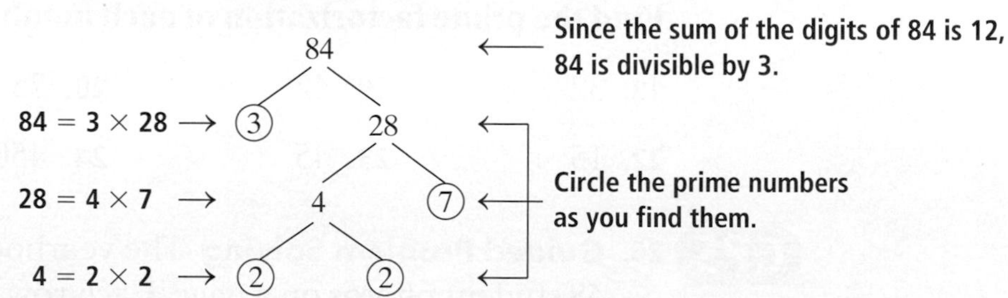

The prime factorization of 84 is $2 \times 2 \times 3 \times 7$, or $2^2 \times 3 \times 7$.

Quick Check

3. Find the prime factorization of 27.

Check Your Understanding

1. **Vocabulary** How is a prime number different from a composite number?

2. Find two prime numbers between 10 and 20, with a difference of 2.

3. Which number is not a composite number? Explain.

55	51	82	7

4. **Number Sense** Can two numbers have the same prime factorization? Explain.

Homework Exercises

For more exercises, see Extra Skills and Word Problems.

GO for Help

For Exercises	See Examples
5–13	1
14–17	2
18–25	3

List the factors of each number.

5. 28 6. 21 7. 17 8. 60

9. 48 10. 37 11. 144 12. 450

13. **Earth Science** For a science project, you want to display 36 rocks in rows, with the same number of rocks in each row. Find the arrangements that you can use.

Is each number *prime* or *composite*? Explain.

14. 19 15. 67 16. 57 17. 91

Find the prime factorization of each number.

18. 32 19. 42 20. 75 21. 400

22. 15 23. 45 24. 450 25. 10,000

26. **Guided Problem Solving** The yearbook editor must arrange 48 student photos on a page. Each row must have the same number of photos. What arrangements can she make?
    - **Make a Plan** What method can you use to find the factor pairs for 48?
    - **Check the Answer** How do you know that you have found all the factor pairs?

Calculator **Find the number with the given prime factorization.**

27. $7 \times 11 \times 13$

28. $2^3 \times 5^2 \times 7 \times 11$

29. A clerk arranges 81 apples in a square crate. Each row has the same number of apples. How many rows does he make?

30. **Parades** A group has 36 ceremonial guards. When they march, they form rows of equal numbers of guards. What numbers of rows can they make? How many guards will be in each row?

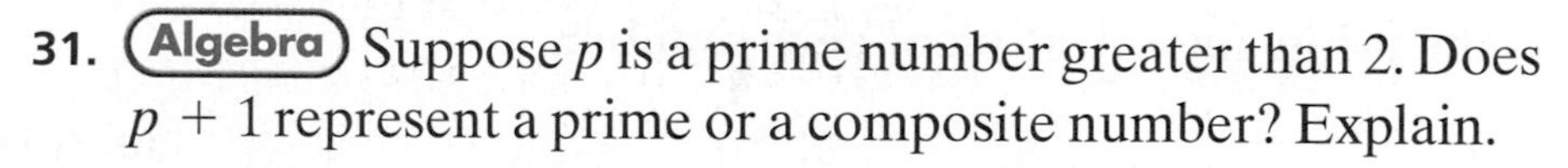

31. **Algebra** Suppose p is a prime number greater than 2. Does $p + 1$ represent a prime or a composite number? Explain.

32. **Landscaping** A homeowner buys 116 square tiles to build a rectangular patio. The same number of tiles are in each row. What are the arrangements of tiles that he can make?

33. **Challenge** Find the pairs of prime numbers with a difference of two, between 1 and 100.

Test Prep and Mixed Review

Practice

Multiple Choice

34. What is the prime factorization of 48?
    (A) $12 \cdot 4$ (B) $6 \cdot 2^4$ (C) $3 \cdot 2 \cdot 2^2$ (D) $2^4 \cdot 3$

35. The graph below shows the results of a student survey. Which statement is supported by the graph?
    (F) More students prefer pop or rock than jazz.
    (G) More students prefer jazz than country.
    (H) About half of the students prefer country and jazz.
    (J) 100 students prefer pop or rock.

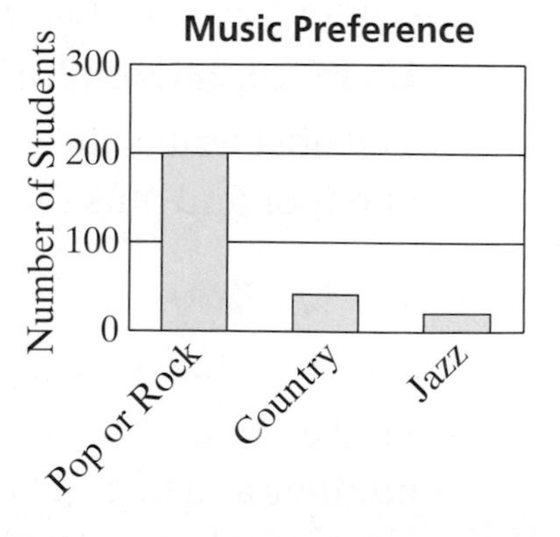

36. Which number is NOT a factor of 30?
    (A) 2 (B) 4 (C) 6 (D) 15

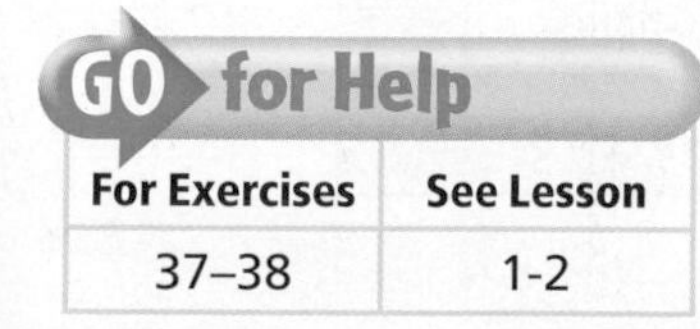

GO for Help

For Exercises	See Lesson
37–38	1-2

Use <, =, or > to complete each statement.

37. $(8 + 10) \div 2$ ■ $14 \div (2 + 5)$

38. $3.5 + 2.5 \times 2$ ■ $24 \div 4 + 3$

Online lesson quiz, PearsonSuccessNet.com

Checkpoint Quiz 1

Lessons 3-1 through 3-3

Test each number for divisibility by 2, 3, 5, 9, and 10.

1. 375
2. 1,402
3. 240

Simplify each expression.

4. 4^3
5. $5 + (2^3 - 3)$
6. 5^5
7. $(6 + 2)^2$

Find the prime factorization of each number.

8. 40
9. 80
10. 1,000

11. A photographer is arranging 105 students in rows for a class picture. She wants the same number of students in each row. What are the different arrangements of students she can make?

MATH GAMES

Triple Prime Time

Getting Started

- Draw a 4-by-4 grid.
- Arrange the following numbers on your grid. Put each number in any square on the grid.
  12, 18, 20, 28, 30, 42, 45, 50, 63, 66, 70, 75, 105, 110, 154, 165
- The host writes the prime numbers **2, 3, 5, 7,** and **11** on slips of paper and puts the slips in a container.

How to Play

- The host draws a prime number, calls it out, and replaces it.
- Find a number on your grid that has the chosen prime number as a factor. Write the prime factor in that square. Each number on your grid has three prime factors.
- The host continues to draw slips and call numbers.
- When you record all three prime factors for a number, cross out the square. For example, you can cross out the square with 28 when you record 2, 2, and 7.
- The first player to cross out four squares in a row wins.

20	154	66	30
2, 2, 7 ~~28~~	18	5 50	165
63	110	12	2 42
70	75	45	105

3-4 Greatest Common Factor

1. Vocabulary Review Write a sentence about math using the words *factor* and *product*.

Find the prime factorization.

2. 45

3. 21

4. 99

Lesson 3-3

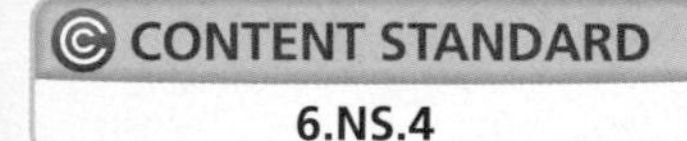

6.NS.4

What You'll Learn

To find the GCF of two or more numbers

New Vocabulary common factor, greatest common factor (GCF)

Why Learn This?

A stamp club president distributes equally one set of 18 stamps and another set of 30 stamps to members present at a meeting. No stamps are left over. You can use factors to find the greatest possible number of club members at the meeting.

To find the greatest possible number of club members, you can find the factors that 18 and 30 share. A factor that two or more numbers share is a **common factor.**

The **greatest common factor (GCF)** of two or more numbers is the greatest factor shared by all the numbers. You can find the GCF of two numbers by listing their factors.

EXAMPLE Using Lists of Factors

1 Find the greatest common factor of 18 and 30.

List the factors of 18 and the factors of 30. Then circle the common factors.

Factors of 18: (1), (2), (3), (6), 9, 18
Factors of 30: (1), (2), (3), 5, (6), 10, 15, 30

← **The common factors are 1, 2, 3, and 6.**

The greatest common factor (GCF) is 6.

Quick Check

1. List the factors to find the GCF of each pair of numbers.

a. 6, 21 **b.** 18, 49 **c.** 14, 28

You can also use a division ladder or factor trees to find the greatest common factor of two or more numbers.

EXAMPLE Using a Division Ladder

2 **Gridded Response** Find the GCF of 42 and 56. Use a division ladder.

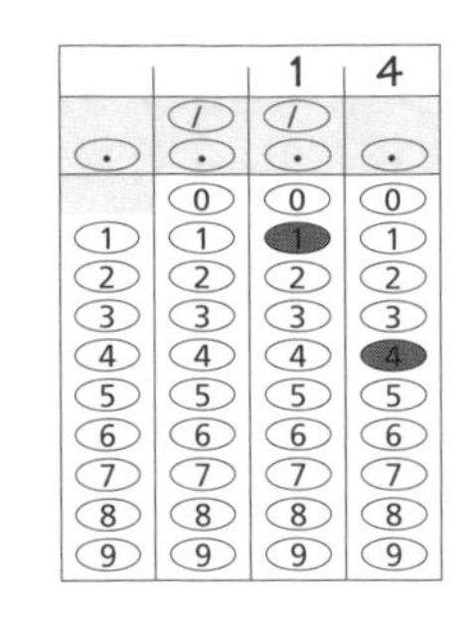

Test Prep Tip

You can use one of the two methods shown in the examples to find the GCF. Then check your answer using the other method.

$2\overline{)42 \quad 56}$ ← **Divide by 2, a common factor of 42 and 56.**
$7\overline{)21 \quad 28}$ ← **Divide by 7, a common factor of 21 and 28.**
$\quad 3 \quad 4$ ← **3 and 4 have no common factors.**

Multiply the common factors: 2 × 7 = 14.

The GCF of 42 and 56 is 14.

Quick Check

2. You want to cut two ribbons into equal lengths with nothing left over. The ribbons are 18 and 42 inches long. What is the longest possible length of ribbon you can cut?

EXAMPLE Using Factor Trees

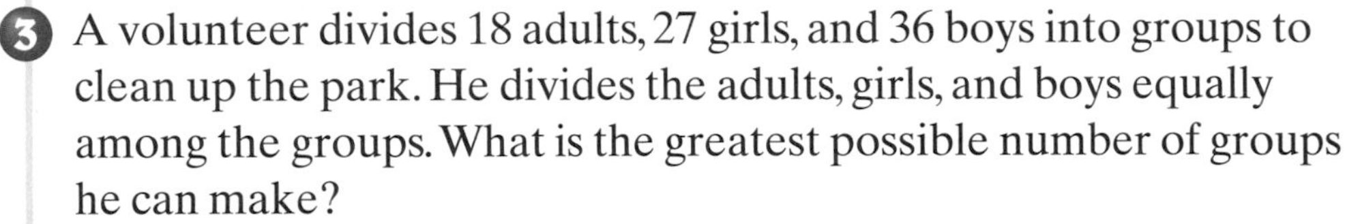

3 A volunteer divides 18 adults, 27 girls, and 36 boys into groups to clean up the park. He divides the adults, girls, and boys equally among the groups. What is the greatest possible number of groups he can make?

Make a factor tree for each number.

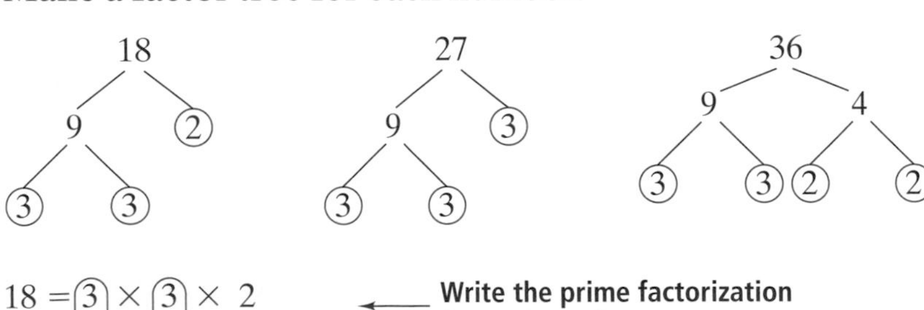

18 = 3 × 3 × 2
27 = 3 × 3 × 3
36 = 3 × 3 × 2 × 2

← **Write the prime factorization for each number.**

Identify common factors.

The GCF of 18, 27, and 36 is 9. The greatest number of groups is 9.

Quick Check

3. Use a factor tree to find the GCF.

a. 48, 80, 128 **b.** 36, 60, 84

Check Your Understanding

1. **Vocabulary** Explain why the GCF of two numbers is sometimes 1.

2. **Open-Ended** Write two numbers with a GCF of 4.

Match each pair of numbers to the GCF.

3. 18, 3 — A. 22
4. 8, 12 — B. 3
5. 22, 110 — C. 4

Homework Exercises

For more exercises, see Extra Skills and Word Problems.

GO for Help

For Exercises	See Examples
6–11	1
12–17	2
18–23	3

List the factors to find the GCF of each set of numbers.

6. 14, 35
7. 24, 45
8. 26, 34
9. 30, 35
10. 48, 88
11. 36, 63

Use a division ladder to find the GCF of each set of numbers.

12. 10, 18
13. 24, 60
14. 11, 23
15. 27, 30
16. 12, 16, 28
17. 33, 55, 132

Use factor trees to find the GCF of each set of numbers.

18. 20, 60
19. 54, 84
20. 72, 120
21. 64, 125
22. 117, 130
23. 45, 150

GPS 24. **Guided Problem Solving** You want to make bouquets of balloons. You choose 18 yellow, 30 blue, and 42 red balloons. Each bouquet will have the same number of each color. What is the greatest possible number of bouquets you can make?
- What method can you use to find the GCF?
- What is the GCF? How many bouquets can you make?

25. Three groups of friends go to a movie. Each ticket costs the same amount. Each group spends a different total amount for tickets. The amounts are $27, $36, and $81. At most how much does each ticket cost?

Find the GCF of each set of numbers.

26. 300, 450 **27.** 280, 420 **28.** 200, 300, 400

29. **Writing in Math** Ninc people plan to share equally 24 stamps from one set and 36 stamps from another set. Explain why 9 people cannot share the stamps equally.

30. Three friends pool their money to buy baseball cards. Brand A has 8 cards in each pack, Brand B has 12 cards, and Brand C has 15 cards. If they want to split each pack of cards equally, which two brands should they buy? Explain.

31. **Summer Camp** A camp director splits 14 counselors and 77 campers into activity groups. Each group should have the same number of counselors and the same number of campers. At most how many groups can she make? How many campers are in each group?

32. **Reasoning** Which number less than 50 has the most factors? Justify your answer.

33. **Challenge** There are four two-digit numbers that end with 6 and are less than 50. Find the GCF of the numbers.

Test Prep and Mixed Review

Practice

Gridded Response

34. You have 36 photos from a trip and 54 photos from a party. What is the GCF of 36 and 54?

35. The heights of several sixth-grade students are shown in the table. What is the difference in height between the tallest and shortest student?

Student	Height (in meters)
Rachael	1.52
Jose	1.47
Oscar	1.60
Penelope	1.50
Malik	1.44
Phillip	1.42
Sandra	1.55
Lucy	1.57

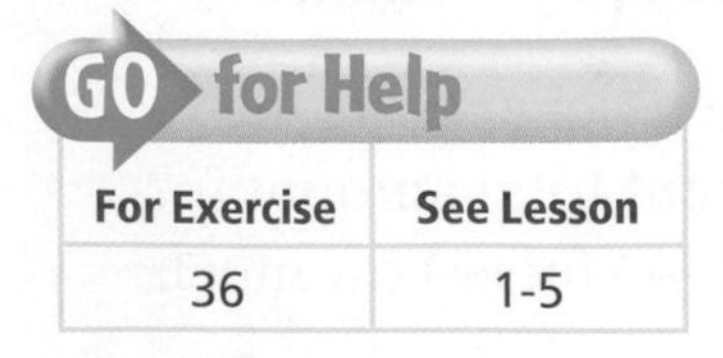
GO for Help

For Exercise	See Lesson
36	1-5

36. You buy 3 packs of notebook paper for $1.25 each and a binder for $1.50. Write an expression for the total cost of the items. Then find the total cost.

3-5 Least Common Multiple

Check Skills You'll Need

1. **Vocabulary Review** How can you use a factor tree to find the *prime factorization* of a number?

Find the prime factorization of each number.

2. 80 **3.** 32

4. 208 **5.** 500

GO for Help Lesson 3-3

CONTENT STANDARD

6.NS.4

What You'll Learn

To find the LCM of two or more numbers

New Vocabulary multiple, common multiple, least common multiple (LCM)

Why Learn This?

You can use common multiples to make coordinating schedules easier.

Carmen gets her hair cut every four weeks. Maria gets her hair cut every six weeks. They both had their hair cut last week. How long will it be before they both get their hair cut again in the same week?

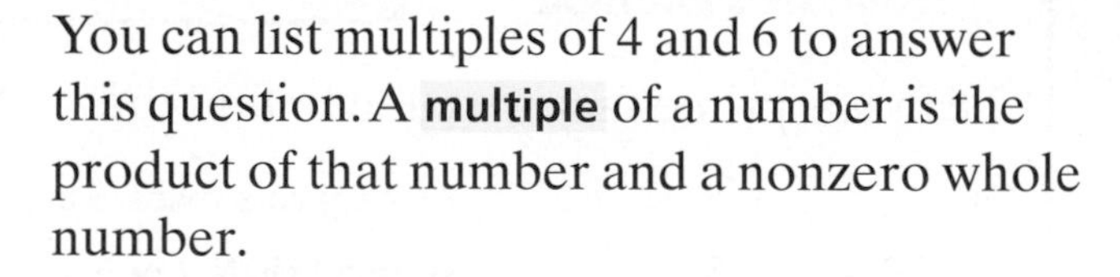

You can list multiples of 4 and 6 to answer this question. A **multiple** of a number is the product of that number and a nonzero whole number.

Multiples of 6
$6 \times 1 = 6$
$6 \times 2 = 12$
$6 \times 3 = 18$
$6 \times y = 6y$

A number that is a multiple of each of two or more numbers is a **common multiple.** The **least common multiple (LCM)** of two or more numbers is the least multiple that is common to all the numbers.

EXAMPLE Find the LCM Using Lists of Multiples

1 Find the least common multiple of 4 and 6.

multiples of 4: 4, 8, (12), 16, 20, (24)

multiples of 6: 6, (12), 18, (24)

← **List multiples of each number. 12 and 24 are common multiples.**

The least common multiple is 12.

Quick Check

1. List multiples to find the LCM.
   a. 10, 12 b. 7, 10

REGULAR SERVICE	
	EVERY
YELLOW LINE	8 MIN
GREEN LINE	10 MIN
PURPLE LINE	20 MIN

EXAMPLE Using Prime Factorizations

2 **Scheduling** A train for each of the train lines shown in the table on the left has just arrived. In how many minutes will a train for each line arrive at the same time again?

Write the prime factorizations for 8, 10, and 20. Then circle each different factor where it appears the greatest number of times.

$8 = (2 \times 2 \times 2)$ ← **2 appears the most often here (three times).**

$10 = 2 \times (5)$ ← **5 appears once.**

$20 = 2 \times 2 \times 5$ ← **Don't circle 5 again.**

$2 \times 2 \times 2 \times 5 = 40$ ← **Multiply the circled factors.**

The LCM is 40. The trains will arrive together in 40 minutes.

Quick Check

2. Use prime factorization to find the LCM of 6, 8, and 12.

More Than One Way

Find the LCM of 20, 30, and 45.

Michael's Method

I can use prime factorization to find the LCM.

$20 = (2 \times 2) \times (5)$ ← **2 appears twice. 5 appears once.**

$30 = 2 \times 3 \times 5$ ← **Don't circle 2 or 5 again.**

$45 = (3 \times 3) \times 5$ ← **3 appears twice.**

$2 \times 2 \times 3 \times 3 \times 5 = 180$ ← **Multiply the circled factors.**

The LCM of 20, 30, and 45 is 180.

Amanda's Method

The greatest number is 45. I can list the multiples of 45 until I find one that is also a multiple of 20 and 30.

45, 90, 135, 180 ← **180 is a multiple of both 20 and 30.**

(90) ← **90 is a multiple of 30, but not of 20.**

So the LCM of 20, 30, and 45 is 180.

Choose a Method

Find the LCM of 6, 9, and 10. Explain why you chose your method.

Check Your Understanding

1. **Vocabulary** Use the word *multiple* in a sentence about math.

List four multiples of each number.

2. 7
3. 8
4. 11

5. Find the LCM of 16 and 24 using prime factorizations.

Homework Exercises

For more exercises, see Extra Skills and Word Problems.

GO for Help

For Exercises	See Examples
6–17	1
18–27	2

List multiples to find the LCM of each set of numbers.

6. 4, 9
7. 5, 6
8. 12, 15
9. 10, 16
10. 14, 21
11. 20, 30
12. 25, 75
13. 8, 10
14. 3, 8, 12, 15
15. 4, 7, 12, 21
16. 25, 50, 125
17. 2, 3, 5, 7, 11

Use prime factorizations to find the LCM of each set of numbers.

18. 9, 21
19. 18, 24
20. 75, 100
21. 8, 14
22. 22, 55
23. 18, 108
24. 7, 12
25. 4, 7, 20
26. 30, 50, 200

27. **Shopping** You buy paper plates, napkins, and cups for a party. Plates come in packages of 15. Cups come in packages of 20, and napkins come in packages of 120. You want to have the same number of plates, cups, and napkins. How many packages of each item do you need to buy?

28. **Guided Problem Solving** Two ships sail between New York and London. One makes the round trip in 12 days. The other takes 16 days. They both leave London today. In how many days will both ships leave London together again?
    - How can you use multiples to solve this problem?
    - What are the multiples of 12 and 16?

29. **Business** During a promotion, a music store gives a free CD to every fifteenth customer and a free DVD to every fortieth customer. Which customer will be the first to get both gifts?

Find the LCM of each set of numbers or expressions.

30. 35, 45 **31.** 6, 8, 16 **32.** $2^2 \times 7,\ 2 \times 7^2$

33. Number Sense A number N has both 8 and 10 as factors.
  a. Name three factors of the number N, other than 1.
  b. What is the smallest number N could be?

34. Fitness You lift weights every third day and swim every fourth day. If you do both activities today, in how many days will you do both activities again on the same day?

35. Algebra The LCM of 3 and 6 is 6. The LCM of 5 and 10 is 10. The LCM of x and $2x$ is ■ when x is a nonzero whole number.

36. Writing in Math What is the LCM for two numbers that have no common factors greater than 1? Explain your reasoning.

37. Challenge Find the LCM of $25xy$ and $200xy$.

Test Prep and Mixed Review — Practice

Multiple Choice

38. What is the least common multiple of 24 and 28?
Ⓐ 4 Ⓑ 84 Ⓒ 168 Ⓓ 336

39. On January 1, Rosa waters all of her plants. She waters her cactus every 60 days, her fern every 4 days, and her violets every 3 days. How many times in a year will she water all her plants on the same day?
  Step K Find the least common multiple.
  Step L Divide 365 by the least common multiple.
  Step M Find the prime factorizations for 3, 4, and 60.

Which list shows the steps in the correct order?
Ⓕ K, M, L Ⓗ K, L, M
Ⓖ M, K, L Ⓙ M, L, K

40. Jon paid a membership fee of $30 to use a skate park. Each time he skated, he paid $2.50. Which equation can be used to find c, the cost of skating for s visits?
Ⓐ $c = 2.5s + 30$ Ⓒ $c = 30s + 2.5$
Ⓑ $c = 30(s + 2.5)$ Ⓓ $c = 2.5(s + 30)$

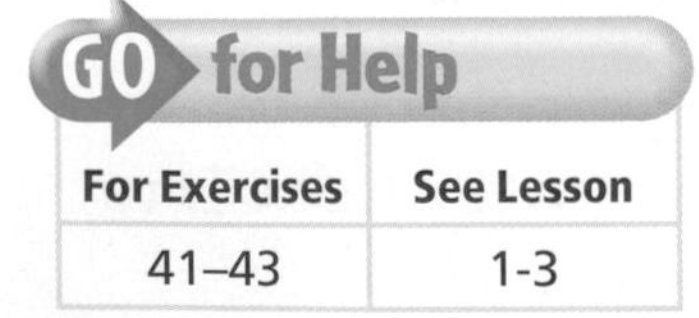
GO for Help

For Exercises	See Lesson
41–43	1-3

Write each decimal in expanded form.

41. 0.51 **42.** 2.35 **43.** 8.752

Algebra

3-6 The Distributive Property

Check Skills You'll Need

1. Vocabulary Review What is an *algebraic expression*?

Evaluate each expression for $x = 3$.

2. $4x + 10$

3. $2x - 5$

4. $6x \div 2$

GO for Help Lesson 2-1

CONTENT STANDARDS
6.EE.2.b, 6.EE.3, 6.EE.4

What You'll Learn

To use the Distributive Property to simplify expressions in problem solving situations

New Vocabulary Distributive Property, equivalent expressions

Why Learn This?

The amount you earn depends on the number of hours you work. The Distributive Property helps you use mental math to calculate your earnings quickly. The **Distributive Property** shows how multiplication affects addition or subtraction.

KEY CONCEPTS The Distributive Property

Arithmetic	Algebra
$8 \times (4 + 6) = (8 \times 4) + (8 \times 6)$	$a(b + c) = ab + ac$
$7 \times (6 - 2) = (7 \times 6) - (7 \times 2)$	$a(b - c) = ab - ac$

Notice that $a(b + c)$ is a product of two factors, a and $(b + c)$. You can look at $(b + c)$ as both a single entity (because the two variables are within parentheses) and a sum of two numbers. For example, $3(1 + 4)$ is a product of 3 and $(1 + 4)$; $(1 + 4)$ is its own unit, and when you add the two numbers within parentheses you get a sum of 5.

EXAMPLE Using the Distributive Property with Algebraic Expressions

1 Write an equivalent expression for $2(6x - 3y + 7)$.

$2(6x - 3y + 7) = 2 \cdot 6x - 2 \cdot 3y + 2 \cdot 7$ ← Use the Distributive Property.

$= 12x - 6y + 14$ ← Multiply.

Check

$2(6x - 3y + 7) \stackrel{?}{=} 12x - 6y + 14$ ← Check if the two expressions are equivalent.

$2(6 \cdot 2 - 3 \cdot 3 + 7) \stackrel{?}{=} 12 \cdot 2 - 6 \cdot 3 + 14$ ← Substitute values, such as 2 for x and 3 for y.

$20 = 20$ ← They are equivalent; your expression is correct.

Quick Check

1. Simplify each expression.
   a. $4(3n + 6)$ b. $8(7 - 3m + 4p)$ c. $12(2a + 3b - 5)$

Equivalent expressions have the same value. They name the same number regardless of which number the variable stands for.

The Distributive Property can also be used in reverse. Applying the Distributive Property this way is called factoring.

EXAMPLE Factoring Numeric Expressions

2 Factor $20 + 8$.

$20 = 5 \times 2 \times 2$
$8 = 2 \times 2 \times 2$ ← Find the GCF of 20 and 8. The GCF is $2 \times 2 = 4$.

$20 + 8 = 4(5) + 4(2)$ ← Write each term as a product of the GCF and its remaining factors.

$= 4(5 + 2)$ ← Use the Distributive Property.

Test Prep Tip

Check your solution by evaluating the original expression and the solution to see if they have the same value. $20 + 8 = 28$ and $4(5 + 2) = 4(7) = 28$, so the answer checks.

Quick Check

2. Factor each expression.
   a. $18 + 24$ b. $56 + 49$ c. $84 + 60$

GO Online

Video Tutor Help
PearsonSuccessNet.com

EXAMPLE Factoring Algebraic Expressions

3 Factor $27x + 18 + 36y$.

$27x = 3 \cdot 3 \cdot 3 \cdot x$
$18 = 3 \cdot 3 \cdot 2$
$36y = 3 \cdot 3 \cdot 2 \cdot 2 \cdot y$ ← Find the GCF of $27x$, 18, and $36y$. The GCF is $3 \cdot 3 = 9$.

$27x + 18 + 36y = 9(3x) + 9(2) + 9(4y)$ ← Write each term as a product of the GCF and its remaining factors.

$= 9(3x + 2 + 4y)$ ← Use the Distributive Property.

Quick Check

3. Factor each expression.
   a. $3n + 21$ b. $72 + 16h$ c. $48y + 80z + 64$

You can use the Distributive Property to multiply mentally.

EXAMPLE Application: Wages

Calculator Tip

Many calculators have a parenthesis key to help you solve problems.

4 **Multiple Choice** A summer job as an assistant camp counselor pays \$6.50 per hour. How much does the counselor earn for working 8 hours?

Ⓐ \$14.50 Ⓑ \$48.00 Ⓒ \$50.00 Ⓓ \$52.00

$6.50 \times 8 = (6.00 + 0.50) \cdot 8$ ← **Write 6.50 as 6.00 + 0.50.**

$= (6.00 \times 8) + (0.50 \times 8)$ ← **Use the Distributive Property.**

$= 48.00 + 4.00$ ← **Simplify within parentheses.**

$= 52.00$ ← **Add.**

The counselor earns \$52 for working 8 hours.
The answer is D.

Quick Check

4. A local bookstore charges \$2.80 for each used book. What is the charge for 5 used books?

Check Your Understanding

1. **Number Sense** In the expression $(4 + 5) \times 7$, what is true about $(4 + 5)$?

Ⓐ It is a sum and a product.
Ⓑ It is not a factor of 63.
Ⓒ It is a sum and a factor.
Ⓓ It is equal to 63.

2. **Error Analysis** Who simplified $2 \times (3 + 5)$ correctly? Explain.

Thomas
$(2 \times 3) + (2 \times 5)$

Brian
$(2 + 3) \times (2 + 5)$

Use the Distributive Property to write an equivalent expression for each expression.

3. $2(4 + t)$

4. $5(x + 3)$

5. $4(g - 9 + 5h)$

6. **Mental Math** Rebecca pays \$3.50 per gallon for 12 gallons of gas. How much did Rebecca pay in all for the gas?

Homework Exercises

For more exercises, see Extra Skills and Word Problems.

GO for Help

For Exercises	See Examples
7–15	1
16–24	2
25–33	3
34	4

Use the Distributive Property to write an equivalent expression for each of the following.

7. $3(x + 5)$ **8.** $7(2x + 4)$ **9.** $7(3 + 4n)$

10. $8(2x - 3 - y)$ **11.** $5(c + 7)$ **12.** $(4d - 15) \times 10$

13. $(3 + 4n) \times 8$ **14.** $9(2y - 4z + 8)$ **15.** $(5a - 2b) \times 4$

Factor each expression. Check your solution.

16. $12 + 16$ **17.** $100 + 75$ **18.** $66 + 44$

19. $70 + 98 + 42$ **20.** $8 + 28$ **21.** $5 + 65$

22. $4 + 34$ **23.** $99 + 6 + 3$ **24.** $108 + 45 + 36$

Factor each expression. Check your solution.

25. $9x + 12$ **26.** $60x + 16$ **27.** $36 + 78x$

28. $45n + 90 + 135q$ **29.** $15x + 9$ **30.** $12 + 20x$

31. $80x + 64$ **32.** $48 + 24m + 42n$ **33.** $56c + 24 + 72d$

34. Six students plan to go to a skating rink. The rink charges $4.50 per person. Find the total cost for the group.

35. **Guided Problem Solving** The expression $10v + 15w$ represents the cost of admission to a museum for 10 adults and 15 students. Factor $10v + 15w$.
- What is the GCF of $10v$ and $15w$?
- $10v + 15w = \square(\square v + \square w)$

36. The expression $80p + 30q + 10r$ can represent the area covered by 80 small tiles, 30 medium tiles, and 10 large tiles. Factor $80p + 30q + 10r$.

37. **Reasoning** Use the Distributive Property to simplify the expression $2x + 7x$.

38. **Writing in Math** Describe two ways to think about the quantity $(2x - 4)$ in the expression $3(2x - 4)$.

39. **Fundraising** There are 50 people walking in a fundraising event. Each participant walks 5.3 miles. How many miles do the participants walk in all?

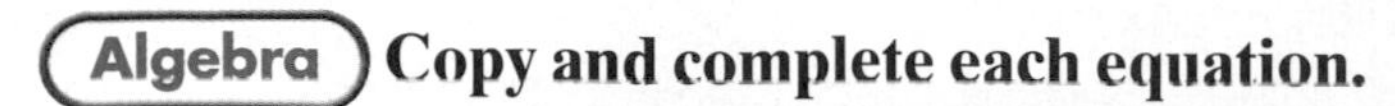

Algebra **Copy and complete each equation.**

40. $4(7 - y) = (4 \cdot 7) - (4 \cdot \blacksquare)$ 41. $9(a + b) = (\blacksquare \cdot a) + (9 \cdot \blacksquare)$

42. The table shows the amount of fabric Felicia needs to make each size couch cover. The amount needed for a large cover is unknown. She plans to make 4 of each size. Write an expression for the total amount of fabric Felicia needs and write an equivalent expression for the expression you wrote.

Size	Fabric (in yards)
Small	5
Medium	7
Large	x

43. Your class is selling calendars for $2.90 each. How much money does your class collect for selling 8 calendars?

44. **Gardening** Your school's ecology club plants 8 rows of trees in a vacant lot. Each row has 27 trees. Find the total number of trees that the ecology club plants.

45. **Reasoning** What property is shown by $a \times (b + c) = (b + c) \times a$? Explain your thinking and use an example to show that the equation is true.

46. **Challenge** Which expression is NOT equivalent to the others?
   A $(-3a \times c) + (-3b \times c)$
   B $(b + a) \times -3c$
   C $-3b \times (c + a)$
   D $(a + b) \times -3c$

Test Prep and Mixed Review

Practice

Multiple Choice

47. Maria works at a local department store and earns $7.50 per hour. She works 24 hours per week. How much does Maria earn per week?
   A $148.00 B $168.00 C $180.00 D $188.00

48. Which property is used in this statement? $(3 + 5) \times 7 = 7 \times (3 + 5)$
   F associative
   G commutative
   H distributive
   J identity

49. Which expression has a value of 105?
   A $(9 + 8) \times 7 - (6 \times 5) + 4 \times (3 + 2)$
   B $(9 + 8) \times (7 - 6) \times 5 + 4 \times 3 + 2$
   C $9 + (8 \times 7) - 6 \times 5 + (4 \times 3) + 2$
   D $(9 + 8) \times (7 - 6) \times 5 + 4 \times (3 + 2)$

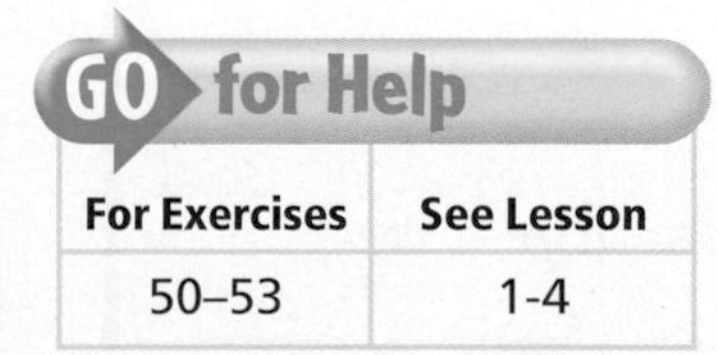

GO for Help

For Exercises	See Lesson
50–53	1-4

Find each sum. Estimate first.

50. $0.85 + 3.0 + 4.43$ 51. $1.1 + 2.02 + 3.13$

52. $0.05 + 0.5 + 0.55$ 53. $2.3 + 3.7 + 0.8$

Vocabulary Builder

Making Word Lists

You can learn new vocabulary by making a word list using index cards.

- Write the term. Then write the definition.
- Include any math symbols related to the term.
- Give an example of the term.
- Give a nonexample showing how the term might *not* apply.

Greatest Common Factor (GCF)

Definition: The GCF of two or more numbers is the greatest factor shared by all the numbers.

Example: The GCF of 12 and 20 is 4.

Nonexample: 2 is a common factor of 12 and 20, but 2 is not the GCF.

For the vocabulary terms on page 85, make a word list with cards like the one shown above.

Checkpoint Quiz 2

Lessons 3-4 through 3-6

Find the GCF of each set of numbers.

1. 45, 80 **2.** 24, 72 **3.** 9, 18, 51 **4.** 18, 48

Find the LCM of each set of numbers.

5. 5, 9 **6.** 12, 18 **7.** 4, 8, 12 **8.** 15, 50, 75

Use the Distributive Property to write an equivalent expression for each of the following.

9. $(15x - 4) \times 2$ **10.** $6(7 + 3c)$ **11.** $8(9r - 10)$ **12.** $5(2a - 12b + 5)$

Factor each expression. Check your solution.

13. $8x + 24$ **14.** $25x + 15$ **15.** $64x - 14y + 30$ **16.** $40p + 90$

Algebra

3-7 Simplifying Algebraic Expressions

Check Skills You'll Need

1. **Vocabulary Review** What is true about *equivalent expressions*?

Use the order of operations to simplify each expression.

2. $8 - 4 + 6 \div 3$
3. $3 \cdot 8^2 + 12 \div 4$
4. $(40 + 24) \div 8$

GO for Help
Lesson 1-2

CONTENT STANDARDS
6.EE.2.b, 6.EE.3, 6.EE.4

What You'll Learn

To simplify algebraic expressions

New Vocabulary term, coefficient

Why Learn This?

Simplifying algebraic expressions makes them easier to evaluate.

In an algebraic expression such as $-2x + 8$, the parts that are separated by an addition or subtraction operation are called terms. A **term** is a number, a variable, or the product of a number and one or more variables. The number before a variable is the **coefficient**.

$7x^2 + 3y$ — terms: $7x^2$, $3y$; coefficients: 7, 3

Think of an expression such as $a - 3b$ as the sum $a + (-3b)$ to determine that the coefficient of b is -3. When there is no number in front of the variable, it is *understood* that "1" is in front of it. For example, x is the same as $1x$ and $-y$ is the same as $-1y$.

Like terms have exactly the same variable factors. In the algebraic expression $3x + 4x + 14$, the like terms are $3x$ and $4x$. In $40y + 12 - 8$, the like terms are 12 and -8.

You can simplify expressions by using properties of operations to combine like terms. The simplified expressions are equivalent to the original expressions.

KEY CONCEPTS Properties for Simplifying Algebraic Expressions

Property	Addition	Multiplication
Commutative	$a + b = b + a$	$ab = ba$
Associative	$(a + b) + c = a + (b + c)$	$(ab)c = a(bc)$

	Addition	Subtraction
Distributive	$a(b + c) = ab + ac$	$a(b - c) = ab - ac$

EXAMPLE Generating Equivalent Expressions

Vocabulary Tip

$6x + (7 + 3x)$ and $9x + 7$ are equivalent expressions because they name the same number regardless of which value is substituted for x.

1 Simplify $6x + (7 + 3x)$ by combining like terms.

$$
\begin{aligned}
6x + (7 + 3x) &= 6x + (3x + 7) && \leftarrow \text{Commutative Property.}\\
&= (6x + 3x) + 7 && \leftarrow \text{Associative Property.}\\
&= x(6 + 3) + 7 && \leftarrow \text{Distributive Property.}\\
&= x(9) + 7 && \leftarrow \text{Simplify.}\\
&= 9x + 7 && \leftarrow \text{Commutative Property.}
\end{aligned}
$$

The expression $9x + 7$ is equivalent to $6x + (7 + 3x)$.

Quick Check

1. Find an equivalent expression for each expression by simplifying.
   a. $2b + 3b + 4b$ **b.** $2c + 8 + 4c - 3$

Remember, you can rewrite subtraction as addition to help you identify whether a coefficient is positive or negative. For example, when you combine $3r$ and $-r$ it is like adding $3r + (-1r)$. So you get $2r$, not $4r$.

EXAMPLE Application: Perimeter

Test Prep Tip

Notice that choice A and choice C both have the same value. The problem states that you should simplify your answer. So choice C is correct.

2 **Multiple Choice** Mr. Shrake needs to find the perimeter of his yard so he can install a fence. The dimensions of his yard are shown in the figure at the right. What is the perimeter of Mr. Shrake's yard? Simplify your answer.

Ⓐ $4x + 6x$ Ⓒ $10x$

Ⓑ $10x - 2y$ Ⓓ $5x - 2y$

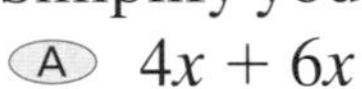

You want to find the yard's perimeter. P = sum of the side lengths.

$3x + 2x + 3x - y + y + y + 2x - y$ ← Write an expression for the sum of the side lengths.

$x(3 + 2 + 3 + 2) + y(-1 + 1 + 1 - 1)$ ← Distributive Property.

$x(10) + y(0)$ ← Simplify.

$10x$ ← Commutative Property.

The correct answer is C.

Quick Check

2. A drawing of Mrs. Stefano's yard is shown in the figure at the right. What is its perimeter?

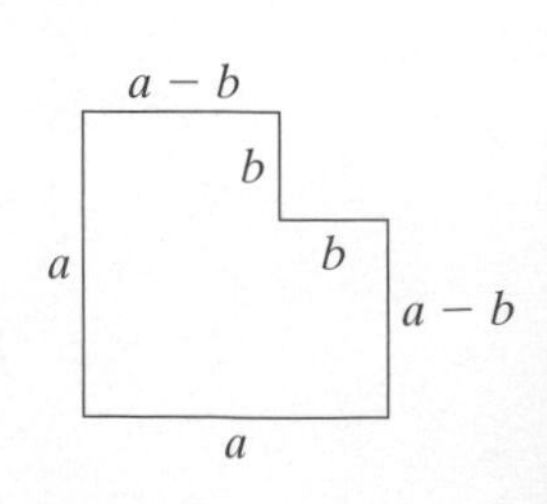

Check Your Understanding

1. **Vocabulary** What is the coefficient in the term $5x$?

Find an equivalent expression for each expression by simplifying.

2. $3x + 9x - 2$
3. $22y - 19y + 15$
4. $123 + 13a - 7a$
5. $10x + 5x - 45 + 7y$
6. **Open-Ended** Explain why it can be helpful to simplify an algebraic expression.

Homework Exercises

For more exercises, see Extra Skills and Word Problems.

GO for Help

For Exercises	See Examples
7–14	1
15	2

Find an equivalent expression for each expression by simplifying.

7. $7b + b + b$
8. $8y + y + 2y$
9. $3x + 4x - 2x$
10. $6c - 4c + 5c$
11. $3x - 3x + 1$
12. $8 + 4x - 8$
13. $j - 2 + 11j$
14. $7 - 3w + 3$
15. Carlos is in charge of placing a banner around the perimeter of the stage for the middle school play. The dimensions of the stage are shown in the diagram on the right. Write an expression to represent the length Carlos needs to make the banner. Simplify your expression. (Hint: You need to find the perimeter of the stage.)

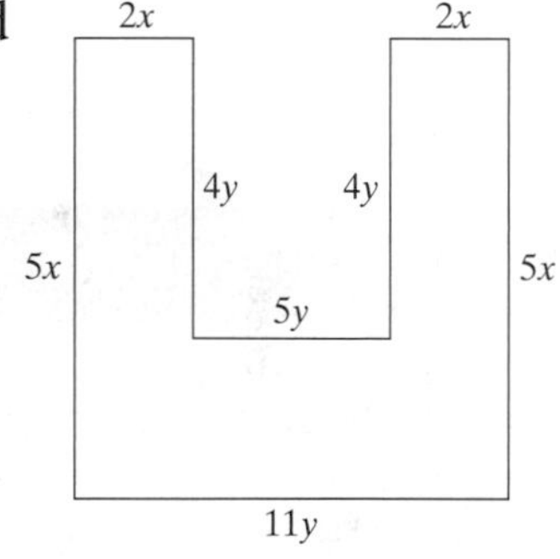

16. **Guided Problem Solving** Simplify $6x - 5y + 8x + 2y + 11y + 4$.
    - How many different groups can you combine?
    - Check your answer by evaluating the original expression and your answer when $x = 3$ and $y = 5$.
17. If s is the area of a circle and t is the area of a square, write an expression for the area of the circles and squares.

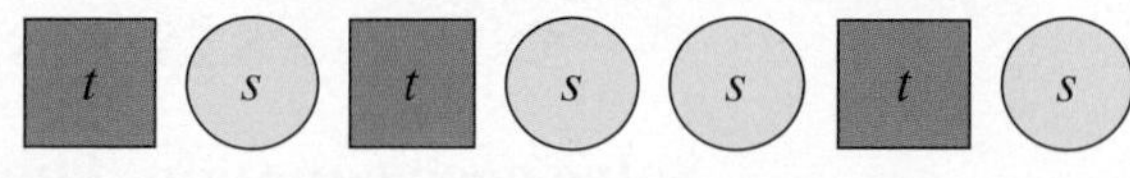

18. **Writing in Math** Describe the steps, including the properties of operations, that you would use to generate an expression equivalent to $8.1b + 6.7a + 2.5 + 7 + 0.9a - 2.8b$.

GO Online
Homework Video Tutor
PearsonSuccessNet.com

19. **Error Analysis** Madeline simplified the expression $3r + 6 - r + 2$ as shown below.

$$3r + 6 - r + 2 = 3r - r + 6 + 2$$
$$= 3 + 6 + 2$$
$$= 11$$

Explain the error that Madeline made.

20. **Open Ended** Write an expression that is equivalent to $x + y$.

21. **Number Sense** Compare the Commutative Property and the Associative Property by describing how you can use them to change expressions.

22. **Algebra** Three consecutive even numbers can be represented by the expressions $2n, 2n + 2$, and $2n + 4$, where n is a whole number. Write the shortest algebraic expression that represents the sum of the three consecutive even numbers.

23. **Challenge** The diagram at the right shows a pool deck surrounding a pool. What is the area of the pool deck? Simplify your answer.

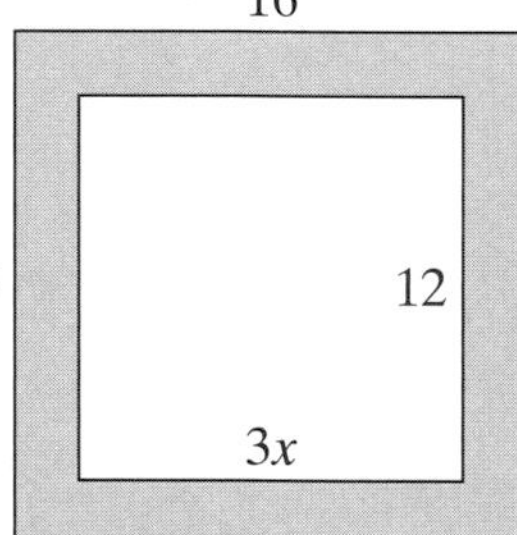

Test Prep and Mixed Review

Practice

Multiple Choice

24. Which shows the simplified form of $4n + 2p + 15n - 4n - p$?
   - (A) $n(4 + 2 + 15 - 4) - p$
   - (B) $21n - p$
   - (C) $15n$
   - (D) $15n + p$

25. What is the product of 2.13×3.5?
   - (F) 5.63
   - (G) 6.39
   - (H) 7.455
   - (J) 74.55

26. Justin buys 8 cantaloupes for \$2.25 each at the local fruit stand. Which of the following correctly uses the Distributive Property to find the total amount Justin pays for the cantaloupe?
   - (A) $2.25(4 × 4) = $36
   - (B) 8($2 + $.25) = $18
   - (C) 8 + ($2 + $.25) = $10.25
   - (D) 8($2 × $.25) = $4

Solve each equation. Then check the solution.

GO for Help

For Exercises	See Lesson
27–32	2-4

27. $53 = x + 19$

28. $n + 14.5 = 22.4$

29. $32 + y = 102$

30. $18.1 = 12.3 + d$

31. $b + 201 = 360$

32. $g + 80 = 118$

Practice Solving Problems

During the late 1800s, bicycles known as High Wheeler bicycles were popular. The front wheel was much larger than the back wheel. Suppose the circumferences of the wheels were 54 in. and 12 in. How many revolutions will each wheel make before the red spokes, shown below, are in the same position again, at the same time?

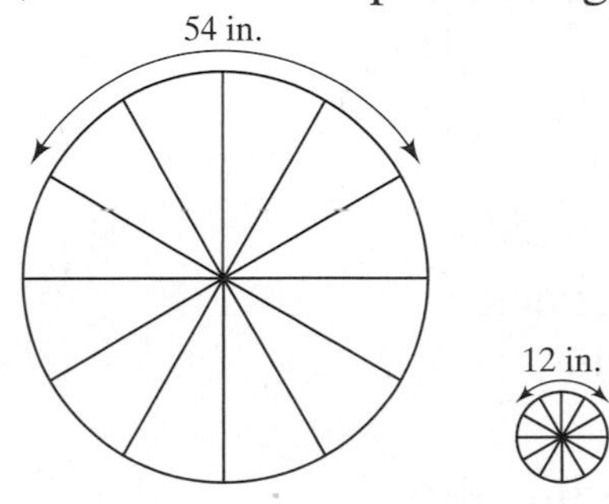

What You Might Think	What You Might Write
What do I know?	One wheel has a circumference of 54 in. The other has a circumference of 12 in.
What do I want to find?	How many revolutions will each wheel make before the red spokes are in the same position at the same time?
How can I show how far each wheel will travel for every complete turn?	Make a list of the multiples of 54 and 12. multiples of 54: 54, **108**, 162, 216, 270 multiples of 12: 12, 24, 36, 48, 60, 72, 84, 96, **108**, 120
How can I solve the problem?	The LCM is 108. When each wheel travels 108 in., the red spokes will be in the same position again.
What is the solution?	108 is the second multiple of 54. This means the large wheel will make 2 revolutions. 108 is the ninth multiple of 12, so the small wheel will make 9 revolutions.

Think It Through

1. Is the answer reasonable? Explain.
2. **Reasoning** Suppose the smaller wheel had a circumference of 36 in. How many revolutions would each wheel make before the red spokes are in the same position at the same time again?

Exercises

3. Mrs. Kane buys one box with 45 snacks and another with 36. She uses all the snacks to make snack bags for a field trip. All snack bags must have the same number of each snack. What is the greatest number of snack bags Mrs. Kane can make?
   a. Which will help you find the answer to the problem, finding the LCM or finding the GCF? Explain.
   b. Which method will you use to solve the problem? Explain.
4. Alex and Katie go the library at regular intervals over the summer. Alex goes to the library every 3 days and Katie goes every 5 days. They see each other at the library on June 30. On what date with Alex and Katie see each other at the library again?
   a. Which will help you find the answer to the problem, finding the LCM or finding the GCF? Explain.
   b. How will you determine the date when Alex and Katie will see each other again?
5. Jaylen has some fruit shown at the right. He is making packages, all with the same number of oranges and the same number of apples. What is the greatest number of packages Jaylen can make without any fruit left over? How many of each fruit will be in each package?

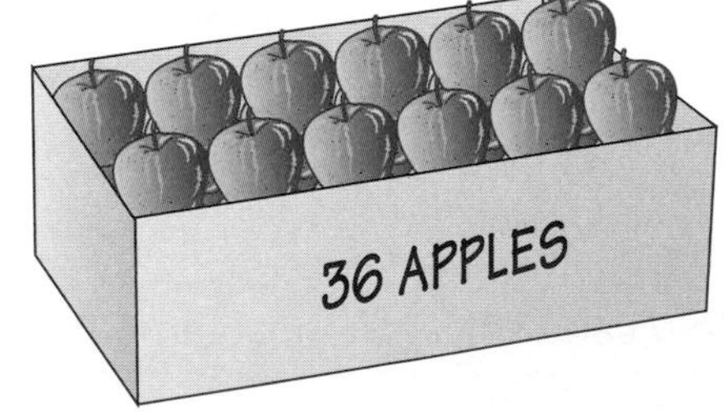

6. Mr. Wexler goes to the grocery store every 4 days and to the gas station every 6 days. He just went to both the grocery store and gas station today. How many days will it be until the next time he goes to both places on the same day?

Test-Taking Strategies

Writing Extended Responses

An extended-response question in this book is worth a total of 4 points. To get full credit, you must show your work and explain your reasoning.

EXAMPLE

Mary plans to fence 80 square feet of her backyard for her dog. She wants the length and width to be whole numbers (in feet). What dimensions can she use? Tell how you know that you have found all possible pairs.

Here are four responses with the points each received.

4 points

1 ft by 80 ft, 2 ft by 40 ft,
4 ft by 20 ft, 5 ft by 16 ft, and
8 ft by 10 ft

These are all the pairs because there are no other whole numbers that divide 80 without a remainder.

The 4-point response shows all of the correct whole-number factors of 80 and the student's explanation of why the answer is complete.

3 points

8 and 10, 4 and 20, 5 and 14,
2 and 40, 1 and 80

There are no other whole numbers that divide 80 with no remainder, so this must be the answer.

The 3-point response has one error, and the student's explanation of the answer is complete.

2 points

8 ft by 10 ft, 1 ft by 80 ft,
2 ft by 40 ft, 5 ft by 16 ft,
and 4 ft by 20 ft

The 2-point response gives all pairs of factors but does not have an explanation.

1 point

2 and 40, 1 and 80, 8 and 10

The 1-point response is missing some pairs and does not have an explanation.

Exercises

1. Read the 3-point response. What error did the student make?
2. Read the 1-point response. Which dimensions are missing?

Chapter 3 Review

Vocabulary Review

base (p. 90)
coefficient (p. 113)
common factor (p. 99)
common multiple (p. 103)
composite number (p. 94)
divisible (p. 86)
Distributive Property (p. 107)
equivalent expressions (p. 108)
even number (p. 87)
exponent (p. 90)
factor (p. 94)
greatest common factor (GCF) (p. 99)
least common multiple (LCM) (p. 103)
multiple (p. 103)
odd number (p. 87)
power (p. 90)
prime factorization (p. 95)
prime number (p. 94)
term (p. 113)

Go Online
For vocabulary quiz
PearsonSuccessNet.com

Choose the correct vocabulary term to complete each sentence.

1. Expressions that represent the same amount are _?_.
2. A factor that two or more numbers share is a(n) _?_.
3. The _?_ of 42 is $2 \times 3 \times 7$.

Skills and Concepts

Lesson 3-1

- To check for divisibility using mental math and to use divisibility to solve problems

You can use divisibility rules to solve problems.

Test each number for divisibility by 2, 3, 5, 9, and 10.

4. 207
5. 585
6. 756
7. 3,330

Lessons 3-2 and 3-3

- To use exponents and to simplify expressions with exponents
- To factor numbers and to find the prime factorization of numbers

You can use an **exponent** to show how many times a number, or **base,** is used as a factor. A number expressed using an exponent is called a **power.**

Simplify each expression.

8. $3^2 + 2^3$
9. $(15 - 1) - 3^2$

A **prime number** has exactly two factors, 1 and the number itself. A **composite number** has more than two factors. Writing a composite number as a product of prime numbers gives the **prime factorization** of the number.

Find the prime factorization of each number.

10. 28
11. 51
12. 100
13. 250

Lesson 3-4

- To find the GCF of two or more numbers

The **greatest common factor (GCF)** of two or more numbers is the greatest factor shared by all the numbers.

Find the GCF of each set of numbers.

14. 18, 28 **15.** 12, 62 **16.** 25, 35 **17.** 16, 40

Lesson 3-5

- To find the LCM of two or more numbers

A number that is a multiple of each of two or more numbers is a **common multiple**. The **least common multiple (LCM)** of two or more numbers is the least multiple that is common to all the numbers.

Find the LCM of each set of numbers.

18. 12, 22 **19.** 10, 20, 35

Lessons 3-6 and 3-7

- To use the Distributive Property to simplify expressions in problem solving situations
- To simplify algebraic expressions

The **Distributive Property** states that multiplying a sum by a number is the same as multiplying each addend by the number and then adding the products. Using the Distributive Property in reverse is called factoring. You can simplify expressions by using properties of operations to combine like terms. The simplified expressions are equivalent to the original expressions. **Equivalent expressions** name the same number when any value is substituted for the variable.

Use the Distributive Property to write an equivalent expression for each expression.

20. $2(x - 3y + 7)$ **21.** $5(2x + 6)$ **22.** $7(4 + 2n)$ **23.** $8(3x + 2y - 8)$

Factor each expression. Check your solution.

24. $8 + 22$ **25.** $100 + 50$ **26.** $18x + 63$ **27.** $56n + 48$

Find an equivalent expression for each expression by simplifying.

28. $5x + 6x - 4x$ **29.** $8c - 6c + 7c$ **30.** $5b + 3c + 16b - c$

31. $k - 3 + 10k$ **32.** $10 - 6t + 7$ **33.** $4f + 2g - 3f + g - 3 + 9g$

Chapter 3 Test

Go Online For online chapter test PearsonSuccessNet.com

Test each number for divisibility by 2, 3, 5, 9, and 10.

1. 70 2. 405 3. 628 4. 837

State whether each number is prime or composite.

5. 19 6. 39 7. 51 8. 67

Find the prime factorization of each number.

9. 72 10. 80 11. 120

Find the GCF of each set of numbers.

12. 24, 36 13. 20, 25, 30 14. 7, 19

15. For a writing workshop, 15 coaches and 35 students will be split into groups, each with the same number of coaches and the same number of students. At most how many groups can there be?

16. Eight friends want to go horseback riding. The stable charges $23 per person. Find the total cost for the group to go horseback riding.

Write each expression using an exponent. Name the base and the exponent.

17. $10 \times 10 \times 10 \times 10$

18. $p \cdot p \cdot p \cdot p \cdot p \cdot p$

Simplify each expression.

19. $4^3 - 1$ 20. 2×3^2

21. $150 \div 5^2$ 22. $36 - (8 - 6)^4$

23. **Lawns** Today, two neighbors water their lawns. One neighbor waters her lawn every four days. The other neighbor waters his lawn every three days. In how many days will they water their lawns on the same day again?

24. You are helping to set up chairs for a class performance. There are 6 rows of chairs. Each row has 16 chairs. Find the total number of chairs.

25. Use the Distributive Property to simplify 5×52.

26. **Writing in Math** Explain how to use prime factorizations to find the LCM of two numbers. Include an example.

Find the LCM for each set of numbers.

27. 4, 8 28. 6, 11 29. 10, 12, 15

Simplify each expression by combining like terms.

30. $3m + 4m + 5m$ 31. $3d + 9 + 5d - 4$

32. $4x + 10x - 3$ 33. $21r - 18r + 14$

34. If r is the area of a rectangle and t is the area of a triangle, write an expression for the area of the rectangles and triangles.

35. Jamal bought 7 tickets to a baseball game. Each ticket cost $15. To find the cost, he added the product 7×10 to the product 7×5, for a total of $105. Which property did Jamal use?

Test Prep **Practice**

Reading Comprehension

Read each passage and answer the questions that follow.

16	3	2	a
5	b	11	c
d	6	7	e
f	15	14	1

Sum Art Artists have often used mathematics in their work. The artist M.C. Escher used math ideas in many of his drawings. In the early sixteenth century, Albrecht Dürer included a 4×4 number square in one of his engravings, *Melancholia.* A number square has numbers arranged so that each row, column, and main diagonal has the same sum. Part of Dürer's number square is shown at the left.

1. What must be the sum of each row, column, and diagonal in Dürer's number square?
   - (A) 21
   - (B) 23
   - (C) 34
   - (D) 38

2. What numbers do a and f represent?
   - (F) 13 and 6
   - (G) 14 and 4
   - (H) 14 and 3
   - (J) 13 and 4

3. What is the sum of $b + c$?
   - (A) 15
   - (B) 16
   - (C) 17
   - (D) 18

4. Two squares next to each other contain the year that Dürer made the engraving. In what year did Dürer engrave *Melancholia?*
   - (F) 715
   - (G) 911
   - (H) 1112
   - (J) 1514

Something to Prove One of the most famous unsolved math problems is Goldbach's Conjecture. In 1742, Christian Goldbach made the conjecture that every even number greater than 2 can be written as the sum of two prime numbers. For example, $6 = 3 + 3$ and $10 = 3 + 7$. Today, mathematicians are still trying to prove Goldbach's Conjecture.

5. To which of the following numbers does Goldbach's Conjecture apply?
   - (A) 1
   - (B) 2
   - (C) 3
   - (D) 4

6. Which of the following illustrates Goldbach's Conjecture for 100?
   - (F) $100 = 35 + 65$
   - (G) $100 = 37 + 63$
   - (H) $100 = 39 + 61$
   - (J) $100 = 41 + 59$

7. Which of the following does NOT illustrate Goldbach's Conjecture for 30?
   - (A) $30 = 7 + 23$
   - (B) $30 = 21 + 9$
   - (C) $30 = 11 + 19$
   - (D) $30 = 17 + 13$

8. Which of the following odd numbers would NOT be used to illustrate Goldbach's Conjecture?
   - (F) 5
   - (G) 7
   - (H) 9
   - (J) 11

CHAPTER 4 Fraction Operations

What You've Learned

- In Chapter 1, you multiplied and divided decimals and solved problems using multiplication and division.
- In Chapter 2, you solved equations using models.
- In Chapter 3, you found the greatest common factor (GCF) of two or more numbers.

Check Your Readiness

GO for Help

For Exercises	See Lesson
1–6	2-4
7–12	2-6
13–18	3-4

Modeling Equations

Draw a model to represent each equation. Solve.

1. $f + 9 = 18$ **2.** $12 = h + 4$ **3.** $14 = 7 + k$

4. $16 + r = 18$ **5.** $11 + q = 14$ **6.** $15 + z = 20$

Solving Equations

Solve each equation.

7. $3a = 12$ **8.** $5x = 25$

9. $p \div 3 = 4$ **10.** $14 = x \div 8$

11. $0.1n = 10$ **12.** $2 = g \div 0.3$

Finding the Greatest Common Factor

Find the GCF of each pair of numbers.

13. 12, 24 **14.** 28, 35 **15.** 27, 24

16. 80, 100 **17.** 36, 66 **18.** 21, 42

What You'll Learn Next

- In this chapter you will multiply and divide fractions and mixed numbers.
- You will use multiplication and division to solve problems involving fractions and mixed numbers.
- You will use equations to solve problems with fractions.

Key Vocabulary

- reciprocal (p. 136)

4-1a Activity Lab

Hands On

Modeling Fraction Multiplication

You can use a model to multiply fractions.

Use a model to find $\frac{1}{2} \times \frac{3}{4}$.

Step 1 Fold a sheet of paper in half. Then fold it in half again.

Step 2 Your paper should be divided into four equal columns. Shade three of the four columns to represent $\frac{3}{4}$.

Step 3 Next, fold the paper in half. Unfold your paper. Shade one of the two rows to represent $\frac{1}{2}$.

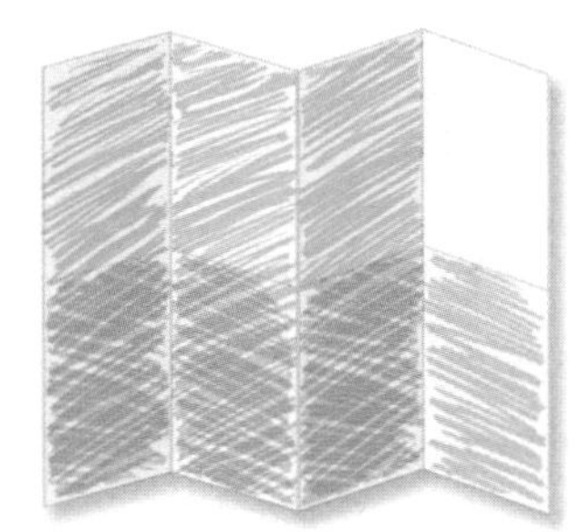

1. a. How many small rectangles did you make?
   b. How many small rectangles did you shade twice?
   c. What fraction of the small rectangles did you shade twice?

2. How can you use your answer in Exercise 1 to find the product $\frac{1}{2} \times \frac{3}{4}$? What is $\frac{1}{2} \times \frac{3}{4}$?

Exercises

1. Find the product shown in the model.

Use a model to find each product.

2. $\frac{1}{2} \times \frac{2}{3}$
3. $\frac{1}{3} \times \frac{1}{4}$
4. $\frac{1}{3} \times \frac{1}{2}$
5. $\frac{1}{6} \times \frac{3}{4}$
6. Write a rule you can use to multiply two fractions without using a model.

4-1 Multiplying Fractions and Mixed Numbers

Check Skills You'll Need

1. Vocabulary Review How do you find the least common multiple (LCM) of two or more numbers?

Find the LCM of each set of numbers.

2. 3, 9 **3.** 6, 8

4. 12, 15 **5.** 40, 50

GO for Help Lesson 3-5

CONTENT STANDARD
Essential for understanding 6.NS.1

What You'll Learn

To solve problems by multiplying fractions and multiplying mixed numbers

Why Learn This?

Suppose you are building a model. You want to know the length of half of a $\frac{5}{6}$-inch piece of wood. You can multiply fractions to find part of a fractional quantity.

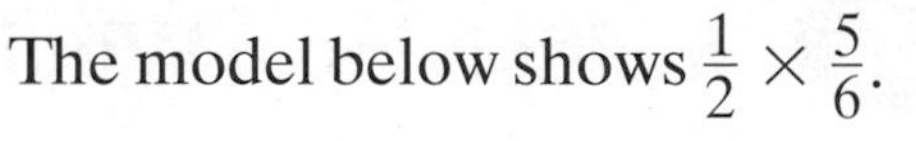

The model below shows $\frac{1}{2} \times \frac{5}{6}$.

$\frac{5}{6}$ **of the columns are shaded with diagonal lines.**

$\frac{1}{2}$ **the columns are shaded blue.**

5 out of 12 of the squares include both types of shading.

So $\frac{1}{2} \times \frac{5}{6} = \frac{5}{12}$. You can also find this product by multiplying the numerators and multiplying the denominators.

EXAMPLE **Multiplying Two Fractions**

$\frac{1}{2}$

$\frac{3}{5}$

1 Find $\frac{3}{5}$ of $\frac{1}{2}$.

$\frac{3}{5} \cdot \frac{1}{2} = \frac{3 \cdot 1}{5 \cdot 2}$ ← **Multiply the numerators.** ← **Multiply the denominators.**

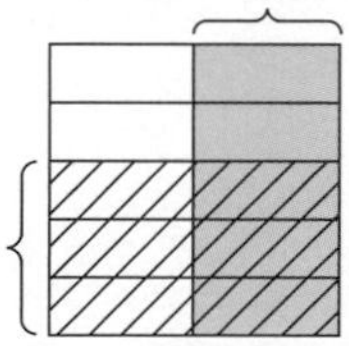

$= \frac{3}{10}$ ← **Simplify.**

Quick Check

1. a. Find $\frac{3}{5} \cdot \frac{1}{4}$.

b. Find $\frac{2}{9} \times \frac{5}{7}$.

KEY CONCEPTS Multiplying Fractions

Arithmetic	Algebra
$\frac{3}{4} \times \frac{1}{2} = \frac{3 \times 1}{4 \times 2} = \frac{3}{8}$	$\frac{a}{b} \cdot \frac{c}{d} = \frac{ac}{bd}$, where b and d are not zero.

Vocabulary Tip

The word *of* usually suggests multiplication.

When the numerators and the denominators have a common factor, you can simplify before multiplying fractions.

$$\frac{3}{8} \cdot \frac{2}{5} = \frac{3 \cdot \cancel{2}^{1}}{{}_{4}\cancel{8} \cdot 5} \quad \leftarrow \text{Divide 8 and 2 by their GCF, 2.}$$

$$= \frac{3 \cdot 1}{4 \cdot 5} \quad \leftarrow \text{Multiply the numerators and the denominators.}$$

$$= \frac{3}{20} \quad \leftarrow \text{Simplify.}$$

To multiply a fraction by a whole number, write the whole number as an improper fraction with a denominator of 1.

EXAMPLE Multiplying a Whole Number

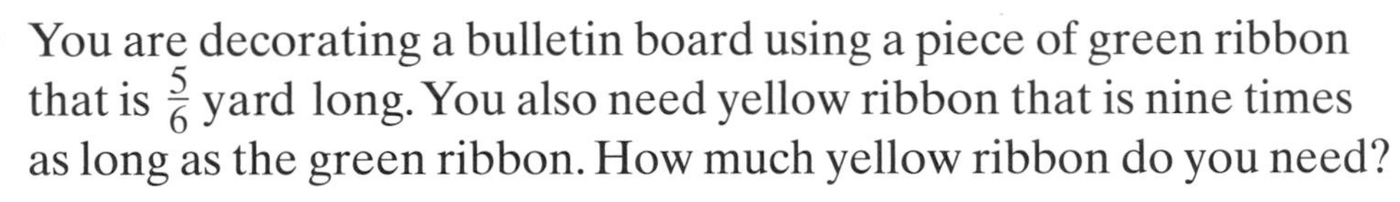

2 You are decorating a bulletin board using a piece of green ribbon that is $\frac{5}{6}$ yard long. You also need yellow ribbon that is nine times as long as the green ribbon. How much yellow ribbon do you need?

Draw a picture to help see how these lengths are related.

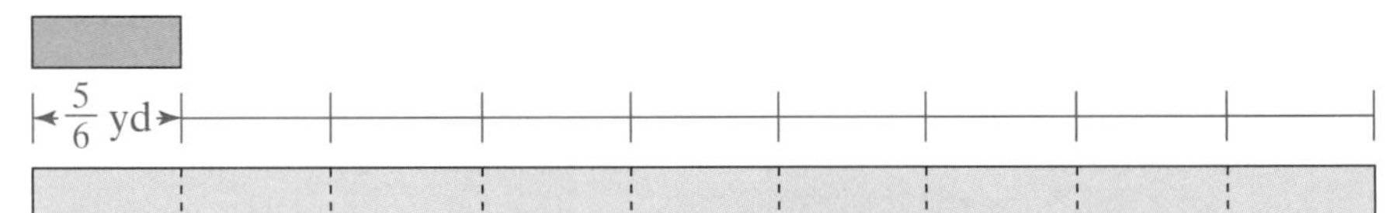

Find the length of the yellow ribbon by multiplying 9 and $\frac{5}{6}$.

$$9 \cdot \frac{5}{6} = \frac{9}{1} \cdot \frac{5}{6} \quad \leftarrow \text{Write 9 as } \tfrac{9}{1}.$$

$$= \frac{{}^{3}\cancel{9}}{1} \cdot \frac{5}{\cancel{6}_{2}} \quad \leftarrow \text{Divide 9 and 6 by their GCF, 3.}$$

$$= \frac{3 \cdot 5}{1 \cdot 2} \quad \leftarrow \text{Multiply the numerators and denominators.}$$

$$= \frac{15}{2}, \text{ or } 7\frac{1}{2} \quad \leftarrow \text{Simplify. Write as a mixed number.}$$

The yellow ribbon is $7\frac{1}{2}$ yards long.

Quick Check

2. A baby alligator is $\frac{5}{6}$ foot long. An adult alligator is 12 times as long as the baby alligator. How long is the adult alligator?

To find the product of mixed numbers, write each mixed number as an improper fraction before multiplying.

EXAMPLE Multiplying Mixed Numbers

3 Find the product $2\frac{2}{3} \times 3\frac{1}{4}$.

Estimate $2\frac{2}{3} \times 3\frac{1}{4} \approx 3 \times 3$, or 9

$2\frac{2}{3} \times 3\frac{1}{4} = \frac{8}{3} \times \frac{13}{4}$ ← **Write the mixed numbers as improper fractions.**

$= \frac{\overset{2}{\cancel{8}}}{3} \times \frac{13}{\underset{1}{\cancel{4}}}$ ← **Divide 8 and 4 by their GCF, 4.**

$= \frac{26}{3}$, or $8\frac{2}{3}$ ← **Multiply the numerators and the denominators. Then write the product as a mixed number.**

Check for Reasonableness $8\frac{2}{3}$ is near the estimate of 9, so the answer is reasonable.

Test Prep Tip

Estimate first. Then compare your computation to your estimate to decide if your answer is reasonable.

Online active math

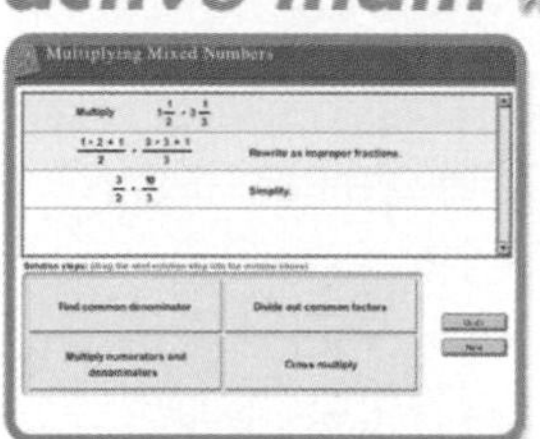

For: Mixed Numbers Activity
Use: Interactive Textbook, 4-1

Quick Check

3. a. Find $10\frac{1}{4} \times 2\frac{3}{4}$.

b. Find $7\frac{1}{3} \times 3\frac{3}{4}$.

EXAMPLE Application: Skiing

4 A student skis $3\frac{1}{2}$ miles in an hour. An instructor can ski $1\frac{1}{3}$ times as far in an hour. How far does the instructor ski in an hour?

The diagram shows the distance that the student skis in one hour. The instructor skis $1\frac{1}{3}$ times as far as the student skis.

Student
$3\frac{1}{2}$ miles
Instructor

number of miles the instructor skis $= 1\frac{1}{3} \times$ number of miles the student skis

$= 1\frac{1}{3} \times 3\frac{1}{2}$

$= \frac{4}{3} \times \frac{7}{2}$ ← **Write the mixed numbers as improper fractions.**

$= \frac{\overset{2}{\cancel{4}}}{3} \times \frac{7}{\underset{1}{\cancel{2}}}$ ← **Divide 4 and 2 by their GCF, 2.**

$= \frac{14}{3}$, or $4\frac{2}{3}$ ← **Multiply the numerators and the denominators. Then write the product as a mixed number.**

The instructor skis $4\frac{2}{3}$ miles in one hour.

Quick Check

4. How many miles can the student ski in $\frac{3}{4}$ hour?

Check Your Understanding

1. **Number Sense** If you multiply 6 by $\frac{1}{2}$, is the answer greater than or less than the result of multiplying 6 by $\frac{1}{3}$? Explain.

Change each mixed number to an improper fraction.

2. $1\frac{2}{5}$
3. $3\frac{1}{3}$
4. $2\frac{2}{3}$

Find each product.

5. $\frac{2}{3} \cdot \frac{3}{4}$
6. $2\frac{1}{2} \times 1\frac{2}{3}$
7. $2\frac{1}{2} \cdot 1\frac{1}{4}$

Homework Exercises

For more exercises, see Extra Skills and Word Problems.

GO for Help

For Exercises	See Examples
8–10	1-2
11–20	3-4

Find each product.

8. $\frac{1}{2} \times \frac{3}{8}$
9. $\frac{5}{11} \times 2$
10. $\frac{3}{4} \times \frac{11}{12}$
11. $7\frac{1}{2} \cdot 8\frac{2}{3}$
12. $5\frac{1}{3} \times 2\frac{1}{4}$
13. $3\frac{1}{9} \cdot 3\frac{3}{8}$
14. $2\frac{4}{5} \times 12\frac{1}{2}$
15. $1\frac{1}{3} \cdot 10\frac{1}{2}$
16. $3\frac{1}{5} \cdot 1\frac{7}{8}$

17. **Budgets** The graph at the right describes Paul's monthly spending. He makes $2,712 each month. How much does Paul spend each month on his rent and car combined?

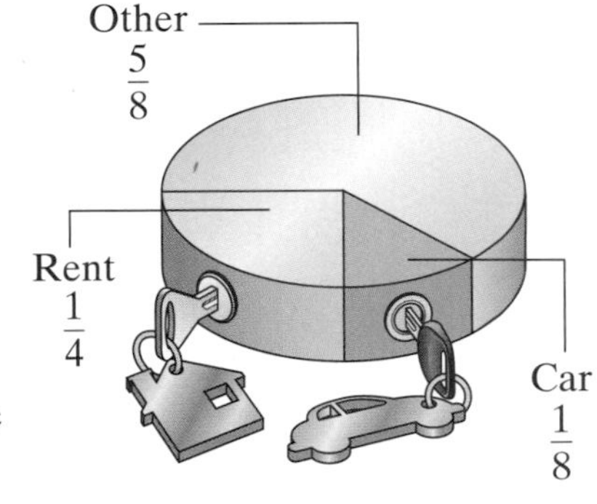

18. **Sewing** A quilt pattern has squares with $7\frac{1}{2}$-inch sides. You want to make squares that are $\frac{2}{3}$ of the pattern's size. Find the new dimensions of a square.

19. **Guided Problem Solving** A carpenter needs six pieces of wood $3\frac{1}{2}$ feet long. The carpenter has two 10-foot boards. Does the carpenter have enough wood? Explain.
    - What is the total length of wood needed?
    - What is the total length of wood the carpenter has?

20. **Track and Field** A women's long-jump record is about $1\frac{1}{6}$ the distance of the 15–16-year-old girls' record of $20\frac{13}{24}$ feet. Find the distance of the women's record to the nearest foot.

GO Online
Homework Video Tutor
PearsonSuccessNet.com

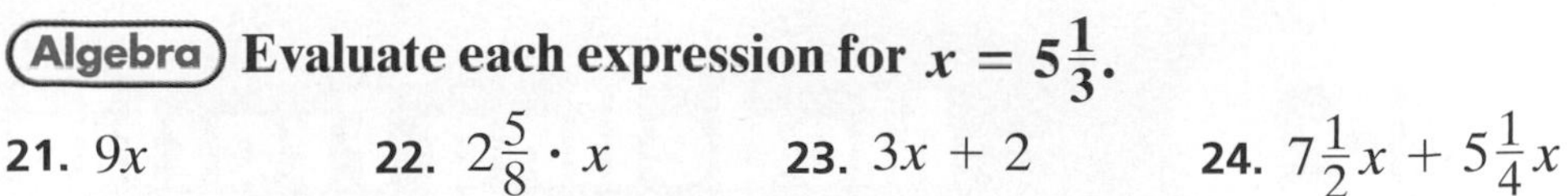

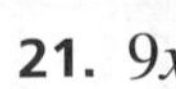

Algebra **Evaluate each expression for $x = 5\frac{1}{3}$.**

21. $9x$ **22.** $2\frac{5}{8} \cdot x$ **23.** $3x + 2$ **24.** $7\frac{1}{2}x + 5\frac{1}{4}x$

25. a. A mother is $1\frac{3}{8}$ times as tall as her daughter. The girl is $1\frac{1}{3}$ times as tall as her brother. The mother is how many times as tall as her son?

b. If the son is 3 feet tall, how tall is his mother?

26. Design A painting is $1\frac{3}{4}$ feet by $1\frac{5}{8}$ feet. What size will a copy of the painting be if its length and width are $1\frac{1}{3}$ the size of the original?

27. You earn $7.25 per hour. You work $4\frac{1}{2}$ hours each day for 3 days each week. How much money do you earn in two weeks?

28. Writing in Math Is it necessary to have a common denominator when you multiply two fractions? Explain.

29. Challenge Find $\left(2\frac{1}{3}\right) \cdot \left(1\frac{1}{2}\right)^2$.

Test Prep and Mixed Review

Practice

Multiple Choice

30. Which number multiplied by $4\frac{1}{3}$ gives a product closest to 12?

Ⓐ $1\frac{1}{5}$ Ⓑ $2\frac{1}{5}$ Ⓒ $3\frac{1}{5}$ Ⓓ $4\frac{1}{5}$

31. The length of a credit card is $3\frac{3}{8}$ inches. Its width is $2\frac{1}{8}$ inches. Which expression shows how much greater the length of the card is than the width?

Ⓕ $3\frac{3}{8} - 2\frac{1}{8}$ Ⓗ $3\frac{3}{8} + 2\frac{1}{8}$

Ⓖ $3\frac{1}{8} - 2\frac{3}{8}$ Ⓙ $3\frac{1}{8} + 2\frac{3}{8}$

32. Gerry wants to find a number between 90 and 100 that is divisible by 3 and 4. He chooses 92. Why is Gerry's answer incorrect?

Ⓐ 92 is a prime number.

Ⓑ 92 is not divisible by 3.

Ⓒ 92 is divisible by 3 and 4.

Ⓓ 92 is not divisible by 4.

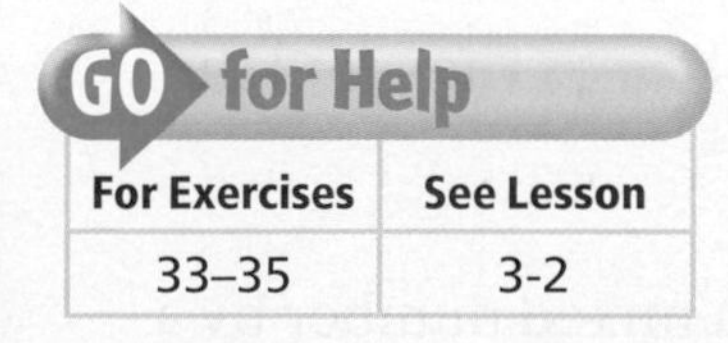

GO for Help

For Exercises	See Lesson
33–35	3-2

Simplify each expression.

33. 8^2 **34.** $(3 + 4)^2$ **35.** $(8 - 6)^4 \times 2.5$

4-2 Modeling Fraction Division

1. Vocabulary Review The __?__ says that if you multiply each side of an equation by the same number, the two sides remain equal.

Solve each equation.

2. $x \div 5 = 6$

3. $m \div 3 = 12$

4. $q \div 25 = 350$

5. $x \div 0.4 = 1.8$

Lesson 2-6

6.NS.1

Vocabulary Tip

In the division expression $3 \div \frac{1}{8}$, 3 is the *dividend* and $\frac{1}{8}$ is the *divisor*. The result is the *quotient*.

What You'll Learn

To use models to interpret and perform fraction division and to solve word problems involving fraction division

Why Learn This?

You know that $15 \div 5$ is 3. When you divide by a fraction, the answer may not be so clear. For instance, suppose you have one and a half large submarine sandwiches that you want to share with your friends. You can use a model to help you find the answer.

EXAMPLE Dividing a Whole Number by a Unit Fraction

1 Make a model to represent the expression $3 \div \frac{1}{8}$. Then find the quotient.

Step 1 Draw 3 matching circles to represent the dividend 3.

Step 2 Divide each circle into eighths to represent the divisor $\frac{1}{8}$.

Step 3 Find the total number of pieces you have. You have 3 circles. Each circle is divided into eighths. So you have 24 pieces altogether.

Step 4 This shows that $3 \div \frac{1}{8} = 24$.

Quick Check

1. Make a model to represent the expression $8 \div \frac{1}{4}$. Then find the quotient.

You can use fraction bars to help you divide a mixed number by a unit fraction.

EXAMPLE Dividing a Mixed Number by a Unit Fraction

2 Suppose you have $1\frac{1}{2}$ large submarine sandwiches to share. Use a model to find how many fourths you can cut from the sandwich. Then write the division problem shown in the model.

Step 1 In the top row, use $1\frac{1}{2}$ unit bars to represent the $1\frac{1}{2}$ sandwiches.

Step 2 Place $\frac{1}{4}$ bars in the second row to represent the fourths you can cut from the sandwiches.

1					
1/4	1/4	1/4	1/4	1/4	1/4

Step 3 Find the number of $\frac{1}{4}$ bars that make up the $1\frac{1}{2}$ unit bars. The model shows that there are six $\frac{1}{4}$-bars that make up the $1\frac{1}{2}$ unit bars.

Step 4 Write the division problem. This shows that $1\frac{1}{2} \div \frac{1}{4} = 6$.

Quick Check

2. Suppose you have $1\frac{3}{4}$ sheets of wrapping paper to cut for wrapping gifts. Use a model to find how many eighths you can cut from the sheets. Then write the division problem shown in the model.

More Than One Way

Make a model to represent the expression $2\frac{2}{3} \div \frac{1}{6}$. Then find the quotient.

Luis's Method

I can draw $2\frac{2}{3}$ matching circles and divide each circle into sixths. To find the quotient $2\frac{2}{3} \div \frac{1}{6}$, I can count the total number of pieces I have.

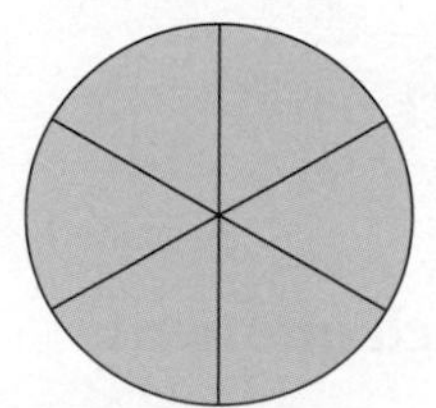
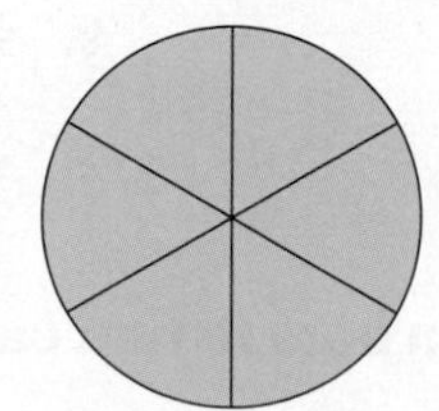
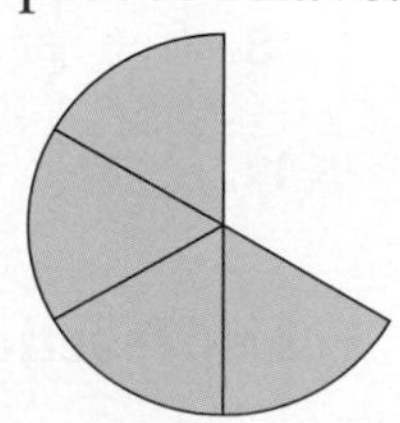

According to the model, $2\frac{2}{3} \div \frac{1}{6} = 16$.

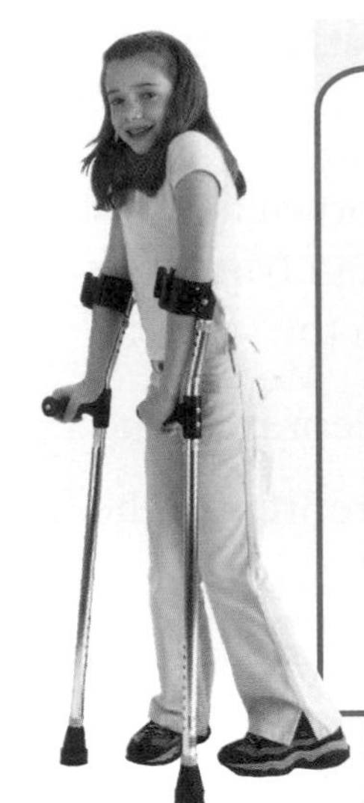

Jessica's Method

I can use fraction bars. The unit bars in the top row represent the dividend $2\frac{2}{3}$. The $\frac{1}{6}$ bars in the bottom row represent the divisor $\frac{1}{6}$. To find the quotient $2\frac{2}{3} \div \frac{1}{6}$, I can count the total number of $\frac{1}{6}$ bars that make up the $2\frac{2}{3}$ unit bars.

1						1									
1/6	1/6	1/6	1/6	1/6	1/6	1/6	1/6	1/6	1/6	1/6	1/6	1/6	1/6	1/6	1/6

According to the model, $2\frac{2}{3} \div \frac{1}{6} = 16$.

Choose a Method

Use a model to find the quotient $3\frac{3}{4} \div \frac{1}{8}$.

Check Your Understanding

1. **Reasoning** What division expression is represented by the model? What is the quotient?

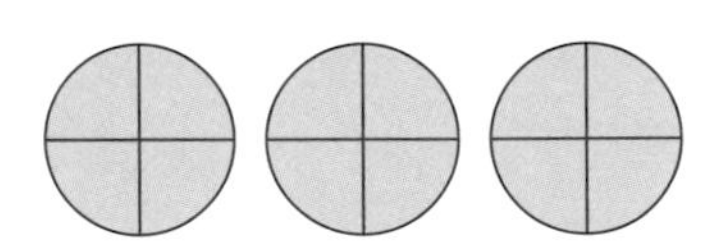

Match each division expression with the correct model.

2. $1\frac{1}{2} \div \frac{1}{6}$
3. $2\frac{2}{3} \div \frac{1}{3}$
4. $1\frac{1}{2} \div \frac{1}{4}$

A. 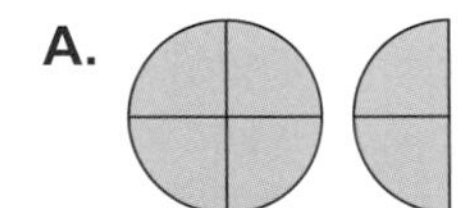

B. 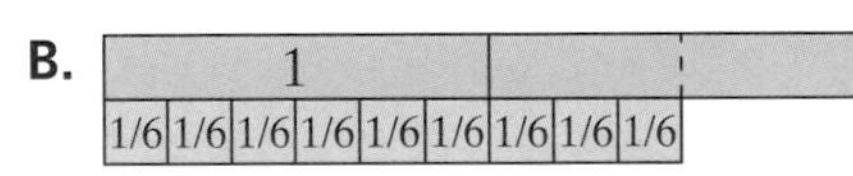

C.

1			1			1	
1/3	1/3	1/3	1/3	1/3	1/3	1/3	1/3

Homework Exercises

For more exercises, see Extra Skills and Word Problems.

GO for Help

For Exercises	See Example
5–13	1
14–22	2

Use circle models to find each quotient.

5. $4 \div \frac{1}{3}$
6. $5 \div \frac{1}{2}$
7. $2 \div \frac{1}{4}$
8. $6 \div \frac{1}{5}$
9. $8 \div \frac{1}{6}$
10. $2 \div \frac{1}{8}$
11. $2 \div \frac{1}{3}$
12. $3 \div \frac{1}{12}$
13. $7 \div \frac{1}{10}$

Use fraction bars to find each quotient.

14. $1\frac{1}{3} \div \frac{1}{6}$
15. $2\frac{1}{2} \div \frac{1}{8}$
16. $1\frac{1}{4} \div \frac{1}{12}$
17. $1\frac{1}{5} \div \frac{1}{10}$
18. $1\frac{1}{4} \div \frac{1}{8}$
19. $2\frac{1}{3} \div \frac{1}{9}$
20. $2\frac{2}{3} \div \frac{1}{3}$
21. $3\frac{1}{2} \div \frac{1}{4}$
22. $3\frac{1}{4} \div \frac{1}{8}$

23. **Guided Problem Solving** Find the quotient $2 \div \frac{2}{3}$.

- **Understand the Problem** Draw a model to help you understand the problem.
- How many $\frac{1}{3}$ make up $\frac{2}{3}$?
- **Make a Plan** How can you find the quotient using your model?

Use a model to find each quotient.

24. $3 \div \frac{3}{4}$
25. $4 \div \frac{2}{5}$
26. $5 \div \frac{5}{8}$

Online
Homework Video Tutor
PearsonSuccessNet.com

27. a. Draw three, four, five, and six circles. Divide each set of circles into halves. Copy and complete the table.

Number of Circles	Fraction	Number of Pieces	Division Problem
3	$\frac{1}{2}$	■	$3 \div \frac{1}{2} =$ ■
4	$\frac{1}{2}$	■	■
5	$\frac{1}{2}$	■	■
6	$\frac{1}{2}$	■	■

b. **Patterns** How does the number of pieces relate to the number of circles in the table?

c. What happens when you divide a number by $\frac{1}{2}$?

28. **Writing in Math** Suppose you have $\frac{7}{16}$ of a tube of dough. You have enough to make 14 cookies. Explain how you can use a model to find the fraction of the original tube of dough that you will use for each cookie.

29. **Challenge** You have $12\frac{3}{8}$ yards of fabric to cut into $2\frac{1}{4}$-yard lengths. How many lengths can you cut from the fabric?

Test Prep and Mixed Review

Practice

Multiple Choice

30. A carpenter cuts two 1-foot square pieces of wood into equal-sized pieces. He ends up with 18 pieces. What is the area of the square face of each piece of wood?

Ⓐ 1 in.^{2} Ⓑ 4 in.^{2} Ⓒ 16 in.^{2} Ⓓ 144 in.^{2}

31. Carmen received scores of 9.5, 8.5, 9, 9, and 9.5 on her diving routine. What is the mean of her scores?

Ⓕ 45.4 Ⓖ 9 Ⓗ 9.1 Ⓙ 1

GO for Help

For Exercise	See Lesson
32–34	2-4

Solve each equation.

32. $5 + x = 39$
33. $z + 16 = 64$
34. $w + 19 = 30$

4-3 Dividing Fractions

Check Skills You'll Need

1. **Vocabulary Review** How do you find the *greatest common factor* of 4 and 15?

Find each product.

2. $8 \times \frac{3}{4}$
3. $\frac{4}{5} \cdot \frac{1}{4}$
4. $\frac{1}{3}$ of $\frac{3}{7}$
5. $\frac{10}{11} \cdot \frac{2}{5}$

for Help
Lesson 4-1

CONTENT STANDARD
6.NS.1

What You'll Learn

To divide fractions and to solve problems by dividing fractions

New Vocabulary reciprocal

Why Learn This?

Suppose you have half of a cake to share. You can find how many eighths you can cut from the cake by dividing by $\frac{1}{8}$.

The model below shows that there are four eighths in $\frac{1}{2}$. So $\frac{1}{2} \div \frac{1}{8} = 4$.

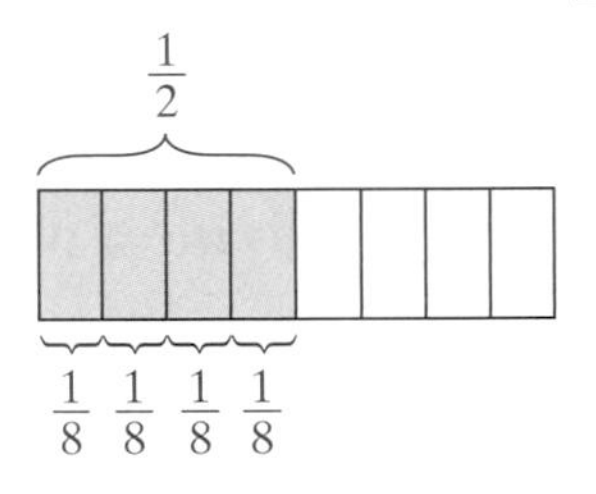

You can also use reciprocals to divide fractions. Two numbers are **reciprocals** if their product is 1. The numerators and denominators are switched in reciprocals such as $\frac{2}{3}$ and $\frac{3}{2}$.

Video Tutor Help
PearsonSuccessNet.com

EXAMPLE 1 Writing a Reciprocal

Write the reciprocal of each number.

a. 9

Since $9 \times \frac{1}{9} = 1$, the reciprocal of 9 is $\frac{1}{9}$.

b. $\frac{7}{8}$

Since $\frac{7}{8} \times \frac{8}{7} = 1$, the reciprocal of $\frac{7}{8}$ is $\frac{8}{7}$.

Quick Check

1. **a.** Find the reciprocal of $\frac{3}{4}$. **b.** Find the reciprocal of 7.

To divide by a fraction, multiply by the reciprocal of the fraction. You can remember this by thinking "invert and multiply."

Test Prep Tip

When dividing fractions, write whole numbers as improper fractions.

KEY CONCEPTS **Dividing Fractions**

Arithmetic	Algebra
$\frac{3}{5} \div \frac{1}{3} = \frac{3}{5} \cdot \frac{3}{1}$	$\frac{a}{b} \div \frac{c}{d} = \frac{a}{b} \cdot \frac{d}{c}$, where b, c, and d are not 0.

EXAMPLES Dividing With Fractions

2 Find $\frac{5}{10} \div \frac{5}{6}$.

$\frac{5}{10} \div \frac{5}{6} = \frac{5}{10} \times \frac{6}{5}$ ← Multiply by $\frac{6}{5}$, the reciprocal of $\frac{5}{6}$.

$= \frac{\cancel{5}^1}{{}_5\cancel{10}} \times \frac{\cancel{6}^3}{\cancel{5}_1}$ ← Divide the numerator 5 and the denominator 5 by their GCF, 5. Divide 10 and 6 by their GCF, 2.

$= \frac{1 \cdot 3}{5 \cdot 1}$ ← Multiply.

$= \frac{3}{5}$ ← Simplify.

3 **Feeding Birds** You have 7 cups of birdseed. You use $\frac{2}{3}$ cup of seed each week. How long will your birdseed last?

You want to find how many $\frac{2}{3}$-cup portions are in 7 cups of seed, so divide 7 by $\frac{2}{3}$.

$7 \div \frac{2}{3} = \frac{7}{1} \div \frac{2}{3}$ ← Write 7 as $\frac{7}{1}$.

$= \frac{7}{1} \times \frac{3}{2}$ ← Multiply by $\frac{3}{2}$, the reciprocal of $\frac{2}{3}$.

$= \frac{21}{2}$ ← Multiply.

$= 10\frac{1}{2}$ ← Simplify.

The birdseed will last $10\frac{1}{2}$ weeks.

Quick Check

2. a. Find $\frac{9}{16} \div \frac{3}{4}$. **b.** Find $\frac{4}{5} \div \frac{1}{3}$.

3. Your art teacher cuts $\frac{5}{6}$ yard of fabric into five equal pieces. How long is each piece of fabric?

Check Your Understanding

1. **Vocabulary** The product of reciprocals always equals __?__.

2. **Error Analysis** Find and correct the error in the work at the right.

$$\frac{11}{9} \div \frac{2}{3} = \frac{{}^{3}\cancel{9}}{11} \times \frac{2}{\cancel{3}_{1}} = \frac{6}{11}$$

3. **Open-Ended** Write a fraction and its reciprocal.

Find each quotient.

4. $5 \div \frac{3}{8}$

5. $\frac{10}{16} \div \frac{5}{16}$

Homework Exercises

For more exercises, see Extra Skills and Word Problems.

GO for Help

For Exercises	See Examples
6–10	1
11–23	2–3

Write the reciprocal of each number.

6. $\frac{2}{5}$

7. $\frac{1}{7}$

8. 11

9. $\frac{5}{3}$

10. $\frac{4}{11}$

Find each quotient. You may find a model helpful.

11. $7 \div \frac{3}{5}$

12. $9 \div \frac{4}{9}$

13. $6 \div \frac{2}{5}$

14. $8 \div \frac{3}{7}$

15. $\frac{8}{9} \div \frac{1}{3}$

16. $\frac{1}{4} \div \frac{1}{4}$

17. $\frac{11}{2} \div \frac{3}{4}$

18. $\frac{1}{5} \div \frac{1}{4}$

19. $\frac{4}{9} \div \frac{2}{3}$

20. $\frac{9}{2} \div \frac{1}{2}$

21. $\frac{8}{9} \div \frac{4}{5}$

22. $\frac{3}{4} \div \frac{1}{8}$

23. A piece of iron $\frac{2}{3}$ yard long is cut into six equal pieces. How long is each piece in feet?

24. **Guided Problem Solving** A road crew has $\frac{3}{4}$ ton of stone to divide evenly among four sidewalks. How much stone does the crew use for each sidewalk?
    - What amount are you dividing evenly?
    - Into how many groups are you dividing the stone?

25. **Measurement** How many $\frac{1}{4}$ inches are in $\frac{1}{2}$ foot? Draw a diagram that models the problem.

26. **Writing in Math** Explain how dividing a number by 2 and dividing a number by $\frac{1}{2}$ are different. Include a diagram.

Homework Video Tutor
PearsonSuccessNet.com

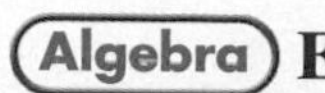

Evaluate each expression for $a = \frac{1}{2}$, $b = \frac{1}{4}$, and $c = \frac{3}{8}$.

27. $a \div b$ **28.** $b \div c$ **29.** $c \div b$

30. Baking A recipe for a loaf of banana bread requires $\frac{2}{3}$ cup of vegetable oil. You have 3 cups of oil. How many loaves of banana bread can you make with the oil?

Use the table for Exercises 31–32.

31. How many times as many people live in Argentina as in Peru?

32. The population of Brasilia, Brazil's capital, is about $\frac{1}{85}$ of the country's population. What fraction of the total population of South America lives in Brasilia?

South American Population

Country	Portion of South America's Population
Brazil	$\frac{1}{2}$
Colombia	$\frac{1}{9}$
Argentina	$\frac{1}{10}$
Peru	$\frac{1}{13}$

SOURCE: U.S. Census Bureau.

33. Challenge Simplify $\left(\frac{2}{7}\right)^2 \div \left(\frac{1}{7}\right)^2$.

Test Prep and Mixed Review

Practice

Multiple Choice

34. You want to buy enough fabric to make three stuffed bears. Each bear requires a certain amount of fabric. You want to know how much the fabric will cost for the three stuffed bears.

Step P Multiply the number of yards needed for each bear by 3.
Step Q Multiply the cost of the fabric by the total number of yards you need.
Step R Identify the cost of the fabric and the amount of fabric needed for each bear.

Which list shows the steps in the correct order for finding how much the fabric for the stuffed bears will cost?

(A) R, P, Q (B) R, Q, P (C) Q, P, R (D) Q, R, P

35. You buy 2 shirts for $7.99 each and a pair of pants for $19.99. How much do you spend before tax?

(F) $27.98 (G) $35.97 (H) $39.98 (J) $55.96

GO for Help

For Exercises	See Lesson
36–39	3-1

Test each number for divisibility by 2, 3, 5, 9, or 10.

36. 1,250 **37.** 372

38. 55,600 **39.** 445

Online lesson quiz, PearsonSuccessNet.com

4-4 Dividing Mixed Numbers

Check Skills You'll Need

1. **Vocabulary Review** How do you know that $\frac{5}{7}$ and $\frac{7}{2}$ are *not reciprocals?*

Find each quotient.

2. $8 \div \frac{2}{7}$
3. $\frac{7}{8} \div \frac{3}{1}$
4. $\frac{2}{3} \div 4$
5. $\frac{15}{4} \div \frac{11}{8}$

GO for Help Lesson 4-3

What You'll Learn

To estimate and compute the quotient of mixed numbers

Why Learn This?

You may need to divide mixed numbers in measurements to make home repairs or change a recipe.

To estimate the quotient of two mixed numbers, round each number to the nearest whole number. Then divide.

CONTENT STANDARD
6.NS.1

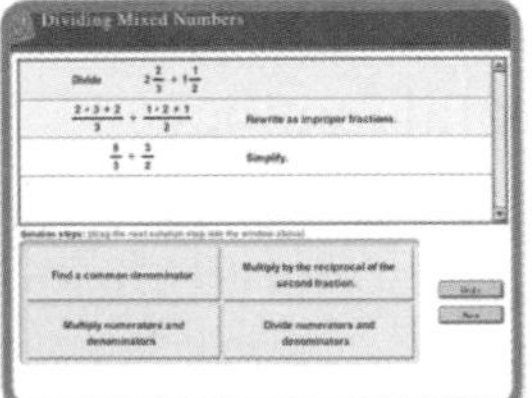

For: Dividing Mixed Numbers Activity
Use: Interactive Textbook, 4-4

EXAMPLE Estimating Quotients

1 **Carpentry** A homeowner wants to cover a wall $59\frac{1}{2}$ inches wide with wood panels. Each wood panel is $4\frac{3}{8}$ inches wide. Estimate the number of panels needed to cover the wall.

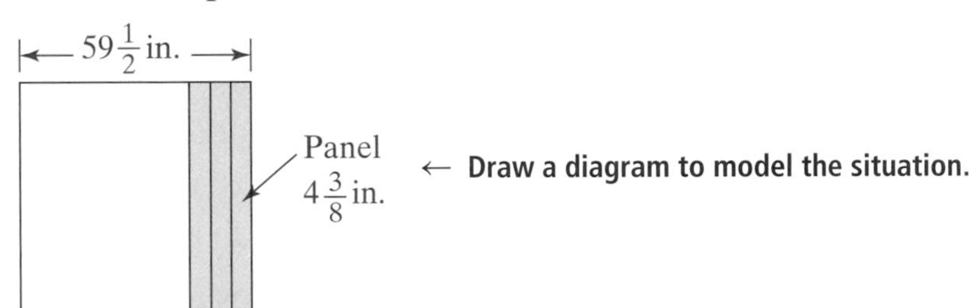

← **Draw a diagram to model the situation.**

$59\frac{1}{2} \div 4\frac{3}{8}$ ← **Round each mixed number to the nearest whole number.**

$60 \div 4 = 15$ ← **Divide.**

About 15 panels are needed to cover the wall.

Quick Check

1. a. Estimate $7\frac{2}{5} \div 1\frac{3}{7}$.
   b. Estimate $14\frac{9}{16} \div 3\frac{8}{19}$.

To divide with mixed numbers, start by writing the numbers as improper fractions.

EXAMPLE Application: Baking

2 **Multiple Choice** A baker has $2\frac{1}{4}$ cups of blueberries to make three batches of muffins. How many cups of blueberries should the baker put into each batch?

(A) $\frac{4}{27}$ (B) $\frac{3}{4}$ (C) $\frac{4}{3}$ (D) $6\frac{3}{4}$

Estimate Since $2\frac{1}{4} < 3$, the quotient is less than 1.

blueberries ÷ batches ← **Divide the number of cups by the number of batches.**

$2\frac{1}{4} \div 3 = \frac{9}{4} \div \frac{3}{1}$ ← **Write the numbers as improper fractions.**

$= \frac{9}{4} \times \frac{1}{3}$ ← **Multiply by $\frac{1}{3}$, the reciprocal of 3.**

$= \frac{\cancel{9}^{3}}{4} \times \frac{1}{\cancel{3}_{1}}$ ← **Divide 9 and 3 by their GCF, 3.**

$= \frac{3}{4}$ ← **Multiply.**

The baker should put $\frac{3}{4}$ cup of blueberries into each batch. The correct answer is choice B.

Quick Check

2. The baker has $3\frac{3}{4}$ cups of walnuts to make three batches of muffins. How many cups of walnuts should go into each batch?

EXAMPLE Dividing Mixed Numbers

3 Find $10\frac{1}{2} \div 1\frac{3}{4}$.

$10\frac{1}{2} \div 1\frac{3}{4} = \frac{21}{2} \div \frac{7}{4}$ ← **Write the mixed numbers as improper fractions.**

$= \frac{21}{2} \times \frac{4}{7}$ ← **Multiply by $\frac{4}{7}$, the reciprocal of $\frac{7}{4}$.**

$= \frac{\cancel{21}^{3}}{\cancel{2}_{1}} \times \frac{\cancel{4}^{2}}{\cancel{7}_{1}}$ ← **Divide 21 and 7 by their GCF, 7. Divide 2 and 4 by their GCF, 2.**

$= \frac{6}{1}$ ← **Multiply.**

$= 6$ ← **Simplify.**

GO Online

Video Tutor Help
PearsonSuccessNet.com

Quick Check

3. a. Find $7 \div 1\frac{1}{6}$.

b. Find $6\frac{5}{6} \div 3\frac{1}{3}$.

Check Your Understanding

1. **Estimation** Estimate $8\frac{3}{4} \div 3\frac{1}{3}$.
2. **Open-Ended** Write a word problem that you can solve using $2\frac{1}{2} \div 1\frac{1}{4}$. Explain what each number represents.
3. **Error Analysis** Who is correct, Jocelyn or Annie?

Jocelyn	Annie
$4\frac{1}{2} \div 1\frac{1}{3} = \frac{8}{2} \div \frac{4}{3}$	$4\frac{1}{2} \div 1\frac{1}{3} = \frac{9}{2} \div \frac{4}{3}$
$= \frac{\overset{1}{\cancel{2}}\overset{2}{\cancel{8}}}{\underset{1}{\cancel{2}}} \cdot \frac{3}{\cancel{4}}$	$= \frac{9}{2} \cdot \frac{3}{4}$
$= 3$	$= \frac{27}{8}$
	$= 3\frac{3}{8}$

Homework Exercises

For more exercises, see Extra Skills and Word Problems.

GO for Help

For Exercises	See Examples
4–8	1
9–11	2
12–17	3

Estimate each quotient.

4. $50\frac{1}{4} \div 5\frac{3}{16}$
5. $48\frac{8}{10} \div 7\frac{3}{7}$
6. $99 \div 8\frac{2}{3}$
7. During a storm the level of a river rose $10\frac{1}{2}$ inches in $4\frac{1}{2}$ hours. Estimate how many inches per hour the level rose.
8. The average adult's height is about 8 times the length of the person's head. A man is $6\frac{1}{2}$ feet tall. About how long is his head?

Find each quotient.

9. $3\frac{1}{6} \div 2$
10. $2\frac{1}{2} \div 7$
11. $1 \div 4\frac{1}{2}$
12. $3\frac{1}{3} \div 1\frac{1}{2}$
13. $7\frac{1}{3} \div 1\frac{5}{6}$
14. $3\frac{1}{4} \div 1\frac{1}{2}$
15. $2\frac{1}{2} \div 1\frac{1}{8}$
16. $10\frac{1}{3} \div 3\frac{1}{3}$
17. $2\frac{1}{10} \div 4\frac{2}{3}$

Test Prep Tip

Drawing a model may help you solve a problem.

18. **Guided Problem Solving** Sunlight takes about $8\frac{1}{2}$ minutes to travel approximately 93 million miles from the sun to Earth. How many miles does light travel in one minute?
    - What operation can you use to find the number of miles light travels in one minute?
    - How can you use estimation to check your answer?

Online Homework Video Tutor
PearsonSuccessNet.com

Find the number that completes each equation.

19. $2\frac{3}{5} \div 2\frac{1}{2} = \blacksquare$ **20.** $2\frac{3}{5} \div \blacksquare = 1$ **21.** $\blacksquare \div \frac{1}{2} = 1\frac{3}{4}$

22. Construction An attic ceiling 24 feet wide needs insulation. Each strip of insulation is $1\frac{1}{3}$ feet wide. Find the number of insulation strips that are needed.

23. Gardening A gardener is building a border for a flower garden with a row of red bricks. The row is $136\frac{1}{2}$ inches long. Each brick is $10\frac{1}{2}$ inches long and costs \$.35. How much will the border cost?

24. Writing in Math Explain how you can use mental math to find $12 \div \frac{1}{5}$.

25. Books A bookstore has a shelf that is $37\frac{1}{2}$ inches long. Each book is $1\frac{1}{4}$ inches thick. How many books can fit on the shelf?

26. Challenge Evaluate each expression for $x = 1\frac{1}{3}$.

a. $(x + x) \div \frac{1}{2}$ **b.** $(x + 1) \div 1\frac{1}{2}$

Test Prep and Mixed Review

Practice

Multiple Choice

27. You serve three different kinds of pizza for dinner. The shaded areas show the amount of pizza left over. The leftover pizza is divided into 3 equal portions. How much of the pizza is in each portion?

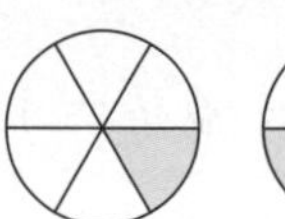

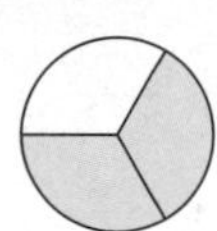

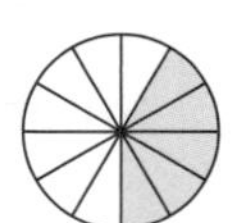

(A) $\frac{5}{12}$ (C) $1\frac{1}{12}$

(B) $\frac{7}{12}$ (D) $1\frac{1}{4}$

28. Mr. Perez is driving 380 miles home from vacation at an average speed of 60 miles per hour. Which method can Mr. Perez use to find how long it will take him to drive home?

(F) Add 380 and 60. (H) Multiply 380 by 60.

(G) Divide 380 by 60. (J) Subtract 60 from 380.

29. Find the greatest common factor of 12 and 20.

 (A) 2  (B) 3 (C) 4 (D) 5

GO for Help

For Exercises	See Lesson
30–33	3-3

Find the prime factorization of each number.

30. 144 **31.** 98 **32.** 276 **33.** 5,000

Online lesson quiz, PearsonSuccessNet.com

Technology

Using a Calculator for Fractions

Many calculators do not have fraction keys. You can use a calculator without fraction keys to check your computations with fractions by changing the fractions to decimals. The example below is for a calculator that follows the order of operations.

Round repeating decimals to several decimal places. When you compute with rounded decimals, results may be slightly different.

EXAMPLES

1 Check $2\frac{3}{8} \times 4\frac{7}{10} = 11\frac{13}{80}$.

Change the fraction part to a decimal by dividing the numerator by the denominator. Then add the quotient to the whole number.

$$2\frac{3}{8} \qquad \times \qquad 4\frac{7}{10} \qquad \stackrel{?}{=} \qquad 11\frac{13}{80}$$

2 [+] 3 [÷] 8 [=] 2.375 4 [+] 7 [÷] 10 [=] 4.7 11 [+] 13 [÷] 80 [=] 11.1625

2.375 [×] 4.7 [=] 11.1625 ← **Use a calculator to find 2.375 × 4.7.**

Since $2.375 \div 4.7 = 11.1625$, and $11\frac{13}{80} = 11.1625$, the answer checks.

2 Check $2\frac{2}{7} \div 1\frac{1}{3} = 1\frac{5}{7}$.

Find the decimal equivalent of each fraction. Use three decimal places.

$$2\frac{2}{7} \qquad \div \qquad 1\frac{1}{3} \qquad \stackrel{?}{=} \qquad 1\frac{5}{7}$$

2 [+] 2 [÷] 7 [=] 2.285 . . . 1 [+] 1 [÷] 3 [=] 1.333 . . . 1 [+] 5 [÷] 7 [=] 1.714 . . .

2.285 [÷] 1.333 [=] 1.714 ← **Use a calculator to find 2.285 ÷ 1.333.**

Since 1.714 is equal to 1.714, the answer $1\frac{5}{7}$ checks.

Exercises

Write a decimal number equation to check each fraction equation. Round repeating decimals to three decimal places.

1. $3\frac{1}{5} \times 1\frac{3}{4} = 5\frac{3}{5}$ **2.** $9\frac{3}{10} - 3\frac{2}{5} = 5\frac{9}{10}$ **3.** $6\frac{1}{2} \div 1\frac{3}{5} = 4\frac{1}{16}$ **4.** $2\frac{5}{7} + 7\frac{1}{2} = 10\frac{3}{14}$

Checkpoint Quiz 1

Lessons 4-1 through 4-4

Find each product or quotient.

1. $\frac{5}{12}$ of 36
2. $5\frac{1}{4} \times 4\frac{1}{2}$
3. $24 \div \frac{3}{8}$
4. $1\frac{1}{9} \div 6\frac{2}{3}$
5. $\frac{2}{7} \cdot 5\frac{1}{3}$
6. $2\frac{2}{5} \div 4$
7. $8\frac{1}{6} \times 2$
8. $7\frac{4}{9} \div 3\frac{1}{3}$
9. $5\frac{2}{3} \div \frac{1}{6}$
10. $\frac{3}{5} \cdot 7\frac{1}{2}$
11. $3\frac{3}{10} \div 1\frac{1}{2}$
12. $5\frac{1}{6} \times 3$
13. How tall is a tree that is 9 times as tall as a $4\frac{1}{3}$-foot sapling?
14. How many $\frac{1}{2}$-inch-thick cookies can you slice from 1 foot of cookie dough? Solve by using a model.
15. You must cover a wall $72\frac{3}{8}$ inches wide with wood panels. If each panel is $5\frac{5}{8}$ inches wide, about how many panels will you need?

MATH GAMES

Estimate That Product!

What You'll Need

- 20 cards or paper slips, each with a fraction or mixed number written on it
- fraction calculator (optional)

How To Play

- Three students are needed to play. One student acts as the judge. Two students are the players.
- The judge shuffles the cards and then turns over two cards.
- Players have 10 seconds to write an estimate for the product.
- The judge finds the product. The judge also computes the difference between each estimate and the actual product.
- The player with the estimate closer to the actual product earns one point. If there is a tie, each player gets one point.
- The first player to earn five points wins.

4-5 Equations With Fractions

Check Skills You'll Need

1. **Vocabulary Review** The *inverse operation* of addition is __?__.

Solve each equation.

2. $17 + x = 43$
3. $4.2 + x = 8$
4. $10.7 = x + 8.2$

for Help Lesson 2-4

CONTENT STANDARDS

6.EE.6, 6.EE.7

What You'll Learn

To solve equations with fractions

Why Learn This?

Weather reports include information such as temperature, humidity, and rainfall. You can use equations with fractions to find rainfall amounts.

Sometimes you can use mental math to solve equations that involve fractions or mixed numbers. Remember, you can also use a model to help you solve equations.

EXAMPLE Using Mental Math in Equations

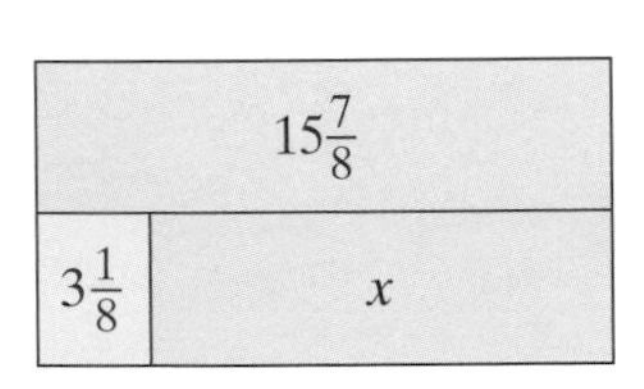

1 Solve $3\frac{1}{8} + x = 15\frac{7}{8}$ using mental math.

$3 + 12 = 15$ ← **Use mental math to find the missing whole number.**

$\frac{1}{8} + \frac{6}{8} = \frac{7}{8}$ ← **Use mental math to find the missing fraction.**

$x = 12\frac{6}{8}$ ← **Combine the two parts.**

Quick Check

1. Solve each equation using mental math.

a. $x - 1\frac{3}{8} = 1\frac{3}{8}$ **b.** $14\frac{1}{4} + x = 25\frac{1}{2}$ **c.** $5\frac{5}{6} - x = 2\frac{1}{6}$

You can use inverse operations to get the variable alone on one side of the equation.

EXAMPLE Solving Equations With Fractions

2 Solve $x - \frac{1}{3} = \frac{5}{6}$.

$x - \frac{1}{3} + \frac{1}{3} = \frac{5}{6} + \frac{1}{3}$ ← **Add $\frac{1}{3}$ to each side.**

$x = \frac{5}{6} + \frac{2}{6}$ ← **The LCD is 6. Write $\frac{1}{3}$ as $\frac{2}{6}$.**

$x = \frac{7}{6}$ ← **Add.**

$x = 1\frac{1}{6}$ ← **Simplify.**

Quick Check

2. a. Solve $n + \frac{1}{3} = \frac{11}{12}$.

b. Solve $\frac{2}{5} + a = \frac{13}{20}$.

EXAMPLE Solving Equations by Multiplying

3 **Multiple Choice** Solve $\frac{x}{8} = 20$.

Ⓐ $2\frac{1}{2}$ Ⓑ 12 Ⓒ 20 Ⓓ 160

Recall that the fraction $\frac{x}{8}$ can also be written as $x \div 8$.

$\frac{x}{8} = 20$

$8 \cdot \frac{x}{8} = 8 \cdot 20$ ← **Multiply each side by 8 to undo the division and get x by itself.**

$\frac{\cancel{8}^{1}}{1} \cdot \frac{x}{\cancel{8}_{1}} = 160$ ← **Write 8 as $\frac{8}{1}$.**

$\frac{x}{1} = 160$ ← **Multiply the numerators and the denominators.**

$x = 160$ ← **Simplify.**

The solution is 160. The correct answer is choice D.

Quick Check

3. a. Solve $\frac{x}{2} = 15$.

b. Solve $\frac{n}{6} = 12$.

To solve $\frac{2}{3}x = 8$, multiply each side of the equation by the reciprocal of $\frac{2}{3}$, or $\frac{3}{2}$.

EXAMPLE Using Reciprocals to Solve Equations

4 Solve $\frac{2}{3}x = 8$. Check the solution.

$$\frac{2}{3}x = 8$$

$$\frac{3}{2} \cdot \left(\frac{2}{3}x\right) = \frac{3}{2} \cdot (8)$$ ← Multiply each side by $\frac{3}{2}$, the reciprocal of $\frac{2}{3}$.

$$1 \cdot x = 12$$ ← Multiply.

$$x = 12$$ ← Simplify.

Check $\frac{2}{3}x = 8$ ← Start with the original equation.

$$\frac{2}{3} \cdot (12) \stackrel{?}{=} 8$$ ← Substitute 12 for x in the original equation.

$$8 = 8 \checkmark$$ ← The solution checks.

GO for Help

For help multiplying fractions, go to Lesson 4-1, Example 2.

Quick Check

4. Solve $\frac{7}{8}x = 42$. Check the solution.

EXAMPLE Writing and Solving Equations

5 A volunteer group has 6 yards of material to make flags for Community Day. Each flag uses $\frac{5}{8}$ yard of material. How many flags can the group make?

Words yards per flag × number of flags = total yards

Let b = number of flags

Equation $\frac{5}{8} \times b = 6$

$$\frac{5}{8}b = 6$$ ← Write the equation.

$$\frac{8}{5} \cdot \left(\frac{5}{8}b\right) = \frac{8}{5} \cdot \frac{6}{1}$$ ← Multiply each side by $\frac{8}{5}$, the reciprocal of $\frac{5}{8}$. Write 6 as $\frac{6}{1}$.

$$1 \cdot b = \frac{48}{5}$$ ← Multiply.

$$b = 9\frac{3}{5}$$ ← Simplify.

The group can make 9 flags.

GO for Help

For help writing an equation, go to Lesson 2-6, Example 3.

Quick Check

5. How many flags can the group make with 13 yards of material?

Check Your Understanding

1. **Writing in Math** Without solving the problem, how can you tell that the solution to $\frac{b}{4} = 2.5$ is greater than 8?

Name the reciprocal you use to solve each equation.

2. $\frac{m}{3} = 9$

3. $\frac{2}{5}x = 5$

4. $\frac{5}{9}z = 30$

Solve each equation. If possible, use mental math.

5. $\frac{v}{4} = 11$

6. $\frac{s}{5} = 35$

7. $\frac{4}{5}y = 8$

Homework Exercises

For more exercises, see Extra Skills and Word Problems.

GO for Help

For Exercises	See Examples
8–13	1-2
14–19	3–4
20	5

Solve each equation. Check the solution.

8. $x = \frac{2}{7} + \frac{5}{6}$

9. $\frac{2}{5} - \frac{1}{9} = x$

10. $x - \frac{5}{6} = \frac{7}{8}$

11. $\frac{5}{24} + g = \frac{1}{3}$

12. $\frac{4}{9} = y - \frac{2}{5}$

13. $t - \frac{7}{9} = \frac{1}{3}$

14. $\frac{x}{3} = 12$

15. $\frac{x}{15} = 3$

16. $\frac{r}{12} = 1.5$

17. $\frac{2}{3}r = 10$

18. $\frac{3}{5}n = 9$

19. $\frac{3}{20}x = 5$

20. **Coin Collecting** The value of Gerald's coins is $\frac{7}{12}$ the value of his brother's coins. Gerald's coins are worth \$14. What is the value of his brother's coins? Write and solve an equation.

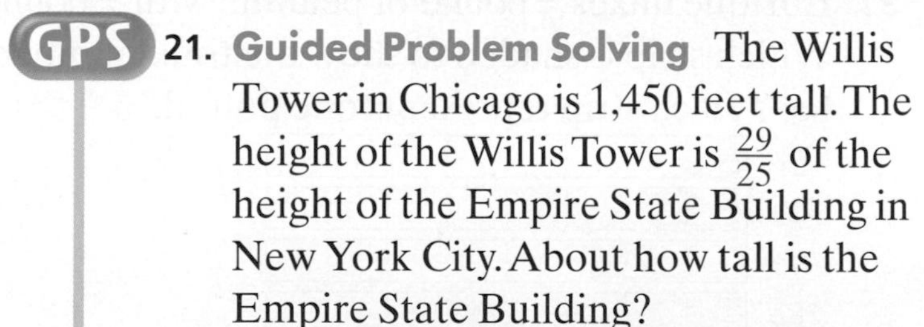

GPS

21. **Guided Problem Solving** The Willis Tower in Chicago is 1,450 feet tall. The height of the Willis Tower is $\frac{29}{25}$ of the height of the Empire State Building in New York City. About how tall is the Empire State Building?
    - **Understand the Problem** What information do you have? What information do you want to find?
    - **Check the Answer** Estimate the height of the Empire State Building.

22. **Costumes** A costume uses $\frac{5}{6}$ yard of ribbon. You have 9 costumes to make. How many yards of ribbon do you need?

Solve each equation. Check the solution.

23. $2\frac{2}{5}p = 10$ **24.** $\frac{1}{6}m = \frac{3}{20}$ **25.** $\frac{2}{7}n = \frac{1}{14}$

Write and solve an equation.

26. Shopping The price of a shirt is $\frac{5}{6}$ of the price of a pair of pants. The shirt costs \$12.50. How much do the pants cost?

27. A local bike race is broken into 12 stages. Each stage is $14\frac{1}{2}$ miles. What is the total distance of the bike race?

28. Travel Use the map. The distance from Cleveland to Pittsburgh is about $\frac{2}{5}$ of the distance from Cleveland to Chicago. About how far is Cleveland from Chicago?

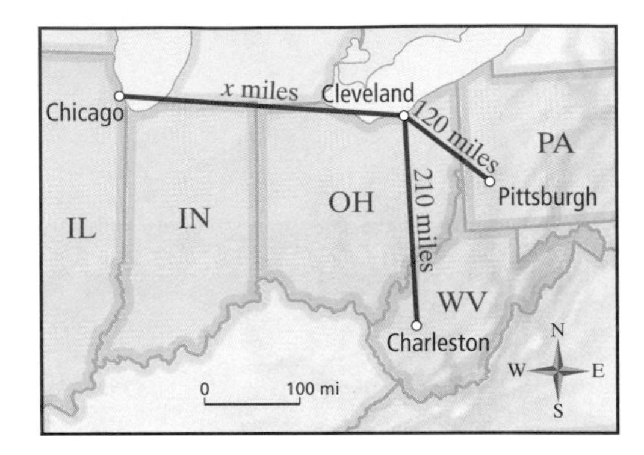

29. Challenge Solve the equation $2\frac{5}{8}y = 10\frac{1}{2}$. Check the solution.

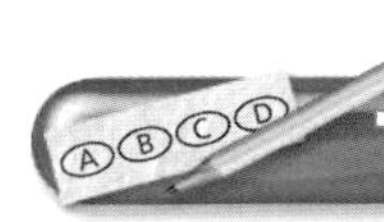

Test Prep and Mixed Review

Practice

Multiple Choice

30. Bridget needs $1\frac{1}{4}$ yards of solid fabric and $4\frac{5}{8}$ yards of print fabric. Which equation can you use to find out how much fabric Bridget needs?

(A) $4\frac{5}{8}f = 1\frac{1}{4}$
(B) $4\frac{5}{8} - 1\frac{1}{4} = f$
(C) $1\frac{1}{4} + 4\frac{5}{8} = f$
(D) $1\frac{1}{4}f = 4\frac{5}{8}$

31. Enrique mixes $\frac{1}{4}$ pound of peanuts with $\frac{1}{8}$ pound of cashews. Which strip is shaded to show the total number of pounds he has? Each strip represents one pound.

(F)
(G)
(H)
(J)

32. Suchin has three pieces of string to tie up newspapers for recycling. The lengths are 10 feet, 36 feet, and 22 feet. Estimate the amount of string Suchin has.

(A) 55 ft (B) 60 ft (C) 70 ft (D) 75 ft

GO for Help

For Exercises	See Lesson
33–35	4-1

Find each product.

33. $\frac{7}{9}$ of 21 **34.** $\frac{1}{6} \cdot 6$ **35.** $\frac{3}{10} \times 45$

GPS Guided Problem Solving

Practice Solving Problems

Movies The table below shows the total earnings for five movies. How many times greater were the earnings for *Shrek 2* than for *Finding Nemo?*

Movie	Earnings ($100 millions)
Shrek 2	$4\frac{2}{5}$
Spider-Man	$4\frac{1}{25}$
Finding Nemo	$3\frac{2}{5}$
Pirates of the Caribbean	$3\frac{1}{20}$
Home Alone	$2\frac{9}{10}$

SOURCE: *U.S. Almanac*

What You Might Think

How can I use a diagram to show this situation?

I can use division to find how many times $3\frac{2}{5}$ fits into $4\frac{2}{5}$. What equation can I write and solve?

What is the answer?

What You Might Write

$4\frac{2}{5}$

$3\frac{2}{5}$

Let x = the number of times $3\frac{2}{5}$ fits into $4\frac{2}{5}$.

$$x = 4\frac{2}{5} \div 3\frac{2}{5}$$

$$x = \frac{22}{5} \div \frac{17}{5}, \text{ or } \frac{22}{5} \times \frac{5}{17}$$

$$x = \frac{22}{17}, \text{ or } 1\frac{5}{17}$$

The earnings for *Shrek 2* were $1\frac{5}{17}$ times greater than the earnings for *Finding Nemo.*

Think It Through

1. Why should you use division to solve the problem?
2. **Number Sense** Before solving the problem, should you expect your answer to be *greater than* or *less than* 1? Explain.
3. **Check for Reasonableness** How can you use estimation to decide whether the answer is reasonable?

Exercises

4. **Picnic Fare** You buy 12 pounds of beef for a class picnic. You use $5\frac{1}{2}$ pounds to make burgers and $4\frac{2}{3}$ pounds to make tacos.
   a. What equation represents this situation?
   b. How much beef have you used in all?

5. A lap around a motocross track is $\frac{3}{4}$ mile. How many laps do you need to complete to finish a 6-mile race?

6. How high is a stack of 12 pieces of lumber if each piece is $1\frac{1}{4}$ inches thick?

7. **Running** The table below shows a relay team's times in minutes.

Relay Team Times (in minutes)

Kim	$1\frac{1}{2}$
Alison	$1\frac{3}{8}$
Laura	$1\frac{3}{4}$
Jamie	$1\frac{1}{4}$

   a. What was the total time in minutes?
   b. Did the relay team beat their best total time of 6 minutes? Explain.

Write and solve an equation for each problem.

8. **Apples** One student can eat $\frac{1}{2}$ of an apple in $\frac{1}{3}$ of a minute. At this rate, how many apples can three students eat in two minutes?

9. **Survey** Your teacher asks your class to name one of the three primary colors.
   - $\frac{2}{5}$ of the class chooses yellow
   - $\frac{1}{3}$ of the class chooses blue

   What fraction of the class chooses red?

Test-Taking Strategies

Eliminating Answers

In a multiple-choice problem, you can often eliminate some of the answer choices.

EXAMPLE

A plant that you bought two years ago is $3\frac{1}{6}$ feet tall. It was $1\frac{3}{4}$ feet tall when you bought it. How many feet has the plant grown since you bought it?

Ⓐ $\frac{1}{4}$ foot Ⓑ 1 foot Ⓒ $1\frac{5}{12}$ feet Ⓓ 4 feet

- The plant is $3\frac{1}{6}$ feet tall. So it could not have grown 4 feet. Eliminate choice D.
- $3\frac{1}{6}$ feet is about 3 feet and $1\frac{3}{4}$ feet is about 2 feet. So the plant has grown about 1 foot. Eliminate choice A, which is much less than the estimate.
- $1\frac{3}{4}$ feet + 1 foot is less than $3\frac{1}{6}$ feet. Eliminate choice B.
- The correct answer is choice C.

Exercises

Identify two choices that you can easily eliminate. Explain why. Then solve the problem.

1. A truck is carrying a load that weighs $15\frac{3}{5}$ tons. The total weight of the truck and the load is $36\frac{1}{2}$ tons. How many tons does the truck weigh?

   Ⓐ $14\frac{9}{10}$ Ⓑ $20\frac{9}{10}$ Ⓒ $21\frac{1}{10}$ Ⓓ $52\frac{1}{10}$

2. The height of a door is $7\frac{1}{6}$ feet. A person standing in the doorway is $4\frac{5}{12}$ feet tall. Find the approximate distance in feet between the person's head and the top of the door.

   Ⓐ 1 foot Ⓑ 2 foot Ⓒ 3 feet Ⓓ 4 feet

3. You have already run $1\frac{3}{8}$ miles. You want to run a total of $3\frac{1}{4}$ miles. How many miles do you still have to run?

   Ⓐ 3 miles Ⓑ $1\frac{7}{8}$ miles Ⓒ $1\frac{1}{2}$ miles Ⓓ $\frac{7}{8}$ miles

Chapter 4 Review

Vocabulary Review

reciprocal (p. 136)

Skills and Concepts

Lesson 4-1

- To solve problems by multiplying fractions and multiplying mixed numbers

To multiply fractions, multiply the numerators and then multiply the denominators.

To multiply with mixed numbers, first write the mixed numbers as improper fractions. Then multiply the fractions.

Estimate each product.

1. $3\frac{1}{3} \times 4\frac{1}{8}$ **2.** $5\frac{2}{3} \cdot 1\frac{5}{6}$ **3.** $8\frac{3}{8} \times 9\frac{11}{15}$ **4.** $7\frac{10}{23} \cdot 12\frac{3}{16}$

Find each product.

5. $\frac{1}{2} \cdot \frac{3}{5}$ **6.** $\frac{12}{13} \times \frac{1}{18}$

7. $25 \cdot \frac{7}{10}$ **8.** $5\frac{1}{6} \times \frac{3}{4}$

9. $3\frac{1}{3} \times 2\frac{2}{25}$ **10.** $4\frac{5}{11} \cdot 4\frac{9}{14}$

11. Dessert A recipe for fruit salad calls for $\frac{2}{3}$ cup peaches. How many cups of peaches do you need to make $\frac{1}{2}$ of the original recipe?

Go Online
For vocabulary quiz
PearsonSuccessNet.com

Lesson 4-2

- To use models to interpret and perform fraction division and to solve word problems involving fraction division

To divide fractions, use models such as fraction bars, fraction strips, or circles to find the quotient.

Use a model to find each quotient.

12. $3 \div \frac{1}{4}$ **13.** $1\frac{1}{3} \div \frac{1}{6}$

1							
1/6	1/6	1/6	1/6	1/6	1/6	1/6	1/6

14. Anna has 2 yards of fabric. She needs $\frac{2}{3}$ yard to make a wallet. How many wallets can she make? Solve by using a model.

15. Marcus wants to make shelves for his room. He has an 8 ft long piece of plywood. He needs $2\frac{3}{4}$ feet of plywood for each shelf. Does he have enough wood for 3 shelves? Solve by using a model.

Lesson 4-3

- To divide fractions and to solve problems by dividing fractions

Two numbers are **reciprocals** if their product is 1. The numbers $\frac{2}{3}$ and $\frac{3}{2}$ are reciprocals, as are $\frac{1}{5}$ and 5. To divide by a fraction, multiply by the reciprocal of the fraction.

Find each reciprocal.

16. $\frac{1}{3}$ 17. $\frac{4}{16}$ 18. $\frac{1}{6}$ 19. $\frac{36}{5}$

Find each quotient.

20. $8 \div \frac{1}{2}$ 21. $4 \div \frac{12}{17}$ 22. $\frac{3}{11} \div \frac{3}{5}$ 23. $\frac{5}{6} \div \frac{15}{16}$

24. $\frac{4}{7} \div \frac{2}{5}$ 25. $\frac{18}{25} \div 9$ 26. $3\frac{3}{4} \div \frac{13}{15}$ 27. $4\frac{1}{7} \div \frac{1}{3}$

28. You can pick a bucket of tomatoes every $\frac{1}{6}$ hour. How many buckets can you pick in $3\frac{1}{3}$ hours?

Lesson 4-4

- To estimate and compute the quotient of mixed numbers

To divide mixed numbers, first write the numbers as improper fractions. Then multiply by the reciprocal of the divisor.

Estimate each quotient. Then find the quotient.

29. $2\frac{1}{5} \div 2\frac{1}{3}$ 30. $8\frac{2}{3} \div 3\frac{2}{11}$ 31. $12\frac{2}{7} \div 3\frac{5}{9}$ 32. $13\frac{1}{2} \div 7\frac{5}{16}$

33. A hair stylist schedules appointments every $\frac{1}{3}$ hour. About how many appointments can a hair stylist schedule in $6\frac{1}{2}$ hours?

Lesson 4-5

- To solve equations with fractions

To solve an equation, get the variable alone on one side. To solve equations in which a variable is multiplied by a fraction, multiply both sides of the equation by the reciprocal of the fraction.

If the variable is multiplied by a mixed number, write the mixed number as an improper fraction. Then solve.

Solve each equation.

34. $\frac{11}{12} = n + \frac{2}{3}$ 35. $\frac{5}{8} = a + \frac{1}{3}$ 36. $3\frac{1}{5} = x - \frac{12}{25}$ 37. $y - 2\frac{8}{9} = \frac{5}{6}$

38. $\frac{m}{6} = 16$ 39. $\frac{2}{5}x = 10$ 40. $\frac{3}{8}k = \frac{3}{4}$ 41. $\frac{6}{7}y = \frac{9}{14}$

Chapter 4 Test

Go Online For online chapter test PearsonSuccessNet.com

Find the reciprocal of each number.

1. 6
2. $\frac{7}{12}$
3. 32
4. $\frac{8}{6}$

Find each product.

5. $\frac{3}{8}$ of 32
6. $\frac{5}{6} \cdot \frac{12}{25}$
7. $\frac{7}{9} \cdot 5\frac{4}{7}$
8. $3\frac{1}{3} \times 2\frac{3}{4}$
9. **Building Design** A log cabin has walls built with 12 logs lying horizontally on top of one another. If each log is $\frac{3}{4}$ foot thick, how high is each wall?
10. Jolene weighs 96 pounds. Jolene's father weighs $1\frac{7}{8}$ times as much as she does. How much does her father weigh?

Find each quotient.

11. $15 \div \frac{9}{11}$
12. $\frac{2}{5} \div \frac{8}{25}$
13. $\frac{5}{7} \div 25$
14. $6\frac{3}{4} \div 4\frac{1}{2}$

Estimate each quotient.

15. $10\frac{4}{17} \div 4\frac{5}{9}$
16. $30\frac{2}{7} \div 15\frac{1}{10}$
17. **Encyclopedias** Several volumes of an encyclopedia fill a shelf. Each volume is $1\frac{1}{4}$ inches wide, and the shelf is $27\frac{1}{2}$ inches long. How many volumes are in the encyclopedia?

Solve for x.

18. $\frac{1}{3} + x = \frac{4}{5}$
19. $\frac{2}{3}x = \frac{7}{24}$
20. $2\frac{1}{3} = x - \frac{1}{2}$
21. $\frac{x}{3} = 8$
22. Instead of walking from school to the grocery store, Scott walks 2 miles from school to the video store. His walk is $\frac{5}{6}$ of the distance to the grocery store. How far from school is the grocery store?
23. There are $1\frac{1}{3}$ times as many girls as there are boys at a party. If there are 18 boys, how many people are at the party?

Match each expression with its product.

24. $\frac{1}{4} \times \frac{1}{3}$ A. $\frac{3}{8}$
25. $\frac{2}{3} \cdot \frac{2}{5}$ B. $\frac{4}{15}$
26. $\frac{1}{2} \times \frac{3}{4}$ C. 6
27. $\frac{6}{7} \cdot 7$ D. $\frac{1}{12}$
28. **Writing in Math** Explain how you can estimate to find $7\frac{2}{5} \times 5$.
29. **Buttons** Joan has $\frac{5}{6}$ yard of ribbon. She needs $\frac{1}{12}$ yard to decorate each button. How many buttons can she decorate? Solve by using a model.
30. **Model** Draw a diagram or a model to find $8 \div \frac{2}{3}$.

Reading Comprehension

Read each passage and answer the questions that follow.

In the Dough Here is a recipe for making modeling dough.

1 cup flour	$1\frac{1}{2}$ teaspoons cream of tartar
$\frac{1}{2}$ cup salt	1 tablespoon vegetable oil
1 cup water	a few drops of food coloring

Heat the vegetable oil in a pan. Then add the other ingredients. Stir constantly. Let dough cool. Store in an airtight container.

1. How many cups of flour, salt, and water does the recipe call for?
   (A) $1\frac{1}{2}$ cups (B) 2 cups (C) $2\frac{1}{2}$ cups (D) $2\frac{3}{4}$ cups

2. Suppose you only have enough flour to make half a batch of dough. How much salt would you need?
   (F) $\frac{1}{4}$ cup (G) $\frac{1}{2}$ cup (H) $\frac{3}{4}$ cup (J) 1 cup

3. Suppose you only have 1 teaspoon of cream of tartar. By what fraction will you need to multiply the other ingredients in order to make dough with the same consistency?
   (A) $\frac{1}{3}$ (B) $\frac{1}{2}$ (C) $\frac{2}{3}$ (D) $\frac{3}{4}$

4. What fraction of a cup of cream of tartar does the recipe call for? (There are 48 teaspoons in 1 cup.)
   (F) $\frac{1}{32}$ (G) $\frac{1}{16}$ (H) $\frac{1}{3}$ (J) $\frac{1}{2}$

Video Value Carlos, Lisa, and Lenny found a box of used computer games at a yard sale. Carlos wanted four of the games, Lisa wanted two of them, and Lenny wanted the other six. The price for the box of computer games was $18. They planned to split the cost according to how many games each person wanted.

5. What fraction of the computer games did Lisa pick?
   (A) $\frac{1}{6}$ (B) $\frac{1}{4}$ (C) $\frac{1}{3}$ (D) $\frac{2}{3}$

6. How much should Lenny pay?
   (F) $4 (G) $6 (H) $9 (J) $12

7. How much should Lisa pay?
   (A) $3 (B) $4 (C) $6 (D) $8

8. What fraction of the computer games did Lenny and Carlos pick together?
   (F) $\frac{2}{3}$ (G) $\frac{3}{4}$ (H) $\frac{5}{6}$ (J) $\frac{7}{8}$

CHAPTER 5 Ratios and Percents

What You've Learned

- In Chapter 1, you used multiplication and division to solve problems involving decimals.
- In Chapter 4, you solved equations with fractions and used multiplication and division to solve problems involving fractions and mixed numbers.

GO for Help

For Exercises	See Lessons
1–4	2-6
5–8	3-5
9–12	3-4
13–16	4-1, 4-3

Solving Equations

Solve for n.

1. $n \div 8 = 6$ **2.** $\frac{n}{7} = 6$

3. $3 \times n = 72$ **4.** $6n = 54$

Finding the Least Common Multiple

Find the LCM of each set of numbers.

5. 3, 9 **6.** 4, 16 **7.** 12, 18 **8.** 20, 25

Finding the Greatest Common Factor

Find the GCF of each set of numbers.

9. 10, 28 **10.** 16, 48 **11.** 15, 25 **12.** 75, 100

Multiplying and Dividing Fractions

Find each product or quotient.

13. $\frac{4}{7} \times \frac{2}{3}$ **14.** $\frac{12}{14} \times \frac{7}{12}$ **15.** $\frac{7}{9} \div \frac{1}{5}$ **16.** $\frac{11}{12} \div \frac{2}{9}$

What You'll Learn Next

- In this chapter, you will use multiplication and division to solve problems involving ratios and rates.
- You will find equivalent ratios and rates using tables and diagrams.
- You will use ratios to convert measurements.
- You will use the relationship between fractions, decimals, and percents to solve problems.

Key Vocabulary

- double number line diagram (p. 161)
- equivalent ratios (p. 170)
- percent (p. 179)
- rate (p. 166)
- ratio (p. 160)
- tape diagram (p. 161)
- unit cost (p. 167)
- unit rate (p. 166)

5-1 Ratios

1. **Vocabulary Review** What do the *numerator* and the *denominator* of a fraction represent?

Write the fraction each drawing represents.

2.

3.

CONTENT STANDARDS
6.RP.1, 6.RP.3

What You'll Learn

To write ratios to compare real-world quantities

New Vocabulary ratio, tape diagram, double number line diagram

Why Learn This?

In recipes, the amounts of the ingredients are related to each other. You can use ratios to compare these amounts.

PARTY MIX
Makes 6 cups
4 cups cereal
2 cups pretzels
3 tbsp Worcestershire sauce

A **ratio** is a comparison of two numbers by division. The table below shows three ways to write the ratio of cups of party mix to cups of pretzels. All three ratios are read "six to two."

Statement	Ways to Write a Ratio		
	In Words	With a Symbol	As a Fraction
6 cups party mix to 2 cups pretzels	6 to 2	6 : 2	$\frac{6}{2}$

EXAMPLE Three Ways to Write a Ratio

1 **Recipes** Use the party mix recipe above. Write the ratio of cups of cereal to cups of pretzels in three ways.

The recipe calls for 4 cups of cereal and 2 cups of pretzels.

cereal to pretzels → 4 to 2 or 4 : 2 or $\frac{4}{2}$

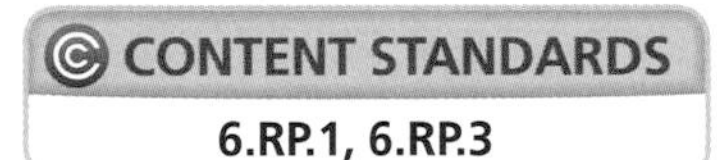

Video Tutor Help
PearsonSuccessNet.com

Quick Check

1. Use the recipe above. Write each ratio in three ways.
   a. pretzels to cereal
   b. pretzels to party mix

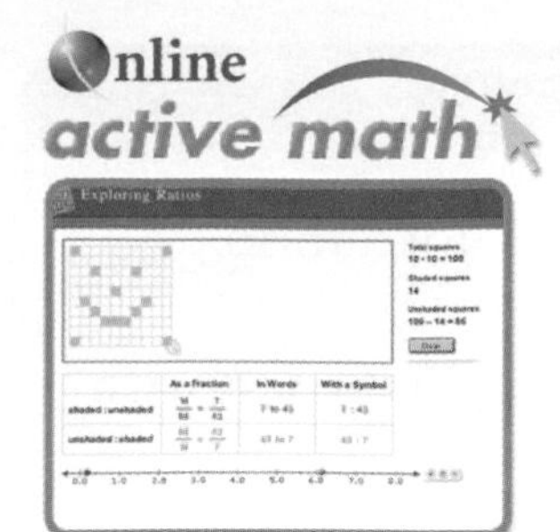

For: Exploring Ratios Activity
Use: Interactive Textbook, 5-1

A **tape diagram** is one way to represent ratios that uses length to show how two different quantities are related.

EXAMPLE Ratios on a Tape Diagram

2 The tape diagram shows the ratio of dogs to cats at an animal shelter. How can you describe the ratio of dogs to cats?

Dogs

Cats

For every 4 dogs at the animal shelter, there are 3 cats.

Quick Check

2. The tape diagram below shows the ratio of dollars earned to dollars saved.
How can you describe this ratio?

Dollars Earned

Dollars Saved

A **double number line diagram** is another way to represent ratios that shows how two quantities in different units are related.

EXAMPLE Using a Double Number Line Diagram

3 Kat works at a bookstore. Using the double number line, describe the ratio of hours Kat works to the money she earns.

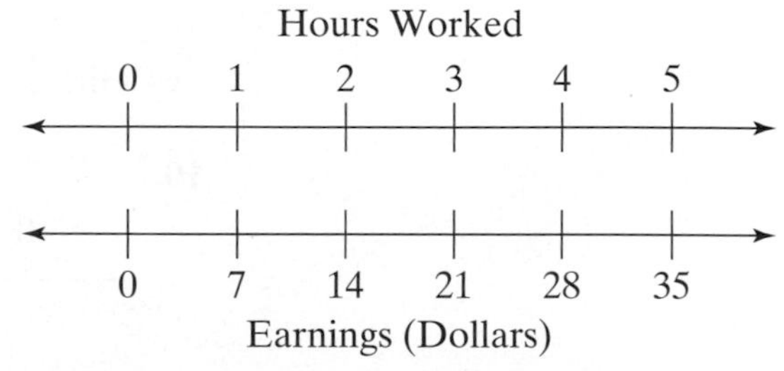

The ratio of hours worked to dollars earned is 1 : 7. For every hour Kat works, she earns $7.

Quick Check

3. The double number line shows Emma's speed during a track event. Describe this ratio.

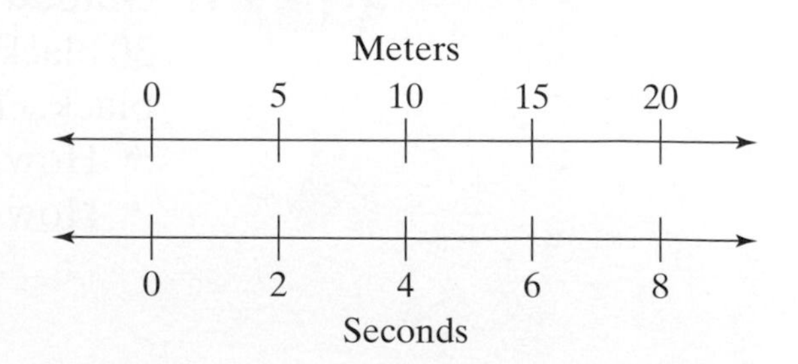

Check Your Understanding

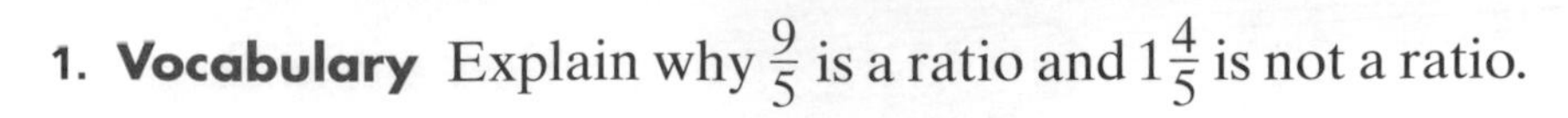

1. **Vocabulary** Explain why $\frac{9}{5}$ is a ratio and $1\frac{4}{5}$ is not a ratio.

Use the picture at the left. Match each relationship on the left with the correct ratio on the right.

2. cups to bowls — A. 5 to 15
3. coasters to blue cups — B. 4 to 2
4. yellow cups to blue bowls — C. 2 to 3
5. bowls to total number of items — D. 6 to 5

Homework Exercises

For more exercises, see Extra Skills and Word Problems.

GO for Help

For Exercises	See Examples
6–8	1
9	2
10	3

Use the table for Exercises 6–8. Write each ratio in three ways.

School Play Ticket Sales

Students	35
Adults	24
Seniors	11

6. students to adults
7. adults to seniors
8. seniors to total number of people

Describe the ratio shown in each diagram.

9.

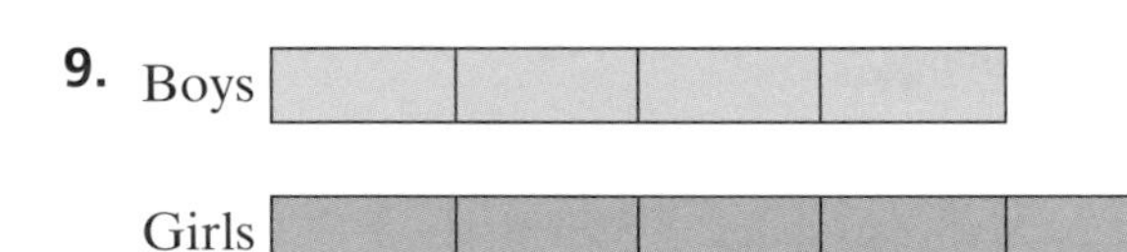

10. Pages Kyle Read

0 15 30 45

0 2 4 6

Days

11. **Guided Problem Solving** A jar contains 20 white marbles, 30 black marbles, and some red marbles. Half of the marbles are black. Find the ratio of white marbles to red marbles.
    - How many marbles are in the jar?
    - How can you find the number of red marbles?

Online
Homework Video Tutor
PearsonSuccessNet.com

12. A typical adult cat has 12 fewer teeth than a typical adult dog. An adult dog has 42 teeth. Write the ratio of an adult cat's teeth to an adult dog's teeth.

13. **Writing in Math** A flower arrangement has an equal number of red roses and white roses. Without knowing the total number of roses, is it possible to represent the number of red roses to white roses as a ratio? Explain.

14. **Science** Of the 20 students in Rae's science class, 13 students choose to make a volcano for their science project. Rae represents the ratio of students making a volcano to students making another science project as 13 : 20. Is this correct? Explain.

15. **Open-Ended** Write a ratio of the number of vowels to the number of consonants in your first name.

16. **Challenge** A fruit punch recipe calls for $3x$ ounces of apple juice for every x ounces of grape juice. Make a double number line diagram to show the ratio of apple juice to grape juice.

Test Prep and Mixed Review — Practice

Multiple Choice

17. The table shows participation in three races. Which fraction represents the ratio of the number of 5-km runners to the number of 10-km runners?

Fun Run

Distance (km)	Number of Runners
10	96
5	128
1	52

Ⓐ $\frac{96}{128}$ Ⓑ $\frac{128}{96}$ Ⓒ $\frac{52}{96}$ Ⓓ $\frac{96}{52}$

18. The final score of a basketball game is 60 to 48. A prize is given to the person in the seat numbered with the least common multiple of 60 and 48. What is the prize-winning seat number?

Ⓕ 12 Ⓖ 120 Ⓗ 240 Ⓙ 480

19. Anders bought a can of juice labeled "12 fluid ounces." How many cups of juice are in the can?

Ⓐ $\frac{1}{2}$ cup Ⓑ $\frac{3}{4}$ cup Ⓒ $1\frac{1}{2}$ cups Ⓓ $1\frac{3}{4}$ cups

GO for Help

For Exercises	See Lesson
20–23	4-1

Write each product in simplest form.

20. $\frac{2}{5} \times \frac{3}{7}$ 21. $\frac{3}{4} \times \frac{5}{8}$ 22. $\frac{1}{6}$ of $\frac{3}{5}$ 23. $\frac{3}{16} \cdot \frac{16}{21}$

Modeling Ratios

You can use paper strips to model ratios. Cut four strips of paper with equal lengths. Fold and shade the paper strips to represent ratios.

EXAMPLE Modeling Part to Part

1 A punch recipe calls for 4 oranges and 2 lemons.

- The ratio of oranges to lemons can be written as $4 : 2$, 4 to 2, or $\frac{4}{2}$.

EXAMPLE Modeling Part to Whole

2 Five out of eight students walk to school.

- The ratio of walkers to students can be written as $5 : 8$, 5 to 8, or $\frac{5}{8}$.

Exercises

Use paper strips to model each ratio. Write each ratio in three different ways.

1. For every five kittens in a litter, three are male.
2. For every ten high school seniors, seven take a science course.
3. For every four pairs of shoes sold in the summer, one pair are sandals.
4. Use the drawing of the blue jays and goldfinches at the right. Write three different ratios to describe the drawing.

5. **Writing in Math** You are given a part-to-part ratio, as in Example 1. Explain how to find the total number of parts.
6. **Reasoning** The ratio of girls to boys in a class is 6 to 8. Does this mean there are 14 students in the class? Explain.

Vocabulary Builder

High-Use Academic Words

High-use academic words are words that you will see often in textbooks and on tests. These words are not math vocabulary terms, but knowing them will help you to succeed in mathematics.

Direction Words

Some words tell what to do in a problem. I need to understand what these words are asking so that I give the correct answer.

Word	Meaning
Define	To give an accurate meaning with sufficient detail
Classify	To assign things to different groups based on their characteristics
Contrast	To show how two things are different; to include details or examples

Exercises

1. Define *salad.*
2. Classify each object as a fruit or a vegetable.
   a. apple **b.** carrot **c.** lettuce **d.** banana **e.** corn
3. Contrast a fruit salad and a vegetable salad.
4. Define *ratio.*
5. Classify each pair of ratios as equivalent or not equivalent. Draw a double number line diagram to help you.
   a. $\frac{1}{2}, \frac{3}{6}$ **b.** $\frac{2}{5}, \frac{4}{10}$ **c.** $\frac{5}{6}, \frac{1}{12}$ **d.** $\frac{1}{3}, \frac{3}{9}$
6. **Word Knowledge** Think about the word *comparison.*
   a. Choose the letter for how well you know the word.
      A. I know its meaning.
      B. I've seen it, but I don't know its meaning.
      C. I don't know it.
   b. Research Look up and write the definition of *comparison.*
   c. Use the word in a sentence involving mathematics.

5-2 Unit Rates

1. Vocabulary Review Which operation is used in a ratio?

Divide the numerator of each ratio by its denominator.

2. $\frac{48}{12}$ **3.** $\frac{36}{9}$

4. $\frac{75}{15}$ **5.** $\frac{42}{7}$

Lesson 5-1

CONTENT STANDARDS

6.RP.2, 6.RP.3, 6.RP.3.b

What You'll Learn

To find and use unit rates and unit costs

New Vocabulary rate, unit rate, unit cost

Why Learn This?

Exercise is important for good health. You can use unit rates to find your heart rate.

A **rate** is a ratio involving two quantities in different units. The rate $\frac{\text{150 heartbeats}}{\text{2 minutes}}$ compares heartbeats to minutes. The rate for one unit of a given quantity is called the **unit rate.**

Divide 150 by 2.

$150 \div 2 = 75$

150 heartbeats in 2 minutes = 75 heartbeats in 1 minute

The unit rate is 75 heartbeats per minute.

EXAMPLE Finding a Unit Rate

1 A box of wheat crackers contains 6 servings and has a total of 420 Calories. Find the number of Calories in 1 serving.

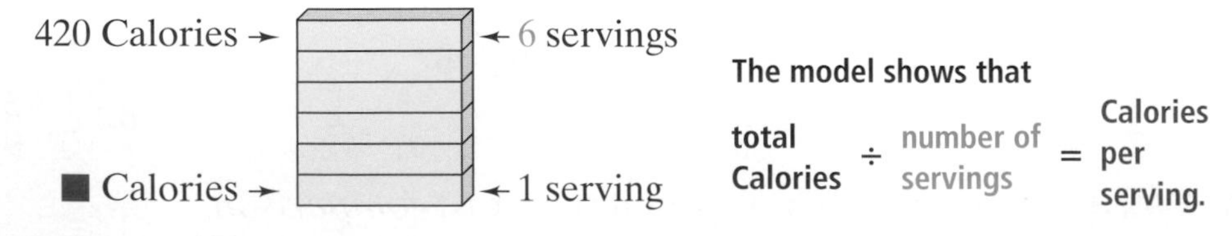

Divide 420 by 6.

420 Calories ÷ 6 servings = 70 calories per serving

The unit rate is 70 Calories per serving.

Quick Check

1. Find the unit rate for $2.37 for 3 pounds of grapes.

A unit rate that gives the cost per unit is a **unit cost.** Unit costs help you compare prices.

EXAMPLE Comparing Unit Cost

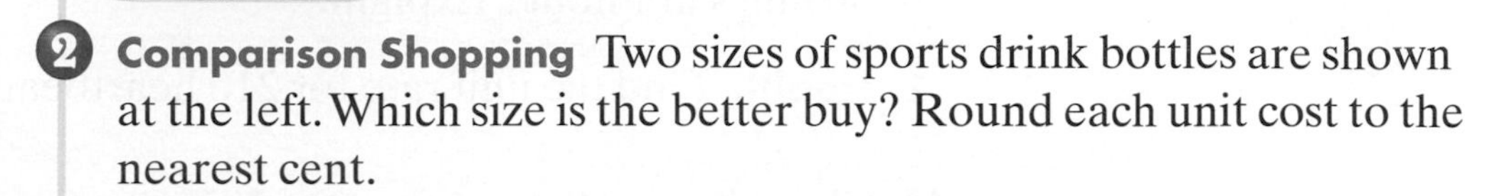

2 Comparison Shopping Two sizes of sports drink bottles are shown at the left. Which size is the better buy? Round each unit cost to the nearest cent.

Divide to find the unit cost for each size. First express each cost in cents.

$$\begin{matrix}\text{price} \rightarrow \\ \text{size} \rightarrow\end{matrix} \frac{120¢}{24 \text{ oz}} = 5¢ \text{ per fluid ounce}$$

$$\begin{matrix}\text{price} \rightarrow \\ \text{size} \rightarrow\end{matrix} \frac{129¢}{32 \text{ oz}} \approx 4¢ \text{ per fluid ounce}$$

The better buy costs less per fluid ounce. Since $.04 is less than $.05, the 32-ounce bottle is the better buy.

Quick Check

2. You can buy 6 ounces of yogurt for $.68, or 32 ounces of yogurt for $2.89. Find each unit cost. Which is the better buy?

When you know a unit rate, you can use multiplication to solve a problem.

EXAMPLE Using a Unit Rate

3 Multiple Choice A car travels about 25 miles on 1 gallon of gas. About how far can the car travel on 8 gallons of gas?

Ⓐ $3\frac{1}{3}$ miles Ⓑ 8 miles Ⓒ 33 miles Ⓓ 200 miles

Multiply the number of miles the car gets on 1 gallon of gas by the number of gallons.

25 miles per gallon $\times$ 8 gallons $=$ 200 miles

The car can travel 200 miles on 8 gallons of gas. The correct answer is choice D.

Quick Check

3. Solve the problem using unit rates.
   a. You earn $5 in 1 hour. How much do you earn in 5 hours?
   b. You can type 25 words in 1 minute. How many words can you type in 10 minutes?

Check Your Understanding

1. **Vocabulary** Which is a unit rate, 160 miles in 4 hours or 40 miles in 1 hour? Explain.

2. **Health** Find the unit rate for 210 heartbeats in 3 minutes.

Match each price to the correct unit cost.

3. peaches: 6 for $3.84
4. bananas: 4 for $1.96
5. oranges: 3 for $2.16
6. pears: 5 for $2.90

A. 49¢ each
B. 58¢ each
C. 64¢ each
D. 72¢ each

Homework Exercises

For more exercises, see Extra Skills and Word Problems.

GO for Help

For Exercises	See Examples
7–10	1
11–13	2
14–16	3

Find the unit rate for each situation. You may find a model helpful.

7. 92 desks in 4 classrooms
8. $19.50 for 3 shirts
9. 45 miles in 5 hours
10. $29.85 for 3 presents

Comparison Shopping **Find each unit cost. Round to the nearest cent. Then determine the better buy.**

11. crackers: 16 ounces for $2.39; 20 ounces for $3.19
12. juice: 48 fluid ounces for $2.07; 32 fluid ounces for $1.64
13. apples: 3 pounds for $1.89; 1 pound for $.79
14. A book costs $6.75. Find the cost of 8 books.
15. There are 3 feet in 1 yard. Find the number of feet in a 15-yard run by a football player.
16. Five buses leave on a field trip. There are about 45 students per bus. About how many students are on the 5 buses?

GPS

17. **Guided Problem Solving** You earn $44.55 in 9 hours. Your friend earns $51 in 12 hours. How much do you and your friend earn together if you each work 20 hours?
    - What is your unit rate for earnings? What is your friend's unit rate?
    - How can you use unit rates to find the total?

For Exercises 18–21, tell which unit rate is greater.

18. Dee reads 60 pages in 2 hours. Teri reads 99 pages in 3 hours.

19. Damian types 110 words in 5 minutes. Howard types 208 words in 8 minutes.

20. Jan bikes 18 miles in 2 hours. Nikki bikes 33 miles in 3 hours.

21. Tanya scores 81 points in 9 games. Tamaira scores 132 points in 12 games.

22. Jump Rope Crystal jumps 255 times in 3 minutes. The United States record for 11-year-olds is 882 jumps in 3 minutes.

a. Find Crystal's unit rate for jumps per minute.

b. Find the record-holder's unit rate for jumps per minute.

c. How many more times per minute did the record-holder jump than Crystal?

23. Estimation A car travels 279.9 miles on 9.8 gallons of gasoline. Estimate the car's unit rate of miles per gallon. Explain how you found your estimate.

24. Writing in Math Explain why the speed limit on a highway is an example of a unit rate.

25. Challenge An airplane flies 2,750 miles in 5 hours. Find the unit rate in miles per second. Round your answer to the nearest hundredth.

Test Prep and Mixed Review — Practice

Multiple Choice

26. There are 54 students and 18 computers in a classroom. Which ratio accurately compares the number of students to the number of computers?

Ⓐ 1 : 3   Ⓑ 3 : 1   Ⓒ 3 : 4   Ⓓ 4 : 3

27. Each square below is divided into parts of equal size. In which square is the ratio of shaded to unshaded parts 2 : 1?

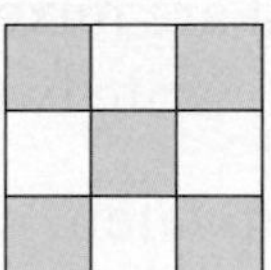
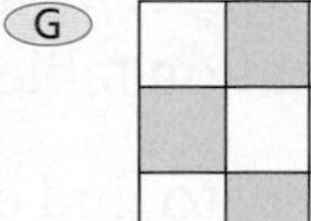
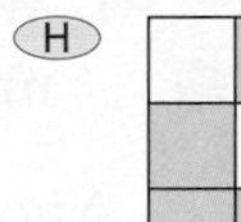
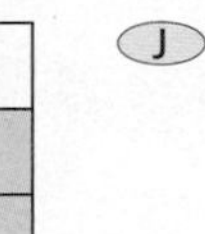
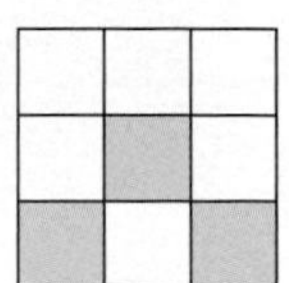

GO for Help

For Exercises	See Lesson
28–30	4-4

Find each quotient.

28. $4\frac{2}{3} \div 1\frac{3}{4}$ **29.** $6\frac{1}{4} \div 2\frac{1}{2}$ **30.** $2\frac{2}{5} \div 7\frac{1}{5}$

Equivalent Ratios and Rates

Check Skills You'll Need

1. **Vocabulary Review** What is a *ratio*?

Write each ratio in two other ways.

2. $\frac{4}{12}$
3. 6 to 10
4. 12 : 17
5. 8 to 3

GO for Help Lesson 5-1

CONTENT STANDARDS
6.RP.3, 6.RP.3.a

What You'll Learn

To use equivalent ratios and rates to solve real-world and mathematical problems

New Vocabulary equivalent ratios

Why Learn This?

Painters use ratios when they are mixing paints to make new colors.

Two ratios that name the same number are **equivalent ratios.** You can use a multiplication table to find equivalent ratios.

EXAMPLE Using a Multiplication Table

1 Red and blue paint are mixed in a ratio of 3 to 5. Use a multiplication table to find 4 ratios equivalent to 3 to 5.

×	1	2	3	4	5	6
1	1	2	3	4	5	6
2	2	4	6	8	10	12
3	3	6	9	12	15	18
4	4	8	12	16	20	24
5	5	10	15	20	25	30
6	6	12	18	24	30	36

Make a table of equivalent ratios. Use the rows for 3 and 5 in the multiplication table.

Red	3	6	9	12	15	18
Blue	5	10	15	20	25	30

The equivalent ratios are 6 to 10, 9 to 15, 12 to 20, 15 to 25, and 18 to 30.

Quick Check

1. White and green paint are mixed in a ratio of 2 to 3. Use a multiplication table to write two equivalent ratios for the ratio 2 to 3.

Another way to find equivalent ratios is to multiply or divide each term of a ratio by the same nonzero number.

Multiply each term by 3. → 6 : 8 (×3, ×3) → 18 : 24

6 : 8 (÷2, ÷2) → 3 : 4 ← **Divide each term by 2.**

You can use this process to make tables, coordinate graphs, number lines, and diagrams to help you solve problems with equivalent ratios.

EXAMPLE Solving Rate Problems

2 Todd earns $7 for each hour he works. How much will he earn for 6 hours?

Method 1 Make a table of equivalent ratios.

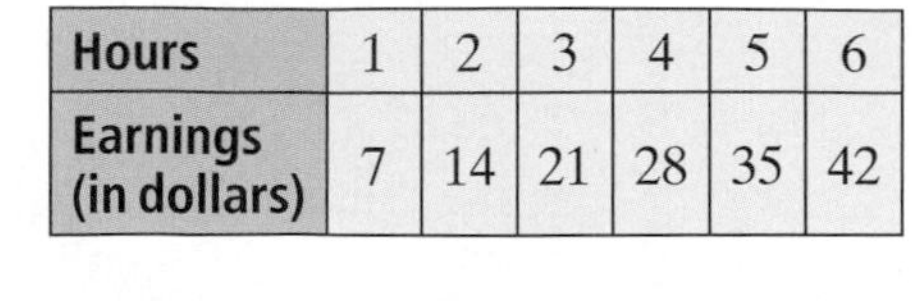

Hours	1	2	3	4	5	6
Earnings (in dollars)	7	14	21	28	35	42

Todd will earn $42.

Method 2 Make a double number line.

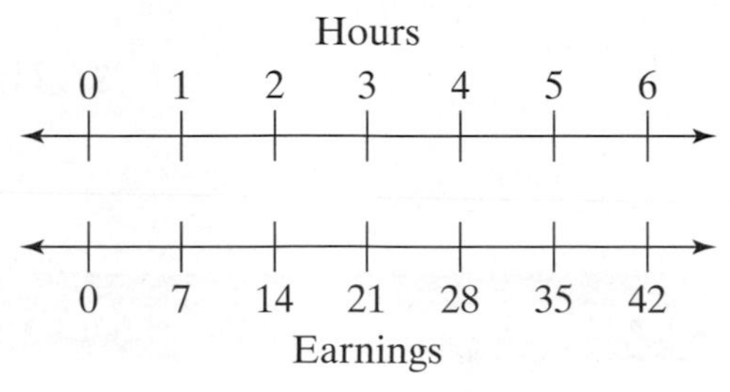

Todd will earn $42.

Method 3 Plot equivalent ratios on a coordinate graph. Use one term in the ratio as x and the other term in the ratio as y. This graph shows that Todd will earn $42 for working 6 hours.

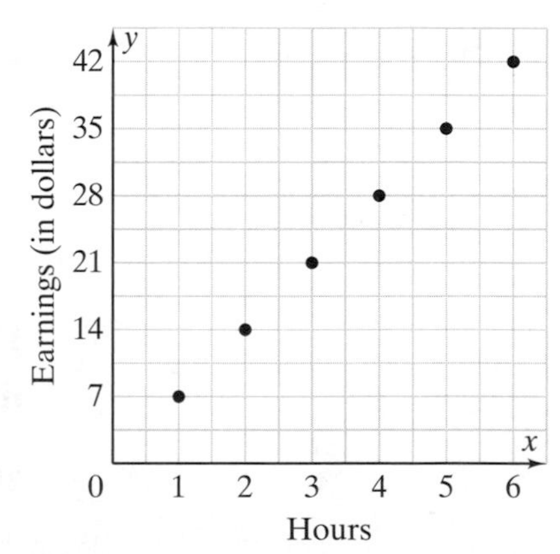

Video Tutor Help
PearsonSuccessNet.com

Quick Check

2. Sonia can read 3 pages in 8 minutes. At that rate, how many pages will she read in 24 minutes?

Some ratio problems can be solved by using a tape diagram.

EXAMPLE Using a Tape Diagram

3 The ratio of round tables to square tables at a party is 6 : 1. The total number of tables is 35. How many round tables are there?

Draw a tape diagram.

Round Tables: 5 | 5 | 5 | 5 | 5 | 5

Square Tables: 5

7 parts

Think:
7 parts → 35 tables
1 part → 35 tables ÷ 7 = 5 tables
6 parts → 6 × 5 tables = 30 tables

There are 30 round tables.

3. The ratio of nickels to dimes in a coin bank is $\frac{5}{3}$. The total number of nickels and dimes is 40. How many nickels are there?

Check Your Understanding

1. **Vocabulary** Give an example of two equivalent ratios.
2. Use a multiplication table to write 3 ratios that are equivalent to 2 to 5.
3. The ratio of girls to boys in a gym class is 1 to 2. If there are 30 students in the class, how many girls are in the class?

Homework Exercises

For more exercises, see Extra Skills and Word Problems.

GO for Help

For Exercises	See Examples
4–9	1
10–12	2
13–15	3

Use a multiplication table to write 4 ratios equivalent to each ratio.

4. 2 to 5
5. 5 to 4
6. $\frac{3}{9}$
7. $\frac{4}{1}$
8. 3 : 8
9. 8 : 7

For Exercises 10–15, use a multiplication table, a double number line, or a tape diagram to help you solve.

10. **Biking** Jackson bikes 2 miles in 15 minutes. At that rate, how many miles will he bike in 45 minutes?
11. **Earth Science** A glacier moves about 3 inches every 9 hours. At that rate, about how far does the glacier move in 36 hours?
12. **Groceries** The cost of 3 quarts of milk is $6.75. How many quarts can you buy with $20.25?
13. **Cooking** Trey used dried fruit and nuts to make 42 ounces of trail mix. The ratio of fruit to nuts is 4 : 3. How many ounces of nuts did he use?
14. **Painting** A painter mixed 56 quarts of blue and yellow paint using a ratio of 3 blue to 11 yellow. How many quarts of blue paint were used?
15. The ratio of roses to tulips in an arrangement is $\frac{2}{3}$. The total number of flowers is 25. How many tulips are there?

16. **Guided Problem Solving** Roberto can read 4 pages in 6 minutes. Casey can read 6 pages in 9 minutes. Is Roberto's ratio of pages to minutes equivalent to Casey's ratio of pages to minutes? Explain.
    - Make a table of equivalent ratios for each ratio.
    - Are there any ratios in Roberto's table that are equivalent to a ratio in Casey's table?

17. **Graphing** Julia can read 6 pages in 5 minutes. Make a coordinate graph to show how many pages she can read in 30 minutes.

18. **Sports** A team's ratio of wins to losses is 3 to 4. How many losses do they have if they have 12 wins?

19. **Number Sense** A recipe calls for 2 cups of flour to make 3 dozen cookies. Is 4 cups of flour enough to make 70 cookies? Explain.

20. **Algebra** Suppose you know that $\frac{a}{b}$ is equivalent to $\frac{m}{n}$, and $\frac{a}{b}$ is not equivalent to $\frac{x}{y}$. Is $\frac{m}{n}$ equivalent to $\frac{x}{y}$? Explain.

21. **Writing in Math** Explain how you can use fractions in simplest form to tell that $\frac{10}{40}$ and $\frac{25}{100}$ are equivalent ratios.

22. **Reasoning** You charge \$7 to baby-sit for 2 hours. Last night you earned \$17.50. How long did you baby-sit?

23. **Challenge** A package of 50 blank CDs costs \$25. However, the store has run out of 50-packs. The manager agrees to sell you packages of 12 at the same unit price. How much should a 12-pack of CDs cost?

Test Prep and Mixed Review

Practice

Multiple Choice

24. A team's ratio of wins to losses is 5 to 2. Which of the following could be the team's record?
    - (A) 10 wins and 7 losses
    - (B) 15 wins and 6 losses
    - (C) 25 wins and 4 losses
    - (D) 20 wins and 50 losses

25. What is the prime factorization of 200?
    - (F) $2^3 \cdot 5^2$
    - (G) $2^2 \cdot 5$
    - (H) $2^3 \cdot 3$
    - (J) $2^2 \cdot 5^2$

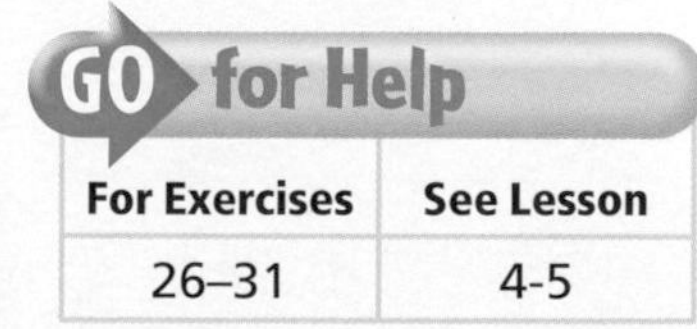

For Exercises	See Lesson
26–31	4-5

Solve each equation.

26. $\frac{2}{5} = s - \frac{1}{2}$

27. $\frac{1}{2} + a = \frac{2}{3}$

28. $\frac{x}{6} = 4$

29. $\frac{3}{4}y = 9$

30. $\frac{2}{3} + b = \frac{5}{6}$

31. $\frac{c}{5} = 9$

5-4 Using Ratios to Convert Measurement Units

1. **Vocabulary Review** Which numerator and denominator in this problem have a *common factor* greater than 1?

$\frac{4}{5} \times \frac{1}{6}$

Find each product.

2. $9 \times \frac{5}{9}$ **3.** $4 \times \frac{1}{4}$

4. $\frac{2}{5} \times 10$ **5.** $\frac{3}{4} \times 20$

Lesson 4-1

CONTENT STANDARD

6.RP.3.d

What You'll Learn

To use ratios to convert from one unit of measure to another

Why Learn This?

When you are increasing the number of servings a fruit punch recipe makes, you may need to convert from quarts to gallons.

To convert from one unit of measure to another, you can use a ratio of equivalent measurements in which the two quantities are equal, but use different units. Here are some examples.

$\frac{1{,}760 \text{ yards}}{1 \text{ mile}} \quad \frac{100 \text{ centigrams}}{1 \text{ gram}} \quad \frac{1 \text{ gallon}}{16 \text{ cups}}$

EXAMPLE Using Ratios to Convert Measures

1 Julia needs 80 cups of orange juice for a punch recipe. How many gallons of orange juice does she need?

First, write a ratio to relate gallons and cups. Write the new unit, gallon, in the numerator.

$$\frac{1 \text{ gallon}}{16 \text{ cups}}$$

Then multiply the given measurement by the ratio.

$$\begin{aligned} 80 \text{ cups} &= 80 \text{ cups} \times \frac{1 \text{ gallon}}{16 \text{ cups}} \\ &= 80 \cancel{\text{cups}} \times \frac{1 \text{ gallon}}{16 \cancel{\text{cups}}} \\ &= \frac{80 \text{ gallons}}{16} = 5 \text{ gallons} \end{aligned}$$

Julia needs 5 gallons of orange juice.

Quick Check

1. A piece of ribbon is 72 inches long. How many feet long is the piece of ribbon?

EXAMPLE Converting Metric Units

2 Convert 5 centimeters to millimeters.

Multiply the given measure by the correct ratio of equivalent measurements. Write the new units, millimeters, in the numerator.

$$5\,\text{cm} = 5\,\text{cm} \times \frac{10\,\text{mm}}{1\,\text{cm}}$$

$$= 5\,\cancel{\text{cm}} \times \frac{10\,\text{mm}}{1\,\cancel{\text{cm}}} = 50\text{ mm}$$

cm 0 1 2 3 4 5
mm 0 10 20 30 40 50

Quick Check

2. Convert 2,500 grams to kilograms.

To solve some problems, you may need to use more than one ratio.

EXAMPLE Using More than One Ratio

Video Tutor Help
PearsonSuccessNet.com

3 Tomas walks 400 yards in 5 minutes. At this rate, how many minutes does it take Tomas to walk 3 miles?

Step 1 Multiply by the correct ratio to find the number of yards in 3 miles. Write the new units, yards, in the numerator.

$$3\,\text{miles} = 3\,\cancel{\text{miles}} \times \frac{1{,}760\,\text{yards}}{1\,\cancel{\text{mile}}}$$

$$= 5{,}280\,\text{yards}$$

Step 2 Use Tomas' walking rate to find the number of minutes he needs to walk 5,280 yards. Since you want to find the number of minutes, use minutes in the numerator.

$$5{,}280\,\text{yards} = 5{,}280\,\cancel{\text{yards}} \times \frac{5\,\text{minutes}}{400\,\cancel{\text{yards}}}$$

$$= 66\,\text{minutes}$$

It takes Tomas 66 minutes to walk 3 miles.

Quick Check

3. Art drinks 2 quarts of milk every 3 days. How many days will it take him to drink 3 gallons of milk?

Check Your Understanding

1. **Reasoning** Explain why the ratio $\frac{100\,\text{g}}{1\,\text{kg}}$ is *not* a ratio of equivalent measurements.

2. **Time** What ratio of equivalent measurements would you use to convert 2 hours to minutes?

Convert each measurement.

3. 48 ounces to pounds
4. 8 grams to milligrams

Homework Exercises

For more exercises, see Extra Skills and Word Problems.

GO for Help

For Exercises	See Examples
5–8	1
9–12	2
13–16	3

Convert each measurement.

5. 48 inches to feet
6. 12 cups to quarts
7. 6 pints to cups
8. 5 miles to yards
9. 1,550 meters to kilometers
10. 350 centiliters to liters
11. 1.5 grams to milligrams
12. 7 meters to centimeters

13. An ant walks 42 feet in 3 minutes. How long will it take the ant to walk 28 yards?

14. **Veterinary Medicine** A dog needs 2 teaspoons of medicine for every 10 pounds of weight. How many teaspoons of medicine are needed for a 240-ounce dog?

15. **Aviation** An airplane is flying at 450 miles per hour. How many yards does the airplane fly in 30 minutes?

16. A cleaning solution uses 2 cups of vinegar for every 3 quarts of water. How many cups of vinegar are needed to make a cleaning solution containing 3 gallons of water?

17. **Guided Problem Solving** Suppose 1 milliliter of ink can print 30 pages of text. How many pages of text could you print with 2 quarts of ink? Use 1 liter $\approx$ 1.06 quarts. Round your answer to the nearest whole page.
    - Use ratios of equivalent measurements to convert milliliters to liters.
    - Convert liters to quarts.
    - Find the number of pages.

18. **Cooking** Mina has a tablespoon and a cup for measuring her ingredients. A recipe calls for 500 milliliters of water. How many tablespoons is this? How many cups is this? Use the ratios of equivalent measures below. Round your answers to the nearest tenth.

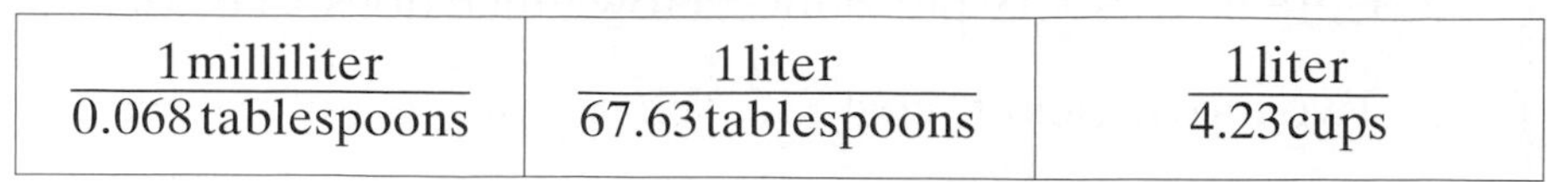

$\frac{1 \text{ milliliter}}{0.068 \text{ tablespoons}}$	$\frac{1 \text{ liter}}{67.63 \text{ tablespoons}}$	$\frac{1 \text{ liter}}{4.23 \text{ cups}}$

GO Online
Homework Video Tutor
PearsonSuccessNet.com

19. **Number Sense** A faucet leaks 75 milliliters of water per minute. How many liters of water does the faucet leak in $3\frac{1}{2}$ hours?

20. **Writing in Math** When converting x miles to an equivalent distance in y feet, is $x > y$ or is $y > x$? Explain.

21. **Reasoning** Mr. Wilson weighs 185 pounds. What do you need to know in order to find Mr. Wilson's weight in kilograms?

22. **Challenge** A remote control car travels 3,696 feet in 1 minute 10 seconds. What is the car's speed in miles per hour?

Test Prep and Mixed Review

Practice

Multiple Choice

23. A motorcycle can travel 104 miles on 2 gallons of gas. How many miles can the motorcycle travel on 2 quarts of gas?
    - (A) 8 miles
    - (B) 26 miles
    - (C) 52 miles
    - (D) 208 miles

24. Misha ate 455 grams of grapes last week. How many kilograms of grapes did she eat?
    - (A) 45.5 kilograms
    - (B) 4.55 kilograms
    - (C) 0.455 kilograms
    - (D) 0.0455 kilograms

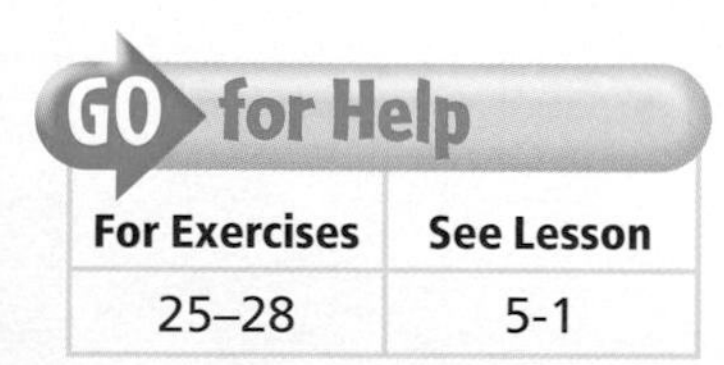

GO for Help

For Exercises	See Lesson
25–28	5-1

Use the table for Exercises 25–28. Write each ratio in three ways.

Hiro's Movie Collection

Type of Movie	Comedy	Science Fiction	Animated
Number of Movies	20	17	9

25. comedy to science fiction
26. animated to comedy
27. animated to total movies
28. science fiction to total movies

Checkpoint Quiz 1

Lessons 5-1 through 5-4

1. Write 18 : 40 in words and as a fraction.
2. Cereal costs $.19 per ounce. How much does 15 oz of cereal cost?
3. Two movie tickets cost $15. What is the cost of six tickets?

Write two ratios that are equivalent to each ratio.

4. 4 to 8
5. $\frac{2}{3}$
6. 7 : 10
7. 9 to 5

Convert each measurement.

8. 24 cups to quarts
9. 5 grams to milligrams

10. The speed of an ocean wave is measured by an oceanographer. The wave travels 30 meters in 10 seconds. How many meters will the wave travel in 2 minutes?

Match Those Ratios!

What You'll Need

- 20 note cards

How to Play

- Find 4 equivalent ratios and write them on 4 different cards. Make a total of 5 different sets of 4 equivalent ratios.
- Mix the 20 cards and place them face down in a 4 by 5 array. Take turns flipping two cards to find pairs of equivalent ratios. If the two ratios are equivalent, take the cards. If the ratios are not equivalent, turn the cards back over.
- The number of points earned for each pair of cards equals the lesser denominator of the pair of equivalent fractions. The student with the greatest number of points at the end wins.

5-5 Understanding Percents

Check Skills You'll Need

1. **Vocabulary Review** What are *equivalent ratios?*

Find two equivalent ratios for each ratio.

2. $\frac{2}{5}$
3. $\frac{13}{50}$
4. $\frac{3}{25}$
5. $\frac{1}{10}$

GO for Help Lesson 5-3

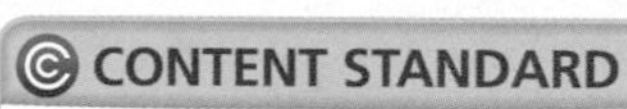

CONTENT STANDARD

6.RP.3.c

What You'll Learn

To model percents and to write percents using equivalent ratios

New Vocabulary percent

Why Learn This?

Percents make ratios easier to understand and compare. You can use a percent to represent the floor space needed for each piece of furniture in a room.

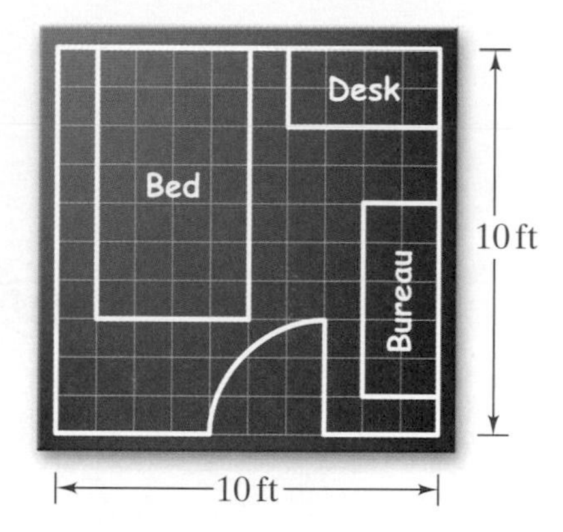

A **percent** is a ratio that compares a number to 100. You can model a percent using a 10 × 10 grid. The symbol for percent is %. You can write a percent as a ratio with a denominator of 100.

EXAMPLES Using Models With Percents

1 The floor plan above shows a bedroom with an area of 100 ft². Find the percent of floor space needed for each piece of furniture.

Count the number of grid spaces for each piece. Write each number as a ratio to the total number of grid spaces, 100. Then write it as a percent.

Bed $\frac{28}{100} = 28\%$ Bureau $\frac{10}{100} = 10\%$ Desk $\frac{8}{100} = 8\%$

Vocabulary Tip

Percent means "per hundred." The root *cent* appears in words such as century, centimeter, and centipede.

2 Model 25% on a 10 × 10 grid.

Shade 25 of the 100 grid spaces. →

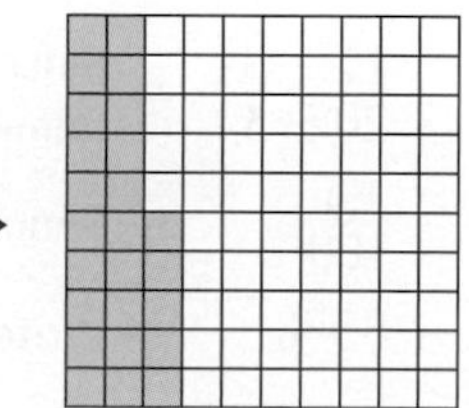

Quick Check

1. Write a ratio and a percent to represent the unused floor space.
2. Model 80% on a 10 × 10 grid.

The factors of 100 are 1, 2, 4, 5, 10, 20, 25, 50, and 100. Any ratio written as a fraction with a denominator that is a factor of 100 is easy to write as a percent. You can use common multiples to write an equivalent ratio that has a denominator of 100. When you have a fraction with a denominator of 100, look at the numerator to find the percent.

EXAMPLE Finding Percents Using Models

3 What percent does each shaded area represent?

a. 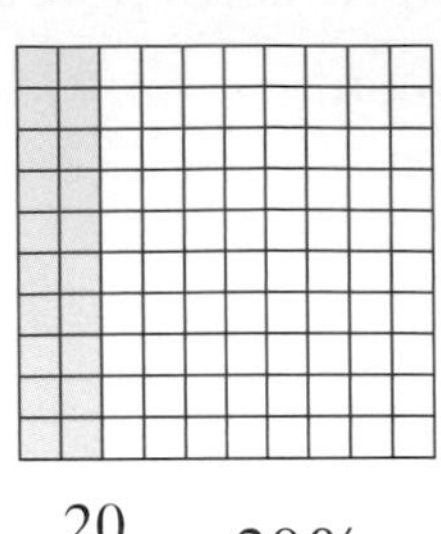

b. 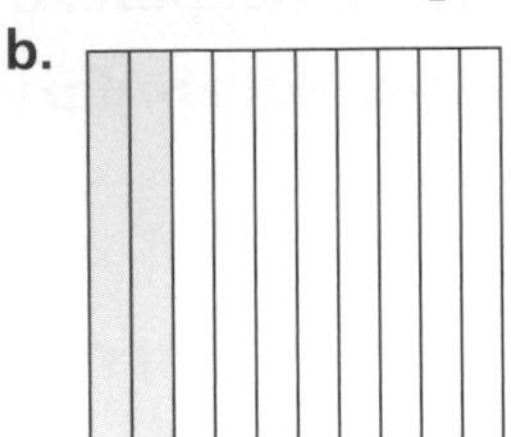

c. 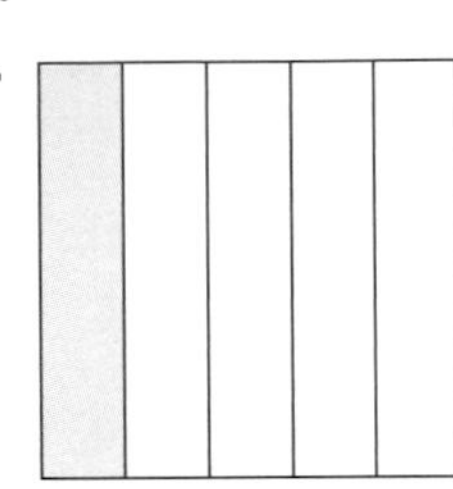

a. $\frac{20}{100} = 20\%$

b. $\frac{2}{10} = \frac{20}{100} = 20\%$

c. $\frac{1}{5} = \frac{20}{100} = 20\%$

Quick Check

3. Write a ratio and a percent for each shaded area.

a. 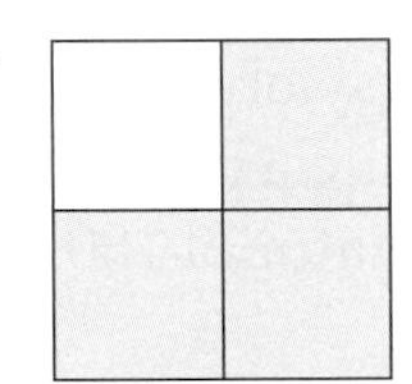

b. 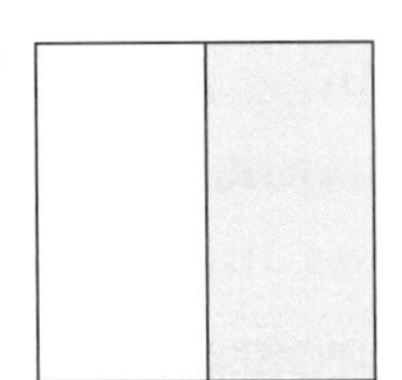

c. 

EXAMPLE Using Equivalent Ratios

When answering questions in gridded format, enter only the numerical portion of your answer in the grid.

		8	5
	/	/	
.	.	.	.
	0	0	0
1	1	1	1
2	2	2	2
3	3	3	3
4	4	4	4
5	5	5	●
6	6	6	6
7	7	7	7
8	8	●	8
9	9	9	9

4 **Gridded Response** You take a quiz that has 20 questions and get only 3 incorrect answers. What is your percent grade on the quiz?

First find the number of correct answers. Then write a ratio.

$\frac{17}{20}$ ← number of correct answers / ← total number of answers

$\frac{17 \cdot 5}{20 \cdot 5}$ ← Since 20 · 5 is 100, multiply numerator and denominator by 5.

$\frac{85}{100}$ ← Simplify.

85% ← Write as a percent.

Your percent grade is 85%. Fill in 85 on your answer grid.

Quick Check

4. A tennis team played a total of 25 games and won 20 of them. What percent of the games did the team win?

Check Your Understanding

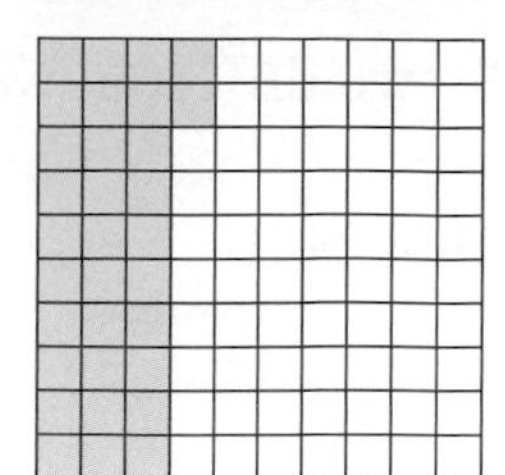

1. Write a ratio and a percent for the shaded area in the diagram.
2. Model 15% on a 10×10 grid.

Write each ratio as a percent.

3. $\frac{67}{100}$ 4. $\frac{4}{5}$ 5. $\frac{9}{10}$

6. **Reasoning** How can you use percents to compare two ratios with different denominators?

Homework Exercises

For more exercises, see Extra Skills and Word Problems.

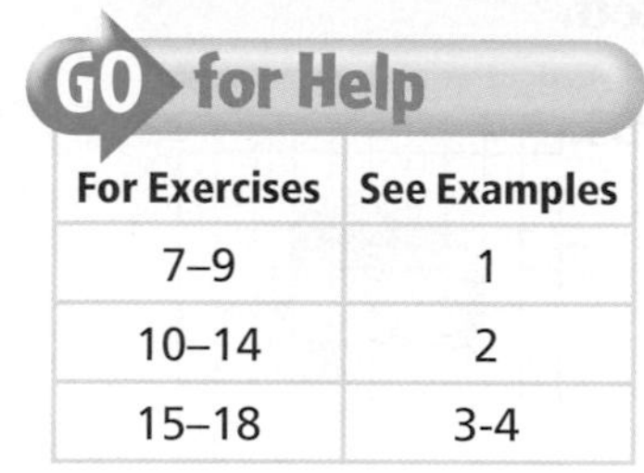

GO for Help

For Exercises	See Examples
7–9	1
10–14	2
15–18	3-4

Write a ratio and a percent for each shaded figure.

7. 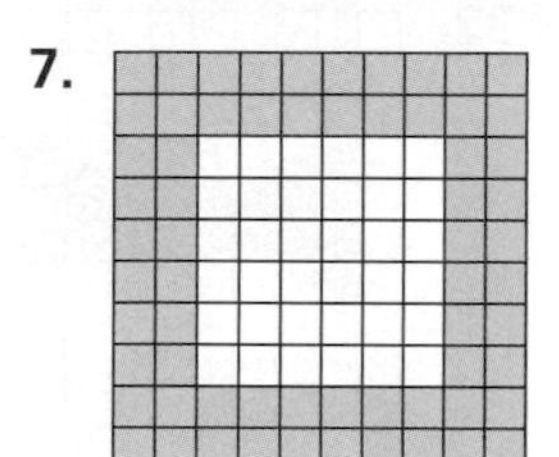
8. 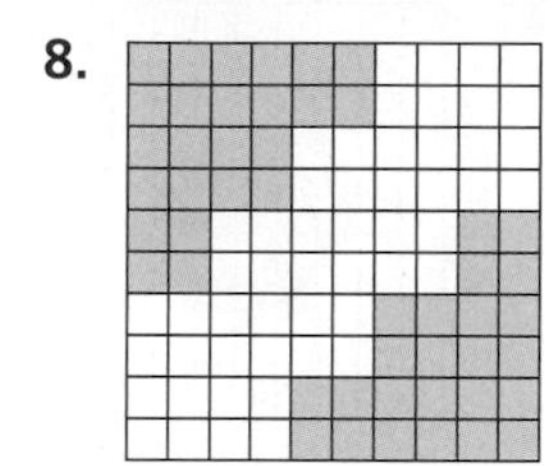
9. 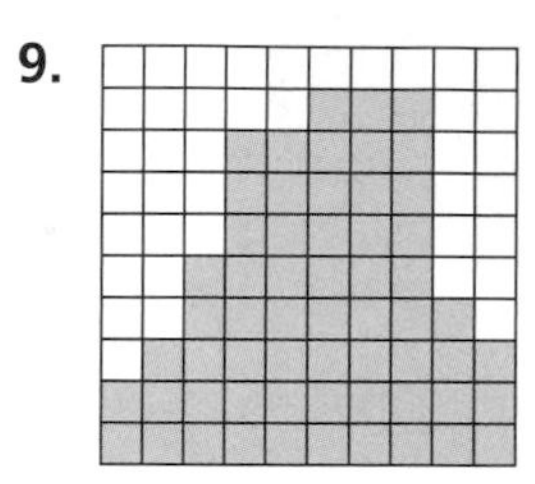

Model each percent on a 10 × 10 grid.

10. 35% 11. 78% 12. 10% 13. 8% 14. 90.5%

Write a ratio and a percent for each shaded area.

15. 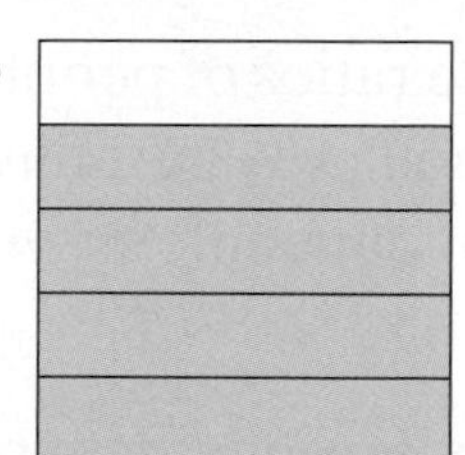
16. 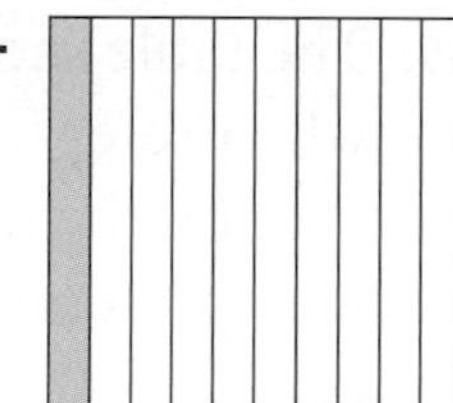
17. 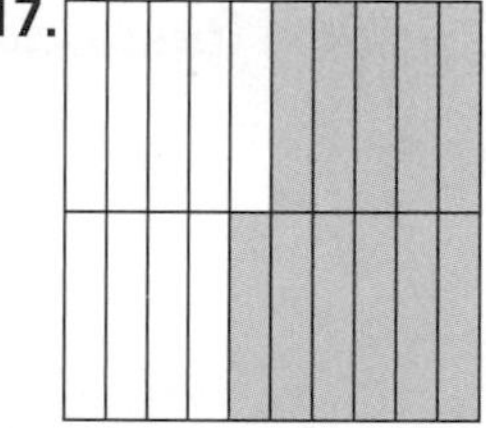

18. **Geography** The area of Argentina is about three tenths the area of the United States. Write this ratio as a percent.

19. **Guided Problem Solving** In a litter of 10 puppies, exactly six puppies are black. What percent of the puppies are not black?
    - How many puppies are not black?
    - How many puppies are in the litter?

20. **Government** An amendment to the U.S. Constitution must be ratified by at least three fourths of the states to become law. Write this ratio as a percent.

Write each ratio as a percent.

21. $\frac{3}{5}$ 22. $\frac{1}{2}$ 23. $\frac{21}{25}$ 24. $\frac{9}{50}$ 25. $\frac{11}{20}$

26. **Writing in Math** Explain how to model 25% two different ways.

Find what percent of a dollar each set of coins makes.

27. 2 quarters and 2 dimes
28. 3 quarters, 1 dime, 3 pennies

29. Your class has 12 boys and 13 girls. What percent of the students in your class are girls?

30. **History** Before the Battle of Tippecanoe, nineteen twentieths of General William Harrison's troops had never before been in a battle. What percent of the troops had previously been in a battle?

Estimate the percent of each figure that is shaded.

31. 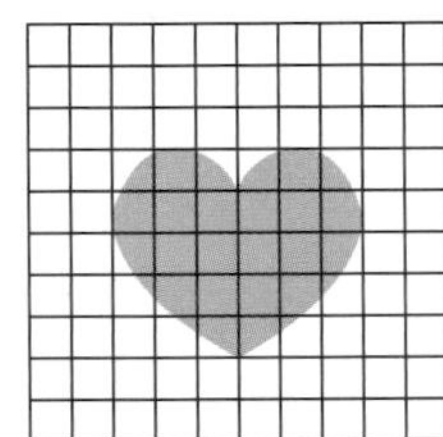

32. 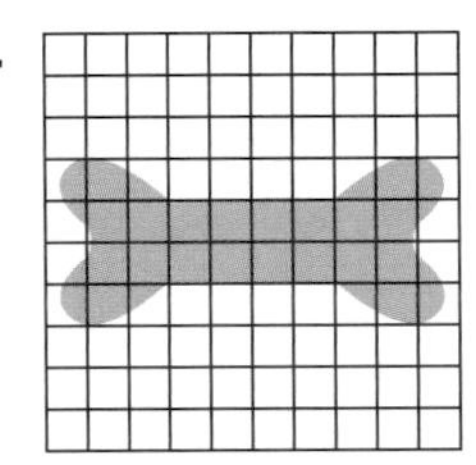

33. 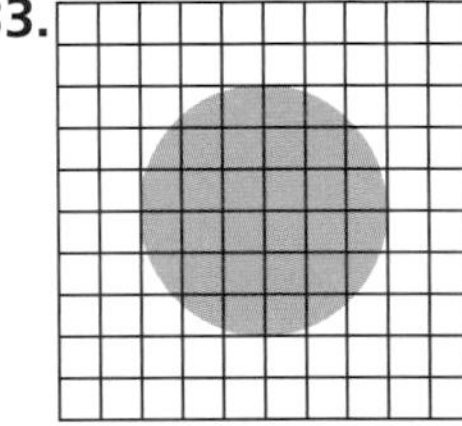

34. **Challenge** You shade four squares in a grid. How many squares are there if the shaded portion represents 20% of the grid?

Test Prep and Mixed Review

Practice

Gridded Response

35. The table shows the ratios of people who prefer four popular yogurt flavors. What is the percent of people surveyed who prefer blueberry?

Most Popular Yogurt Flavors

Personal Favorite	Ratio
Strawberry	$\frac{2}{5}$
Blueberry	$\frac{3}{25}$
Vanilla	$\frac{3}{50}$
Peach	$\frac{3}{100}$

36. Five students in Ms. Power's class ran for charity. The distances they ran were as follows: 5.8 mi, $4\frac{1}{2}$ mi, 2.4 mi, $3\frac{9}{10}$ mi, and 7 mi. What was the distance, in miles, the students ran altogether?

37. Arthur scored 87 on each of his first three tests. He scored 93 and 95 on his next two tests. What was the mean score of all his tests?

GO for Help

For Exercises	See Lesson
38–40	3-2

Simplify each expression.

38. 4^2 39. $(4 + 1)^3$ 40. $(6 - 2)^2 + 4$

5-6a Activity Lab

Hands On

Modeling Percents

You can write a fraction or a decimal as a percent.

In the grid model at the right, each small square represents $\frac{1}{100}$ of the whole. Forty-one of the 100 squares are shaded. This can be written as $\frac{41}{100}$, 0.41, or 41%.

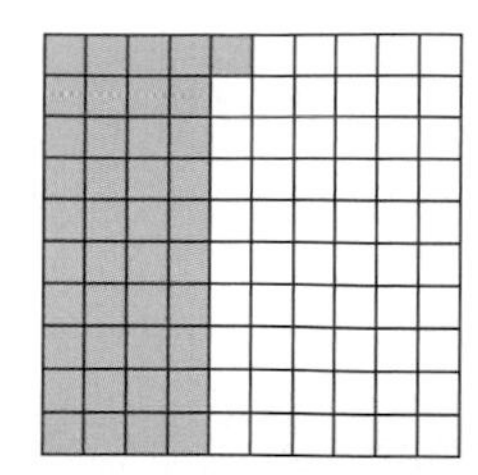

Each column contains 10 squares. Shade 4 columns and 1 additional square.

ACTIVITY

1. On a piece of graph paper, draw a 10-by-10 grid model.
2. Suppose 50% of students in your school like broccoli. Use your grid model to represent 50%. How many squares will be shaded?
3. Write 50% as a fraction and as a decimal.
4. Make four grid models of the values in the table. Copy the table. Use your models to complete the table.

Fraction	$\frac{5}{100}$	■	■	■
Decimal	■	0.75	■	■
Percent	■	■	37%	100%

Exercises

Model each situation with a grid model.

1. A basketball player makes 82% of her free throws.
2. 67% of the seats in an auditorium are filled.
3. **Reasoning** Describe a grid model that represents 150%.
4. a. What percent of the grid at the right is shaded?
   b. What percent of the grid at the right is not shaded?
   c. **Writing in Math** Explain how you found your answer to part (b).

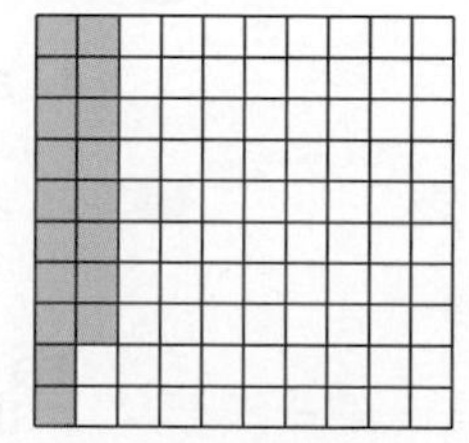

5-6 Percents, Fractions, and Decimals

1. **Vocabulary Review** How do you read the *decimal* 0.24?
2. Write a decimal for the model.

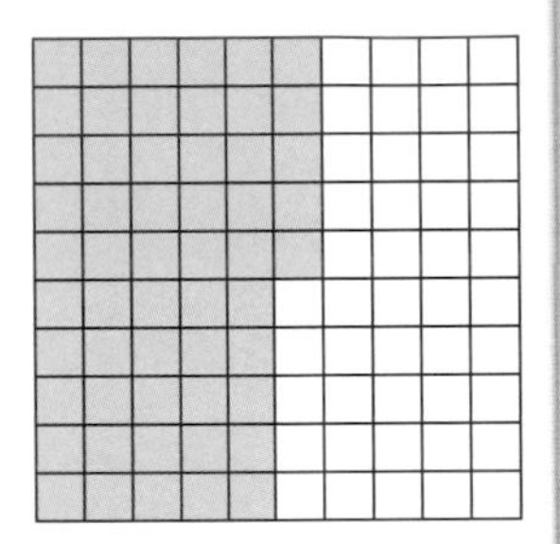

CONTENT STANDARD
Essential for understanding 6.RP.3.c

Test Prep Tip
Test answer choices are often expressed in simplest form.

What You'll Learn

To find equivalent forms of fractions, decimals, and percents

Why Learn This?

Newspapers use percents, fractions, and decimals to report data. To compare the data, you need to be able to convert from one form to another.

Recall that you can write a percent as a fraction with a denominator of 100.

EXAMPLES Representing Percents

1 Write 36% as a fraction. Write your answer in simplest form.

$36\% = \frac{36}{100}$ ← **Write the percent as a fraction with a denominator of 100.**

$= \frac{9}{25}$ ← **Write the fraction in simplest form.**

2 **Gridded Response** You read 36% of a book. Express this amount as a decimal.

$36\% = \frac{36}{100}$ ← **Write the percent as a fraction with denominator 100.**

$= 0.36$ ← **Write the fraction as a decimal.**

Quick Check

1. **a.** Write 55% as a fraction. **b.** Write 4% as a fraction.
2. **a.** Write 25% as a decimal. **b.** Write 2% as a decimal.

To write a decimal as a percent, you write a fraction first.

EXAMPLE Writing a Decimal as a Percent

3 Write 0.07 as a percent.

$0.07 = \frac{7}{100} = 7\%$ ← **Write the decimal as a fraction with a denominator of 100.**

Quick Check

3. Write each decimal as a percent.
   a. 0.52 b. 0.05 c. 0.5

You can use equivalent fractions to convert a fraction to a percent.

EXAMPLE Writing a Fraction as a Percent

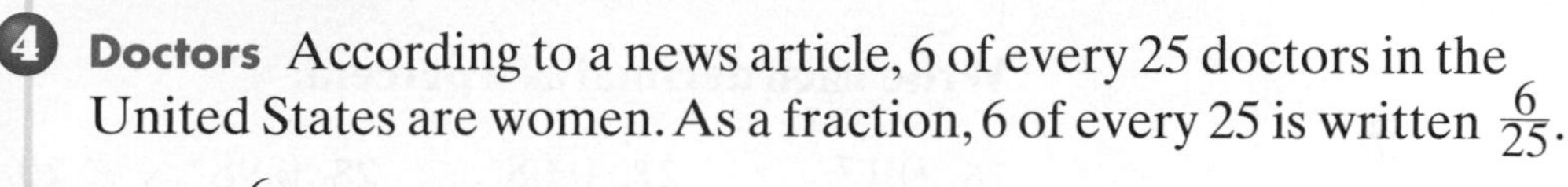

4 **Doctors** According to a news article, 6 of every 25 doctors in the United States are women. As a fraction, 6 of every 25 is written $\frac{6}{25}$. Write $\frac{6}{25}$ as a percent.

Careers Physicians measure heart rate and blood pressure.

$\frac{6}{25} \overset{\times 4}{=} \frac{24}{100}$ ← **Find the fraction with a denominator of 100 equal to $\frac{6}{25}$.**

$\frac{6}{25} = \frac{24}{100}$

$= 24\%$ ← **Write using a percent symbol.**

In the United States, 24% of the doctors are women.

Quick Check

4. The same article said that 1 of every 20 neurosurgeons in the United States is a woman. Write the fraction $\frac{1}{20}$ as a percent.

Check Your Understanding

1. **Vocabulary** Explain why the ratio 4 : 10 is NOT a percent.
2. Which numbers at the left are equivalent to 20%?
3. **Open-Ended** Write a fraction and a decimal greater than 80%.
4. **Mental Math** Write 50% as a fraction in simplest form.

$\frac{1}{5}$ 0.02 $\frac{20}{50}$ 0.20 $\frac{4}{12}$
0.2 $\frac{6}{24}$ 0.4 $\frac{20}{100}$ 0.05

Homework Exercises

For more exercises, see Extra Skills and Word Problems.

GO for Help

For Exercises	See Example
5–14	1
15–25	2
26–30	3
31–36	4

Write each percent as a fraction in simplest form.

5. 70% **6.** 88% **7.** 5% **8.** 33% **9.** 14%

10. 15% **11.** 75% **12.** 18% **13.** 2% **14.** 42%

Write each percent as a decimal.

15. 15% **16.** 22% **17.** 82% **18.** 63% **19.** 10%

20. 40% **21.** 3% **22.** 7% **23.** 12% **24.** 100%

25. Quality Control A shipment of radios is packed incorrectly, and 6% arrive damaged. Write this amount as a decimal.

Write each decimal as a percent.

26. 0.17 **27.** 0.08 **28.** 0.98 **29.** 0.22 **30.** 0.44

Write each fraction as a percent.

31. $\frac{19}{20}$ **32.** $\frac{27}{50}$ **33.** $\frac{1}{4}$ **34.** $\frac{19}{25}$ **35.** $\frac{7}{25}$

36. School Play Three of every five students who tried out for a play made the cast. Write $\frac{3}{5}$ as a percent.

37. Guided Problem Solving About $\frac{7}{10}$ of Earth's surface is covered by water. What percent of Earth's surface is NOT covered by water?

- You can draw a picture to model this problem.

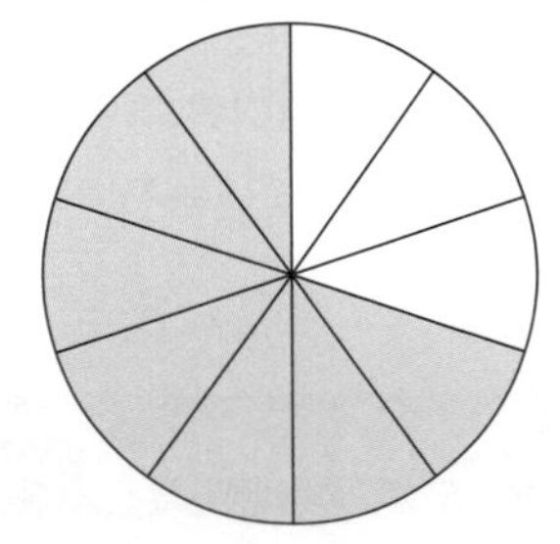

Write the letter of the point on the number line that represents each number.

0 A B C D 1

38. 0.4 **39.** 60% **40.** $\frac{5}{6}$ **41.** 18%

Homework Video Tutor
PearsonSuccessNet.com

The dodo once lived on the island of Mauritius in the Indian Ocean. It has been extinct since the late 1600s. New research suggests the bird was slimmer than shown in this drawing.

Order each set of numbers from least to greatest.

42. $46\%, \frac{1}{2}, 0.53, 5\%$

43. $\frac{1}{4}, 22\%, 0.24, \frac{1}{5}$

44. $63\%, \frac{3}{5}, 0.58, \frac{31}{50}$

45. $\frac{17}{20}, 95\%, 0.9, \frac{22}{25}$

46. Biology At least ninety-nine percent of all the kinds of plants and animals that have ever lived are now extinct. Write ninety-nine percent as a fraction and as a decimal.

47. Copy and complete the table below.

Fraction	$\frac{11}{50}$	$\frac{39}{50}$	$\frac{22}{25}$	■	■	$\frac{4}{5}$
Decimal	■	0.78	■	0.45	■	■
Percent	22%	■	■	■	42%	■

48. You answer 32 questions correctly on a 45-question test. You need a score of at least 70% to pass. Do you pass? Explain.

49. Fuel Gauge Use the fuel gauge below. What percent of the tank is full?

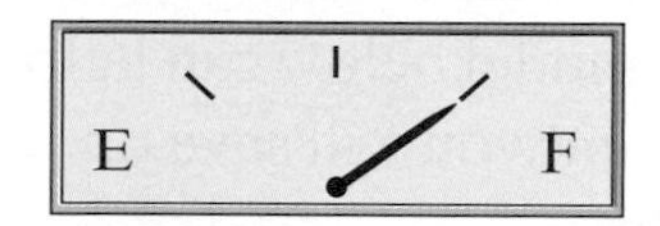

50. Writing in Math Explain how to write a decimal as a percent.

51. Challenge Find the percent of numbers from 1 to 100 that are prime numbers.

Test Prep and Mixed Review

Practice

Gridded Response

52. The formula $i = \frac{127}{50}c$ can be used to convert a measurement from centimeters to inches. Write a decimal equal to $\frac{127}{50}$.

53. Eric finishes a swimming race in 51.4 seconds. Bobby finishes the same race in 48.6 seconds. How much faster is Eric's time than Bobby's time, in seconds?

54. Billie Jean earns $12 for baby-sitting for 3 hours. How much will she earn in 4 hours, in dollars?

GO for Help

For Exercises	See Lesson
55–58	4-3

Find each quotient.

55. $8 \div \frac{2}{3}$

56. $\frac{1}{3} \div \frac{2}{3}$

57. $\frac{2}{5} \div \frac{4}{9}$

58. $\frac{1}{4} \div \frac{3}{8}$

5-7 Finding the Percent of a Number

Check Skills You'll Need

1. Vocabulary Review How do you write a *percent* as a decimal?

Write each percent as a fraction in simplest form.

2. 50% **3.** 35%

4. 48% **5.** 66%

for Help
Lesson 5-6

CONTENT STANDARD
6.RP.3.c

What You'll Learn

To use percents to find part of a whole

Why Learn This?

Advertisements often include percents such as "Save 25%" or "All items 40% off!" You can use percents to find discounts.

A store has all baseball equipment on sale for 40% off. The model below can help you find the amount you will save on a $32 baseball glove.

EXAMPLE Using a Model

1 **Retail Sales** Find 40% of $32.

The bar model shows the total cost of the glove and the percent you will save.

40% = ?

10%	10%	10%	10%	10%	10%	10%	10%	10%	10%

100% = $32

10 parts = $32

1 part = $32 ÷ 10 = $3.20

40% is 4 parts and 4 × $3.20 = $12.80.

You will save $12.80 on the baseball glove.

Quick Check

1. a. You buy a $40 shirt on sale for 20% off. Find 20% of $40.
b. You buy a $120 bicycle on sale for 25% off. Find 25% of $120.

Vocabulary Tip

The words "percent of" tell you to multiply.

You can find a percent of a number by using a decimal.

EXAMPLE Using a Decimal

2 Find 22% of 288.

$$22\% = 0.22 \quad \leftarrow \text{Write 22\% as a decimal.}$$
$$0.22 \times 288 = 63.36 \quad \leftarrow \text{Multiply.}$$

So 22% of 288 is 63.36.

Quick Check

2. a. Find 12% of 91. **b.** Find 18% of 121.

The percents in the table below are found in real-world situations. You can change these to fractions or decimals to use mental math.

Test Prep Tip

Memorizing the values in the table at the right can help you find percents quickly on tests.

Equivalent Expressions for Mental Math

Percent	10%	20%	25%	50%	75%	80%
Fraction	$\frac{1}{10}$	$\frac{1}{5}$	$\frac{1}{4}$	$\frac{1}{2}$	$\frac{3}{4}$	$\frac{4}{5}$
Decimal	0.1	0.2	0.25	0.5	0.75	0.8

EXAMPLE Using Mental Math

3 Suppose 25% of 80 students in a survey vacationed in Florida. Find the number of students who vacationed in Florida.

What you think

$25\% = \frac{1}{4}$; $\frac{1}{4} \times 80 = 20$.

Twenty students vacationed in Florida.

Why it works

$$25\% = \frac{25}{100} = \frac{1}{4} \quad \leftarrow \text{Write 25\% as a fraction in simplest form.}$$
$$\frac{1}{4} \times 80 = \frac{1}{4} \times \frac{80}{1} \quad \leftarrow \text{Multiply } \tfrac{1}{4} \text{ by 80. Rewrite 80 as } \tfrac{80}{1}.$$
$$= \frac{80}{4} \quad \leftarrow \text{Simplify.}$$
$$= 20 \quad \leftarrow \text{Divide.}$$

Quick Check

3. Use mental math to find 75% of 12.

Check Your Understanding

Mental Math **Find each answer.**

1. 50% of 10
2. 25% of 40
3. 3% of 100

Use the table below for Exercises 4–5.

Frequency of Vowels in Written Passages

Letter	A	E	I	O	U
Frequency	8%	13%	6%	8%	3%

4. Find the number of E's expected in a passage of 100 letters.
5. Find the number of I's expected in a passage of 500 letters.

Homework Exercises

For more exercises, see Extra Skills and Word Problems.

GO for Help

For Exercises	See Examples
6–11	1
12–18	2
19–22	3

Find each answer using a model.

6. 40% of 70
7. 60% of 210
8. 20% of 184
9. 70% of 880
10. 15% of 90
11. 65% of 240

Find each answer using a decimal.

12. 7% of 50
13. 18% of 170
14. 44% of 165
15. 43% of 61
16. 55% of 91
17. 30% of 490

18. **Shopping** You go to a sale where all items are 20% off. Your total bill would have cost $80. Find the amount you save.

Find each answer using mental math.

19. 20% of 180
20. 80% of 40
21. 75% of 480

22. **Dance** Suppose 50% of 180 dancers said they prefer modern dance. How many dancers prefer modern dance?

23. **Guided Problem Solving** You earn $240 for your first paycheck. You pay 22% of it in taxes. You decide to put 40% of the remaining money into savings. How much money will you have left to spend?
    - The amount you pay in taxes is ■. The money remaining after taxes is ■.
    - Write an expression to find the amount put into savings.

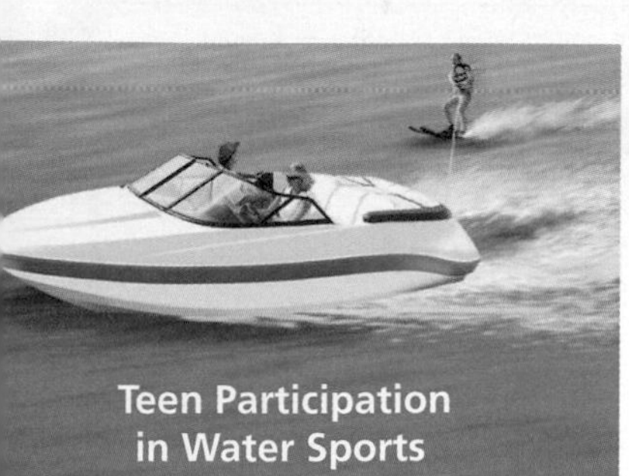

Teen Participation in Water Sports

Water Sport	Boys	Girls
Swimming	62%	76%
Waterskiing	13%	13%
Surfing	7%	3%
Sailboarding	4%	2%

GO Online
Homework Video Tutor
PearsonSuccessNet.com

Recreation The results of a survey of 200 boys and 200 girls are shown at the left.

24. How many boys surf?

25. How many girls surf?

26. How many boys swim?

27. How many girls swim?

28. Travel Of 200 students surveyed, 30% said they have visited SeaWorld in Florida. Of those students, 60% saw Shamu. How many students saw Shamu?

29. Reasoning You want to buy a game that regularly costs \$60. The store has a 40%-off sale. You also have a coupon for 10% off. Is taking 50% off the full price the same as taking 40% off the full price and then 10% off the sale price? Explain.

Money You can find simple interest by multiplying the investment *P*, the yearly rate *r*, and the time *t*. Find the simple interest.

30. $P = \$500,\ r = 1\%,\ t = 2$

31. $P = \$1{,}000,\ r = 3\%,\ t = 4$

32. $P = \$895,\ r = 5\%,\ t = 2$

33. $P = \$4{,}500,\ r = 2\%,\ t = 3$

34. Vision In the United States, about 46% of the population wear glasses or contact lenses. A sample of 85 people is taken.

a. About how many people would you expect to wear glasses or contact lenses?

b. **Writing in Math** How did you find your answer to part (a)?

35. Challenge Store A offers a 60% discount. Store B has a sale for $\frac{2}{3}$ off. Which store gives the greater discount? Explain.

Test Prep and Mixed Review

Practice

Multiple Choice

36. The blood in a human body accounts for about 7% of total body weight. Which number is equal to 7%?

Ⓐ 0.07 Ⓑ 0.7 Ⓒ $\frac{1}{7}$ Ⓓ $\frac{7}{10}$

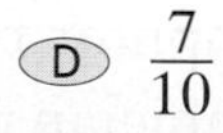

37. How much of the model is shaded?

Ⓕ 54% Ⓗ 50%

Ⓖ 52% Ⓙ 48%

GO for Help

For Exercises	See Lesson
38–41	5-3

Write each ratio in simplest form.

38. $\frac{10}{45}$

39. 36 : 90

40. 18 to 21

41. $\frac{100}{150}$

Checkpoint Quiz 2

Lessons 5-5 through 5-7

Write a ratio and a percent for each shaded area.

1.

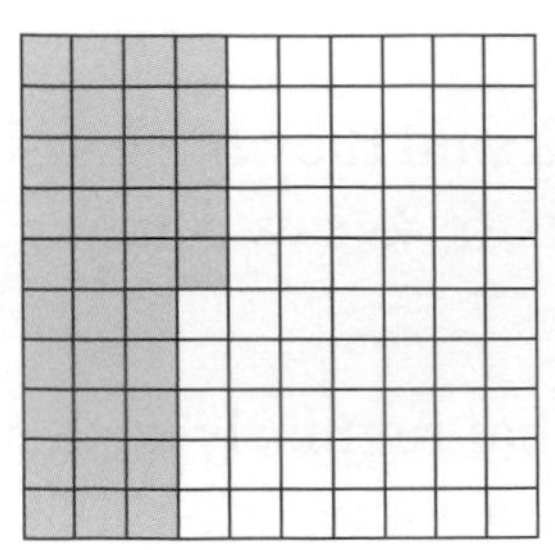

2.

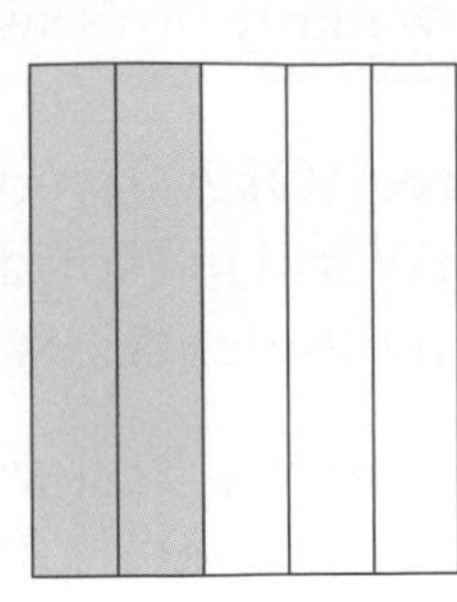

Write each percent as a decimal and as a fraction in simplest form.

3. 74%

4. 6%

5. 60%

Write each fraction as a percent.

6. $\frac{21}{25}$

7. $\frac{7}{10}$

8. $\frac{1}{20}$

9. There were 40 questions on a test. Tina answered 85% of the questions correctly. How many questions did she answer correctly?

10. You buy a pair of shoes that were $42 at 15% off. Find the amount you save.

MATH AT WORK

Help-Desk Technician

Do you enjoy helping your family and friends with their computer-related questions? If so, a career as a help-desk technician might be for you. Help-desk technicians provide support to people who have hardware and software questions.

Help-desk technicians must be able to apply logical reasoning and problem-solving skills in order to assist their customers.

Go Online For information on help-desk technicians PearsonSuccessNet.com

5-8 Finding the Whole

1. Vocabulary Review A ratio that compares a number to 100 can be written as a ____.

Write each percent as a fraction in simplest form.

2. 20% **3.** 5%

4. 25% **5.** 60%

GO for Help Lesson 5-6

6.RP.3.c

What You'll Learn

To solve problems involving finding the whole, given a part and the percent

Why Learn This?

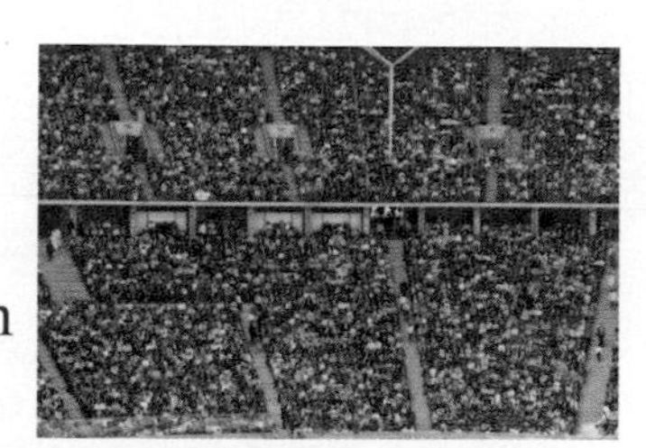

Suppose you know how many people are at a sports stadium and you know the percent of the seats that are filled. You can use this information to find the total number of seats in the stadium.

A percent is a quantity out of 100. Sometimes you know the percent of a number and the part that results, but you do not know the whole quantity.

EXAMPLE Using Equivalent Ratios

1 **Multiple Choice** Tasha paid \$27 for a pair of shoes. This is 45% of the original price. What was the original price of the shoes?

Ⓐ \$12.15 Ⓑ \$18 Ⓒ \$60 Ⓓ \$90

Write a fraction for 45% in simplest form.

$$45\% = \frac{45}{100} = \frac{9}{20}$$

Make a table of equivalent ratios to find the whole.

9×3

Part	45	9	27
Whole	100	20	60

20×3

The original price of the shoes was \$60. The correct answer is C.

Quick Check

1. Michael won 35 chess games. This is 70% of the games he played. How many games did he play? Make a table of equivalent ratios to help you.

Video Tutor Help
PearsonSuccessNet.com

EXAMPLE Using an Equation

2 There are 6,000 people watching a game in a football stadium. If 75% of the seats are filled, how many seats are in the stadium?

Write a fraction in simplest form for 75%. $75\% = \frac{75}{100} = \frac{3}{4}$

Look at the diagram to see how the whole, the part, and the percent are related.

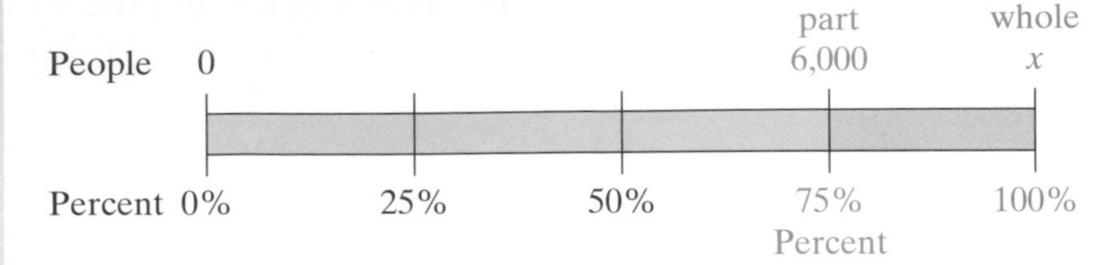

Write an equation. Solve to find the whole, x.

Think: 6,000 is $\frac{3}{4}$ of what number?

$$6{,}000 = \frac{3}{4}x \quad \leftarrow \text{Write the equation.}$$

$$\frac{4}{3} \cdot (6{,}000) = \frac{4}{3} \cdot \left(\frac{3}{4}x\right) \quad \leftarrow \text{Multiply each side by } \frac{4}{3}\text{, the reciprocal of } \frac{3}{4}.$$

$$8{,}000 = 1 \cdot x \quad \leftarrow \text{Multiply.}$$

$$8{,}000 = x$$

There are 8,000 seats in the stadium.

GO for Help

For help using reciprocals to solve equations, go to Lesson 4-5, Example 4.

Quick Check

2. Jordan has walked 6 miles this month. This is 20% of the distance she usually walks in a month. How many miles does she usually walk?

EXAMPLE Using Mental Math

3 Thirty sixth-grade students are on the honor roll. This is 20% of the sixth grade. How many sixth-grade students are there?

What you think

$20\% = \frac{1}{5}$; I need to find a number so that 30 is $\frac{1}{5}$ of that number: $5 \times 30 = 150$. There are 150 students in the sixth grade.

Why it works

$$20\% = \frac{20}{100} = \frac{1}{5}$$

$$n \times \frac{1}{5} = 30$$

$$n = 5 \times 30 = 150$$

Quick Check

3. Six students in a class received a perfect score on a spelling test. If this is 25% of the class, how many are in the class? Use mental math to solve this problem.

Check Your Understanding

Mental Math **Solve each problem.**

1. 9 is 10% of what number?
2. 15 is 50% of what number?
3. Josie has a coupon for 40% off art supplies. With the coupon, she saves $4 on a sketchbook. Copy and complete the diagram below to find the original cost of the sketchbook.

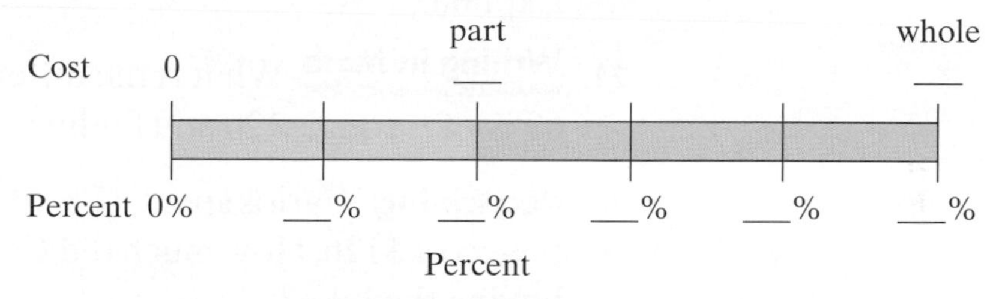

4. Of all the seats in a theater, 20% are empty. If 30 seats are empty, how many seats are in the theater?

Homework Exercises

For more exercises, see Extra Skills and Word Problems.

GO for Help

For Exercises	See Examples
5–12	1-2
13–16	3

Solve each problem.

5. 25 is 10% of what number?
6. 18 is 9% of what number?
7. 75 is 30% of what number?
8. 54 is 30% of what number?
9. 4 is 80% of what number?
10. 21 is 15% of what number?
11. **Camping** Twenty adults went on a camping trip. If 40% of the people on the trip were adults, how many people were on the trip?
12. Suppose you answered 19 questions correctly on a test. If this is 95% of the questions, how many questions were on the test?
13. 36 is 75% of what number?
14. 18 is 25% of what number?
15. 155 is 20% of what number?
16. 90 is 50% of what number?
17. **Shopping** The discounted price of a book is 85% of the original price. This is a savings of $3. A sales tax of 8% will be added to the discounted price. How much sales tax will be added?

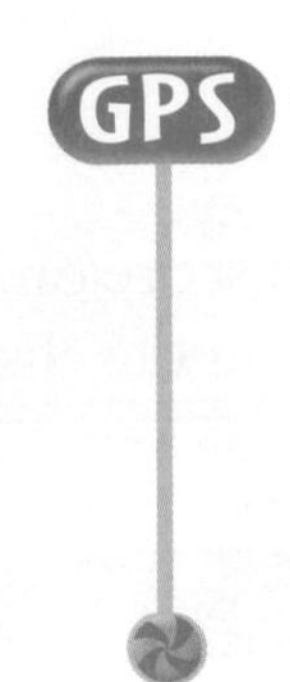

18. Guided Problem Solving The discounted price of a coat is 70% of the original price. This is a savings of $18. What will be the final cost of the coat after the discount is taken and a sales tax of 10% is added?
- What is the percent of discount?
- What is the original price of the coat? What is the discounted price?
- Find the amount of sales tax and the final cost.

19. Mental Math A team won 50% of the games they played, and tied 20% of the games. If the team won 15 games, how many games did they tie?

GO Online
Homework Video Tutor
PearsonSuccessNet.com

20. Error Analysis Nikko knows that 20% of a number is 56. To find the number, she uses the equation $56 = \frac{2}{5}x$. Is Nikko correct? Explain.

21. Writing in Math What is the difference between finding n when 60% of n equals 120 and finding n when 60% of 120 equals n?

22. Reasoning Carlos spent 45% of his savings to buy a bike. The bike cost $126. How much did Carlos have left in his savings after buying the bike?

23. Challenge Mr. Hawkins budgets 12% of his weekly earnings for entertainment. Last week he spent $25 on movies, $12 on a computer game, and $26 at an amusement park. If he stayed within his budget last week, what is the least amount he earns each week?

Test Prep and Mixed Review

Practice

Multiple Choice

24. Cassie has a coupon for 30% off the cost of dinner at a local restaurant. With the coupon, she saves $6 on her dinner. What was the original cost of her dinner?

Ⓐ $1.80 Ⓑ $18 Ⓒ $20 Ⓓ $26

25. A piece of ribbon $\frac{3}{4}$ yard long is cut into 9 equal pieces. How long is each piece in feet?

Ⓕ $\frac{1}{4}$ foot Ⓖ $\frac{1}{8}$ foot Ⓗ 3 feet Ⓙ 12 feet

Convert each measurement.

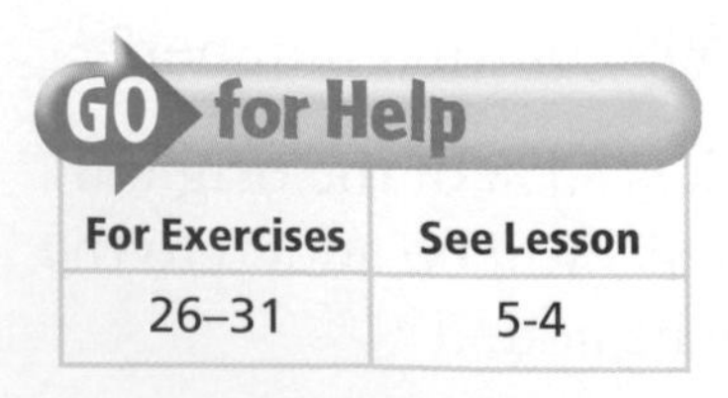

GO for Help

For Exercises	See Lesson
26–31	5-4

26. 72 inches to feet

27. 10 cups to quarts

28. 6 miles to yards

29. 2,650 meters to kilometers

30. 2.6 grams to milligrams

31. 452 centiliters to liters

Practice Solving Problems

Top Jobs A survey identified the four jobs most commonly held by high school sophomores. There were 425 students surveyed. How many students worked as a cashier or a grocery clerk?

Sophomore Job Survey

Job	Percent
Food Service	21
Child Care	13
Cashier or Grocery Clerk	6
Salesperson	4

What You Might Think

What am I trying to find?

How do I solve the problem?

What is the answer? Is it reasonable?

What You Might Write

I want to know what 6% of 425 students equals.

I can use a decimal to find 6% of 425.

6% of 425 = 6% × 425 ← Write as a multiplication expression.

= 0.06 × 425 ← Write 6% as a decimal.

= 25.5 ← Multiply.

About 26 sophomores worked as a cashier or a grocery clerk.

10% of 425 is about 42, so 5% is about 21, which is close to 25.5.

Think It Through

1. What fraction could you have used in the multiplication expression instead of the decimal 0.06?
2. **Reasoning** Why is the answer 26, not 25.5?
3. **Check for Reasonableness** Explain how the estimate was found.

Exercises

4. Use the survey data on the previous page to find how many more students were food service workers than cashiers or grocery clerks. (*Hint*: Find how many students worked in food service.)

5. Thirty-seven percent of the students in the survey on the previous page worked 10 hours or less each week. How many of the students worked more than 10 hours each week? Use the model below.

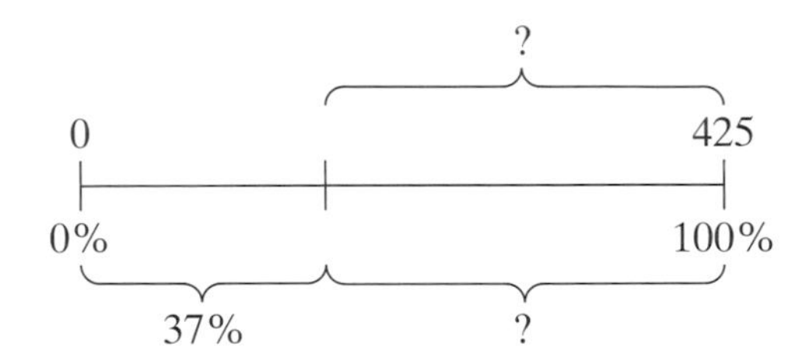

6. Camille drinks 2 quarts of orange juice every 5 days. How many days will it take her to drink 2 gallons of orange juice?

7. Three pounds of apples cost $3.84. Three pounds of peaches cost $5.67. How much will it cost in all to buy 5 pounds of apples and 5 pounds of peaches?

8. You answered $\frac{4}{5}$ of the science test questions correctly. What percent of the questions did you *not* answer correctly?

9. The ratio of quarters to pennies in a bank is $\frac{3}{8}$. The total number of quarters and pennies is 55. How many quarters are there?

10. Jason spent 60% of his allowance on lunch. The cost of lunch was $6. How much did Jason have left of his allowance after buying lunch?

Working Backward

The problem-solving strategy *Work Backward* is useful when taking multiple-choice tests. Work backward by testing each choice in the original problem. You will eliminate incorrect answers. Eventually you will find the correct answer.

EXAMPLE

A fruit stand is selling 8 bananas for $1.25. At this rate, how much will 24 bananas cost?

Ⓐ $1.50 Ⓑ $2.50 Ⓒ $3.75 Ⓓ $5.00

Use mental math to test the choices that are easy to use.

$2.50 is twice $1.25. Twice 8 is only 16, so choice B is not the answer.

$5.00 is four times $1.25. Three times 8 is 24, so choice D is not the correct answer.

Since 24 is between 16 and 32, the cost must be between $2.50 and $5.00. The correct answer is choice C.

Exercises

1. Omar made an overseas phone call. The rate was $2.40 for the first minute and $.55 for each additional minute. His bill was $6.80. How can Omar find the total amount charged for additional minutes?
   Ⓐ Subtract 2.40 from 6.80.
   Ⓑ Add 0.55 and 6.80.
   Ⓒ Subtract 0.55 from 6.80.
   Ⓓ Add 2.40 and 6.80.

2. At a copy center, 100 copies cost $4.00. At this rate, how much will 450 copies cost?
   Ⓕ $16.00 Ⓖ $18.00 Ⓗ $20.00 Ⓙ $22.00

3. The ratio of tennis balls to golf balls in a bucket is 7 to 1. There are 48 balls. How many are golf balls?
   Ⓐ 49 Ⓒ 40
   Ⓑ 42 Ⓓ 6

Chapter 5 Review

Vocabulary Review

double number line diagram (p. 161)
equivalent ratio (p. 170)
percent (p. 179)
rate (p. 166)
ratio (p. 160)
tape diagram (p. 161)
unit cost (p. 167)
unit rate (p. 166)

Choose the correct vocabulary term to complete each sentence.

1. Finding the __?__ can help you compare prices.
2. A __?__ can help you visualize numbers in a ratio.
3. An example of a __?__ is 25 miles per hour.
4. You can use a __?__ to compare a number to 100.

A. tape diagram
B. unit rate
C. percent
D. unit cost

Go Online
For vocabulary quiz
PearsonSuccessNet.com

Skills and Concepts

Lesson 5-1

- To write ratios to compare real-world quantities

A **ratio** compares two numbers by division. A **tape diagram** and a **double number line diagram** are two ways to show ratios.

A jar contains 8 tacks, 15 bolts, and 23 nails. Write each ratio in three ways.

5. bolts to nails
6. bolts to tacks
7. nails to tacks
8. bolts to total

9. **Fruit** Describe the ratio shown in the tape diagram.

Lemons	▭	▭	▭	▭	▭
Oranges	▭	▭	▭		

Lessons 5-2 and 5-3

- To find and use unit rates and unit costs
- To use equivalent ratios and rates to solve real-world and mathematical problems

A **rate** is a ratio that compares quantities in different units. To find a **unit rate**, divide the numerator by the denominator. A **unit cost** gives the cost per unit. Two ratios that name the same number are **equivalent ratios.**

10. You run 1 mile in 8 minutes. How long do you take to run 5 miles?
11. You earn $400 in 32 hours. How much do you earn in 1 hour?
12. **Compare** One loaf of bread costs $3.09 for 32 ounces, and another costs $1.40 for 24 ounces. Which is the better buy?

Copy and complete the equivalent ratio tables.

13.

2	4	■	8
3	■	9	■

14.

5	10	20	25
6	■	■	■

Lesson 5-4

- To use ratio reasoning to convert from one unit of measure to another and to manipulate and transform units appropriately **when** multiplying or dividing quantities

Use a ratio of equivalent measurements when converting units.

Convert each measurement.

15. 4 pints to cups **16.** 230 centimeters to meters **17.** 3.4 miles to feet

18. Ships The S.S. United States, a passenger ship, is 990 feet long. How many yards long is the ship?

Lessons 5-5 and 5-6

- To model percents and to write percents using equivalent ratios
- To find equivalent forms of fractions, decimals, and percents

A **percent** is a ratio that compares a number to 100.

Write a ratio and a percent to represent each shaded area.

19.

20. 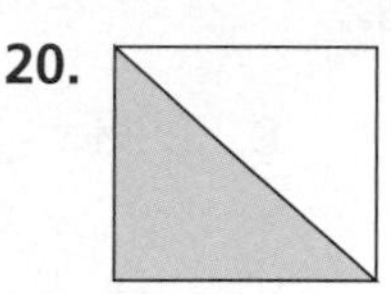

21. 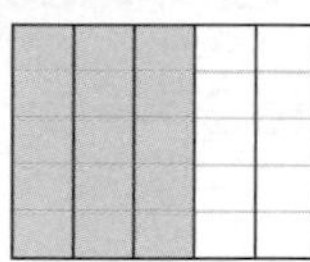

Write each ratio as a percent.

22. $\frac{4}{5}$ **23.** $\frac{3}{4}$ **24.** $\frac{18}{20}$ **25.** $\frac{3}{10}$

Write each percent as a fraction in simplest form and as a decimal.

26. 40% **27.** 25% **28.** 56% **29.** 12%

Write each decimal or fraction as a percent.

30. 0.19 **31.** $\frac{4}{25}$ **32.** 0.04 **33.** $\frac{7}{10}$

Lessons 5-7 and 5-8

- To use percents to find part of a whole
- To solve problems involving finding the whole, given a part and the percent

To find a percent of a number, change the percent to a decimal and then multiply. Sometimes you can use **mental math** to find a percent. When you know the percent of a number and the part that results, you can find the whole by using an equation, equivalent ratios, or mental math.

Find each answer.

34. 20% of 48 **35.** 6% of \$20 **36.** 15% of 144 **37.** 25% of 8

Solve each problem.

38. 16 is 25% of what number? **39.** 39 is 60% of what number?

40. 700 is 35% of what number? **41.** 225 is 50% of what number?

42. Discount Faye paid \$16.00 for a pair of shorts that were 20% off. What was the original price of the shorts?

Chapter 5 Test

Go Online For online chapter test PearsonSuccessNet.com

You have 3 nickels, 11 dimes, and 5 quarters in your pocket. Write each ratio in three ways.

1. nickels to quarters **2.** dimes to nickels

3. dimes to all coins **4.** quarters to dimes

5. Use the figure below. Find the ratio of the shaded region to the whole region.

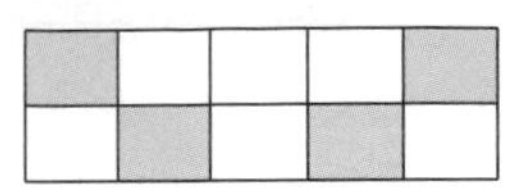

Write each ratio two other ways.

6. 3 to 2 **7.** $\frac{3}{18}$ **8.** 6 : 8

9. A car can travel 28 miles per gallon of gas. How far can the car travel on 8 gallons of gas?

10. A 6-ounce bottle of juice costs \$.96. An 8-ounce bottle costs \$1.12. Which is the better buy?

11. Describe the ratio shown by the tape diagram below.

Ducks

Geese

12. A grocery store sells 6 pounds of apples for \$12. What is the unit price of the apples?

13. **Writing in Math** The ratio of girls to boys in a science class is 5 to 6. Can there be 15 boys in the class? Explain why or why not.

Write each percent as a decimal and as a fraction in simplest form.

14. 25% **15.** 6% **16.** 98%

Write each decimal or fraction as a percent.

17. 0.48 **18.** 0.02 **19.** $\frac{1}{10}$

20. $\frac{3}{25}$ **21.** $\frac{9}{50}$ **22.** 0.7

Find each percent.

23. 5% of 200 **24.** 80% of 8 **25.** 2% of 50

26. **Data Analysis** Suppose 86% of 50 people at a law firm like their job. How many people like their job?

27. Describe the ratio shown by the double number line below.

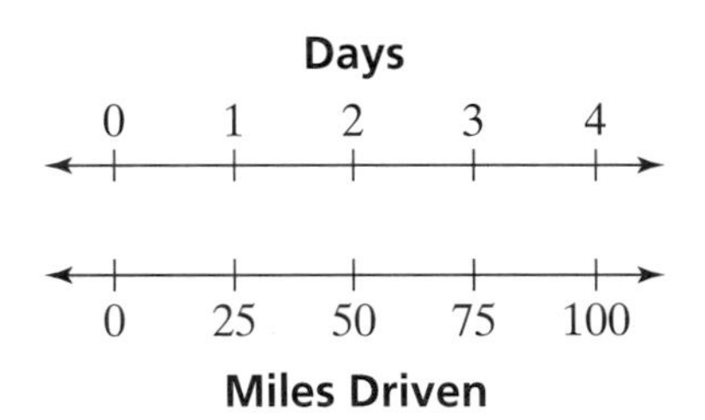

Find a 15% tip for each bill amount rounded to the nearest cent.

28. \$32.00 **29.** \$48.76 **30.** \$12.83

31. Suppose you buy a DVD for \$12.98. The sales tax is 7%. What is the total cost?

32. Colleen can make 3 bracelets in 1 hour. How many bracelets can she make in 5 hours?

33. A tiled area in a kitchen was made with a ratio of 7 black tiles for every 3 white tiles. If 80 tiles were used, how many tiles were black?

34. Hal read 114 pages of his book during vacation. This was 60% of the book. How many pages does Hal have left to read?

Multiple Choice

Choose the correct letter.

1. Find the product of $\frac{2}{9}$ and $\frac{5}{7}$.
   (A) $\frac{10}{63}$ (C) $\frac{14}{45}$
   (B) $\frac{5}{31}$ (D) $3\frac{3}{14}$

2. Which could you use to describe how to find $1\frac{3}{4}$ divided by $\frac{1}{2}$?
   (F) Multiply $\frac{1}{2}$ and $\frac{7}{4}$.
   (G) Multiply $\frac{1}{2}$ and $\frac{4}{7}$.
   (H) Multiply $\frac{4}{7}$ and 2.
   (J) Multiply $\frac{7}{4}$ and 2.

3. You bought a 12-bag variety pack of dried fruit. Each bag of dried fruit contains 6 ounces. How many ounces of dried fruit did you buy?
   (A) 2 (C) 18
   (B) 4 (D) 72

4. Which number is NOT equivalent to 40%?
   (F) $\frac{40}{100}$ (G) 0.04 (H) 0.40 (J) $\frac{2}{5}$

5. Which of the following numbers is divisible by 2, 3, 5, 9 and 10?
   (A) 1,350 (C) 945
   (B) 1,010 (D) 120

6. Myra's dog weighs 65 pounds. What is her dog's weight in ounces?
   (F) 4 (H) 1,040
   (G) 81 (J) 1,056

7. What is the GCF of 250 and 325?
   (A) 10 (B) 25 (C) 75 (D) 125

8. At a car dealer, $\frac{2}{5}$ of the vehicles sold during the year were minivans. What percent of the vehicles sold were minivans?
   (F) 2.5% (H) 25%
   (G) 20% (J) 40%

9. Which decimal represents the portion of the model that is NOT shaded?

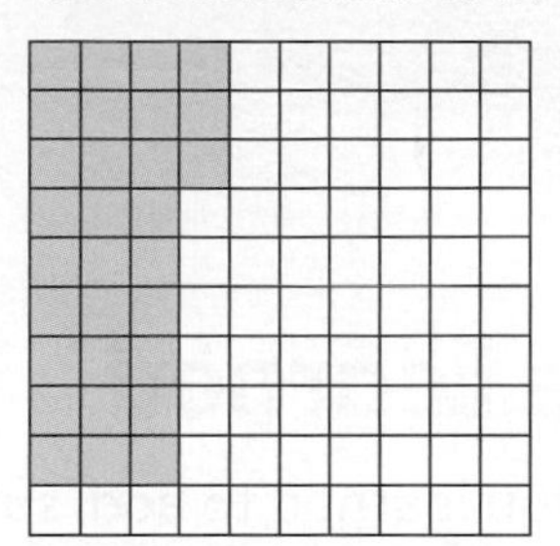

   (A) 0.3 (B) 0.33 (C) 0.67 (D) 0.7

Gridded Response

10. A bank teller spends about 8 minutes helping each customer. How long does the teller spend with 7 customers?

11. What is the LCM of 3 and 16?

12. Summer vacation is 68 days long and $\frac{3}{4}$ of the vacation has gone by. How many days are left?

Short Response

13. A 12-ounce box of crackers costs $2.69 and a 16-ounce box costs $3.79. Which box is the better buy? Explain your answer.

Extended Response

14. Your dinner bill comes to $19.68. What is the total cost for dinner after 5% tax and a 20% tip are added onto the original bill? Explain your reasoning.

15. Walt scored 80% on a math test. He answered 40 problems correctly. How many problems did he miss? Explain how you found your answer.

CHAPTER 6 Integers and Rational Numbers

What You've Learned

- In earlier chapters, you learned to add, subtract, multiply, and divide decimals and fractions.
- You wrote and solved equations.
- You graphed positive numbers on a number line.

GO for Help

For Exercises	See Lessons
1–2	2-4
3–4	2-5
5–10	2-6
11–16	3-5

Algebra Solving Equations

Solve each equation.

1. $a + 13 = 92$

2. $b + 12 = 43$

3. $c - 31 = 8$

4. $d - 23 = 8$

Algebra Solving Multiplication and Division Equations

Solve each equation.

5. $7g = 4.2$

6. $h \div 6 = 11$

7. $8j = 328$

8. $k \div 9 = 8$

9. $16m = 240$

10. $n \div 14 = 18$

Find the Least Common Multiple

Find the least common multiple of each set of numbers.

11. 4, 6

12. 9, 21

13. 8, 16

14. 8, 12

15. 5, 20

16. 8, 10

What You'll Learn Next

- In this chapter, you will use integers, rational numbers, opposites, and absolute values to represent real-world situations.
- You will locate and graph points.
- You will use a number line to compare and order integers, decimals, and fractions.
- You will solve inequalities.

Key Vocabulary

- absolute value (p. 207)
- graph of an inequality (p. 224)
- inequality (p. 223)
- integers (p. 206)
- opposites (p. 206)
- rational number (p. 213)
- solution of an inequality (p. 224)

6-1 Exploring Integers

Check Skills You'll Need

1. **Vocabulary Review** Compare the *identity properties* of addition and multiplication.

Find each missing number.

2. $8 + 9 = \blacksquare + 8$
3. $(10 + 1) + 6 = \blacksquare + (1 + 6)$
4. $140 + \blacksquare = 140$

for Help
Lesson 1-1

CONTENT STANDARDS

6.NS.5, 6.NS.6, 6.NS.6.a, 6.NS.6.c, 6.NS.7.c

What You'll Learn

To use integers, opposites, and absolute values to represent real-world situations

New Vocabulary opposites, integers, absolute value

Why Learn This?

You can use integers to represent real-world situations. In the tug-of-war below, the team on the right has gained 2 feet. The position of the flag is positive 2, or +2. You write +2 as 2.

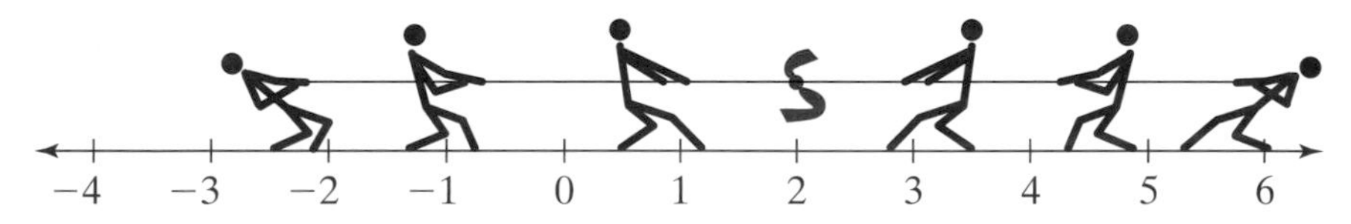

Suppose the team on the right had lost 2 feet instead. The position of the flag would have been negative 2, or −2.

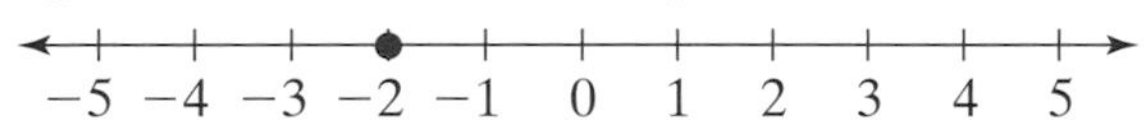

Opposites are two numbers that are the same distance from 0 on a number line but in opposite directions. **Integers** are the set of positive whole numbers, their opposites, and zero. The opposite of 0 is 0.

EXAMPLE Representing Situations with Integers

1 **Multiple Choice** Dry ice is solid carbon dioxide, which freezes at about 109 degrees below zero Fahrenheit. Which integer represents the freezing point of dry ice?

Ⓐ −109 Ⓑ −19 Ⓒ +19 Ⓓ +109

The freezing point is 109 degrees below zero. Use a negative sign for an integer less than zero: −109. The answer is choice A.

The "smoke" that makes a performance exciting is actually from dry ice.

Quick Check

1. The lowest elevation in New Orleans, Louisiana, is 8 feet below sea level. Use an integer to represent this elevation. What does zero represent?

The opposite of a positive number is negative. The opposite of a negative number is positive.

EXAMPLE Identifying Opposites

Calculator Tip

You can use the (–) key or the +/- key on your calculator to express an opposite.

2 Write the opposite of 3.

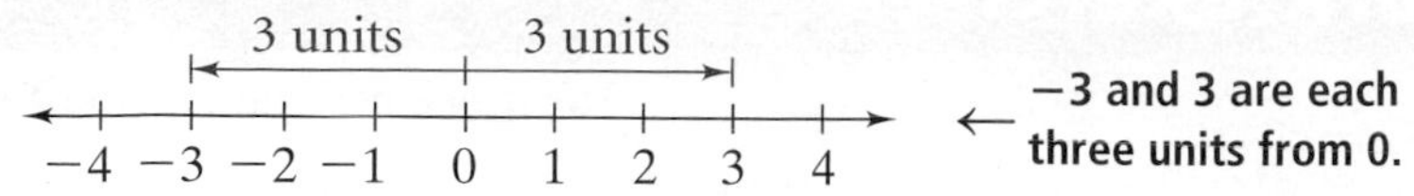

The opposite of 3 is −3.

Quick Check

2. Write the opposite of −5.

The opposite of the opposite of any positive or negative number is the number itself.

The **absolute value** of a number is its distance from 0 on a number line. The symbol for the absolute value of a number n is $|n|$. Opposite numbers have the same absolute value.

EXAMPLE Finding Absolute Value

Test Prep Tip

Drawing a number line can help you answer questions involving integers.

3 A student withdraws \$4 from a savings account. This can be represented by −4. Find $|-4|$ and explain its meaning.

4 units

−4 −3 −2 −1 0 1 2 3 4

Since −4 is 4 units from 0, $|-4| = 4$. $|-4|$ represents the amount of the withdrawal.

Quick Check

3. A bird dives down 12 feet.

a. Write an integer for this situation.

b. Explain the meaning of the absolute value of the integer.

Check Your Understanding

1. Vocabulary Give examples of numbers that are integers and numbers that are *not* integers.

2. Open-Ended Describe two different real-life situations that can be represented by the integer −9.

Match each integer with a point on the number line.

M N P Q

−6 −5 −4 −3 −2 −1 0 1 2 3 4 5 6

3. −6   4. 5   5. 1   6. −4

Homework Exercises

For more exercises, see Extra Skills and Word Problems.

GO for Help

For Exercises	See Examples
7–12	1
13–18	2
19–24	3

Use an integer to represent each situation.

7. earned $100
8. 800 ft gain in elevation
9. 12° below 0°C
10. 4° above 0°F
11. a debt of $25
12. lost 5 pounds

Write the opposite of each integer.

13. −10   14. −21   15. 14   16. 0

17. Write the opposite of the opposite of 8.

18. Write the opposite of the opposite of –4.

Find each absolute value.

19. $|38|$ 20. $|2|$ 21. $|-9|$ 22. $|-97|$

Use this fact for Exercises 23 and 24: the temperature on a winter day is 8 degrees below zero.

23. Write an integer for this situation.

24. Explain the meaning of the absolute value of the integer.

25. **Guided Problem Solving** The reading on a thermometer outside is −7°F at 8:00 A.M. At 3:00 P.M., the reading is 2°F. What integer can you use to represent the change in temperature?
    - You can use a number line to help visualize the problem.

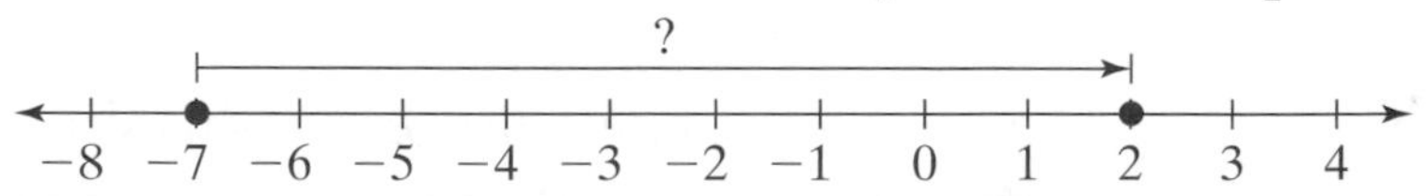

26. Starting at the fourth floor, an elevator goes down 3 floors and then up 8 floors. At which floor does the elevator stop?

27. **Divers** Dean dives 17 feet below the surface of Canyon Lake. Janet dives 25 feet below the lake's surface. Use absolute values to find who dives farther below the surface.

28. **Writing in Math** Can the absolute value of a number be negative? Explain your reasoning.

Write an integer for each point on the number line.

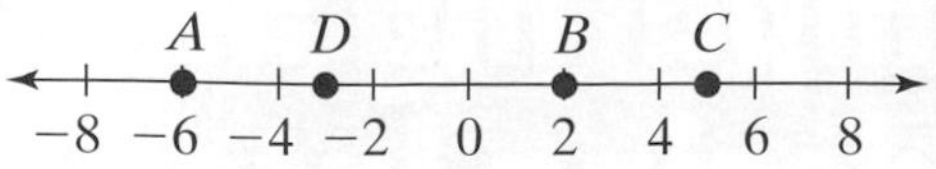

(Number line from −8 to 8 with points A, D, B, C)

29. *A* **30.** *B* **31.** *C* **32.** *D*

Write two numbers that have the given absolute value.

33. 3 **34.** 22 **35.** 101 **36.** 2,004

37. **Algebra** The absolute value of a certain integer n equals the opposite of n. If n does not equal 0, is n positive or negative?

Microchips used in computers are made of silicon, a chemical element found in ordinary beach sand.

38. **History** A timeline is a number line that shows dates.

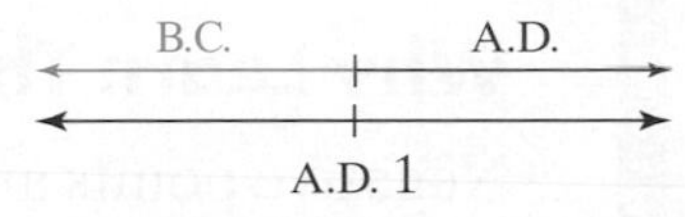

Draw a timeline from 2000 B.C. to A.D. 2000 using intervals of 500 years. Then graph the following events on the timeline.

A.D. 1971 The first microcomputer is introduced.
776 B.C. The first Olympic Games are held.
1600 B.C. Stonehenge is completed.
A.D. 1492 Columbus lands in the New World.
1190 B.C. The city of Troy falls to Greek warriors.

39. **Challenge** What is the opposite of the opposite of $|-7|$? Explain.

Test Prep and Mixed Review

Practice

Multiple Choice

40. Tara was 50 feet below the surface of the ocean. She then swam up 20 feet. Which integer represents her starting depth?

Ⓐ −50 Ⓑ −20 Ⓒ 20 Ⓓ 50

41. 35% of the students in the sixth grade participate in theater or band. What fraction of the students do NOT participate in theater or band?

Ⓕ $\frac{7}{20}$ Ⓖ $\frac{13}{20}$ Ⓗ $\frac{7}{10}$ Ⓙ $\frac{13}{10}$

42. **Crafts** You need $2\frac{1}{3}$ yards of ribbon to decorate one hat. How many yards of ribbon do you need to decorate 6 hats?

43. **Cooking** A potato soup recipe calls for $3\frac{1}{2}$ cups of cream. If you make $2\frac{1}{2}$ times the recipe, how many cups of cream will you need?

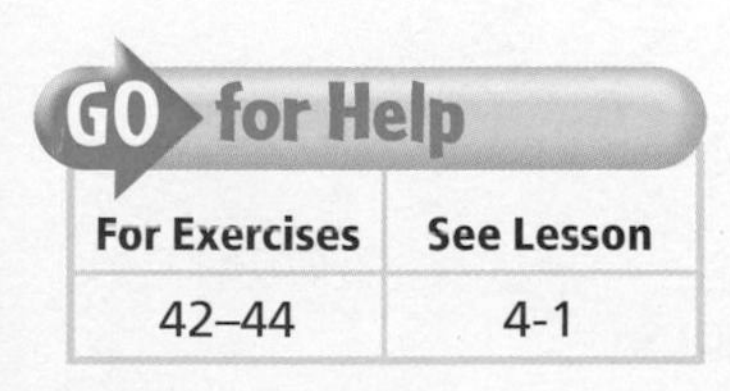

GO for Help

For Exercises	See Lesson
42–44	4-1

44. Matt is $2\frac{1}{3}$ times taller than his sister. His sister is $1\frac{1}{2}$ feet tall. How tall is Matt?

6-2 Comparing and Ordering Integers

Check Skills You'll Need

1. Vocabulary Review Where does it mean for two numbers to be opposites?

Match each integer with a point on the number line.

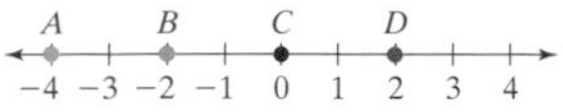

2. 0 **3.** 2

4. −2 **5.** −4

GO for Help Lesson 6-1

CONTENT STANDARD
6.NS.7.a

What You'll Learn

To compare and order integers

Why Learn This?

Negative points and scores are possible in some games. You need to compare and order integers to find who is winning.

You can use a number line to compare integers. As you move to the right on a number line, the numbers become greater.

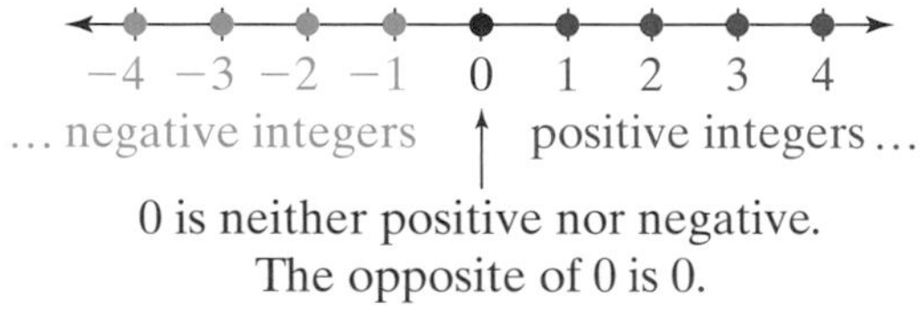

0 is neither positive nor negative.

EXAMPLE Comparing Integers

1 Compare −6 and −4.

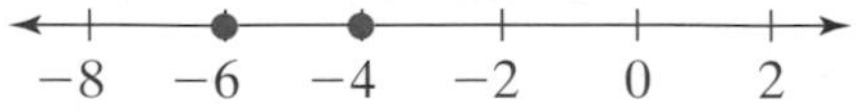

← **Graph −4 and −6 on the same number line.**

Since −6 is to the left of −4 on the number line, $-6 < -4$, or $-4 > -6$.

Quick Check

1. Compare, using < or >.

a. 5 ■ −3 **b.** −12 ■ 9

You can also use a number line to order integers.

EXAMPLE Ordering Integers

2 **Games** Order the scores on the scoreboard from least to greatest.

Tigers	−200
Bulldogs	+300
Lions	−400
Spartans	+100

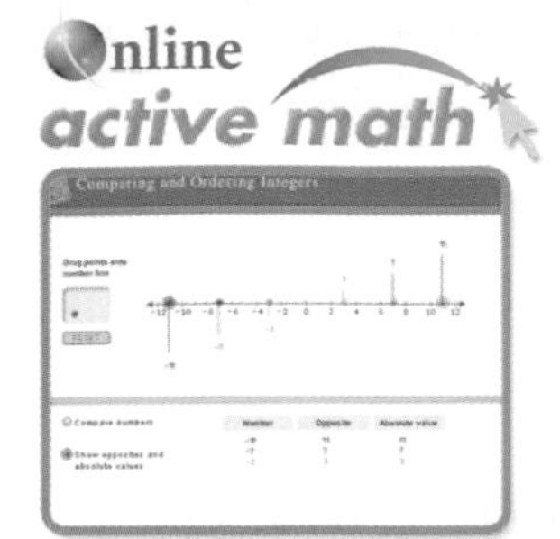

Online active math

For: Comparing Integers Activity
Use: Interactive Textbook, 6-2

Use one hundred as the number line interval.

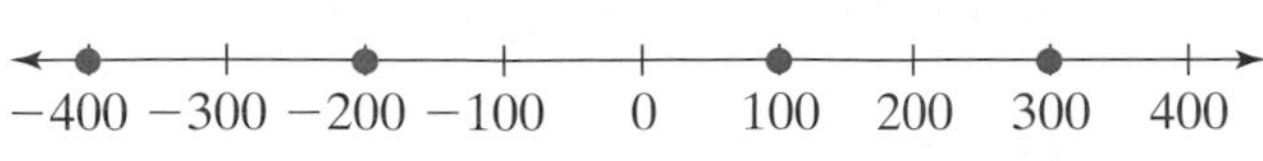

−400, −200, 100, 300 ← **Order the scores from least to greatest.**

In order, the scores are −400, −200, 100, and 300.

Quick Check

2. Order these scores from least to greatest: −25, 100, −50, 75.

Check Your Understanding

1. Which statement is NOT true?
   (A) $-9 < -7$ (B) $-3 < 5$ (C) $-5 > -3$ (D) $-2 < 6$
2. Order −2, 4, 0, and −6 from least to greatest.
3. **Writing in Math** Suppose a is negative and b is positive. Use a number line to explain how you know that $a < b$.

Homework Exercises

For more exercises, see Extra Skills and Word Problems.

GO for Help

For Exercises	See Examples
4–15	1
16–20	2

Compare, using < or >.

4. −7 ■ −8
5. −3 ■ 3
6. 0 ■ −9
7. −7 ■ 0
8. −5 ■ 0
9. 6 ■ −18
10. −12 ■ −2
11. 0 ■ −3
12. 2 ■ −12
13. −9 ■ −17
14. −1 ■ 10
15. −23 ■ −4

Order each set of integers from least to greatest.

16. −9, −12, −4, −15
17. −2, 5, 0, −5, 2
18. 40, −30, 30, −50, −60
19. −28, −16, −33, −13
20. **Golf** In golf, a negative score is called "under par." List the golf scores −1, +2, −3, and +4 from least to greatest.

21. **Guided Problem Solving** Here are the coldest and hottest temperatures on record for four Alaskan cities:
−34°F, 85°F, −62°F, 96°F, −22°F, 90°F, −54°F, 86°F.
Write the temperatures in order from coldest to hottest.
- Separate the list into negative and positive integers.
- Order each group of integers separately.

PearsonSuccessNet.com

22. **Number Sense** What is the greatest negative integer?

23. How many integers are *greater than* −5 and *less than* 5?

24. **Weather** Order the temperatures below from least to greatest.
- Normal body temperature is about 37°C.
- An average winter day on the polar ice cap is −25°C.
- The warmest day on record in Canada was 45°C.
- The coldest day on record in Texas was −31°C.

25. **Algebra** Compare, using $<$ or $>$.
If $x > y$, then the opposite of x ■ the opposite of y.
If $x < y$, then the opposite of x ■ the opposite of y.

26. **Challenge** Write the numbers in order from least to greatest:
$-2, -1.3, \frac{1}{4}, 0, -4, -\frac{1}{2}, -2\frac{3}{4}, 3, -3.5, 2\frac{1}{2}$.

Practice

Multiple Choice

27. The temperature on the moon varies from −387°F to 253°F. Which integer represents the highest moon temperature?
Ⓐ −387 Ⓑ −253 Ⓒ 253 Ⓓ 387

28. Two students measured the length of the shelves in a school library. The results are shown in the table. Which expression can be used to find the length, in yards, of shelf E?
Ⓕ $3n$ Ⓗ $n - 3$
Ⓖ $\frac{3}{n}$ Ⓙ $\frac{n}{3}$

Library Shelves

Shelf	Length (feet)	Length (yards)
A	3	1
B	6	2
C	12	4
D	15	5
E	n	■

Find the percent of the number.

29. 30% of 120
30. 40% of 228
31. 75% of 16

32. You earned $45 mowing the lawn. You spent 25% of your money on a book and you saved the rest. How much money did you save?

GO for Help

For Exercises	See Lesson
29–32	5-7

6-3 Rational Numbers

1. **Vocabulary Review** What are *integers*?

Write an integer to represent each situation.

2. lost 4 pounds
3. earned $10
4. 8° below 0° C
5. 25 feet below sea level

for Help Lesson 6-1

CONTENT STANDARDS

6.NS.5, 6.NS.6, 6.NS.6.c, 6.NS.7.b

What You'll Learn

To show that numbers are rational and to plot rational numbers on a number line

New Vocabulary rational number

Why Learn This?

You see rational numbers when you read prices in ads on the Internet or in the newspaper. Rational numbers are also used in athletes' statistics, temperatures, and the weights of items.

A **rational number** is any number that can be written as a quotient of two integers in which the denominator is not zero. Integers, fractions, mixed numbers, and certain types of decimals are rational numbers. The examples below show how different types of rational numbers can be written as a quotient of two integers.

$1\frac{2}{3}$	0.4	2	-8	-0.38
$\updownarrow$	$\updownarrow$	$\updownarrow$	$\updownarrow$	$\updownarrow$
$\frac{5}{3}$	$\frac{4}{10}$	$\frac{2}{1}$	$\frac{-8}{1}$	$\frac{-38}{100}$

EXAMPLE Showing That Numbers Are Rational

1 Show that each number is a rational number by writing it as a quotient of two integers.

a. $\frac{3}{4}$

$\frac{3}{4}$ is a fraction. It is rational.

b. -3

-3 is an integer and can be written as $\frac{-3}{1}$. It is rational.

c. $-1\frac{2}{5}$

$-1\frac{2}{5}$ can be written as $\frac{-7}{5}$. It is rational.

d. 11.06

11.06 can be written as $\frac{1106}{100}$. It is rational.

Quick Check

1. Show that each number is a rational number by writing it as a quotient of two integers.

   a. -6.4 b. 9 c. $-\frac{5}{7}$ d. -0.75

You previously graphed positive and negative integers on a number line. To graph rational numbers on a number line, divide the integer units into fractional parts.

EXAMPLE Plotting Fractions on a Number Line

2 Plot $\frac{4}{6}$ and $-\frac{5}{6}$ on a number line.

The denominator of $-\frac{5}{6}$ and $\frac{4}{6}$ is 6. So, divide your number line into sixths. Label the sixths.

For positive numbers, count right from 0. Find and plot a point at $\frac{4}{6}$.

For negative numbers, count left from 0. Find and plot a point at $-\frac{5}{6}$.

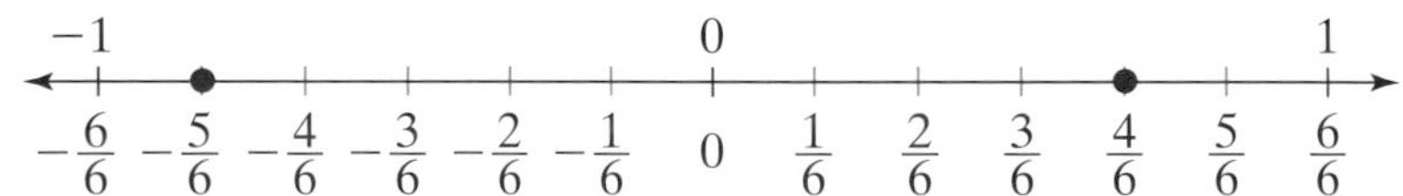

Quick Check

2. Plot each fraction on a number line.

   a. $-\frac{5}{3}$ b. $\frac{3}{8}$ c. $-4\frac{2}{5}$

EXAMPLE Plotting Decimals on a Number Line

3 Vera owes her brother \$1.70. This debt is represented by -1.7. Plot the decimal on a number line.

The smallest place value in -1.7 is tenths. So, divide your number line into tenths. Label the tenths.

For negative numbers, count left from 0. Find and plot a point at -1.7.

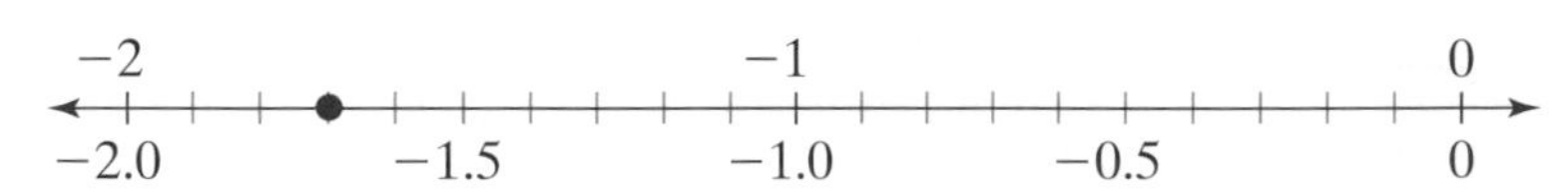

Quick Check

3. Plot each decimal on a number line.

   a. -2.4 b. -0.3 c. 1.52

Number lines can also be vertical. The positive numbers appear above 0 on the line and the negative numbers appear below 0. As you move up on a vertical number line, the numbers become greater.

EXAMPLE Plotting on a Vertical Number Line

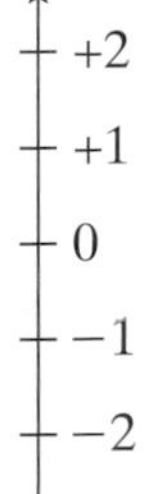

4 Plot −3 on a vertical number line.

Draw a vertical number line. Label the integers.
Count down from 0 to find −3. Plot a point at −3.

Quick Check

4. Plot each rational number on a vertical number line.

a. 6 **b.** $-\frac{7}{12}$ **c.** −3.85

Check Your Understanding

1. Vocabulary Name three different *rational numbers*.

2. Modeling Complete each statement.

a. On a horizontal number line, negative rational numbers appear _____ 0.

b. On a vertical number line, negative rational numbers appear _____ 0.

Match each rational number with a point on the line.

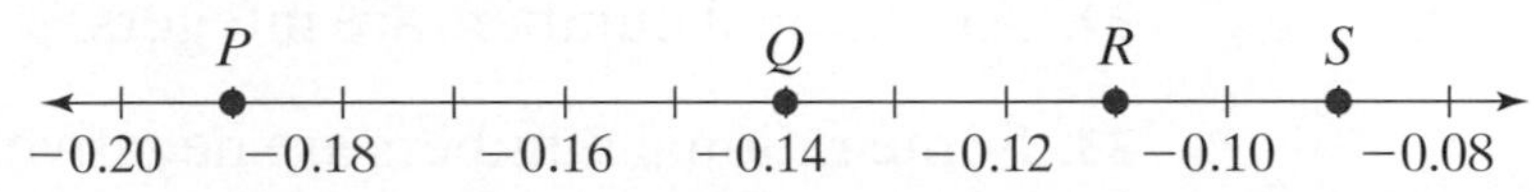

3. −0.14 **4.** −0.11 **5.** −0.19 **6.** −0.09

7. Reasoning Is 0 a rational number? Explain.

Homework Exercises

For more exercises, see Extra Skills and Word Problems.

GO for Help

For Exercises	See Example
8–11	1
12–15	2
16–19	3
20–23	4

Show that each number is a rational number by writing it as the quotient of two integers.

8. 65 **9.** $-1\frac{3}{4}$ **10.** −0.73 **11.** 2.4

Plot each fraction on a number line.

12. $\frac{-1}{4}$ **13.** $\frac{1}{2}$ **14.** $\frac{-7}{12}$ **15.** $-3\frac{3}{5}$

Plot each decimal on a number line.

16. −0.4 **17.** −5.6 **18.** 2.9 **19.** −3.95

Plot each rational number on a vertical number line.

20. $-1\frac{5}{8}$ **21.** 8 **22.** −0.6 **23.** −0.52

24. **Guided Problem Solving** On Monday the low temperature was −4.25°F. Plot the temperature on a number line.
    - How will you decide what to use as a scale on the number line?
    - Between what two integers on a number line does −4.25 lie?
    - On a number line is −4.25 closer to −5 or to −4? Explain.

25. **Number Sense** The batting average of a baseball player is 0.276. Explain how you know that 0.276 is a rational number.

Write each rational number.

26. the opposite of 2.5
27. the opposite of the opposite of −0.16
28. the opposite of $\frac{-5}{9}$
29. the opposite of the opposite of $1\frac{3}{14}$

GO Online
Homework Video Tutor
PearsonSuccessNet.com

30. **Number Sense** Between what two integers on a number line does −3.425 lie? Between what two rational numbers, in tenths, does it lie? Between what two rational numbers, in hundredths, does it lie? Explain.

Reasoning **Write *true* or *false* for each statement. Give an example.**

31. All integers are rational numbers.
32. All rational numbers are integers.
33. Some rational numbers are negative.
34. **Writing in Math** Explain why a mixed number is a rational number. Give an example.
35. **Challenge** Plot these rational numbers on the same number line.
    $-1\frac{2}{3}, -1.6, -1\frac{3}{8}, -1.45, -2, -0.9$

Test Prep and Mixed Review

Practice

Multiple Choice

36. Which rational number lies between points R and S on the number line?

    P Q R S
    −1.0 −0.8 −0.6 −0.4 −0.2 0

    (A) $-\frac{4}{100}$ (B) $-\frac{2}{5}$ (C) $-\frac{5}{6}$ (D) $-\frac{7}{10}$

Find the unit rate for each situation.

GO for Help

For Exercises	See Lesson
37–39	5-2

37. $27 for 18 square feet
38. 297 miles on 9 gallons
39. Which is a better buy: strawberries: 3 pounds for $5.39 or 1 pound for $1.89?

Checkpoint Quiz 1

Lessons 6-1 through 6-3

Find each absolute value.

1. $|-13|$
2. $|64|$

Show that each number is rational by writing it as the quotient of two integers.

3. 0.64
4. $-4\frac{7}{9}$
5. Plot $-1\frac{1}{2}$ on a number line.
6. You write a check for $32. What integer represents the change in your checking account balance?
7. Order 16, −17, 18, −15, and −14 from least to greatest.
8. What is the opposite of the opposite of 6?

MATH GAMES

A Race to the End

What You'll Need

- game board
- two different-colored number cubes
- two different-colored place markers

−10 −9 −8 −7 −6 −5 −4 −3 −2 −1 0 1 2 3 4 5 6 7 8 9 10

How To Play

- Each player places a marker on 0.
- Use one cube to represent positive integers and the other cube to represent negative integers.
- One player rolls the two number cubes.
- The player moves his or her marker forward the number of spaces indicated by the positive integer and then moves the marker back the number of spaces indicated by the negative integer.
- Players take turns rolling both number cubes and moving their markers.
- The first player who reaches or goes past either end of the board wins.

6-4 Comparing and Ordering Rational Numbers

Check Skills You'll Need

1. **Vocabulary Review** What is a *rational number*?

Write each rational number as the quotient of two integers.

2. 6
3. 0.75
4. −0.4
5. $-2\frac{1}{4}$
6. $\frac{-5}{8}$
7. 6.35

Lesson 6-3

CONTENT STANDARDS

6.NS.5, 6.NS.6, 6.NS.6.c, 6.NS.7.a, 6.NS.7.b

What You'll Learn

To compare and order rational numbers

Why Learn This?

You can compare measurements, such as weights or lengths, in different forms when you want to determine the greatest or least amount. Negative rational numbers can represent quantities like debt, temperature below zero, and distance below sea level.

You have plotted positive and negative rational numbers on a number line. A number line can also help you compare and order rational numbers.

EXAMPLE Comparing Decimals

1 Compare –12.4 and –12.65.

Plot both negative decimals on the same number line. Divide the number line into tenths. Locate −12.65 halfway between −12.6 and −12.7.

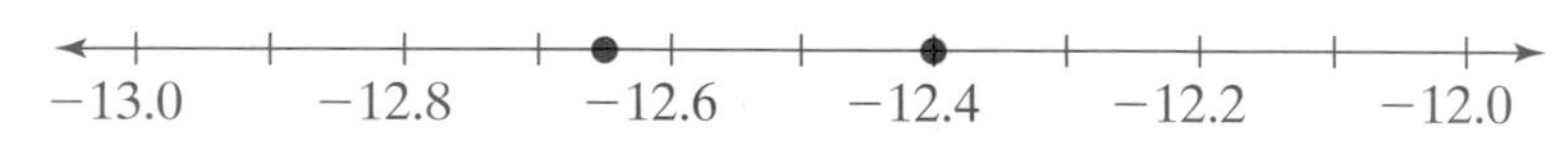

Compare the locations of the points. Since −12.65 is to the left of −12.4 on the number line, −12.65 is less than −12.4.

$-12.65 < -12.4$ or $-12.4 > -12.65$

Quick Check

1. Compare using $<$, $=$, or $>$.
   a. -12.05 ■ -12.5
   b. -12.98 ■ -12.89

EXAMPLE Comparing Fractions

2 Compare $-\frac{5}{6}$ and $-\frac{5}{8}$.

Because the denominators are 6 and 8, divide your number line into sixths and also into eighths. Plot both fractions.

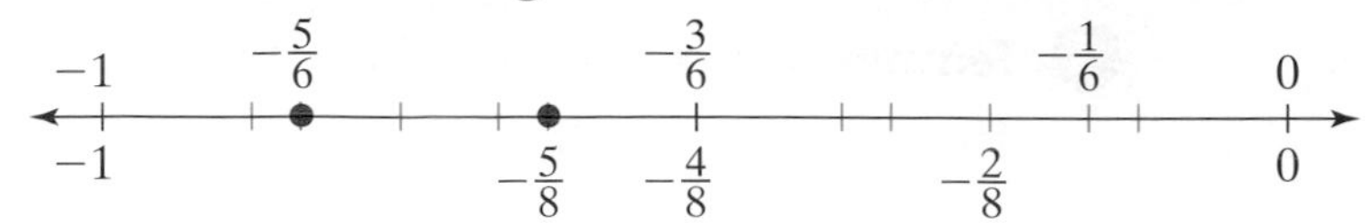

Compare the locations of the points. Since $-\frac{5}{6}$ is to the left of $-\frac{5}{8}$ on the number line, $-\frac{5}{6}$ is less than $-\frac{5}{8}$.

$-\frac{5}{6} < -\frac{5}{8}$ or $-\frac{5}{8} > -\frac{5}{6}$

Quick Check

2. Compare, using $<$, $=$, or $>$.

a. $-\frac{5}{8} \blacksquare -\frac{1}{2}$

b. $-4\frac{7}{12} \blacksquare -4\frac{2}{3}$

EXAMPLE Comparing Decimals and Fractions

3 **Elevation** Two cities are below sea level. City A has an elevation of $-1\frac{2}{3}$ feet. City B has an elevation of -1.8 feet. Which city has a lower elevation?

Locate each elevation on the same number line. The denominator is 3 and the decimal is to the tenths place. Mark off thirds and tenths to plot the numbers.

−2 $-1\frac{2}{3}$ $-1\frac{1}{3}$ −1

−2.0 −1.8 −1.5 −1.0

Then compare the locations of the points.

$-1.8 < -1\frac{2}{3}$

City B has a lower elevation than City A.

Quick Check

3. Solve each problem.

a. City C has an elevation of -1.24 feet. City D has an elevation of $-1\frac{3}{10}$ feet. Which city has a higher elevation?

b. City E has an elevation of -6.8 feet. City F has an elevation of $-6\frac{4}{5}$ feet. Which city has a higher elevation?

You can order rational numbers by plotting all the numbers on the same number line and comparing the locations of the points.

EXAMPLE Ordering Rational Numbers

4 **Temperatures** On Monday, the temperature was $-0.2°C$. On Tuesday, the temperature was $-1\frac{1}{2}°C$. It was $-1°C$ on Wednesday, $2.4°C$ on Thursday, and $1\frac{3}{4}°C$ on Friday. Write the temperatures in order from least to greatest.

STEP 1: Draw a number line from -2 to 3 and divide it into halves. Plot each temperature on a number line. Locate numbers on or in between the labels.

$-1\frac{1}{2}°C$ $-1°C$ $-0.2°C$ $1\frac{3}{4}°C$ $2.4°C$

-2 -1 0 1 2 3

STEP 2: Compare the locations of the points. The least number is on the left.

The temperatures from least to greatest are:

$-1\frac{1}{2}°C, -1°C, -0.2°C, 1\frac{3}{4}°C, 2.4°C.$

Quick Check

4. Order the temperatures from least to greatest.
$-6.45°C, -6\frac{3}{4}°C, 6.2°C, -6.3°C, -6\frac{1}{2}°C$

Check Your Understanding

1. **Vocabulary** Explain how you know $-\frac{3}{5}$ is greater than $-\frac{4}{5}$.

Compare, using <, =, or >.

2. $-\frac{2}{10}$ ■ 0.4

3. -1.64 ■ $-2\frac{6}{10}$

Order each set of rational numbers from least to greatest.

4. $-\frac{30}{100}, -0.32, 1.3$

5. $5.4, -5.19, -5\frac{7}{8}$

6. **Open-Ended** Give one example of a rational number that is greater than -3.2 and one example that is less than -3.2.

Homework Exercises

For more exercises, see Extra Skills and Word Problems.

GO for Help

For Exercises	See Examples
7–9	1
10–12	2
13–15	3
16–18	4

Compare the decimals using <, =, or >.

7. $-6.12 \blacksquare -6.18$ 8. $-0.55 \blacksquare -0.5$ 9. $-2.7 \blacksquare -3.5$

Compare the fractions using <, =, or >.

10. $-\frac{1}{3} \blacksquare -\frac{2}{6}$ 11. $-\frac{4}{5} \blacksquare -\frac{5}{8}$ 12. $-2\frac{3}{8} \blacksquare -2\frac{6}{7}$

Compare the fractions and decimals using <, =, or >.

13. $-\frac{3}{5} \blacksquare -0.3$ 14. $-2.9 \blacksquare -2\frac{4}{5}$

15. The city measures the water level in a lake and considers the average depth of the lake to be 0 ft. After Week 1, the water level was -2.8 ft. In Week 2, the water level was $-2\frac{3}{4}$ ft. Compare the numbers. In which week was the water level lower?

Order each set of rational numbers from least to greatest.

16. $-3.1, -3\frac{2}{10}, -3.02$ 17. $\frac{32}{4}, -8.2, -8\frac{6}{20}$

18. Marty researched the elevations of various places around New Orleans. He found these elevations.

-4.18 ft, $-4\frac{3}{8}$ ft, -4.6 ft, -6 ft, 4.4 ft, $-4\frac{3}{4}$ ft

Order the elevations from least to greatest.

19. **Guided Problem Solving** A marathon is a running event for a distance of 26.2 miles. Lana has run 4 marathons. She ran her first marathon in 3.5 hours. The table shows the number of minutes she reduced her time from her first marathon in each of the next 3 marathons she ran. Order her last three marathon times from fastest to slowest.

Marathon	B	C	D
Time Reduced	4.2 minutes	4.12 minutes	$4\frac{1}{2}$ minutes

- Explain why each value should be considered a negative number for the comparison.
- Plot each value on a number line. How does the number line show the order of marathon times from fastest to slowest?

0.52	-0.52	$-4\frac{1}{2}$	2.5	5.2

20. **Reasoning** Use the information at the left to identify which numbers in the box are A, B, C, D, and E.
- D is greater than E and less than C.
- C and D are opposites.
- At least one number is greater than A.

21. **Number Sense** The students in Mrs. Metz's science class are growing plants under different light, soil, and water conditions. The average plant growth during a week was 3.5 inches. The table shows the difference from the average for some of the students' plants. Order the students' plants from least to greatest. (Recall that 1 in. = 2.54 cm.)

Student	Difference
Ji Sun	$2\frac{1}{4}$ in.
Gayle	$-2\frac{7}{10}$ in.
Stefan	1.5 cm
Ricardo	−2.4 cm

22. **Open-Ended** Use the digits 5, 6, 7 or 8 to complete this inequality. Give at least two possible answers.

$-2 < -\frac{\square}{\square} < -1$

23. **Writing in Math** Suppose you are comparing the fractions $-\frac{26}{8}$ and $-\frac{37}{9}$. Explain how you could use mental math to determine the greater fraction.

24. **Challenge** Complete each inequality with the digit or digits that make it true.

a. $-1.5 < -$ ■.■ < -1.3

b. $-10.6 > -10.9 > -10.$■9

c. $-\frac{4}{10} > -0.$■ $> -\frac{3}{5}$

Test Prep and Mixed Review

Practice

Multiple Choice

25. Which shows the rational numbers listed in order from least to greatest? $3, 3\frac{2}{3}, -4.2, -4\frac{2}{5}$

Ⓐ $3\frac{2}{3}, 3, -4.2, -4\frac{2}{5}$

Ⓑ $-4.2, -4\frac{2}{5}, 3\frac{2}{3}, 3$

Ⓒ $-4\frac{2}{5}, 3\frac{2}{3}, -4.2, 3$

Ⓓ $-4\frac{2}{5}, -4.2, 3, 3\frac{2}{3}$

26. Which statement is NOT true?

Ⓕ $-\frac{4}{5} > -\frac{5}{4}$

Ⓖ $-0.4 < -0.6$

Ⓗ $\frac{1}{10} > -\frac{10}{2}$

Ⓙ $-\frac{9}{3} < -1.8$

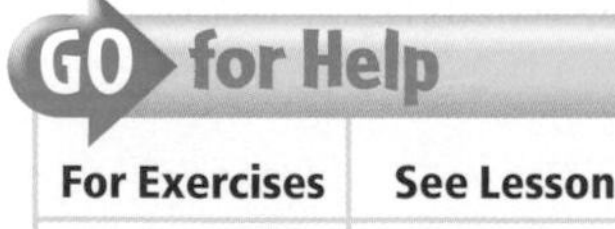

GO for Help

For Exercises	See Lesson
27–30	2-4

Solve each equation. Check your solution.

27. $25 = m + 6.3$

28. $3.2 = 1.6 + h$

29. $x + 9.8 = 15.6$

30. $17 = p + 4.5$

6-5 Inequalities

Check Skills You'll Need

1. Vocabulary Review How can you use a number line to *compare* integers?

Compare using $<$ or $>$.

2. 4 ■ −9

3. −2 ■ −3

4. −94 ■ −93

5. 1,001 ■ 1,010

GO for Help Lesson 6-2

CONTENT STANDARDS
6.EE.5, 6.EE.6, 6.EE.8, 6.NS.7.d

What You'll Learn

To express and identify solutions of inequalities

New Vocabulary inequality, graph of an inequality, solution of an inequality

Why Learn This?

Inequalities can tell you time limits, the height limits for amusement-park rides, and many other things.

Don't cross this field unless
you can do it in 9.9 seconds.
The bull can do it in 10.

An **inequality** is a mathematical sentence that contains $<, >, \leq, \geq,$ or $\neq$. Real-world situations can sometimes be represented by inequalities.

Inequality Symbols			
$<$	less than	$>$	greater than
$\leq$	less than or equal to	$\geq$	greater than or equal to
$\neq$	not equal to		

EXAMPLE Writing an Inequality

1 **Time** The sign above warns you to cross the field in less than 10 seconds. Write an inequality that represents the time limit.

Words your time is less than bull's time

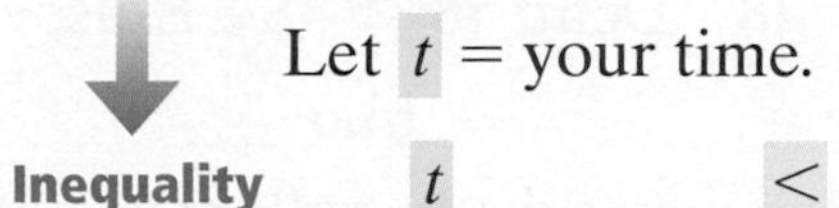

Let t = your time.

Inequality t $<$ 10

The inequality is $t < 10$.

Quick Check

1. Skydivers jump from an altitude of 14,500 feet or less. Write an inequality to express the altitude from which skydivers jump.

The **graph of an inequality** shows all solutions of the inequality. A **solution of an inequality** is any number that makes the inequality true. An open circle on a graph shows that the number is *not* a solution. A closed circle shows that the number *is* a solution.

EXAMPLE Graphing Inequalities

2 Write the inequality. Then graph the inequality.

a. You ride your scooter more than 2 miles.

Let k = your distance.

$k > 2$

(Number line from −1 to 5: open circle at 2, shaded to the right.)

b. The temperature is at most 5 degrees below zero.

Let t = temperature.

$t \leq -5$

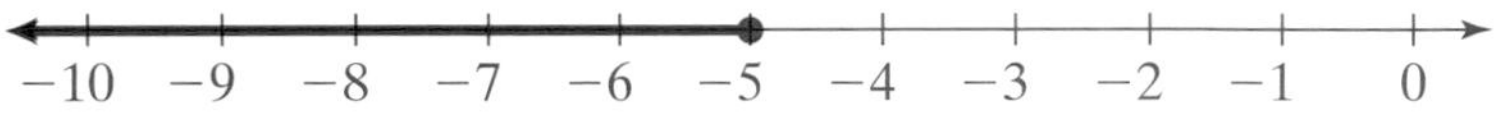

(Number line from −10 to 0: closed circle at −5, shaded to the left.)

Quick Check

2. You spend at least 2 hours studying. Write the inequality for the situation. Then graph the inequality.

You can use an inequality to show which numbers meet a limit.

EXAMPLE Identifying Solutions of an Inequality

3 **Roller Coasters** You must be at least 48 inches tall to ride a certain roller coaster. Which of the children in the table can ride the roller coaster?

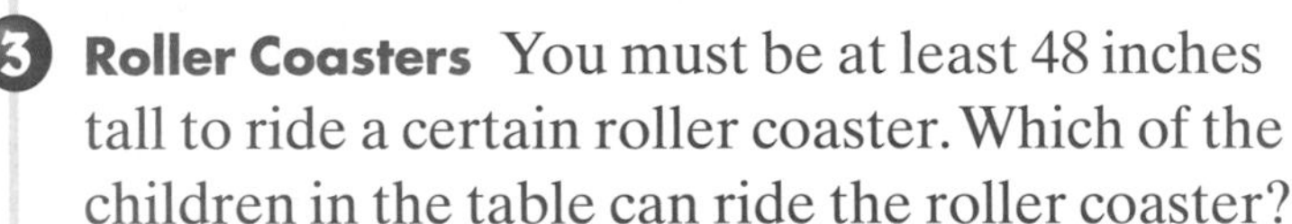

Name	Height
Sally	$48\frac{1}{2}$ in.
Dean	48 in.
Kelsey	$46\frac{3}{4}$ in.

Words child's height | is at least | 48 inches

Let h = the child's height.

Inequality $h \geq 48$

Decide whether the inequality is true or false for each person.

Sally $48\frac{1}{2} \geq 48$ — true

Dean $48 \geq 48$ — true

Kelsey $46\frac{3}{4} \geq 48$ — false

Sally and Dean may ride the roller coaster.

Quick Check

3. Ian is 3 ft 11 in. tall. Is Ian tall enough to ride the roller coaster?

Check Your Understanding

1. **Vocabulary** A graph of an inequality shows all the __?__ of the inequality.
2. **Reasoning** Are the solutions of $x < 3$ and $x \leq 3$ the same? Explain.
3. Write an inequality for the graph.

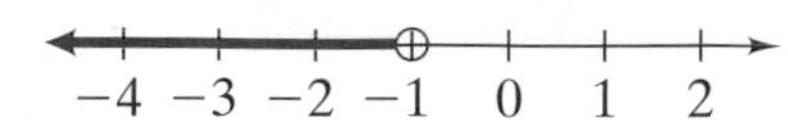

Homework Exercises

For more exercises, see Extra Skills and Word Problems.

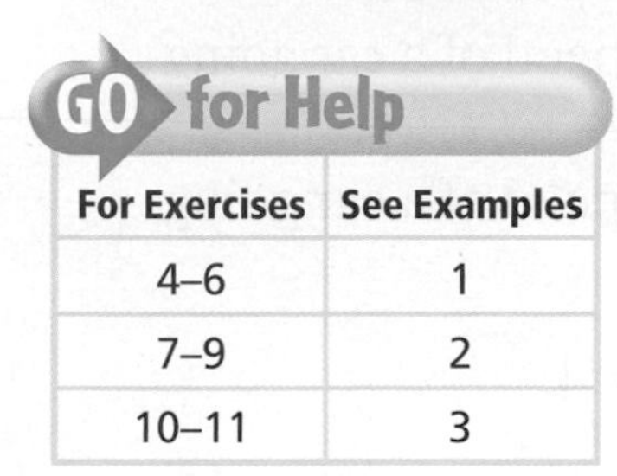

GO for Help

For Exercises	See Examples
4–6	1
7–9	2
10–11	3

Write an inequality for each situation.

4. No more than 45 students work in the car-wash fundraiser.
5. There are more than 15 ladybugs on the windowsill.
6. A sign reads, "Maximum height of vehicles is 12.5 feet."

Write an inequality for each situation. Then graph the inequality.

7. Four people or fewer are allowed on the ride at once.
8. David's account balance shows a debt of at least $40.
9. You must deposit at least $20 to open a bank account.

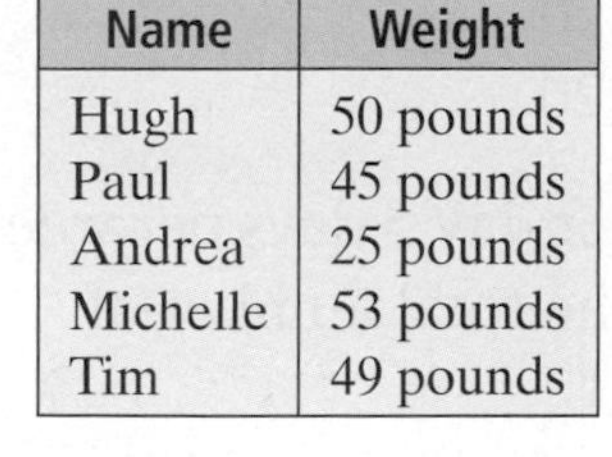

Name	Weight
Hugh	50 pounds
Paul	45 pounds
Andrea	25 pounds
Michelle	53 pounds
Tim	49 pounds

10. Use the table at the left. A child must weigh less than 50 pounds to ride on the playground animals. Who may ride the animals?
11. Kristen has a bank account that shuts down if the balance drops below −$25
    a. Write an inequality for this situation.
    b. Write an inequality that expresses the amount she owes the bank for this situation.

GPS 12. **Guided Problem Solving** Which appliances in the table below use an average of more than 50 kilowatt-hours of energy per month? Write an inequality and graph the solution.

Average Monthly Energy Use

Appliance	VCR	Dryer	Washer	Dishwasher
Energy (kilowatt-hours)	4	100	10	50

- Which symbol can you use to represent "more than"?
- On your graph, should you use an open or closed circle?

Tell whether each inequality is true or false.

13. $-2 \leq 2$

14. $|-5| < 5$

15. $-4^2 < (-4)^2$

16. **Football** You must weigh 120 pounds or less to play in a junior football league. Use the table at the right. Who qualifies to play?

Name	Weight
Aaron	118 lb
Steve	109 lb
Mark	131 lb
James	120 lb

17. **Writing in Math** Describe how to graph $x < -20$.

18. **Driving** The minimum speed limit on an interstate is 45 miles per hour. The maximum speed limit is 65 miles per hour.
   a. Write an inequality that describes the speed of a car going slower than the minimum limit.
   b. Write an inequality that describes the speed of a car going faster than the maximum limit.

19. **Number Sense** Graph the inequality $x \neq 4$.

20. **Challenge** Solve and graph $|x| < 2$.

Test Prep and Mixed Review

Practice

Multiple Choice

21. Nicholas must read at least 20 minutes each night. Which inequality represents this situation?
   (A) $m > 20$
   (B) $m < 20$
   (C) $m \geq 20$
   (D) $m \leq 20$

22. Abby plans to practice piano 30 minutes per day, 5 days per week, over the next 10 weeks. How can she find the total number of minutes she will practice?
   (F) Multiply 30 and 5.
   (G) Multiply 5 and 10.
   (H) Multiply 30, 5, and 10.
   (J) Multiply 0.5, 5, and 10.

23. What is the prime factorization of 300?
   (A) 3×100
   (B) $3 \times 2^2 \times 5^2$
   (C) 5×60
   (D) $2^2 \times 3^2 \times 5^2$

24. A baker has $1\frac{1}{2}$ cups of walnuts to make four batches of muffins. How many cups of walnuts should the baker put into each batch?
   (F) $\frac{1}{8}$ cup
   (G) $\frac{3}{8}$ cup
   (H) $\frac{8}{3}$ cup
   (J) 6 cup

GO for Help

For Exercises	See Lesson
24	4-3

Checkpoint Quiz 2

Lessons 6-4 through 6-5

Compare, using <, =, or >.

1. $-2.5 \blacksquare -2.8$ **2.** $-\frac{7}{8} \blacksquare -0.74$ **3.** $-\frac{5}{10} \blacksquare -\frac{9}{10}$ **4.** $-2\frac{1}{2} \blacksquare -2\frac{3}{5}$

5. Keaton recorded the low temperatures for five days in a table. Write the temperatures in order from greatest to least.

Day	Low Temperature
Mon	$-4\frac{1}{2}$°F
Tue	–5.5°F
Wed	–4.7°F
Thu	–4.2°F
Fri	$-5\frac{1}{4}$°F

6. Write an inequality for the graph.

–5 –4 –3 –2 –1 0 1 2

Write an inequality for each situation.

7. The distance Mr. Delgado drove was no more than 55 miles.

8. You must be at least 48 inches tall to go on the ride at the fair.

MATH GAMES

The Greater Number Wins

2 players

- 20-30 index cards, each with a different rational number.
- Examples: $-0.5, \frac{1}{8}, -2, \frac{4}{5}, \frac{3}{4}, 0.25, \frac{8}{3}, -3.25, 0.2, -2.4, -\frac{1}{8}, \frac{5}{6}, 1.32$

How to Play

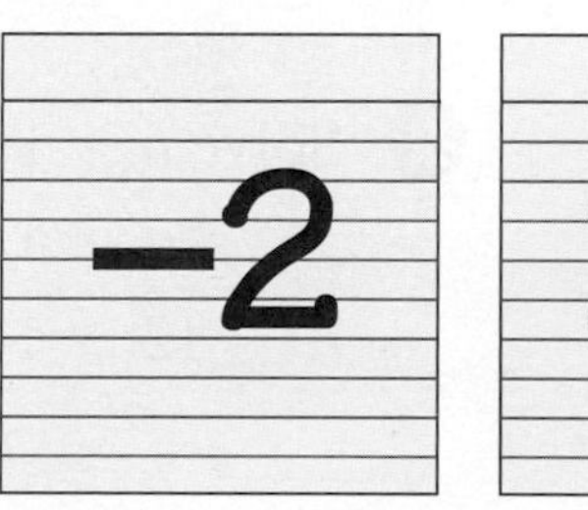

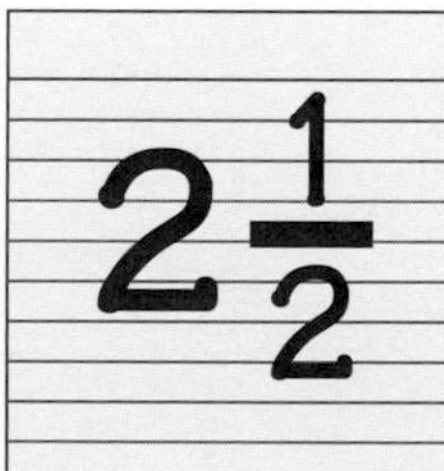

- Shuffle the cards and deal half of the cards face down to each player.
- Each player turns over the top card of their stack and places it down.

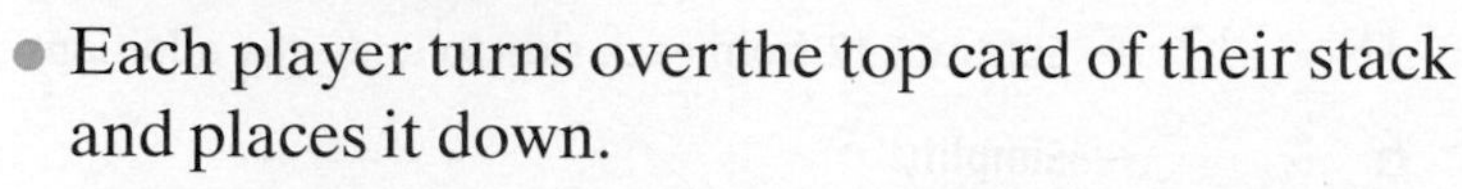

- The player with the greater rational number keeps both cards.

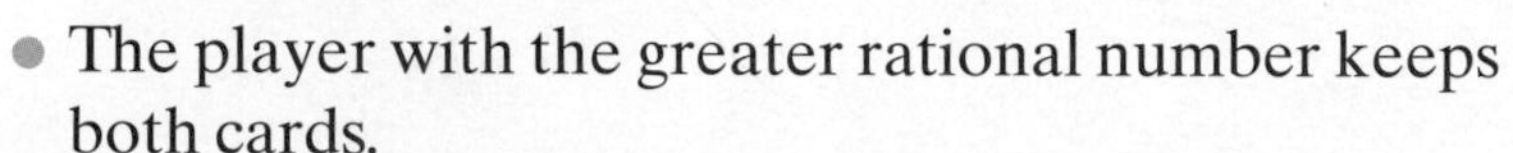

- Play continues until all the cards have been used.
- The player with the most cards wins.

6-6 Solving One-Step Inequalities

1. **Vocabulary Review** What is an inequality?

Write an inequality for each situation.

2. You spend less than \$5.00 for lunch.
3. You want to complete at least 12 math problems tonight.

CONTENT STANDARD
6.EE.5

What You'll Learn

To solve one-step inequalities by adding or subtracting

Why Learn This?

You can solve inequalities when you need to find an unknown amount. For example, you can determine how close you are to meeting a goal in sports or in business.

To solve an inequality, use inverse operations to get the variable alone.

EXAMPLES Solving Inequalities

1 Solve $s - 7 < 3$.

$$s - 7 < 3$$

$$s - 7 + 7 < 3 + 7 \quad \leftarrow \text{Add 7 to each side to undo the subtraction.}$$

$$s < 10 \quad \leftarrow \text{Simplify.}$$

2 Solve $n + 12 \geq 18$.

$$n + 12 \geq 18$$

$$n + 12 - 12 \geq 18 - 12 \quad \leftarrow \text{Subtract 12 from each side to undo the addition.}$$

$$n \geq 6 \quad \leftarrow \text{Simplify.}$$

Quick Check

1. Solve $u - 6 \leq 3$.
2. Solve $z + 15 > 24$.

You can also solve inequalities in real-world situations.

EXAMPLE Application: Running

3 A marathon runner plans to run at least 55 miles this week. He has already run 42 miles. Write and solve an inequality to find how many more miles he plans to run this week.

Words miles run + miles left is at least 55 miles

Let m = number of miles left.

Inequality $42 \quad + \quad m \quad \geq \quad 55$

$$42 + m \geq 55$$

$$42 + m - 42 \geq 55 - 42 \quad \leftarrow \text{Subtract 42 from each side.}$$

$$m \geq 13 \quad \leftarrow \text{Simplify.}$$

The marathon runner plans to run at least 13 more miles this week.

Quick Check

3. A restaurant can serve a maximum of 115 people. There are now 97 people dining in the restaurant. Write and solve an inequality to find how many more people can be served.

Check Your Understanding

Name the operation used to solve each inequality.

1. $c - 4 \geq 8$ **2.** $n + 2 < 13$ **3.** $t + 11 \leq 11$

4. Reasoning What number is a solution of $y + 2 \geq 10$ but is not a solution of $y + 2 > 10$?

5. Mental Math Solve $c - 2 \leq 8$.

Homework Exercises

For more exercises, see Extra Skills and Word Problems.

GO for Help

For Exercises	See Examples
6–11	1
12–18	2–3

Solve each inequality.

6. $x - 2 \geq 5$ **7.** $z - 5 < 0$ **8.** $k - 21 > 1$

9. $j - 2 > 9$ **10.** $n - 96 < 58$ **11.** $s - 4 \leq 8$

12. $r + 5 \geq 7$ **13.** $y + 11 \leq 12$ **14.** $w + 2 > 7$

15. $14 + d \leq 24$ **16.** $7 + f > 13$ **17.** $5 + g \leq 62$

18. You have \$15 to spend on souvenirs. You buy a visor for \$7.99. Write and solve an inequality to find how much more money you can spend.

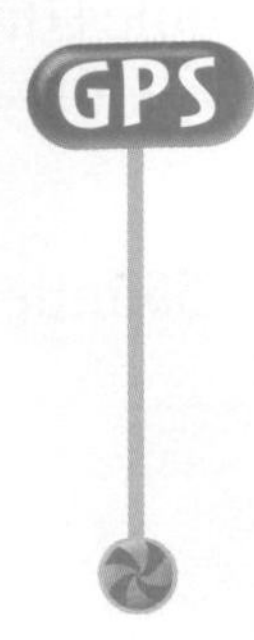

19. **Guided Problem Solving** Your bank requires a minimum of \$250 in an account to avoid fees. You have \$143 in your account. Write and solve an inequality to find how much money you must deposit to avoid fees.
    - **Make a Plan** Decide which operation to use in the inequality. Undo the operation in the inequality.
    - **Check the Answer** Draw a graph of the inequality.

20. **Writing in Math** Explain how you know that $3n > 3n$ has no solutions.

21. To avoid a storm, a pilot of a vintage biplane flies up 2,500 feet but stays below 32,000 feet. Write an inequality to find the maximum original altitude of the plane.

22. **Budgeting** You want to spend less than \$30 on two T-shirts and a pair of shorts. The pair of shorts costs \$13. Each of the T-shirts costs the same amount. Write and solve an inequality to find how much money you can spend on each T-shirt.

23. **Challenge** Which integers are solutions to both $x + 7 \leq 9$ and $x + 7 > 4$?

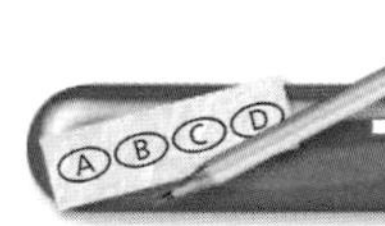

Test Prep and Mixed Review

Practice

Multiple Choice

24. Carl has \$150 to spend on a bicycle and a helmet. The helmet costs \$30. Which inequality represents the amount of money Carl has to spend on a bicycle?

    (A) $x - 30 \geq 150$ (C) $x + 30 \geq 150$
    (B) $x - 30 \leq 150$ (D) $x + 30 \leq 150$

25. The elevation of Death Valley in California is 282 feet below sea level. Mount McKinley in Alaska is 20,320 feet above sea level. What integer represents the elevation of Death Valley?

    (F) −20,320 (H) 282
    (G) −282 (J) 20,320

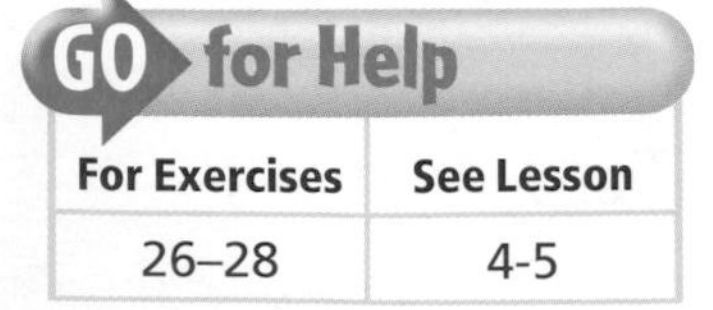

For Exercises	See Lesson
26–28	4-5

Solve each equation using mental math.

26. $x - 2\frac{1}{6} = 2\frac{1}{6}$

27. $12\frac{1}{2} + x = 24\frac{3}{4}$

28. $8\frac{7}{8} - x = 5\frac{3}{8}$

GPS Guided Problem Solving

Practice Solving Problems

Shopping You want to spend a maximum of $35 on school supplies. You have already spent $12 on school supplies. Write and solve an inequality to find out how much more money you can spend on school supplies.

What You Might Think	What You Might Write
What do I know?	I know that I want to spend a maximum of $35 on school supplies. I know that I have already spent $12.
What do I want to find out?	I want to find out how much more money I can spend on school supplies.
How can I show this in words?	Money spent plus money I can still spend is no more than $35.
How can I write the words as an inequality?	First I choose a letter to represent the amount I want to find. Let *m* represent the amount of money I can still spend. Then I use the words to help me write the inequality. $12 + m \leq 35$
How do I solve the inequality?	$12 + m \leq 35$ $12 + m - 12 \leq 35 - 12$ ← Subtract 12 from each side. $m \leq 23$ ← Simplify.
What is the answer?	You can spend at most $23 more dollars on school supplies.

Think It Through

1. Why did you subtract to solve the inequality?
2. **Reasoning** How would the inequality change if you want to spend less than $35 on school supplies?
3. **Check for Reasonableness** How could you check to make sure that the answer to this problem is reasonable?

Exercises

4. A runner plans to run at least 35 miles this week. She has already run 18 miles. Write and solve an inequality to find how many more miles she plans to run this week?
5. A diver sees a sea turtle at 27 feet below the surface of the water. Write an integer to represent the situation.
6. Jake recorded the hottest and coldest temperatures for the first three days of January. Write the temperatures in order from hottest to coldest.

	Jan 1	Jan 2	Jan 3
hottest	–3°F	15°F	18°F
coldest	–12°F	–4°F	6°F

7. Beth wants to make a list of all the integers that are greater than −4 and less than 7. Which integers should she write?
8. Five students named their heights in feet.

   5.25 ft   4.8 ft $5\frac{1}{3}$ ft   5.5 ft $4\frac{2}{3}$ ft

   a. Plot the heights on a number line.
   b. List the heights in order from shortest to tallest.
9. Paulo drew this graph to show *d*, the number of dollars he wants to save from the amount he earns each week.

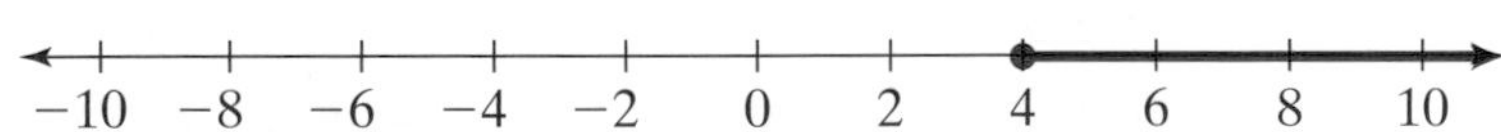

   Write an inequality for the situation.
10. Haley wrote 5 rational numbers.

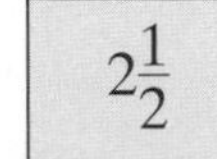

   −1.25   −3.2   3.4 $-2\frac{7}{8}$

   a. Plot the numbers on a number line.
   b. List the numbers in order from greatest to least.

Test-Taking Strategies

Using a Variable

Use a variable to represent the unknown quantity. You can choose a letter that reminds you of what the variable represents. Then write an inequality.

EXAMPLE

A bicyclist plans to bike at least 75 miles this week. She has already biked 36 miles. Which inequality can be used to find how many more miles she plans to bike this week?

(A) $36 + 75 \geq m$

(B) $36 + m \geq 75$

(C) $36 + 75 \geq m$

(D) $36 + m \leq 75$

Words miles biked + miles left is at least 75 miles

Let m = the number of miles left.

Inequality $36 \quad + \quad m \quad \geq \quad 75$

The correct answer is choice B.

Exercises

1. Stephanie scored 7 points in the first half of the basketball game. In all, she scored at least 12 points. Which inequality can you use to find p, the number of points Stephanie scored in the second half?

(A) $p - 7 \geq 12$ (B) $p - 7 > 12$ (C) $7 + p \geq 12$ (D) $7 + p > 12$

2. Chung wants to spend less than $350 to buy a new surfboard. He saved $32 last week. Which inequality can you use to find d, the number of dollars Chung still needs to save to buy the surfboard?

(F) $32 + d \geq 350$ (G) $32 + d > 350$ (H) $32 + d \leq 350$ (J) $32 + d < 350$

3. Russell is playing a computer game. To win the game a player must score at least 125 points. Russell has scored 75 points so far. Which inequality can you use to find g, the number of points he still needs to score to win the game?

(A) $75 + g \geq 125$ (B) $g - 75 \geq 125$ (C) $75 + g \leq 125$ (D) $g - 75 \leq 125$

Chapter 6 Review

Vocabulary Review

absolute value (p. 207)
graph of an inequality (p. 224)
inequality (p. 223)
integers (p. 206)
opposites (p. 206)
rational number (p. 213)
solution of an inequality (p. 224)

Go Online
For vocabulary quiz
PearsonSuccessNet.com

Choose the correct vocabulary term to complete each sentence.

1. A(n) __?__ is a mathematical sentence that contains $<, >, \leq, \geq$, or $\neq$.
2. The numbers $-4, -\frac{2}{3}, 1\frac{5}{8}, 0$, and 5.7 are __?__.
3. -3 and 3 are integers that are __?__
4. The number 7 is the __?__ of both -7 and 7.

Skills and Concepts

Lesson 6-1

- To use integers, opposites, and absolute values to represent real-world situations

Integers are the set of positive whole numbers, their opposites, and 0. The opposite of the opposite of a number is the number itself. The **absolute value** of a number is its distance from 0 on a number line.

Use an integer to represent each situation.

5. 14 degrees below zero
6. gain 6 pounds

Write the opposite of each integer.

7. -4
8. 5
9. -33
10. 20
11. Write the absolute value of the opposite of 9.

Lesson 6-2

- To compare and order integers

You can use a number line to help you compare and order integers.

Compare, using $<$ or $>$.

12. $-5 \blacksquare 0$
13. $-8 \blacksquare 12$
14. $4 \blacksquare |-9|$
15. $-12 \blacksquare -14$

Order each set of integers from least to greatest.

16. $-1, 1, 2, -2$
17. $0, -4, 5, -6$
18. $-3, 5, -7, 9$

Lesson 6-3

- To show that numbers are rational and to plot rational numbers on a number line

A **rational number** is any number that can be written as a quotient of two integers in which the denominator is not zero. Integers, fractions, and certain types of decimals are rational numbers. Rational numbers can be plotted on a horizontal or a vertical number line.

Show that each number is a rational number by writing it as a quotient of two integers.

19. 21 **20.** -3.1 **21.** $1\frac{5}{9}$ **22.** -7

Plot each rational number on a number line.

23. $3\frac{1}{2}$ **24.** -2.3 **25.** $-\frac{5}{8}$ **26.** 0.75

Lesson 6-4

- To compare and order rational numbers

A number line can help you compare and order rational numbers.

Compare, using <, =, or >.

27. -4.6 ■ -4.06 **28.** $-\frac{7}{10}$ ■ $-\frac{9}{10}$

29. -3.5 ■ $-3\frac{1}{5}$ **30.** -5.28 ■ -5.85

31. Order the temperatures from greatest to least.
$-4.9°C, -4\frac{1}{2}°C, -4.3°C, -5°C, -4\frac{1}{4}°C$

Lessons 6-5 and 6-6

- To express and identify solutions of inequalities
- To solve one-step inequalities by adding or subtracting

An **inequality** is a mathematical sentence that contains $<, >, \leq, \geq$, or $\neq$. An inequality shows the relationship between quantities that are not equivalent. A **solution of an inequality** is any number that makes the inequality true.

Tell whether $x \leq -4$ is *true* or *false* for each value for x.

32. $x = 4$ **33.** $x = -10$ **34.** $x = -2$ **35.** $x = -6$

Graph each inequality on a number line.

36. $p > -4$ **37.** $h < 4$ **38.** $k \geq -5$ **39.** $g \leq 3$

To solve an inequality, use inverse operations to isolate the variable.

Solve each inequality.

40. $q + 6 < 9$ **41.** $t - 7 < 2$ **42.** $v - 4 > 12$ **43.** $y + 9 \geq 11$

44. You want to read at least 50 pages in a book this week. You have already read 16 pages. Write and solve an inequality to find how many more pages you need to read this week.

Chapter 6 Test

Go Online For online chapter test PearsonSuccessNet.com

Write an integer to represent each situation.

1. 7° below 0°F
2. received 6 dollars

Write the opposite of each integer.

3. 89
4. –10
5. Write the value of $|-3|$.
6. Write the value of $-|-41|$.
7. What is the opposite of the opposite of –6?

Compare, using <, =, or >.

8. $18 \blacksquare -24$
9. $-13 \blacksquare -16$
10. $\frac{9}{14} \blacksquare \frac{3}{8}$
11. $-3.47 \blacksquare -3.45$
12. $1\frac{3}{4} \blacksquare 1.9$
13. $-0.4 \blacksquare -\frac{1}{2}$
14. Order the integers from least to greatest. $3, -1, -13, 5, 0$

Write an inequality for each situation.

15. Kade has an account balance of less than -25 dollars.
16. Mike wants to read at least 6 books this summer.

Show that each number is rational by writing it as a quotient of two integers.

17. -4.3
18. 7
19. $2\frac{7}{8}$
20. -0.12

Plot each rational number on a number line.

21. 0.65
22. $-3\frac{1}{5}$

Plot each rational number on a vertical number line.

23. $3\frac{1}{4}$
24. -2.5
25. Order from least to greatest. $-\frac{2}{5}, -0.35, -\frac{5}{8}, -0.375$
26. Order from greatest to least. $-6.25, 5\frac{1}{2}, -5.75, 6.3$

Graph each inequality on a number line.

27. $w > -5$
28. $x \leq 4$
29. **Writing in Math** Is $-4\frac{3}{5}$ a rational number? Explain.

Solve each inequality.

30. $y + 4 \geq 9$
31. $k - 6 < 2$
32. $s - 6 < 42$
33. $f + 1 \geq 2$
34. **Temperature** On Monday the temperature was −3°F. On Tuesday the temperature was −5°F. Compare the temperatures, using < or >.
35. **Bank Fees** You have $59 in a bank account. You need at least $200 to avoid bank fees. Write and solve an inequality to find how many more dollars you should deposit.
36. **Test Scores** To earn an A on a two-part test, Dana must score a minimum of 80 points. She scores 65 points on the first part of the test. Write and solve an inequality to find how many points she needs to score on the second part of the test to earn an A.

Multiple Choice

Choose the correct letter.

1. Evaluate the expression $b - a - 8$ when $a = 7$ and $b = 24$.
   (A) -25 (B) -9 (C) 9 (D) 11

2. Which equation is NOT an example of the Distributive Property?
   (F) $18(7.4) + 18(2.3) = 18(7.4 + 2.3)$
   (G) $0.85(4.3) + 0.15(4.3) = 1(4.3)$
   (H) $18.2(70) = 18.2(100) - 18.2(30)$
   (J) $8.4 + 9.4 = 9.4 + 8.4$

3. Suppose you purchase 9 peaches, 6 oranges, 12 pears, and 8 plums. What is the ratio of plums to pears?
   (A) $\frac{2}{3}$ (C) 12 : 8
   (B) 9 to 12 (D) 4 : 2

4. Which number is NOT a factor of 40?
   (F) 4 (G) 6 (H) 8 (J) 10

5. Suppose you have a fresh lemonade stand. During the day, you sell 12 cups of lemonade for \$0.50 each and 14 muffins for \$1.50 each. What is your total sales?
   (A) \$2 (B) \$21 (C) \$27 (D) \$39

6. Mariah has $\frac{3}{4}$ cup of walnuts. She puts $\frac{1}{8}$ cup in each bag of trail mix. How many bags of trail mix does she make?
   (F) 3 (G) (H) 6 (J) 8

7. Solve $x + 3 = 15$.
   (A) $x = 5$ (C) $x = 18$
   (B) $x = 12$ (D) $x = 45$

8. Amy has 36 tomato plants for her vegetable garden. She wants to put the same number of plants in each row. Which is NOT an arrangement she can use?
   (F) 2×16 (H) 4×9
   (G) 3×12 (J) 6×6

9. Which equation is NOT correct?
   (A) $\frac{3}{4} \times 2\frac{1}{2} = \frac{5}{6}$ (C) $1\frac{7}{8} \times 1\frac{5}{6} = 3\frac{7}{16}$
   (B) $3\frac{4}{5} \times \frac{6}{8} = 2\frac{17}{20}$ (D) $5\frac{2}{5} \times 2\frac{1}{3} = 12\frac{3}{5}$

10. Twenty-four students received a perfect score on the math test. If this is 75% of the class, how many students are in the class?
    (F) 28 students (H) 32 students
    (G) 30 students (J) 36 students

11. Solve. $x - 5 \geq 4$
    (A) $x \geq 1$ (C) $x \geq 12$
    (B) $x \geq 9$ (D) $x \geq 20$

Gridded Response

12. What is the opposite of the opposite of -7?

13. Jack saves \$32.75 from his newspaper delivery job. On Saturday, he spends \$23.52 of his savings on a CD. How much does he have left?

Short Response

14. On a scale drawing, the scale shown is 1 in. to 10 ft. The length of a room is 2.5 in. on the drawing. Make a sketch and find the actual length of the room.

15. Write an integer to represent three degrees Fahrenheit below zero. Then graph the integer on a number line.

Extended Response

16. **a.** Kate drew this graph to show how many dollars she has left in her budget this month. Describe in words what the graph shows.

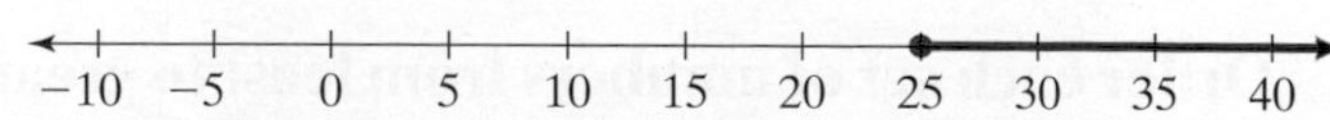

b. Explain how an equation and an inequality are different.

CHAPTER 7 The Coordinate Plane

What You've Learned

- In earlier chapters, you learned to add, subtract, multiply, and divide decimals and fractions.
- You wrote and solved equations.
- You graphed numbers on a number line and used graphs to analyze data.

Check Your Readiness

GO for Help

For Exercises	See Lessons
1–2	2-4
3–4	2-5
5–10	2-6
11–16	6-4

Algebra Solving Equations

Solve each equation.

1. $a + 13 = 92$
2. $b + 12 = 43$
3. $c - 31 = 8$
4. $d - 23 = 8$

Algebra Solving Multiplication and Division Equations

Solve each equation.

5. $7g = 4.2$
6. $h \div 6 = 11$
7. $8j = 328$
8. $k \div 9 = 8$
9. $16m = 240$
10. $n \div 14 = 18$

Comparing and Ordering Fractions

Compare each pair of numbers. Use $<$, $=$, or $>$.

11. $\frac{1}{3} \blacksquare \frac{2}{5}$
12. $\frac{3}{4} \blacksquare \frac{2}{3}$
13. $\frac{2}{16} \blacksquare \frac{1}{8}$

Order each set of numbers from least to greatest.

14. $\frac{1}{8}, \frac{1}{3}, \frac{1}{12}$
15. $\frac{4}{9}, \frac{5}{6}, \frac{7}{12}$
16. $\frac{1}{4}, \frac{6}{7}, \frac{1}{2}$

What You'll Learn Next

- In this chapter, you will locate and graph points and polygons in the coordinate plane using ordered pairs.
- You will represent functions with tables, graphs, and equations.

Key Vocabulary

- coordinate plane (p. 241)
- distance (p. 246)
- function (p. 251)
- horizontal line (p. 246)
- linear function (p. 255)
- ordered pair (p. 241)
- origin (p. 241)
- quadrants (p. 241)
- vertical line (p. 246)
- reflection (p. 245)
- line of reflection (p. 245)

7-1a Activity Lab

Technology

Graphing Points

You can use a graphing calculator to explore how to graph points. An ordered pair is a pair of numbers that describe the location of a point on your screen.

First, prepare your calculator for this activity. Press 2nd [PLOT] 4: PlotsOff to turn off the plots. Press Y= and clear any equations. Press ZOOM 4: ZQuadrant1 to set the window.

ACTIVITY

```
DRAW POINTS STO
1:Pt-On(
2:Pt-Off(
3:Pt-Change(
4:Px1-On(
5:Px1-Off(
6:Px1-Change(
7:Px1-Test(
```

1. First press CLEAR.
2. Press DRAW to select the **Draw** menu. Press ▶ to highlight **Points.** Select 1: Pt-On. Then press ENTER.
3. To graph the point (6, 4), press 6 , 4) ENTER.
4. The ordered pair (6, 4) tells you the location of the point. How far to the right of the vertical line is the point (6, 4)? How far above the horizontal line is the point?
5. Repeat steps 1–3 to graph (4, 5). Describe the location of the point on the screen.

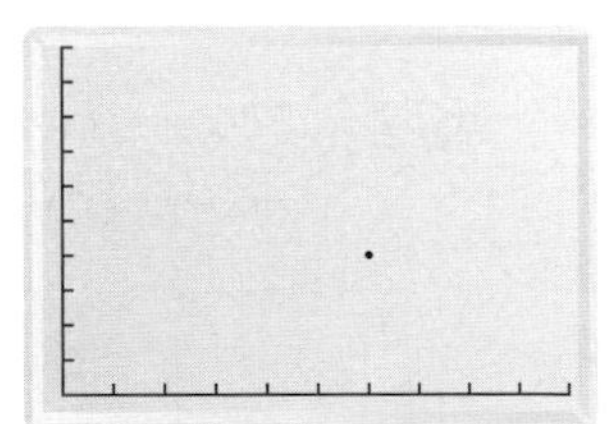

Exercises

Use a graphing calculator to graph each point.

6. (1, 6)
7. (9, 7)
8. (2, 3)
9. (6, 1)
10. **Reasoning** Without using a graphing calculator, describe the location of the point (4, 8). Draw a diagram to check your answer.
11. Graph (0, 4) on a calculator. Why does the point not appear on the screen?
12. **Writing in Math** Your classmate needs to graph (3, 14). Write directions for your classmate explaining how to graph the point on the calculator.

Points in the Coordinate Plane

1. Vocabulary Review *Opposites* are the same distance from __?__ on a number line.

Graph each integer on a number line.

2. −2 **3.** 3

4. 0 **5.** −6

CONTENT STANDARDS

6.NS.6, 6.NS.6.c, 6.NS.8

What You'll Learn

To name and graph points on a coordinate plane

New Vocabulary coordinate plane, quadrants, origin, ordered pair

Why Learn This?

You can use coordinates to find and describe locations on a map.

The **coordinate plane** is a surface formed by the intersection of two number lines. The plane is divided into four regions, called **quadrants.** The **origin** is the point where the two number lines intersect.

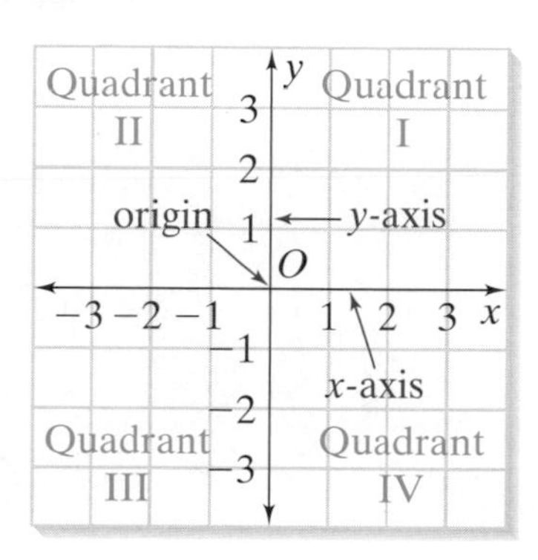

An **ordered pair** is a pair of numbers that describes the location of a point in a coordinate plane. The ordered pair (0, 0) describes the origin.

The x-coordinate tells how far to move right or left along the x-axis.

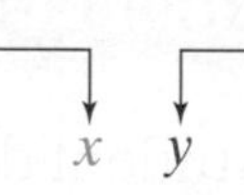

The y-coordinate tells how far to move up or down along the y-axis.

Vocabulary Tip

The plural of *axis* is *axes*.

EXAMPLE Naming Coordinates

1 Find the coordinates of point C.

Point C is 1 unit to the right of the y-axis. So the x-coordinate is 1.

Point C is 3 units above the x-axis. So the y-coordinate is 3.

The coordinates of point B are (1, 3).

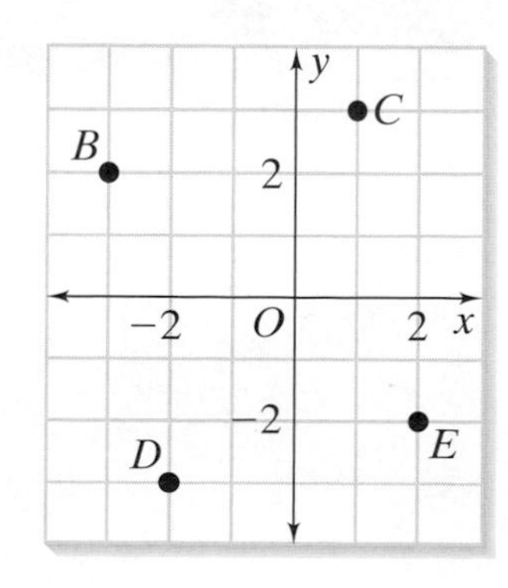

Quick Check

1. Find the coordinates of each point in the coordinate plane.

a. B **b.** D **c.** E

For: Coordinate Plane Activity
Use: Interactive Textbook, 7-1

You can graph points if you know their coordinates. You move right from the *origin* to graph a positive x-coordinate and left from the *origin* to graph a negative x-coordinate. You move up from the x-axis to graph a positive y-coordinate and down from the x-axis to graph a negative y-coordinate.

EXAMPLE Graphing Ordered Pairs

2 Graph point $P(3.5, 2)$ on a coordinate plane.

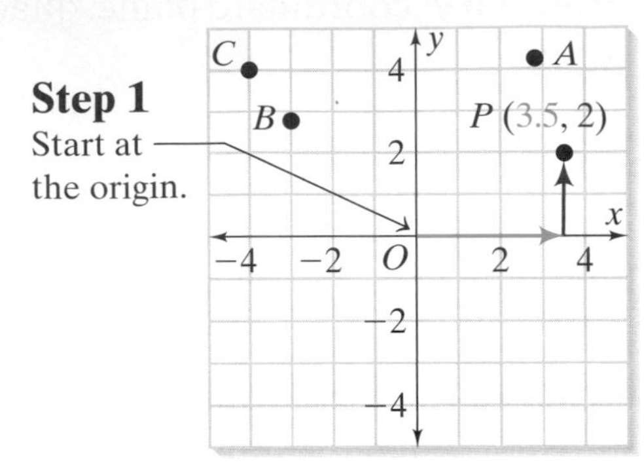

Quick Check

2. Graph each point on the same coordinate plane.
   a. $A(2.8, 4.25)$ b. $B\left(-3, 2\frac{3}{4}\right)$ c. $C(-4, -4)$

EXAMPLE Using Map Coordinates

3 A student drew a map of certain locations in relation to home.

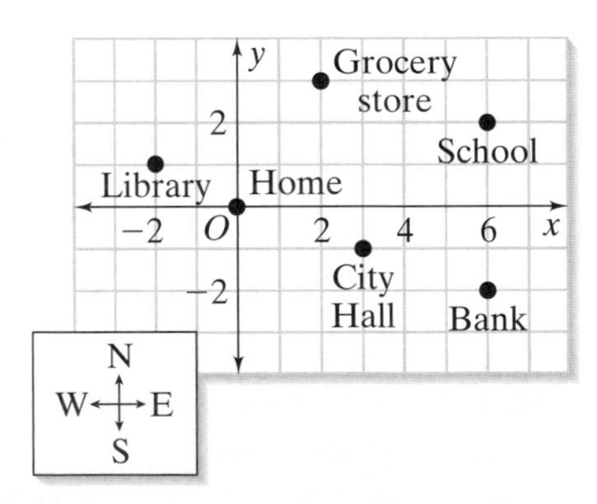

a. Identify the coordinates of the library.

   The library is located at $(-2, 1)$.

b. You leave the library and ride your scooter 2 blocks north and then 4 blocks east. At which building do you arrive?

   You are at the grocery store.

Quick Check

3. a. Suppose you leave the library and walk 5 blocks east and then 2 blocks south. At which building do you arrive?
   b. What are the coordinates of the building?

Check Your Understanding

1. **Vocabulary** Why is order important in an ordered pair?

2. **Open-Ended** Name four points on a coordinate plane that form a square when connected by straight lincs.

3. Which point is NOT in the same quadrant as the other three?
   (A) $(8, -4)$ (B) $(-5, 6)$ (C) $(1, -7)$ (D) $(2, -2)$

Homework Exercises

For more exercises, see Extra Skills and Word Problems.

GO for Help

For Exercises	See Examples
4–11	1
12–17	2
18–20	3

Find the coordinates of each point at the right.

4. B 5. D 6. K 7. Q

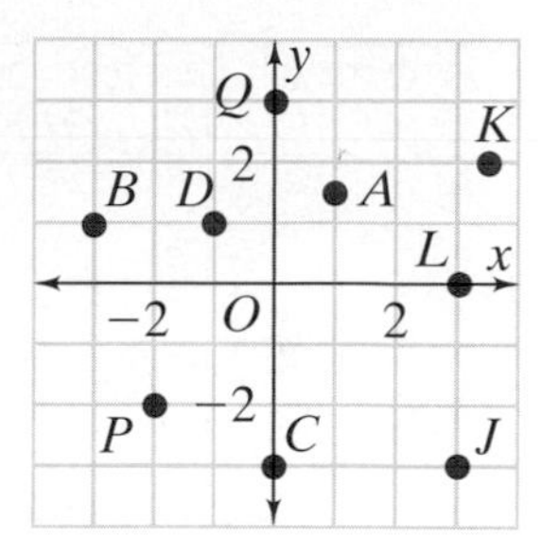

Name the point with the given coordinates in the coordinate plane at the right.

8. $(1, 1.5)$ 9. $(-2, -2)$

10. $(3, -3)$ 11. $(0, -3)$

Graph each point on the same coordinate plane.

12. $A(1, 5\frac{1}{2})$ 13. $B(-5, -3)$ 14. $C(2, -4)$

15. $D(-2, 3)$ 16. $E(1.25, -4)$ 17. $F(-5, 5)$

Use the map below for Exercises 18–20.

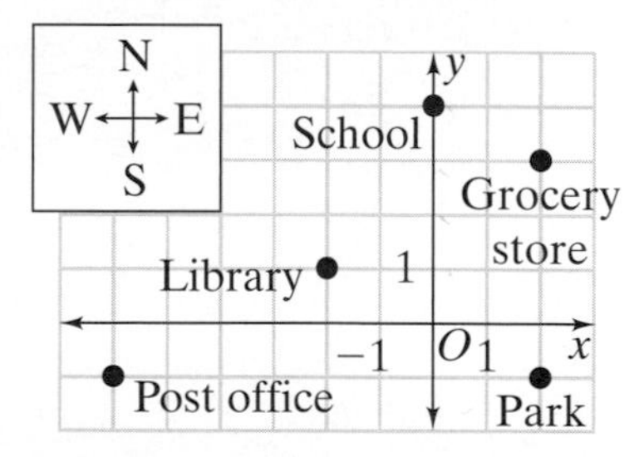

18. You travel 2 units north of the library and 4 units east. Where do you arrive?

19. Find the coordinates of the park.

20. Find the coordinates of the school.

21. **Guided Problem Solving** A police car begins at $(-2, 8)$. It travels 6 blocks east and 10 blocks south to the courthouse. In which quadrant is the courthouse?
    - Which direction on the coordinate plane is east?
    - Which direction on the coordinate plane is south?

22. **Writing in Math** What do all points located on the y-axis have in common? Explain.

Name the quadrant or axis in which each point lies.

23. $(-2, -2)$ **24.** $(6, 4)$ **25.** $\left(0, 4\frac{1}{6}\right)$ **26.** $(-1, 9)$

27. $(-3, 0)$ **28.** $(5.9, \quad 8)$ **29.** $(8, 0)$ **30.** $(0, -10)$

31. Geometry A symmetrical four-pointed star has eight corner points. Seven of the points are $(-1, 1)$, $(0, 3)$, $(1, 1)$, $(3, 0)$, $(1, -1)$, $(0, -3)$, and $(-1, -1)$. What are the coordinates of the missing point?

32. Quilt Making Quilt designers often use coordinate grids to design patterns. Find the coordinates of the pattern shown at the right.

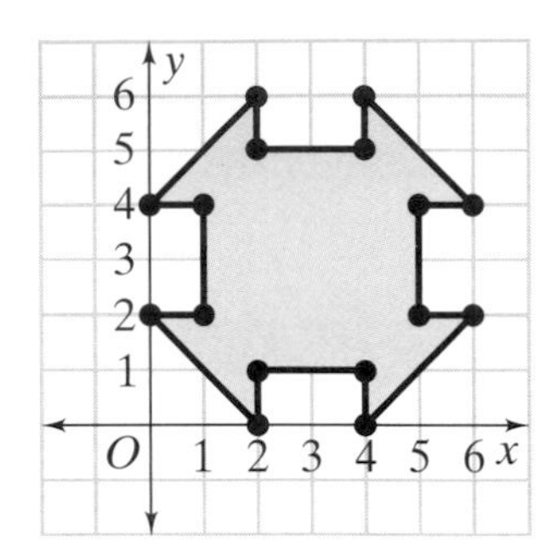

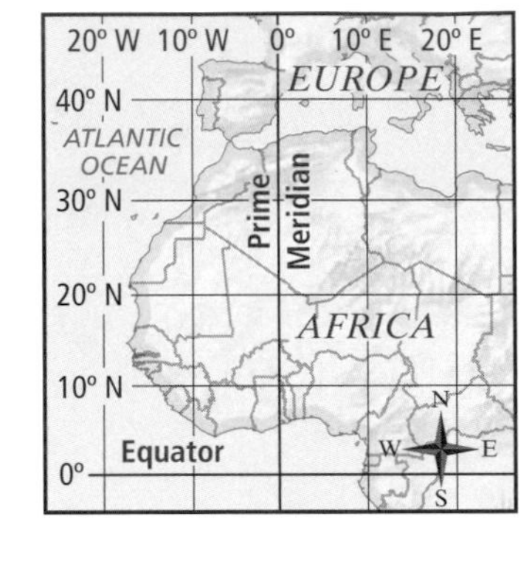

33. Geography Maps of Earth use a coordinate system to describe locations. The horizontal axis is the equator, and the vertical axis is the prime meridian.

a. On what continent is 20° N latitude, 20° E longitude?

b. On what continent is 48° N latitude, 5° E longitude?

34. (Algebra) On which axis does the point $(n, 0)$ lie?

35. Challenge A parallelogram has vertices at $(3, 2)$, $(2, 5)$, and $(6, 5)$. Find three possible points for the fourth vertex.

Test Prep and Mixed Review — Practice

Multiple Choice

36. Which ordered pair represents a point located inside both the circle and the rectangle at the right?

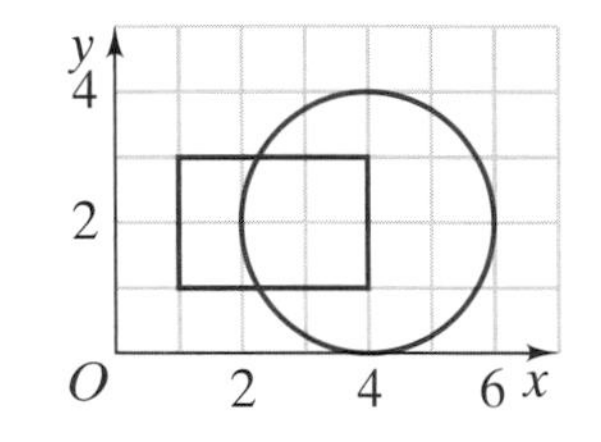

(A) $\left(1\frac{1}{4}, 2\right)$ (B) $\left(3, 2\frac{1}{2}\right)$

(C) $(2, 4)$ (D) $(5, 2)$

37. Belle cut a rectangle from paper for a geometry project.

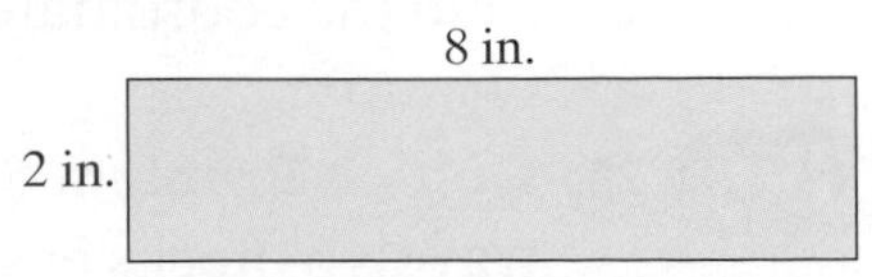

What is the area of the rectangle in square inches?

(F) 6 (G) 10 (H) 16 (J) 20

GO for Help

For Exercises	See Lesson
38–39	6-6

Solve the inequalities.

38. $x - 5 > 10$ **39.** $12 \leq 3r$

7-2a Activity Lab

Reflections in the Coordinate Plane

A **reflection,** or flip, is a transformation that flips a figure over a line called the **line of reflection.** When you use the *x*- or *y*-axis as the line of reflection, there is a relationship between the coordinates of the reflected points.

EXAMPLE

1 List the ordered pairs of the vertices of the parallelograms that are in Quadrants I and II. Find a pattern.

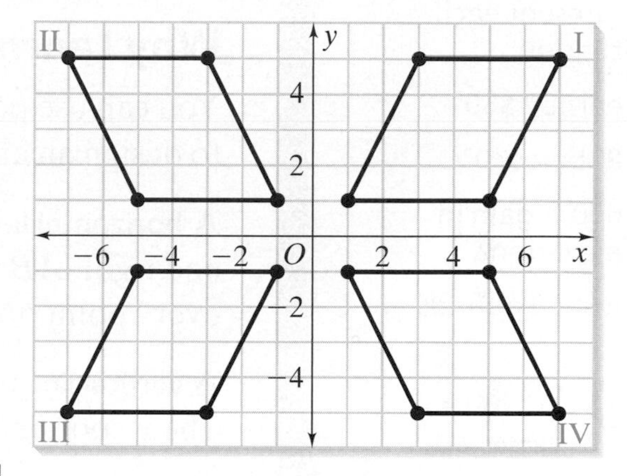

Quadrant I	
x	*y*
1	1
3	5
7	5
5	1

Quadrant II	
x	*y*
−1	1
−3	5
−7	5
−5	1

All corresponding *x*-coordinates are opposites and all corresponding *y*-coordinates are the same.

2 List the ordered pairs of the vertices of the parallelograms that are in Quadrants I and IV. Find a pattern.

Quadrant I	
x	*y*
1	1
3	5
7	5
5	1

Quadrant IV	
x	*y*
1	−1
3	−5
7	−5
5	−1

All corresponding *x*-coordinates are the same and all corresponding *y*-coordinates are opposites.

Exercises

Plot the given points and connect them in order. Reflect the figure over the *y*-axis. Then reflect the original figure over the *x*-axis.

1. (2,2), (4,6), (6,2), (2,2)

2. (−1, −1), (−1, −6), (−7, −6), (−1, −1)

3. (1, −1), (4, −1), (4, −3), (3, −4), (2, −4), (1, −3), (1, −1)

7-2 Polygons in the Coordinate Plane

1. Vocabulary Review What are *integers?*

Use an integer to represent each situation.

2. earned \$50

3. 8° below 0°C

4. 600 ft gain in elevation

5. lost 10 pounds

Lesson 6-1

CONTENT STANDARDS

6.NS.6.b, 6.NS.8, 6.G.3

What You'll Learn

To graph polygons in a coordinate plane

New Vocabulary horizontal line, vertical line, distance

Why Learn This?

You can use polygons in the coordinate plane to design an area.

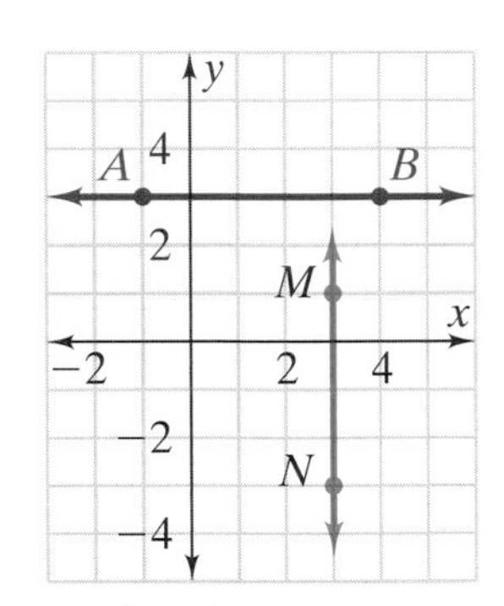

A **horizontal line** is a straight line that extends left and right. $\overleftrightarrow{AB}$ is horizontal. The *y*-coordinates of every point on a horizontal line are the same.

A **vertical line** is a straight line that extends up and down. $\overleftrightarrow{MN}$ is vertical. The *x*-coordinates of every point on a vertical line are the same.

The **distance** between two points is the length of the line segment that connects them. If two points on a horizontal line are on opposite sides of the *y*-axis, such as *A* and *B* above, the distance between them is the sum of the absolute values of the *x*-coordinates. If the points are on the same side of the *y*-axis, the distance between them is the difference of the absolute values of the *x*-coordinates. Since distance is always positive, always subtract the lesser absolute value from the greater absolute value.

Similarly, the distance between two points on a vertical line is the sum (opposite sides of *x*-axis) or the difference (same side of *x*-axis) of the absolute values of the *y*-coordinates.

EXAMPLE Finding Distances

Vocabulary Tip

The word *horizontal* comes from the word horizon.

1 Find the distance from *E* to *F*.

E is located at $(4, -2)$.

F is located at $(4, 3)$.

E and *F* have the same *x*-coordinates, so they are on the same vertical line.

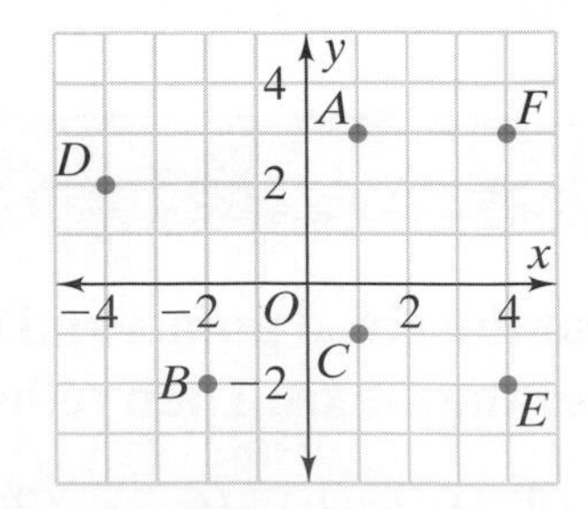

$EF = |-2| + |3| = 2 + 3 = 5$ ← **Points *E* and *F* are on opposite sides of the *x*-axis. Add the absolute values of the *y*-coordinates.**

The distance between *E* and *F* is 5.

Quick Check

1. Find the distance between the points in coordinate plane above.
   a. A and C b. E and B c. F and A

When you draw a polygon in a coordinate plane, you use the given points as vertices. You can use the coordinates to find the lengths of the sides.

EXAMPLE Drawing Polygons

Careers: A landscape designer arranges features of an area for practical and artistic purposes. She could use polygons on a coordinate plane to represent features.

2 **Landscape Designer** A landscape designer uses a rectangle that has coordinates $(-3, 4), (2, 4), (2, 1)$, and $(-3, 1)$ to represent a shed in a yard. What is the perimeter of the shed? Each unit of length represents one meter.

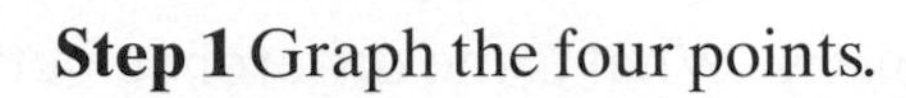

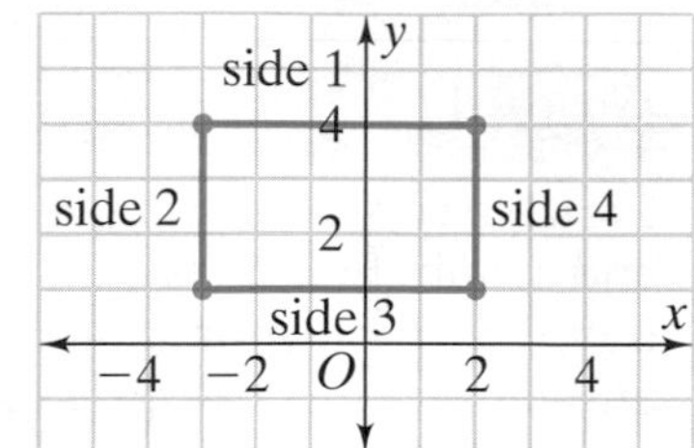

Step 1 Graph the four points.

Step 2 Connect the points to make a rectangle.

Step 3 Find the lengths of the sides.

Sides 1 and 3:

For each segment, the endpoints are on opposite sides of the x-axis. So, add the absolute values of the x-coordinates.

$|2| + |-3| = 5$

Sides 2 and 4:

For each segment, the endpoints are on the same side of the y-axis. So, subtract the absolute values of the y-coordinates.

$|4| - |1| = 3$

Step 4 Add the lengths.

$5 + 3 + 5 + 3 = 16$

The perimeter of the shed is 16 meters.

Quick Check

2. The designer uses a rectangle with coordinates $(3, -3), (5, -3), (5, -5)$ and $(3, -5)$ to represent a flower garden. What is the perimeter of the flower garden? Each unit of length represents one meter.

See Activity Lab 7-2a.

When two ordered pairs have one set of coordinates that are the same and the other coordinates that are opposites, the points are reflections of each other over an axis.

When a point is reflected over the y-axis, the x-coordinates are opposites. When a point is reflected over the x-axis, the y-coordinates are opposites.

EXAMPLE Reflecting Points

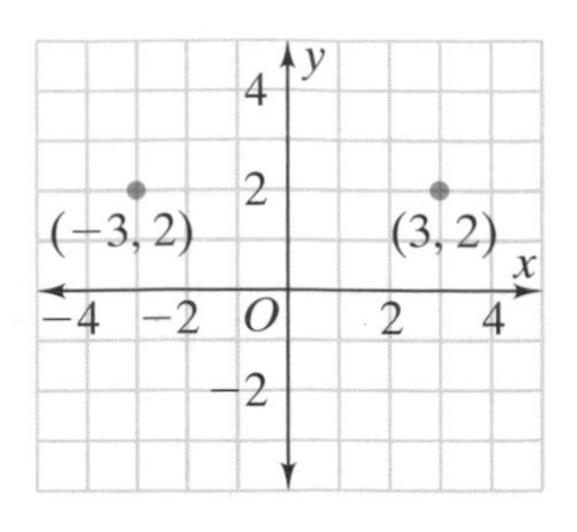

3 How is the point $(3, 2)$ related to $(-3, 2)$?

The y-coordinate for each point is the same, 2.

The x-coordinates, 3 and -3, are opposites.

The point is reflected over the y-axis.

Quick Check

3. How is the point $(2, 5)$ related to the point $(2, -5)$?

Check Your Understanding

Sketch a coordinate plane and graph the points before writing your answer.

1. **Vocabulary** What is the difference between a horizontal line and a vertical line?
2. The points $(-2, 6), (3, 6), (3, -1)$, and $(-2, -1)$ are graphed and connected. What polygon is formed?
3. Suppose the point $(7, -2)$ is reflected over the x-axis. What are the coordinates of its new location?

Homework Exercises

For more exercises, see Extra Skills and Word Problems.

Find the distance between the two points.

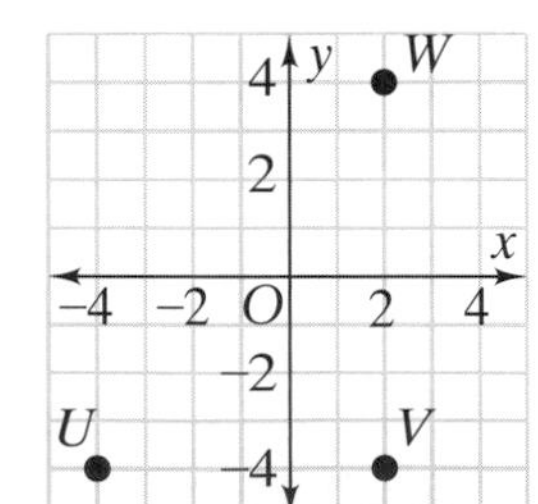

4. points U and V
5. points W and V
6. $(2, 5), (9, 5)$
7. $(4, 0), (4, -12)$
8. $(-7.5, -6.25), (19.5, -6.25)$
9. $(5, 9), (5, 2)$
10. $(0, 0), (0, -7)$
11. $(9.25, 1.5), (-9.25, 1.5)$
12. $(-1.2, -1.2), (-1.2, 3.6)$
13. $(0, 0), (-7, 0)$

For Exercises 14–17, the given points are connected to form a rectangle. Find the perimeter of the rectangle.

14. $(4, 5), (-4, 5), (-4, -5), (4, -5)$
15. $(3, 3), (3, -3), (-3, -3), (-3, 3)$
16. $(-1, 2), (1, 2), (1, -2), (-1, -2)$
17. $(-5, 5), (-5, -5)\ (5, -5), (5, 5)$
18. On a floor plan, a sofa is represented by the rectangle formed by the points $(-5, 2), (1, 2), (-5, 5.5)$, and $(1, 5.5)$. What is the perimeter of the sofa? Each unit represents one foot.

GO for Help

For Exercises	See Examples
4–13	1
14–18	2
19–24	3

For each pair, tell whether the first point was reflected over the x-axis or the y-axis.

19. $(9, 1), (9, -1)$ **20.** $(4, -4), (-4, -4)$ **21.** $(1, 6), (-1, 6)$

22. $(3, 7), (-3, 7)$ **23.** $(8, 5), (8, -5)$ **24.** $(2, -3), (2, 3)$

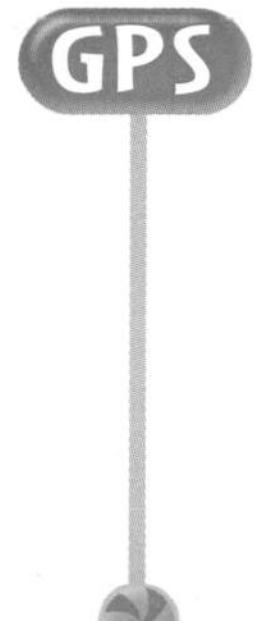

25. Guided Problem Solving Paulo made a diagram of a rectangular vegetable garden he wants to plant on a coordinate plane. His brother accidentally tore off a corner of the paper, and only the points $(-1, 4)$, $(3, 1)$, and $(-1, 1)$ showed. What will be the perimeter of the garden? Each unit of length represents one yard.

- How can you find the fourth point of the garden?
- How can you find the length of each side of the rectangle?
- How do you find the perimeter of the rectangle?

26. Writing in Math What happens to the point $(0, -19)$ when it is reflected across the y-axis? the x-axis?

Homework Video Tutor
PearsonSuccessNet.com

27. Reasoning The point (a, b) reflected over the x-axis, then the y-axis, then the x-axis again, and then the y-axis again. What are the coordinates of the new point?

28. Open-Ended A square has a perimeter of 16 units. One of its vertices is at $(3, -1)$.

a. What is the length of each side of the square?

b. Give possible coordinates for the other three vertices of the square.

c. Is there more than one square that has a perimeter of 16 units and a vertex at $(3, -1)$? Explain.

29. Challenge The points $(-10, 5)$ and $(4, 5)$ are two vertices of a rectangle. Find two other points that make a rectangle with a perimeter of 44 units.

Test Prep and Mixed Review

Practice

Gridded Response

30. The points $(-3, -2)$, $(-3, 4)$, $(2.75, 4)$, and $(2.75, -2)$ are connected to form a rectangle. What is its perimeter?

Solve each equation.

31. $3x = 15$ **32.** $6 = p + 4$ **33.** $\frac{d}{2} = 9$

34. $4 = \frac{h}{3}$ **35.** $35 = 5c$ **36.** $k - 9 = 11$

GO for Help

For Exercises	See Lesson
37–38	6-4

Order each set of numbers from least to greatest.

37. $1\frac{1}{2}, -1.2, -0.12, 2, -1$ **38.** $-4, -\frac{3}{4}, -0.34, -3.4, -3$

Checkpoint Quiz 1

Lessons 7-1 through 7-2

Name the coordinates of each point.

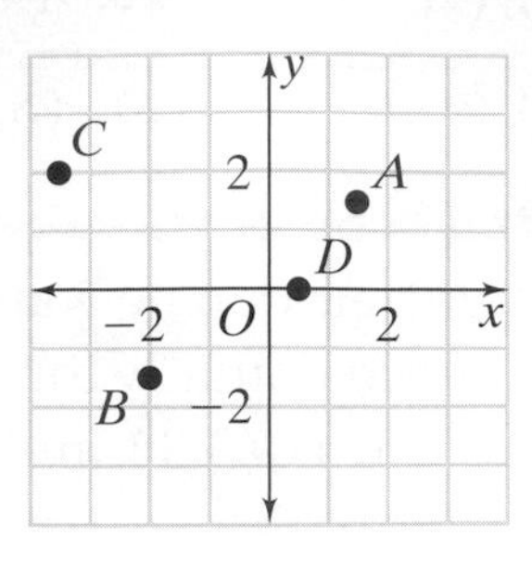

1. A
2. B
3. C
4. D

Find the distance between the points.

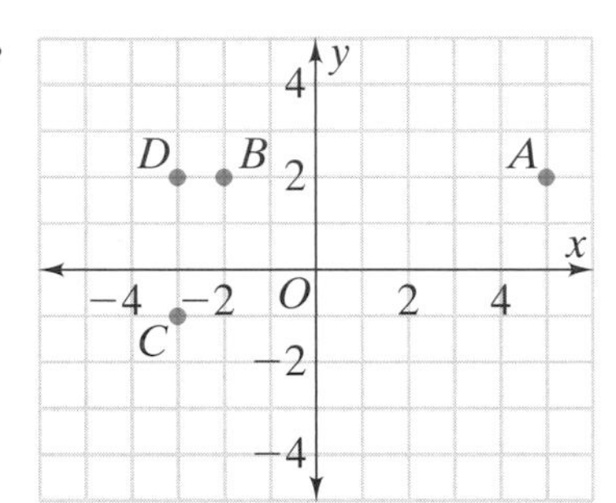

5. A and B
6. C and D
7. B and D
8. A and D
9. The layout of a classroom is plotted on a coordinate plane. The teacher's desk is represented as a rectangle with coordinates $(-5, 3)$, $(-3, 3)$, $(-3, -1)$ and $(-5, -1)$. What is the perimeter of the desk? Each unit represents one foot.
10. What are the coordinates of the new point when you reflect $(-4, 1)$ across
    a. the x-axis?
    b. the y-axis?

MATH AT WORK

Graphic Designer

If you are creative and like art, a career as a graphic designer could be just right for you. Graphic designers use computers to produce images for logos, packaging, or advertising for goods, services, and ideas. Their designs are seen in magazines, posters, newspapers, and television advertisements.

Designers also use mathematical skills. They use coordinates to ensure the exact placement of images.

Go Online For information on graphic designers PearsonSuccessNet.com

7-3 Functions

Check Skills You'll Need

1. **Vocabulary Review** Explain how an *expression* and an *equation* are different.

Evaluate each expression for $x = 3$.

2. $8 + x$
3. $18 \div x$
4. $4x$
5. $21 - x$

Lesson 2-1

CONTENT STANDARD

6.EE.9

What You'll Learn

To make a function table and to write an equation

New Vocabulary function

Why Learn This?

Pretend you have a machine. You can put any number, or input, into the machine. The machine performs an operation on the number and provides a result, or output. A **function** is a rule that assigns exactly one output value to each input value.

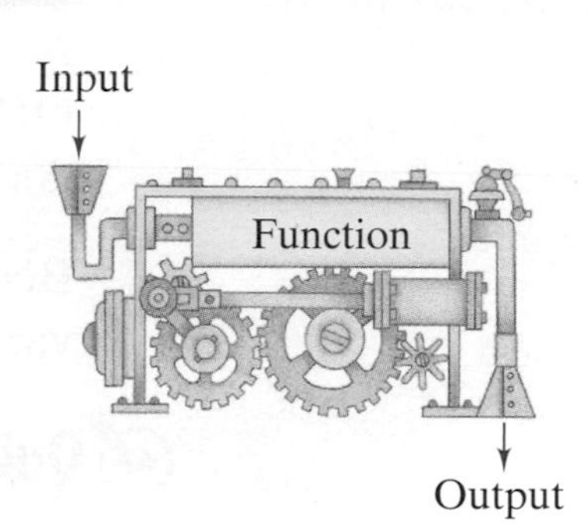

Suppose you tell the machine to multiply by 4. A function table, such as the one at the right, shows the input and output values.

Input	Output
3	12
−7	−28

EXAMPLE Completing a Function Table

1. Complete the function table if the rule is Output = Input · (−2).

Input	Output
−1	2
1	−2
3	−6

← Multiply −1 by −2. Place 2 in the Output column.
← Multiply 1 by −2. Place −2 in the Output column.
← Multiply 3 by −2. Place −6 in the Output column.

Quick Check

1. Complete the function table for each rule.

a. Output = Input ÷ 4

Input	Output
16	■
−24	■
36	■

b. Output = Input − 8

Input	Output
−6	■
−1	■
4	■

The input variable is also called the independent variable. The output variable is the dependent variable because it depends on the input variable.

EXAMPLE Identifying Independent and Dependent Variables

2 Identify the independent and dependent variable.
the age of an octopus and the weight of an octopus

Vocabulary Tip

The independent variable does not depend on the other variable for its value.

Consider the two variables: the age of an octopus and the weight of the octopus.

Think: Which makes more sense?
As an octopus gets older, its weight changes.
OR
As an octopus gets heavier, its age changes.

Because the weight depends on age, weight is the dependent variable and age is the independent variable.

Quick Check

2. Identify the independent variable and dependent variable.
the time spent studying and the test score

You can use variables in a function table to write a function rule. The output (or dependent variable) *depends* on the input (or independent variable).

EXAMPLE Writing Equations for Functions

3 The 8th grade class is selling T-shirts as a fundraiser. They record their daily sales and income in a table. Write an equation for the amount of income the class gets from its sale of T-shirts.

Number of T-shirts	Income ($)
22	242
41	451
50	550
79	869

GO for Help

For help writing algebraic expressions, go to Lesson 2-2.

The income depends on the number of T-shirts sold.
The income is 11 times the number of T-shirts sold.

income = 11 · number of T-shirts sold
$y = 11 \cdot x$

Quick Check

3. The 8th grade class decides to sell hoodies, too. Write an equation for the amount of income the class gets from its sale of hoodies.

Number of Hoodies	Income ($)
14	280
20	400
36	720
49	980

Check Your Understanding

1. **Vocabulary** Explain the difference between independent and dependent variables.

Given the function rule, find the output.

2. Function Rule:
   Output = Input + 100
   What is the output if the input is 147?

3. Function Rule:
   Output = Input ÷ 4
   If the input is –16, what is the output?

x	y
2	4
3	6
4	8
5	10

4. Identify the independent and dependent variables.
   amount of data used on a cell phone and the cost

5. What is the function rule for the table at the left?

Homework Exercises

For more exercises, see Extra Skills and Word Problems.

GO for Help

For Exercise	See Examples
6–7	1
8–10	2
11–14	3

Complete the function table using the rule.

6. Output = Input + 4

Input	Output
−5	■
8	■
31	■

7. Output = Input − 4

Input	Output
−2	■
5	■
14	■

Identify the independent and dependent variables.

8. the outside temperature and the number of people in the park
9. the height of a tree and the number of years since it was first planted
10. the cups of wheat bran you have and the number of muffins you bake

Write an equation for each function table.

11. Carla is converting measurements in inches to measurements in feet.

Number of Inches	Number of feet
24	2
36	3
60	5
108	9

12. Sandra is calculating how much is in her savings account each month.

Number of Months	Total ($)
3	180
6	360
9	540
12	720

13. Kaden is younger than his sister.

Sister's Age	Kaden's Age
3	2
4	3
7	6
10	9

14. A sports drink is made with a number of scoops of powdered drink mix.

Number of Scoops	Gallons of Drink
16	2
32	4
40	5
80	10

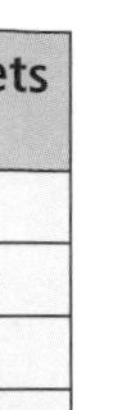

15. **Guided Problem Solving** After lunch each day, the students record the total number of tickets sold to date. Assuming that the pattern continues, how many tickets will be sold in 10 days?
    - What are the independent and dependent variables?
    - What pattern is in the table?
    - What equation could the students use to figure out how many tickets they will have sold after any number of days?

Days	Total Tickets Sold
3	90
4	120
5	150
6	180

16. **Reasoning** Aaron records how much he makes for different numbers of lawns he has mowed. How many lawns were mowed if he earned $368?

Lawns Mowed	$ Earned
2	46
5	115
9	207
?	368

17. **Open-Ended** Describe a situation that can be modeled by the equation $y = x + 10$.

18. **Writing in Math** Explain how you can use an equation to find the independent variable if you know the dependent variable's value.

19. **Challenge** A high school student charges $8 per hour plus a fee of $5 to babysit one child. Make a table, including a row for n hours, and write an equation for this function. How much would the student earn for 8 hours of babysitting?

Test Prep and Mixed Review

Practice

Multiple Choice

20. Which set of ordered pairs will make the data in the table represent the function $y = 3x$?

Input	Output
4	12
■	■
■	■
15	45

    (A) (8, 32), (10, 40)
    (B) (6, 18), (10, 30)
    (C) (5, 10), (12, 36)
    (D) (11, 33), (14, 39)

21. Which point is NOT in the same quadrant as the other three?
    (F) (−3, 5)
    (G) (−1, 6)
    (H) (−4, 0)
    (J) (−2, 7)

22. 264 books are distributed evenly on three library shelves. Use an equation to find the number of books on each shelf.

GO for Help

Exercise	See Lesson
22	2-6

7-4 Graphing Functions

Check Skills You'll Need

1. Vocabulary Review What is the coordinate plane?

Give the coordinates for each point.

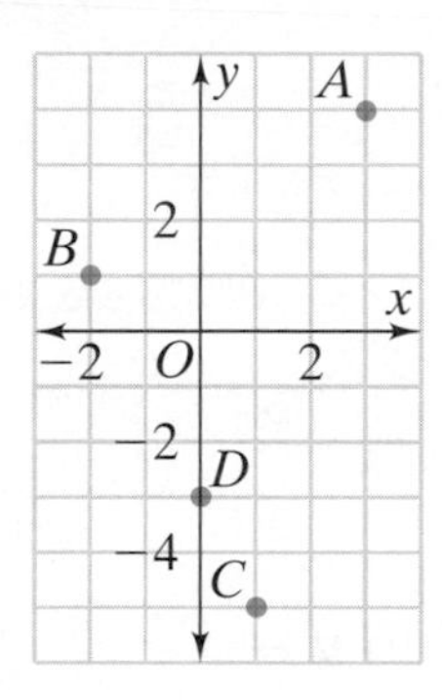

2. *A* **3.** *B*

4. *C* **5.** *D*

Lesson 7-1

CONTENT STANDARD

6.EE.9

Vocabulary Tip

The graph of a *linear* function is a *line*.

What You'll Learn

To graph functions using data in a table.

New Vocabulary linear function

Why Learn This?

You can use the data in a table to graph a function. The graph and the table both model the same function, but in different ways.

x	y
0	1
−2	−1
−4	−3

A function is a **linear function** if its graph is a line. For data in a table, graph the data as points. If you can join the points with a line, then the relationship of the data is a linear function. The data points for a nonlinear function do not fall on a line.

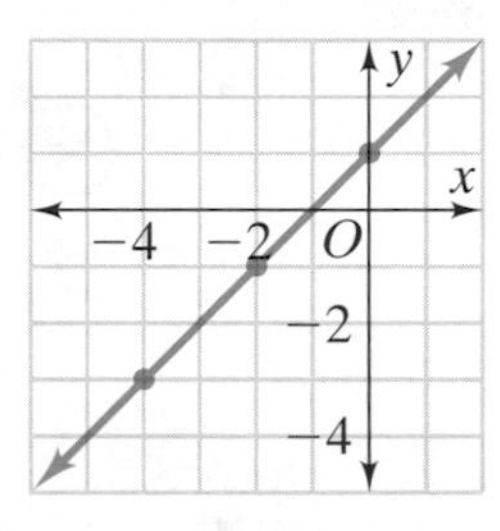

EXAMPLE Graphing a Function from a Table

1 Graph the data in the table. Determine whether the relationship is a linear function.

x	y
−2	1
−1	2
0	3
1	4

Plot the points $(-2, 1)$, $(-1, 2)$, $(0, 3)$, and $(1, 4)$.

Connect the points. These four points lie on the same line.

The function is linear.

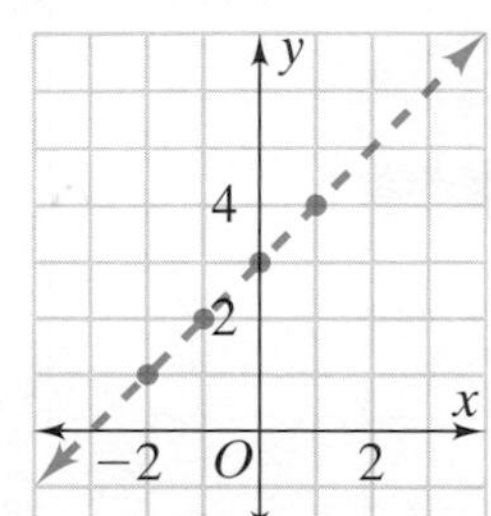

Quick Check

1. Use a graph to determine if the function table represents a linear function.

x	y
−2	3
−1	1
0	0
1	−3

EXAMPLE Graphing a Function

2 Make a table and graph some points of the function $y = x + 3$.

Test Prep Tip

When making a table of values for a function rule, choose lesser values for the independent variable so that you are less likely to make a computation error.

x	y
−2	1
−1	2
0	3
1	4
2	5

← $-2 + 3 = 1$
← $-1 + 3 = 2$
← $0 + 3 = 3$
← $1 + 3 = 4$
← $2 + 3 = 5$

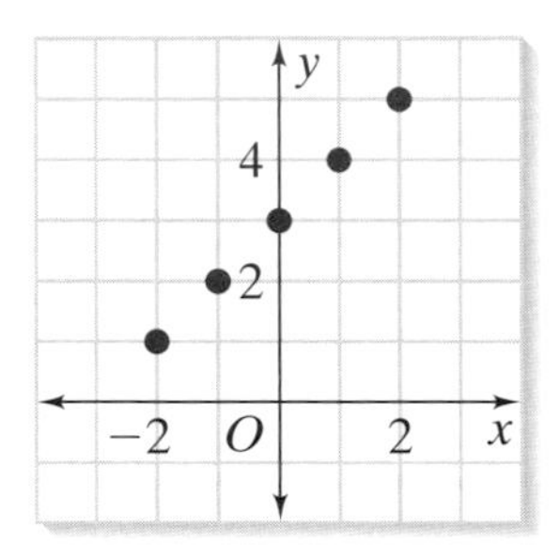

Quick Check

2. Make a table and graph some points of the function $y = x - 3$.

EXAMPLE Application: Salaries

3 A babysitter makes $7 an hour. The function $m = 7h$ shows how the money m he earns relates to the number of hours h he works. Make a table and graph the function.

Hours Worked	Money Earned (dollars)
1	7
2	14
3	21
4	28

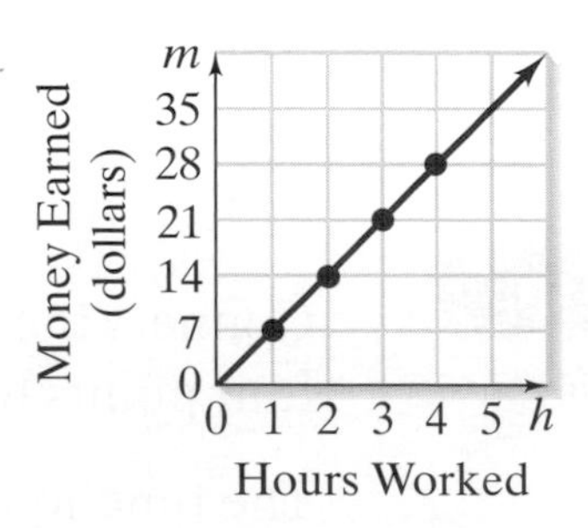

Online active math

For: Graphing Functions Activity
Use: Interactive Textbook, 7-4

Quick Check

3. A car is driven at a steady rate of 45 miles per hour. The function $d = 45t$ shows how time t relates to distance d. Make a table and graph the function.

More Than One Way

A pizza delivery person receives $5 each day he reports to work and $2 for each pizza he delivers. You can express this situation as the function $y = 5 + 2x$, where y = earnings and x = number of pizzas he delivers. How much will the delivery person earn in one day if he delivers 25 pizzas?

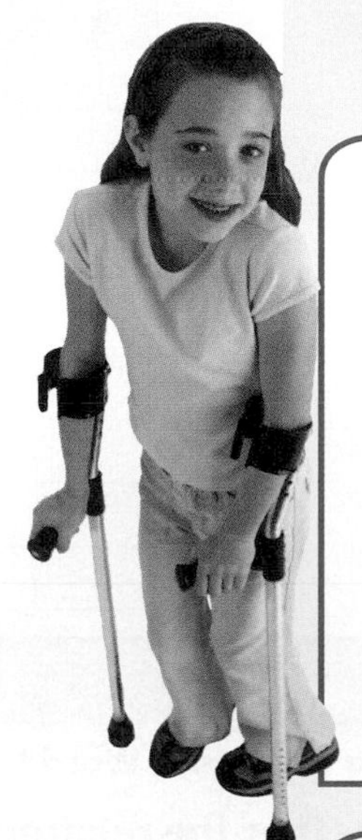

Jessica's Method

I can evaluate the equation to find the amount the delivery person earns. To do so, I replace x with the 25 pizzas he delivers.

$y = 5 + 2x$ ← **Write the equation.**

$y = 5 + 2(25)$ ← **Substitute 25 for x.**

$y = 55$

The delivery person will earn $55 for delivering 25 pizzas.

Leon's Method

If I make a table and a graph, I can tell how much the delivery person earns for delivering different numbers of pizzas.

x	y
0	5
5	15
10	25
15	35

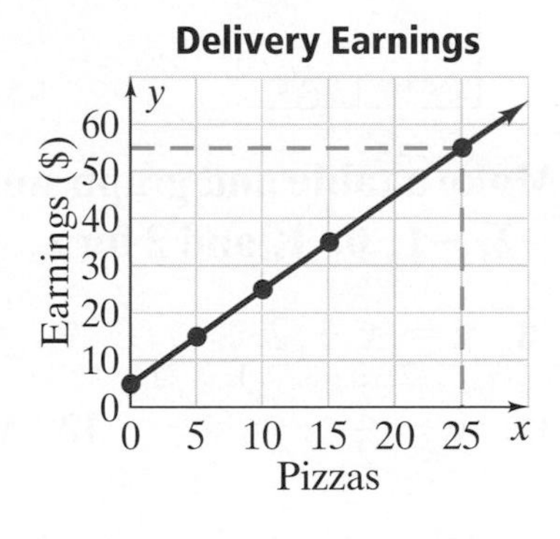

All the points lie on a line, so I can use the graph to find the amount earned for 25 pizzas delivered. When $x = 25$, the y-value is 55. So the delivery person earned $55.

Choose a Method

Tracy is a member of a discount CD club. She pays an annual fee of $30 and $4 for each CD. The function $y = 30 + 4x$ models this situation. If Tracy buys 15 CDs during the year, what will be her total cost? Describe your method and explain why you chose it.

Check Your Understanding

1. **Vocabulary** Describe the graph of a linear function.

2. **Reasoning** How are the graph and table for a function related?

3. Complete the table for the function $y = x + 3$.

x	y
−4	■
−3	■
−2	■
−1	■

4. What are the ordered pairs for the table in Exercise 3?

5. Complete the table and then graph three points of the function $y = 3x$.

x	y
−1	■
0	■
1	■

Homework Exercises

For more exercises, see Extra Skills and Word Problems.

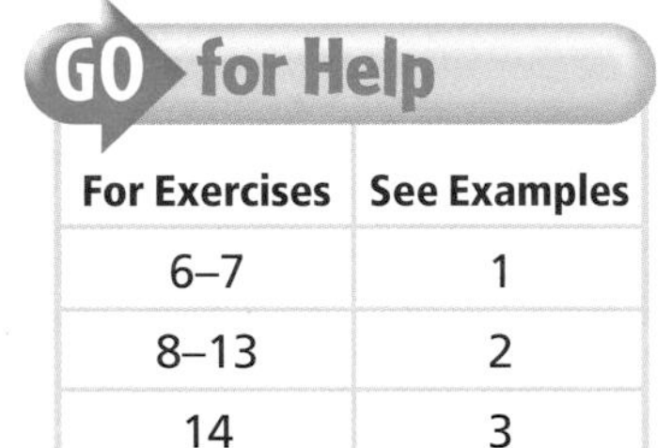
GO for Help

For Exercises	See Examples
6–7	1
8–13	2
14	3

Graph the data in the table. Determine whether the relationship is a linear function.

6.

x	y
−5	−1
8	4
31	35

7.

x	y
−2	−6
5	1
14	10

Make a table and graph some points for each function. Use −2, −1, 0, 1, and 2 for *x*.

8. $y = x + 2$

9. $y = x - 2$

10. $y = 2x$

11. $y = \frac{x}{2}$

12. $y = \frac{x}{2} + 1$

13. $y = -\frac{x}{2}$

GO Online
Homework Video Tutor
PearsonSuccessNet.com

14. **Library** Suppose a library charges a fine of \$0.25 for each day a book is overdue. The function $f = 0.25d$ shows how the number of days d relates to the fine f. Make a table and graph the function.

15. **Guided Problem Solving** You buy shirts for \$9 each. You have a coupon for \$2 off your total purchase. Find the final price of seven shirts.
    - What function models this situation?
    - What number will you substitute for t, the price of a shirt?

16. **Choose a Method** A store sells kicking tees by mail for \$3 each. The shipping charge is \$5. Find the total prices for 2, 3, 4, or 5 tees. Describe your method and explain why you chose it.

Complete each function table. Then write a rule for the function and graph it.

17.

x	y
3	5
4	6
5	7
6	■
7	■

18.

x	y
10	2
15	3
20	4
25	■
30	■

19. **Business** You start a cookie business. You know that the oven and materials will cost \$600. You decide to charge \$.75 for each cookie. The function $p = 0.75c - 600$ relates profit p to the number of cookies c that you sell.
   a. What will be your profit or loss if you sell 400 cookies? If you sell 500 cookies?
   b. How many cookies must you sell to break even?

Writing in Math **Classify each function as *linear* or *nonlinear*. Explain your answer.**

20. $y = x$

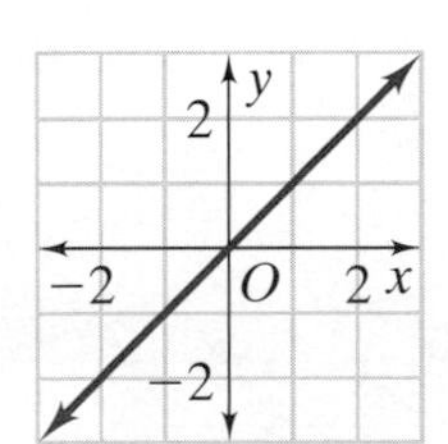

21. $y = x^2$

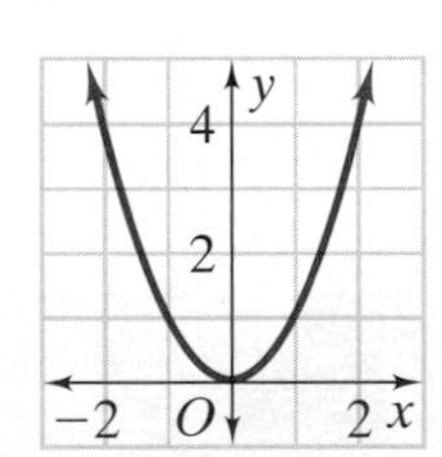

22. $y = \frac{1}{x}$

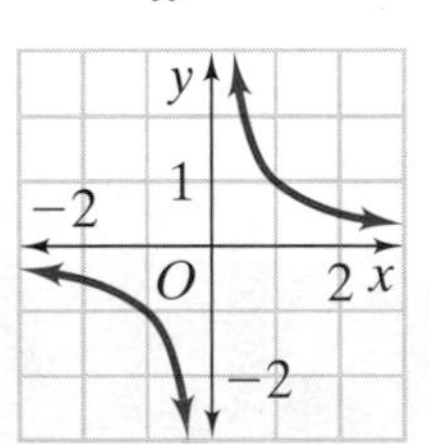

23. **Challenge** Graph $y = -2x$ and $y = -x^2$. What points do the graphs have in common? How are the graphs different?

Test Prep and Mixed Review

Practice

Multiple Choice

24. Which ordered pair shows the coordinates of point P?

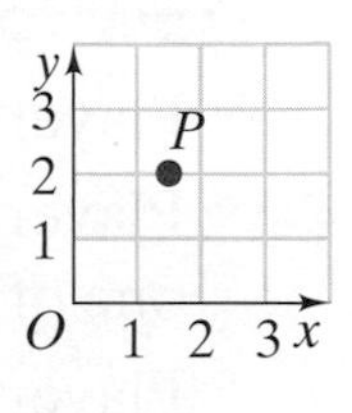

   Ⓐ $\left(1\frac{1}{2}, 2\right)$ Ⓒ $\left(2, 1\frac{1}{2}\right)$
   Ⓑ $\left(1, 2\frac{1}{2}\right)$ Ⓓ $\left(2\frac{1}{2}, 1\right)$

25. Tim drives his car 240 miles in 4 hours. If he travels at this rate, how far will Tim drive in the next 7 hours?
   Ⓕ 1,680 miles   Ⓖ 600 miles   Ⓗ 420 miles   Ⓙ 60 miles

GO for Help

For Exercise	See Lesson
26	6-2

26. Order the following integers from greatest to least.
   $-4, 5, 2, -1, 0$

Checkpoint Quiz 2

Lessons 7-3 through 7-4

Complete the table using the rule.

1. output $= -2 \cdot$ input

Input	Output
12	■
36	■
50	■
105	■

2. $y = x - 15$

Input	Output
64	■
78	■
99	■
120	■

3. $y = \frac{x}{3}$

Input	Output
−9	■
3	■
24	■
30	■

Make a table and graph some points for each function. Use $-2, -1, 0, 1,$ and 2 for x.

4. $y = x + 5$
5. $y = 2x$
6. $y = 8 - x$

7. You are paid $5 per hour for babysitting. The function $p = 5h$ shows how the number of hours h relates to the pay p. Graph the function.

MATH GAMES

Functions

What You'll Need

- Pencil and paper
- 10 index cards

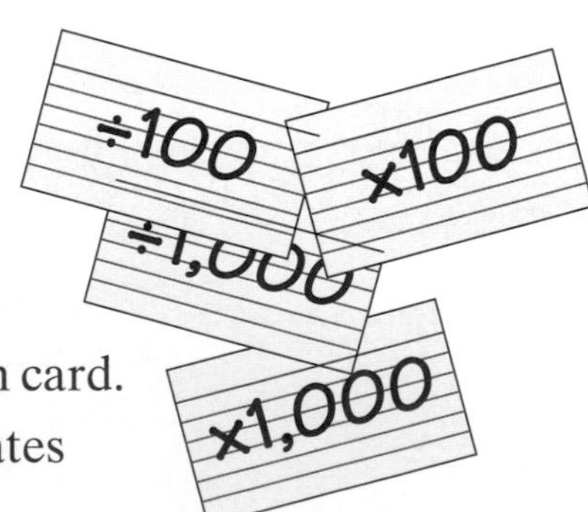

How to Play

- Players each take 5 index cards and write an integer on each card.
- Player 1 draws two cards and writes a function rule that relates one of the cards to the other.
- Player 2 draws one card and applies the function rule to that number. The result is that player's score.
- Players switch roles and repeat. Players take turns until each player has had three turns. Scores from each turn are added.
- The player with the greater score wins.

Algebra

7-5 Functions in the Real World

Check Skills You'll Need

1. **Vocabulary Review** What is an *expression*?

Write an expression for each phrase.

2. six more than a number
3. three times a number
4. four less than twice a number
5. a number divided by twelve

GO for Help Lesson 2-2

CONTENT STANDARD
6.EE.9

What You'll Learn

To use equations, tables, and graphs to represent real-world function situations

Why Learn This?

You can use functions to find how much you earn while working at a job.

Tables, graphs, and equations can represent functions. You can make a table, graph, or equation to represent a situation that can be modeled with a function, such as hours worked and money earned, and then use the representation to solve the problem.

EXAMPLE Using a Table

1 **Wages** Paul works in a pet store during the summer. He earns \$7.50 per hour. Make a table showing the relationship between hours worked and amount earned. How much does he earn in a week if he works 22 hours?

Step 1 Determine the independent and dependent variables. The amount he earns depends on the number of hours he works. So dollars is the dependent variable and hours is the independent variable.

Step 2 Make a table of the possible amounts that he earns. Choose some values for the number of hours worked, including 22 hours. Then, find the amount he earned for each value. To do this, multiply the number of hours by 7.50.

Number of Hours	Dollars Earned
10	75
14	105
22	165
30	225

Step 3 Answer the question.

When Paul works 22 hours, he earns \$165.

Quick Check

1. Helen is a manager at the store. She earns \$12 per hour. Make a table showing the relationship between hours worked and amount earned. How much does Helen earn if she works 40 hours?

EXAMPLE Using a Graph

2 **Traveling** A car travels at 30 miles per hour. How far does the car travel in 5 hours?

Step 1 Determine the independent and dependent variables.
The distance the car travels depends on time of travel. So miles is the dependent variable and hours is the independent variable.

Test Prep Tip

When using a graph to find an answer, draw lines between the graph and the axes to make sure you are reading the point correctly.

Step 2 Make a graph for the situation.

In 0 hours, the car goes 0 miles. $(0, 0)$
In 1 hour, the car goes 30 miles. $(1, 30)$
In 2 hours, the car goes 60 miles. $(2, 60)$

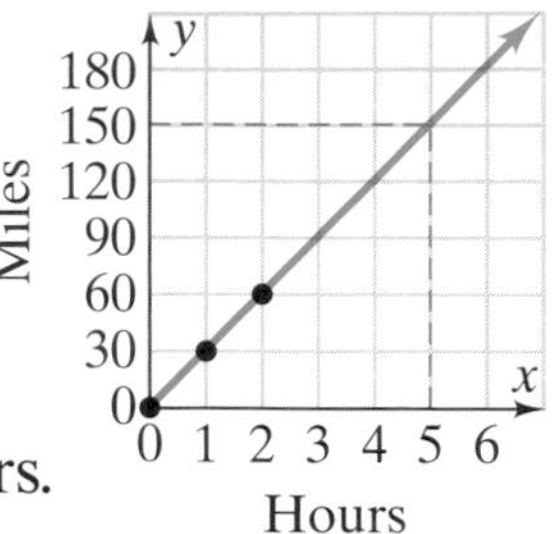

Step 3 Find the point on the line that represents distance when the time is 5 hours.

In 5 hours, the car travels 150 miles.

Quick Check

2. Allen drives his car on vacation. He drives at 55 miles per hour. How far does Allen travel in 3 hours?

EXAMPLE Using an Equation

3 **Buying Tickets** Tickets to the concert cost \$10.50 each. Write an equation showing the relationship between tickets purchased and cost. How much does it cost to buy 5 tickets?

Step 1 Determine the independent and dependent variables.
The cost depends on the tickets purchased. So cost is the dependent variable and number of tickets is the independent variable.

Step 2 Write an equation.
The independent variable (x) is the number of number of tickets purchased, and the dependent variable (y) is the cost.
$y = 5x$

Step 3 Substitute 10.50 for x, and simplify.
$y = 5(10.50) = 52.50$ ← **Substitute 10.50 for x.**

For 5 tickets, the cost is \$52.50.

Quick Check

3. Josh buys tickets to a baseball game. Each ticket costs \$8.75. Write an equation showing the relationship between tickets purchased and cost. How much will it cost Josh to buy 4 tickets?

Check Your Understanding

1. **Vocabulary** Name three ways that you can represent a function to solve a real-world problem.

Use the table for Exercises 2 and 3.

The library is having a used book sale.

Number of Books Sold	Money Received ($)
12	48
19	76
31	124
54	216

2. How much money will the library fund receive if 19 books are sold?
3. How many books must be sold to receive $216?

Use the graph for Exercises 4 and 5.

Kelly tracks how far she has run during the week.

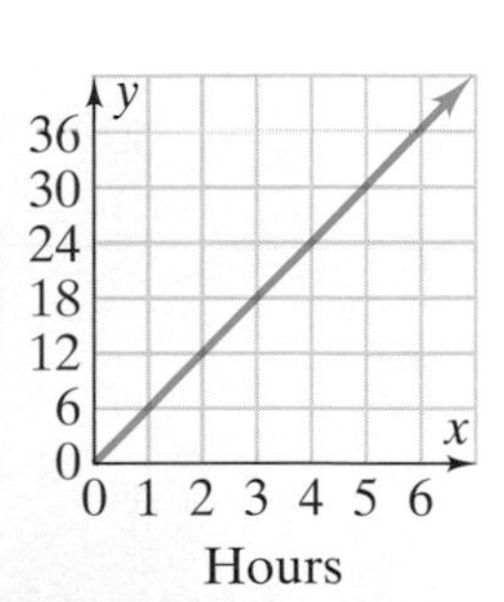

4. How far did she run in 4 hours?
5. How long did it take Kelly to run 36 miles?

Homework Exercises

For more exercises, see Extra Skills and Word Problems.

GO for Help

For Exercises	See Example
6–8	1
9–11	2
12–14	3

Penelope babysits every weekend to earn extra spending money. She earns $6.50 per hour.

6. Make a table showing the relationship between hours worked and amount earned.
7. How much will Penelope earn if she babysits for 5 hours?
8. How much will Penelope earn if she babysits for 9 hours?

Melissa rides her bicycle along a bike trail. She travels at 8 miles per hour.

9. Make a graph showing the relationship between time and distance.
10. How far does Melissa travel in 2 hours?
11. How long does it take Melissa to ride 28 miles?

The bakery is having a sale on muffins. The sale price is $0.75.

12. Write an equation showing the relationship between muffins purchased and cost.
13. How much do 7 muffins cost?
14. How many muffins can you buy for $9.00?

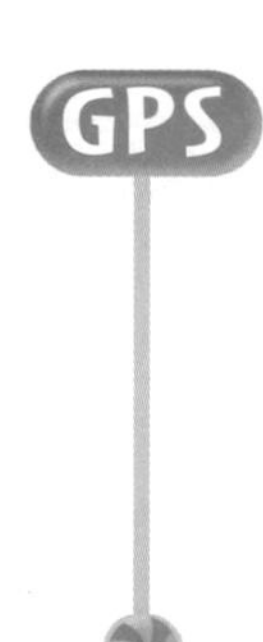

15. **Guided Problem Solving** The French club spends \$5 on flowers for each bouquet they make. They sell the bouquets for \$7.50 each. Use a graph to find the number of bouquets the club will need to sell to make a profit of \$20.00.
    - What is the profit on one bouquet?
    - What variables will you locate on each axis of the graph?
    - Name the coordinates for three points you can plot.
    - How can you check that your answer is reasonable?

16. **Choose a Method** Juanita earns \$5 for each subscription she sells. If she sells 25 subscriptions, will she make enough money to buy a bicycle that costs \$115? Explain. Use a table, graph, or equation to support your answer.

17. **Reasoning** The data at the right shows the amount Caroline earns working. How much did Caroline earn after working 4 hours? Explain three methods you can use to solve the problem.

Hours Worked (x)	Money Earned (y)
1	\$8
2	\$16
3	\$24

18. **Writing in Math** Carl makes \$4 each time he walks the neighbor's dog. He wants to make graph to show how much he can earn for walking the dog various numbers of times. Explain how he might make a graph for the situation.

19. **Challenge** A canoe travels down a river at 4 miles per hour. A kayak traveled 30 miles in 6 hours. Make a graph to determine which boat travels faster. How can you tell which is faster by looking at the graph?

Test Prep and Mixed Review

Practice

Multiple Choice

20. A cell phone plan charges \$25 per month for 250 minutes. For any minutes over 250, the price is 10¢ a minute. Which equation represents this function?

    Ⓐ $y = 250 + 10x$
    Ⓑ $y = 250 + 0.1x$
    Ⓒ $y = 25 + 0.1x$
    Ⓓ $y = 10 + 25x$

Use the number line for Exercises 21 and 22.

D C B A

−5 −4 −3 −2 −1 0 1 2 3

GO for Help

For Exercises	See Lesson
21–22	6-3

21. Which point represents $6\frac{11}{12}$ more than D on the number line?

22. Which point is $1\frac{1}{3}$ greater than C on the number line?

GPS Guided Problem Solving

Practice Solving Problems

Jobs Mandy earns \$6 per hour babysitting, plus \$3 for transportation. How much will she earn for a 1-hour job and a 5-hour job this weekend?

What You Might Think

What do I know?
What am I trying to find out?

How do I show the main idea?

What does the graph look like?

What is the answer?

What You Might Write

Mandy gets \$3 to start and earns \$6 per hour. I want to find out how much she will earn for a 1-hour job and for a 5-hour job.

I will graph $m = 6h + 3$ to show how much money m she earns after h hours of work.

Solve for $h = 1$ and $h = 5$.
If $h = 1$, then $m = 6(1) + 3$, or 9.
If $h = 5$, then $m = 6(5) + 3$, or 33.
Graph (1, 9) and (5, 33). I can connect the points with a solid line because Mandy can get paid for working part of an hour.

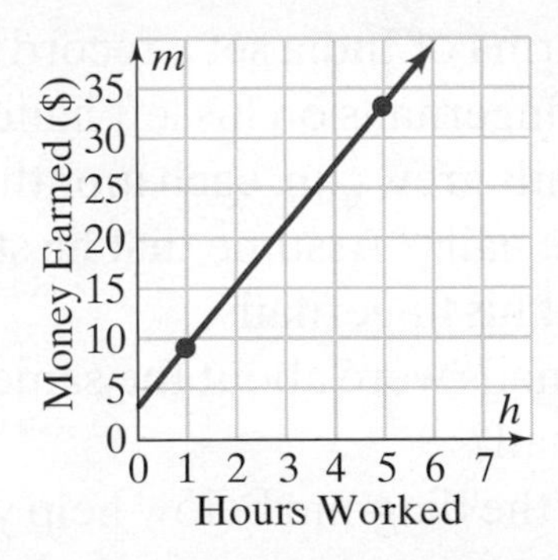

Mandy will earn \$9 for the 1-hour job and \$33 for the 5-hour job.

Think It Through

1. How does the equation $m = 6h + 3$ represent the amount of money m Mandy earns for h hours of work? Explain.
2. How much does Mandy earn for 2 hours, $3\frac{1}{2}$ hours, 4 hours, and $6\frac{1}{4}$ hours of work?

Exercises

Solve each problem. For Exercises 3 and 4, answer the questions first.

3. Fingernails grow an average of 1.5 in. per year. Suppose your nails are $\frac{1}{2}$ in. long on your tenth birthday. You can express this situation as the function $f = 1.5y + 0.5$, where f = length of your fingernails and y = number of years. If you do not cut your nails, how long will they be on your sixteenth birthday?
   a. What do you know? What do you want to find out?
   b. How does graphing the equation give you additional information?

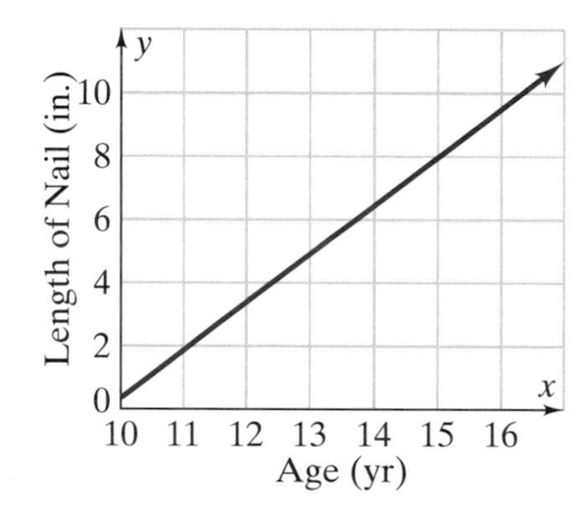

4. Romesh Sharma of India set a record for the longest fingernails. He had five fingernails on his left hand that had a total length of 33 ft. If his nails grew $\frac{1}{8}$ in. each month, about how long did it take to grow those nails? Assume that he started when he was born and never cut his fingernails.
   a. If the five nails were about the same length, about how long was each nail?
   b. How does the diagram below help you decide what to do?

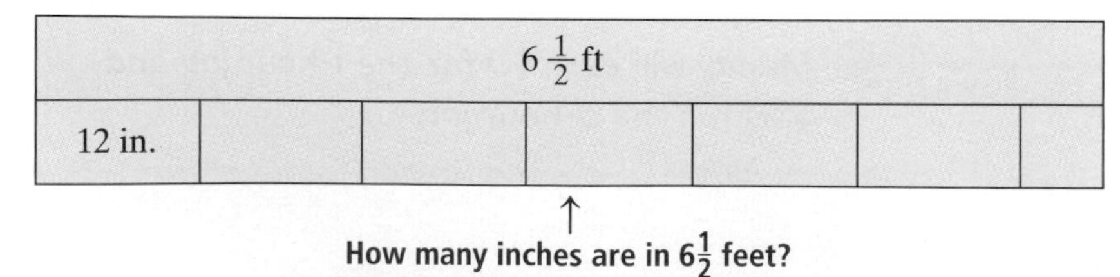

5. In 1982, Larry Walters tied 42 helium balloons to an aluminum lawn chair. He floated above Los Angeles International Airport in his chair for 45 min. If Larry and all his equipment weighed 168 lb, how much did each balloon lift on average?

Test-Taking Strategies

Look for a Pattern

The problem solving strategy Look for a Pattern is useful when taking a test. Patterns can help you complete a table or write a function rule. The table or the function rule can help you solve the problem.

EXAMPLE

Anesh has a coin collection. Last year he had 40 coins. This year he has 65 coins. Each year he adds the same number of new coins to his collection. How many coins does Anesh have 10 years from now?

Ⓐ 105 coins
Ⓑ 290 coins
Ⓒ 400 coins
Ⓓ 105 coins

Look for a pattern to help you find the answer. Each year Anesh adds the same number of coins. Since $65 - 40 = 25$, he adds 25 coins to his collection each year. Make a table to see the pattern.

Number of Years	Number of Coins
0	40
1	65
2	$65 + 25 = 90$
3	$90 + 25 = 115$
...	...
10	$265 + 25 = 290$

The table shows that the number of coins in Anesh's collection each year. Continuing that pattern, you can complete the table for 10 years.

In 10 years, Anesh has 290 coins in his collection. The correct answer choice is B.

Exercises

1. Last year the ticket price for the Fun Times Theme Park was $12. This year the price is $16. The rate of increase remains the same. What will the ticket price be three years from now?
2. A store sells kicking tees by mail for $3 each. There is a shipping charge of $5 no matter how many tees are ordered. What is the cost for 16 tees?

Chapter 7 Review

Vocabulary Review

coordinate plane (p. 241)
distance (p. 246)
function (p. 251)
horizontal line (p. 246)
line of reflection (p. 245)
linear function (p. 255)
ordered pair (p. 241)
origin (p. 241)
reflection (p. 245)
quadrants (p. 241)
vertical line (p.246)

Go Online
For vocabulary quiz
PearsonSuccessNet.com

Choose the vocabulary term that correctly completes each sentence.

1. A(n) _?_ assigns one output value to each input value.
2. A _?_ extends up and down.
3. _?_ are the regions of the coordinate plane.
4. The point $(0, 0)$ is called the _?_.

Skills and Concepts

Lesson 7-1

- To name and graph points on a coordinate plane

A **coordinate plane** is formed by the intersection of an x-axis and a y-axis at the **origin**. An **ordered pair** identifies the location of a point.

Graph each point on the same coordinate plane.

1. $A\ (0, 6)$
2. $B(5, -4)$
3. $C(6, 1)$
4. $D(-2, -3)$

Name the coordinates of each point on the coordinate plane.

5. W
6. X
7. Y
8. Z

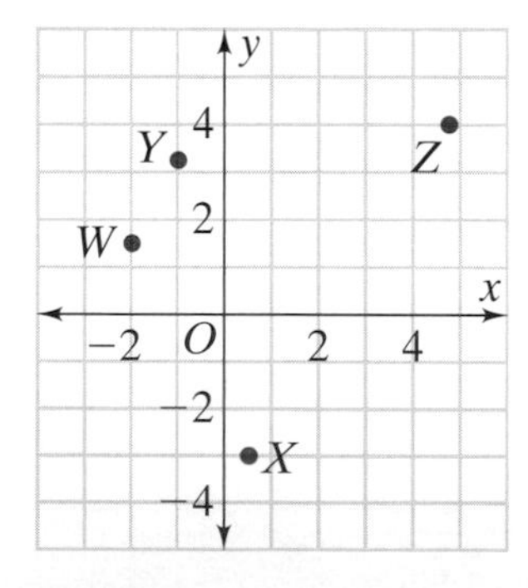

Lesson 7-2

- To graph polygons in a coordinate plane

If two points on a horizontal line are on opposite sides of the y-axis, the **distance** between the points is the sum of the absolute values of the x-coordinates. If the points are on the same side of the y-axis, the distance between the points is the difference of the absolute values of the x-coordinates. Similarly, the distance between two points on a vertical line is the sum (opposite sides of x-axis) or the difference (same side of x-axis) of the absolute values of the y-coordinates.

Find the distance between the two points.

9. $(3, -6)$ and $(-2, -6)$

10. $(4.5, 2)$ and $(4.5, 0)$

11. An architect uses a rectangle with coordinates $(-1, 4)$, $(5, 4)$, and $(5, -3)$, and $(-1, -3)$ to represent a bedroom in a house. What is the perimeter of the bedroom? Each unit of length represents 1 yard.

12. What are the coordinates of the new point when you reflect $(3, -2)$ across
   a. the x-axis?
   b. the y-axis?

Lesson 7-3

- To make a function table and to write an equation

A **function** assigns exactly one output value to each input value.

Complete the function table.

13. Output = Input + 9

Input	Output
16	■
−24	■
13	■

14. Output = $(-3) \bullet$ Input

Input	Output
−12	■
−1	■
4	■

15. Identify the independent and dependent variables: how far you run, the time you spend running.

Lesson 7-4

- To graph functions using data from tables

A function is a **linear function** if its graph is a line.

16. Graph the data in the table at the right. Determine whether the relationship is a linear function.

x	y
−3	−1
0	2
2	4

17. Make a table and graph some points of the function $y = 2x$.

Lesson 7-5

- To use equations, tables, and graphs to represent real-world situations

Tables, graphs, and equations can represent functions.

18. Michael rides his bike at a rate of 7 miles per hour. Make a table showing the relationship between time and distance. How far does Michael ride in 5 hours?

19. Cupcakes cost $1.50 each. Make a graph showing the relationship between cupcakes and cost. How much will it cost to buy 12 cupcakes?

20. Jessie earns $5 an hour babysitting for her cousin. Write an equation showing the relationship between time and money earned. How much will Jessie earn if he babysits for $3\frac{1}{2}$ hours?

Chapter 7 Test

Go Online For online chapter test PearsonSuccessNet.com

Use the coordinate plane below for Exercises 1 and 2.

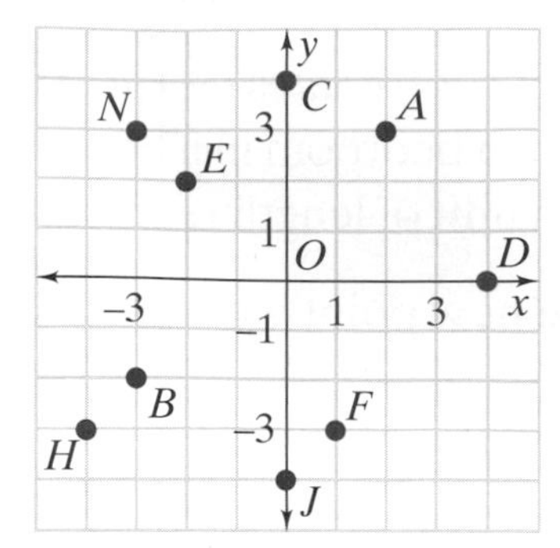

1. Name the point with the given coordinates.
   a. $(0,4)$ b. $(-3,3)$ c. $(-4,-3)$

2. Write the coordinates of each point.
   a. A c. F
   b. B d. J

3. Graph each point on a coordinate plane.
   a. $(-2,-3)$ b. $(4,-5)$ c. $(2,6)$

4. Find the distance between $(-1,1.4)$ and $(-1,2.9)$.
   A -2 B -1 C 1.5 D 4.3

5. Matt draws a rectangle that has coordinates $(-4,1),(5,1),(5,-3)$, and $(-4,-3)$. What is the perimeter of the rectangle? Each unit of length represents one meter.

6. What are the coordinates of the point $(-1,5)$ when it is reflected across the y-axis?
   A $(1,5)$ C $(-1,-5)$
   B $(-1,-5)$ D $(1,-5)$

7. **Carpentry** Franco makes a table to show the conversion from yards to feet. Write an equation for this function table.

Number of Yards	Number of Feet
2	6
3	9
4	12
5	15

8. **Writing in Math** Desmond graphs the time it takes to mow a lawn and the size of the yard he mows. Explain which variable is dependent and how you know.

9. Complete the function table and graph the points. Determine whether the relationship is a linear function.

x	y
1	4
3	12
6	■
7	■

10. Draw a graph for the linear function $y = x - 3$.

11. Caitlyn works in a bookstore. She earns \$11 per hour. Make a table showing the relationship between hours worked and amount earned. How much does Caitlyn earn if she works 35 hours in a week?

12. Hannah collects baseball cards. Each pack of cards costs \$2.75. Write an equation showing the relationship between packs of cards and cost. How much will it cost Hannah to buy 6 packs of cards?

13. A bus travels at 45 miles per hour. Make a graph showing the relationship between time and distance. How far does the bus travel in 6 hours?

Multiple Choice

Choose the correct letter.

1. Evaluate the expression $4.3 + m \div 10$ for $m = 15$.
   - A 1.93
   - B 5.2
   - C 5.8
   - D 29.3

2. Simplify $3 + (4 + 1)^2$.
   - F 13
   - G 25
   - H 28
   - J 64

3. Todd ran around the track in less than 10 minutes. Which is an inequality for the situation?
   - A $t \geq 10$
   - B $t > 10$
   - C $t \leq 10$
   - D $t < 10$

4. Solve the equation $d + 2\frac{1}{2} = 5\frac{3}{4}$.
   - F $3\frac{1}{4}$
   - G $3\frac{3}{4}$
   - H $7\frac{1}{4}$
   - J $8\frac{1}{4}$

5. What is the prime factorization of 24?
   - A $2^3 \cdot 3$
   - B $2^3 \cdot 2$
   - C $2^2 \cdot 6$
   - D $4 \cdot 6$

6. Which number is NOT equivalent to $\frac{5}{25}$?
   - F $\frac{20}{100}$
   - G 20%
   - H 0.20
   - J $\frac{2}{5}$

7. What operation would you perform first in the expression below?

   $12.5 - 1.6 \times 10 + 4 \div 2.5$

   - A Subtract 1.6 from 12.5.
   - B Multiply 1.6 and 10.
   - C Add 10 and 4.
   - D Divide 4 by 2.5.

8. Which statement is NOT true?
   - F $-5 < -2$
   - G $-3 < 7$
   - H $-6 > -2$
   - J $4 > -1$

9. Which point has the coordinates $(-2, 3.5)$?

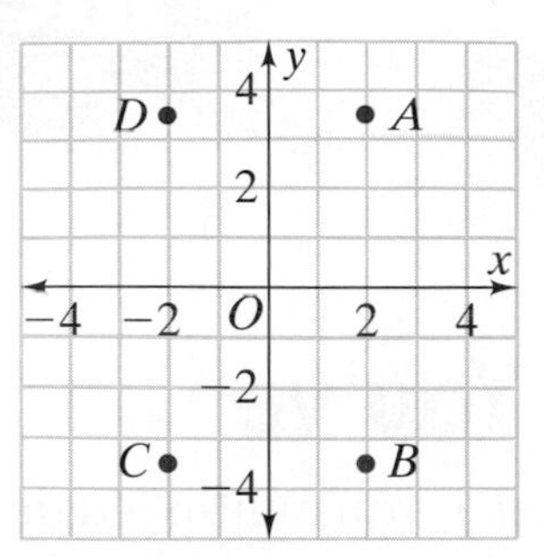

   - A A
   - B B
   - C C
   - D D

Gridded Response

10. Jessie paid \$30 for a pair of shoes that were 25% off. What was the original price of the shoes?

11. Solve the equation $6.8p - 14 = 13.2$ for p.

12. A pound of cheese costs \$5.40 and a pound of ham costs \$6.98. What is the total cost of 1 pound of cheese and 2.5 pounds of ham?

Short Response

13. The diagram shows the ratio of children to adults at the park. Describe the ratio shown in the diagram.

Children ▭▭▭▭▭▭▭

Adults ▭▭▭▭

Extended Response

14. Gabe earns \$54.32 in 8 hours. Brannon \$78.60 in 12 hours.
    a. What is Gabe's unit rate for earnings? What is Brannon's unit rate?
    b. How much will Gabe and Brannon earn together if they each work 15 hours?
    c. Explain how you solved the problem.

CHAPTER 8 Geometry and Measurement

What You've Learned

- In Chapter 1, you multiplied decimals to solve problems.
- In Chapter 2, you evaluated algebraic expressions.
- In Chapter 4, you multiplied fractions and mixed numbers to solve problems.

Check Your Readiness

GO for Help

For Exercises	See Lessons
1–3	1-5
4–7	2-1
8–13	4-1

Multiplying Decimals

Find each product.

1. $\begin{array}{r} 0.8 \\ \times 0.7 \\ \hline \end{array}$

2. $\begin{array}{r} 26 \\ \times 0.4 \\ \hline \end{array}$

3. $\begin{array}{r} 2.5 \\ \times 3.5 \\ \hline \end{array}$

Evaluating Algebraic Expressions

Evaluate each expression.

4. $12s$ for $s = 4$

5. $p + 9$ for $p = 4$

6. $6b - 4$ for $b = 1.2$

7. $c \div 5$ for $c = 20.5$

Multiplying Fractions and Mixed Numbers

Find each product.

8. $\frac{1}{2} \times \frac{2}{5}$

9. $\frac{1}{2} \times 15$

10. $\frac{2}{9} \times \frac{5}{8}$

11. $2\frac{1}{3} \times 5\frac{1}{4}$

12. $5\frac{1}{2} \times 8\frac{3}{4}$

13. $6\frac{2}{5} \times 3\frac{1}{6}$

What You'll Learn Next

- In this chapter, you will find the areas of parallelograms and triangles.
- You will compose and decompose figures to find their areas.
- You will identify three-dimensional figures and find their surface areas and volumes.

Key Vocabulary

- area (p. 275)
- compose (p. 281)
- cone (p. 287)
- cube (p. 286)
- cylinder (p. 287)
- decompose (p. 281)
- edge (p. 286)
- faces (p. 286)
- net (p. 292)
- prism (p. 286)
- pyramid (p. 287)
- sphere (p. 287)
- surface area (p. 293)
- vertex (p. 286)
- volume (p. 299)

8-1a Activity Lab

Hands On

Comparing Areas

In this activity, you will investigate how to find the areas of parallelograms and triangles. The *area* of a figure is the number of square units the figure contains.

ACTIVITY

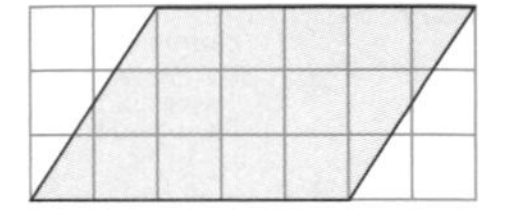

1. On graph paper, draw a parallelogram that does not have a right angle. Cut out your parallelogram.
2. Draw a segment from one vertex that is perpendicular to the opposite base. Cut along that segment.

3. Arrange both pieces of the parallelogram to form a rectangle.
4. **Number Sense** Find the area of your rectangle. Is this area the same as the area of your parallelogram? Explain.
5. Repeat Steps 1–4 using a different parallelogram that does not have a right angle.
6. Write a formula that you can use to find the area of the parallelogram in the diagram on the right. Explain why the formula works. Then find the area of the parallelogram.

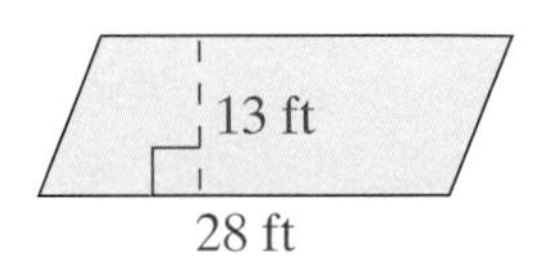

ACTIVITY

7. Draw two identical triangles on graph paper. Cut out both triangles.

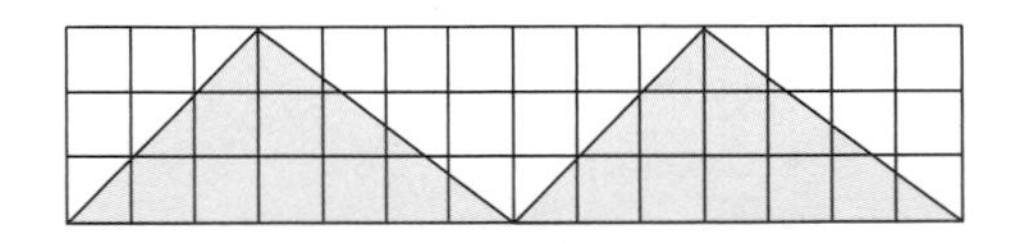

8. Arrange and tape both triangles to form a parallelogram. Then repeat Steps 2–4.
9. Repeat Steps 7 and 8 using a different triangle, such as an isosceles triangle.
10. **Writing in Math** Write a formula that you can use to find the area of the triangle on the right. Explain why the formula works. Then find the area of the triangle.

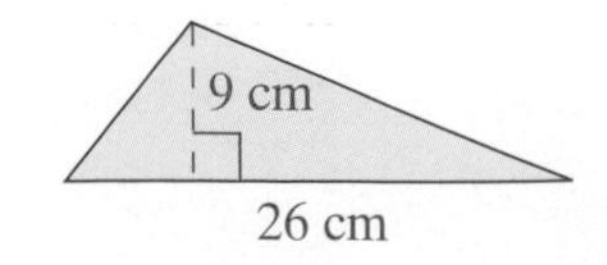

8-1 Areas of Parallelograms and Triangles

Check Skills You'll Need

1. **Vocabulary Review** A mathematical *expression* with one or more variables is a(n)_____ expression.

Evaluate each expression for $a = 5$, $b = 2$ and $c = 6$.

2. $a \times b$
3. $\frac{1}{2}(b \times c)$
4. $\frac{1}{2}b \times a$
5. $c \times b$

GO for Help Lesson 2-1

CONTENT STANDARD
6.G.1

What You'll Learn

To solve problems involving areas of parallelograms, triangles, and complex figures

New Vocabulary area, base of a parallelogram, height of a parallelogram, base of a triangle, height of a triangle

Why Learn This?

Conservation groups purchase land to protect wildlife. The value of the land depends in part on its area.

The **area** of a figure is the number of square units it contains. To find the area of a parallelogram, multiply the base by the height. Any side can be considered the **base of a parallelogram.** The **height of a parallelogram** is the perpendicular distance between opposite bases.

KEY CONCEPTS Area of a Parallelogram

$A = b \times h$

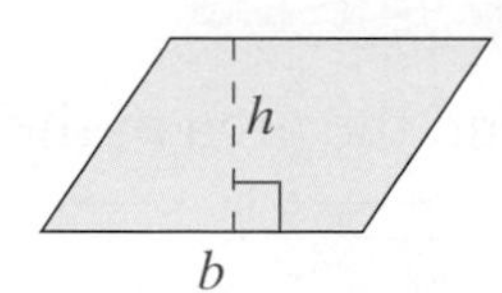

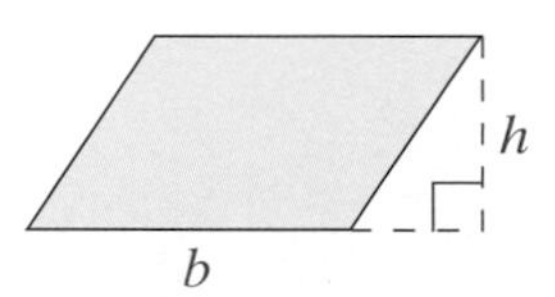

Test Prep Tip

A griddable answer is not always a decimal.

		1	5
	/	/	
.	.	.	.
	0	0	0
1	1	1	1
2	2	2	2
3	3	3	3
4	4	4	4
5	5	5	5
6	6	6	6
7	7	7	7
8	8	8	8
9	9	9	9

EXAMPLE Finding the Area of a Parallelogram

1 **Gridded Response** Find the area of the parallelogram.

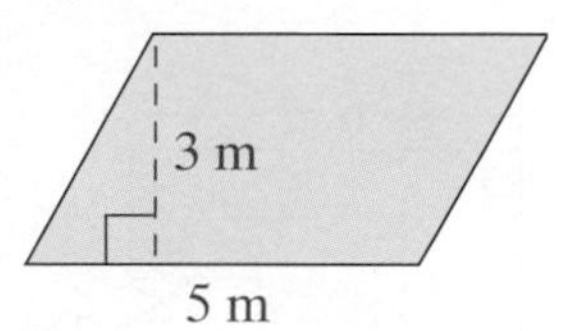

$A = b \times h$ ← Use the formula for the area of a parallelogram.

$= 5 \times 3$ ← Substitute 5 for b and 3 for h.

$= 15$ ← Simplify.

The area of the parallelogram is 15 m^2.

Quick Check

1. Find the area of a parallelogram with $b = 14$ m and $h = 5$ m.

Any side of a triangle can be the **base of a triangle.** The **height of a triangle** is the length of the perpendicular segment from a vertex to the base opposite that vertex.

The diagram at the right shows that the area of a triangle is half of the area of a parallelogram with the same base length and height, or $A = \frac{1}{2}b \times h$.

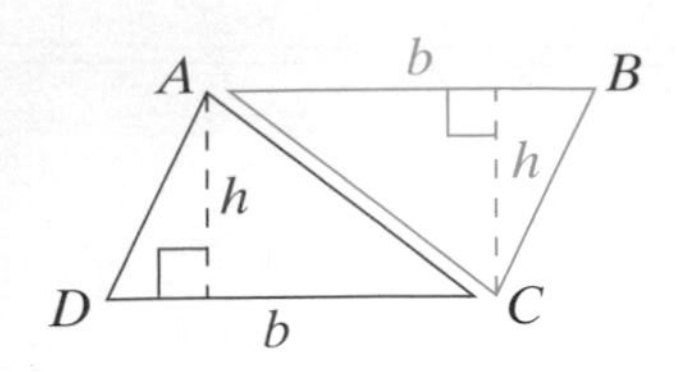

EXAMPLE Finding the Area of a Triangle

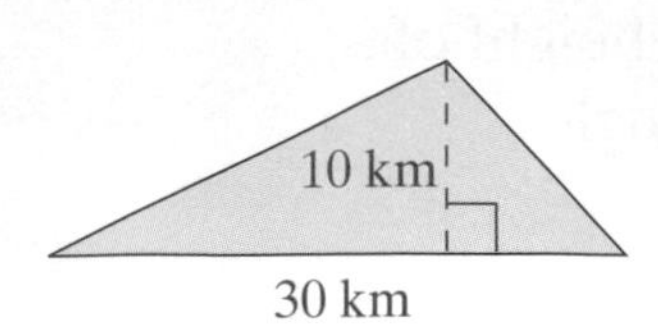

2 **Conservation** A conservation group plans to buy a triangular plot of land shown at the left. What is the area of the plot?

$A = \frac{1}{2}b \times h$ ← **Use the formula for the area of a triangle.**

$= \frac{1}{2} \times 30 \times 10$ ← **Substitute 30 for *b* and 10 for *h*.**

$= 150$ ← **Simplify.**

The area of the plot is 150 km^2.

Quick Check

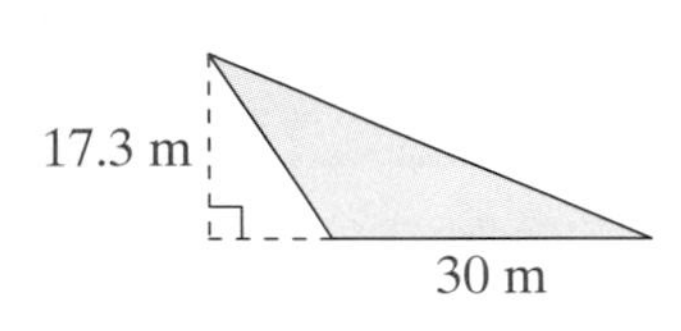

2. The obtuse triangle at the left has a base of 30 m and a height of 17.3 m. Find the triangle's area.

Sometimes you can split a complex figure into smaller polygons.

EXAMPLE Finding the Area of a Complex Figure

3 Find the area of the figure.

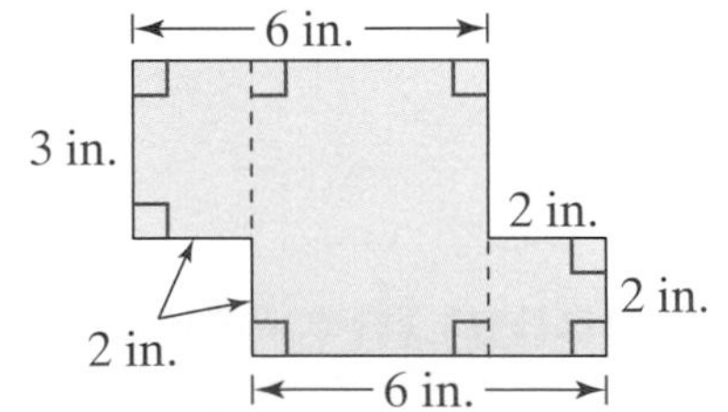

← **Split the polygon into two rectangles and a square, as shown by the dashed lines.**

Area of smaller rectangle: 3×2, or 6 $in.^2$

Area of larger rectangle: 4×5, or 20 $in.^2$

Area of square: 2×2, or 4 $in.^2$

} **Find the area of each polygon.**

The total area is $6 + 20 + 4$, or 30 $in.^2$.

Quick Check

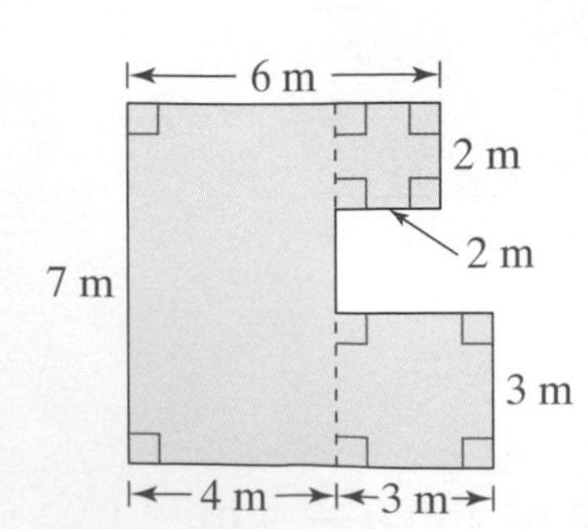

3. Find the area of the figure at the left.

Check Your Understanding

1. **Vocabulary** Explain why the height of a triangle depends on which side you select for the base.

2. If you double the length of the base of a triangle, how does the area of the triangle change?

3. **Reasoning** Draw a triangle and a rectangle that have the same base and the same height. How are the areas of the two figures related?

Homework Exercises

For more exercises, see Extra Skills and Word Problems.

GO for Help

For Exercises	See Examples
4–6	1
7–10	2
11–12	3

Find the area of each parallelogram or triangle.

4.
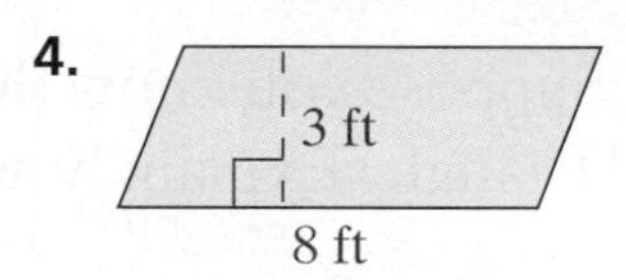

5.
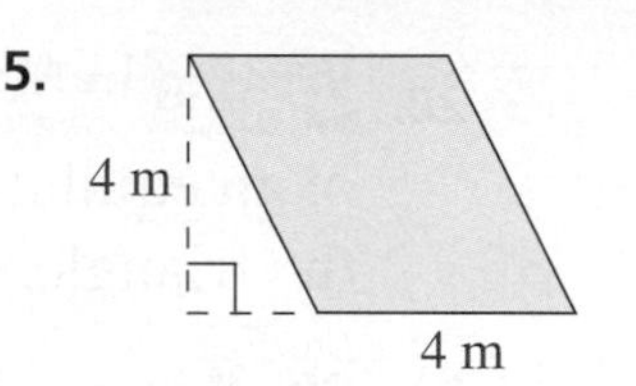

6.
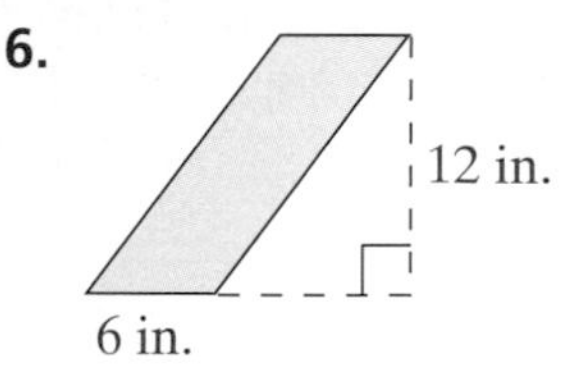

7.
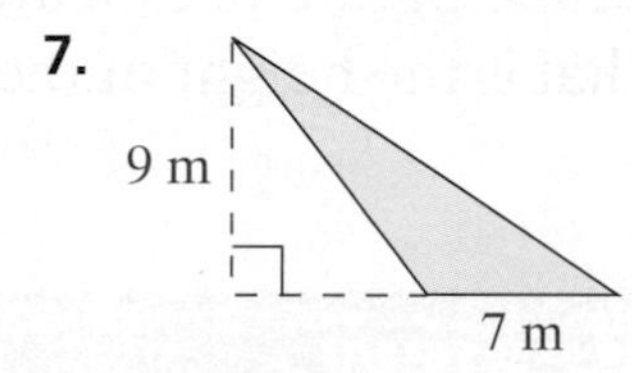

8.
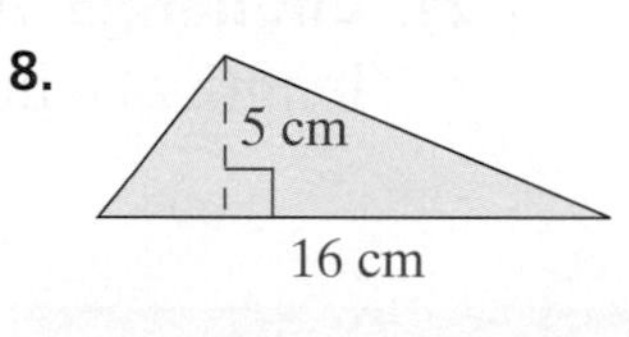

9.
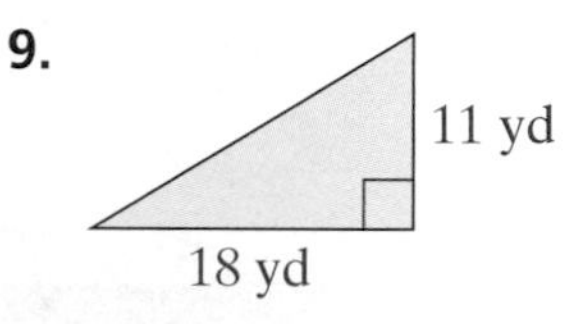

10. **Art** You sprinkle glitter on a triangular area of a card. The triangle has a base of 5 cm and a height of 10 cm. What is the area of the triangle?

Find the area of each complex figure.

11.
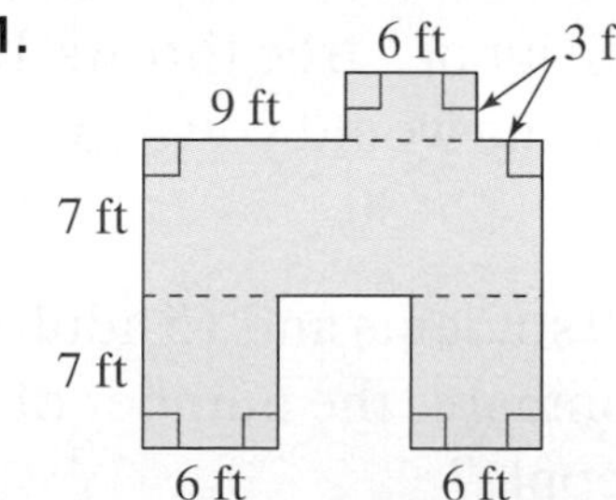

12.
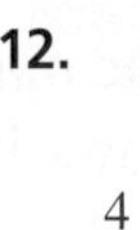
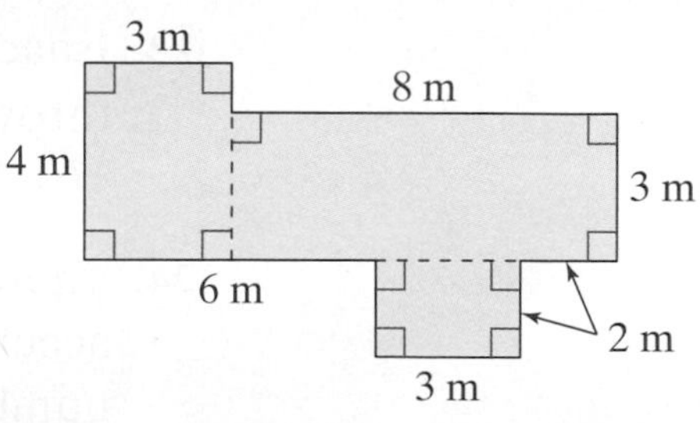

GPS 13. **Guided Problem Solving** Find the area of the figure at the right.
- How can you split the figure into three rectangles?
- Find the area of the three rectangles.

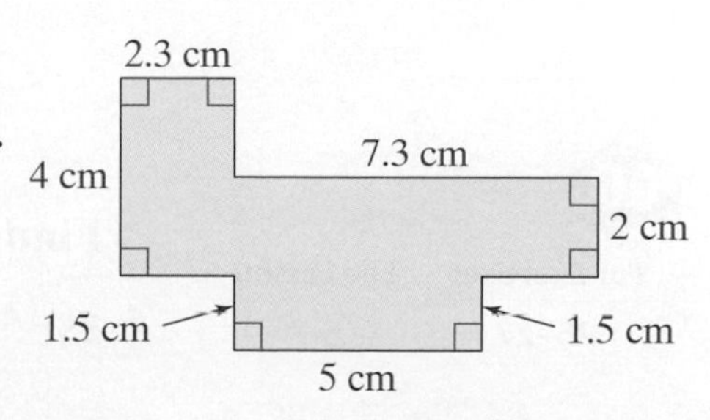

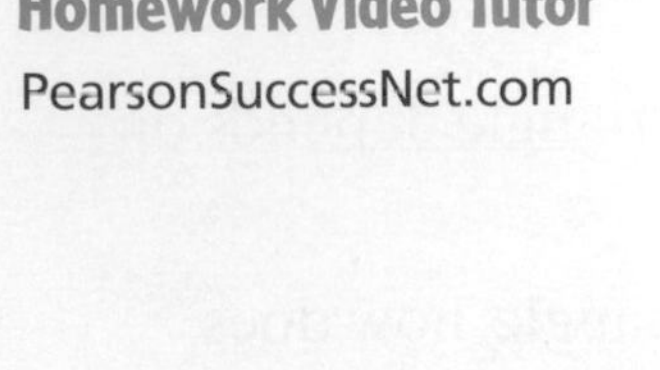

Homework Video Tutor

PearsonSuccessNet.com

Find the area of each figure.

14. 4.2 in. 5 in. 6 in.

15.

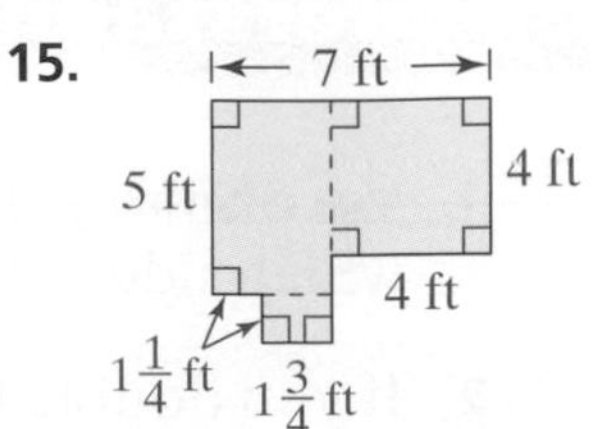

16.

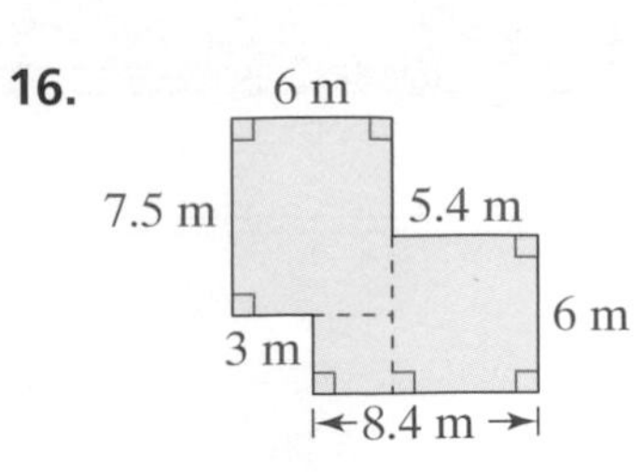

Parking spaces are sometimes shaped like parallelograms.

17. Parking Each space at the left has a width of 10.5 feet and a length of 21 feet. Find the area of a parking space.

18. Number Sense Two parallelograms have the same base length. The height of the first is half the height of the second. What is the ratio of the area of the smaller parallelogram to the area of the larger one?

19. **Algebra** A parallelogram has an area of 66 in.^{2} and a base length of 5 inches. What is the height of the parallelogram?

20. **Writing in Math** Suppose you know the perimeter and the height of an equilateral triangle. Explain how you would find the area of the triangle.

21. Challenge A parallelogram has an area of 4 ft^2 and a base length of 8 in. What is the height of the parallelogram?

Test Prep and Mixed Review

Practice

Multiple Choice

22. Hue cut out the triangle at the right for a craft project. What is the area of the triangle?

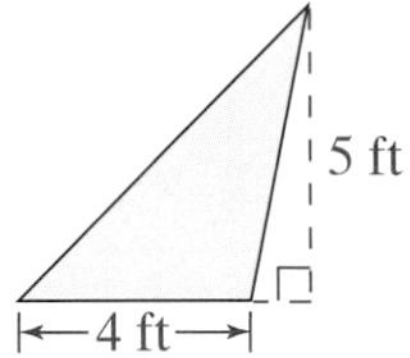

Ⓐ 12 ft^2 Ⓒ 54 ft^2

Ⓑ 24 ft^2 Ⓓ 10 ft^2

23. Isaac makes 3 out of 5 free throws. If he attempts 100 free throws, how many would you expect him to make?

Ⓕ 15 Ⓖ 30 Ⓗ 60 Ⓙ 75

24. There are 120 students and 15 adults on a field trip. Which ratio accurately compares the number of students to the total number of people?

Ⓐ 1 : 8 Ⓒ 8 : 9

Ⓑ 8 : 1 Ⓓ 9 : 8

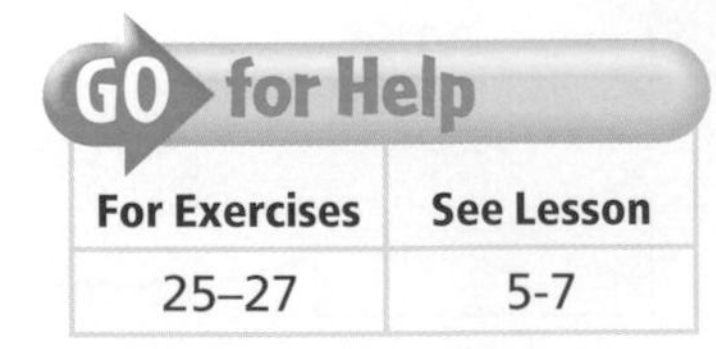

For Exercises	See Lesson
25–27	5-7

Find each answer.

25. 50% of 492 **26.** 35% of 84 **27.** 15% of 120

Vocabulary Builder

Using Concept Maps

One way to show connections among ideas is to draw a diagram called a concept map. The lines in a concept map connect related ideas.

EXAMPLE

Make a concept map with the terms related to ratio from Chapter 5.

- ratio
- rate
- unit rate
- equivalent ratio
- percent

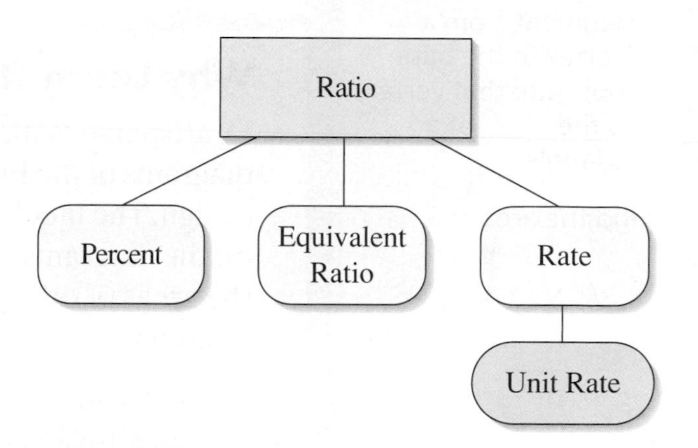

Exercises

1. Use the list below to make a concept map for area.

area	parallelogram	height	width
triangle	rectangle	base	length

2. Complete the concept map at the right as you study the next few lessons. Fill in the ovals with the appropriate terms listed below.
   - three-dimensional figure
   - rectangular prism
   - pyramid
   - base
   - surface area
   - height
   - base
   - net
   - volume

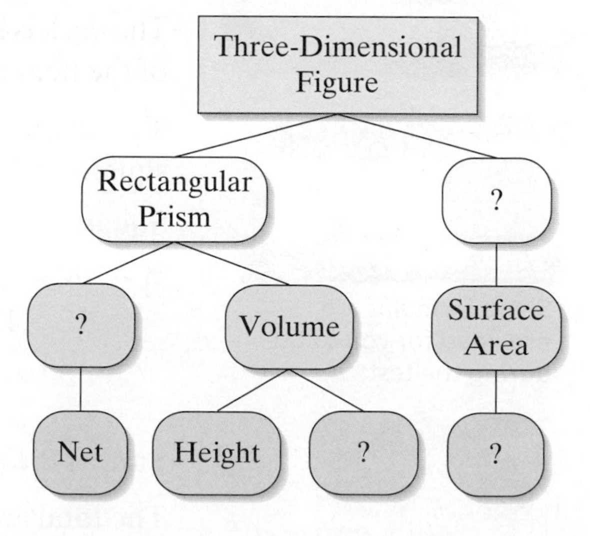

8-2 Areas of Polygons

1. Vocabulary Review The length of the perpendicular segment from a vertex to the base opposite that vertex is the _____ of a triangle.

Find the area.

2.

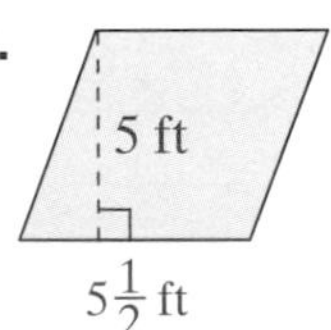

3.

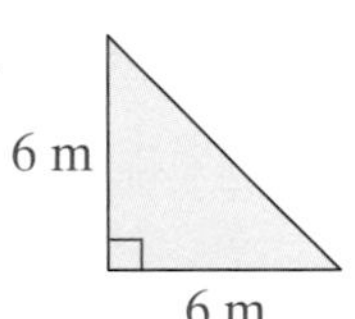

What You'll Learn

To compose and decompose polygons to solve problems involving area

New Vocabulary compose, decompose

Why Learn This?

Draftspersons make detailed diagrams of the buildings architects design. The labeled measurements on the diagrams can be used to find the areas of different parts of the buildings.

CONTENT STANDARD
6.G.1

Test Prep Tip

Some formulas are provided for you to use during the test.

EXAMPLE Making Simpler Shapes

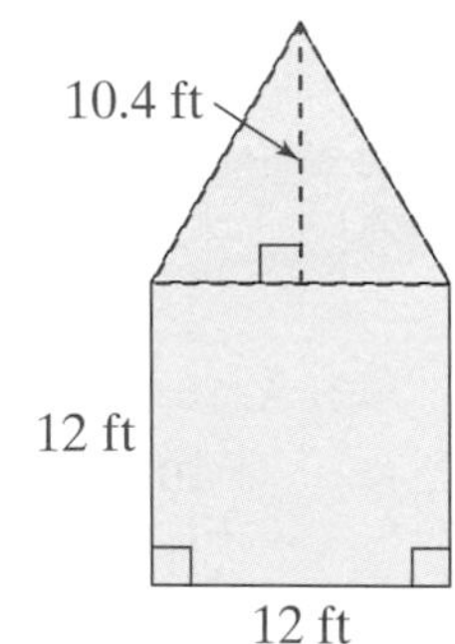

1 Multiple Choice Karl drew this diagram of a deck he's going to build. What is the area of the deck?

Ⓐ 134.4 square feet
Ⓑ 206.4 square feet
Ⓒ 268.8 square feet
Ⓓ 748.8 square feet

The deck is in the shape of a pentagon. You can think of the pentagon as a triangle and a square that share an edge.

To find the area of the deck, find the sum of the areas of the square and the triangle

Square

$$A = b \times h$$
$$= 12 \times 12$$
$$= 144$$

Triangle

$$A = \frac{1}{2} \times b \times h$$
$$= \frac{1}{2} \times 10.4 \times 12$$
$$= 62.4$$

Sum of the areas: $144 + 62.4 = 206.4$

The total area is 206.4 square feet. The correct answer is choice B.

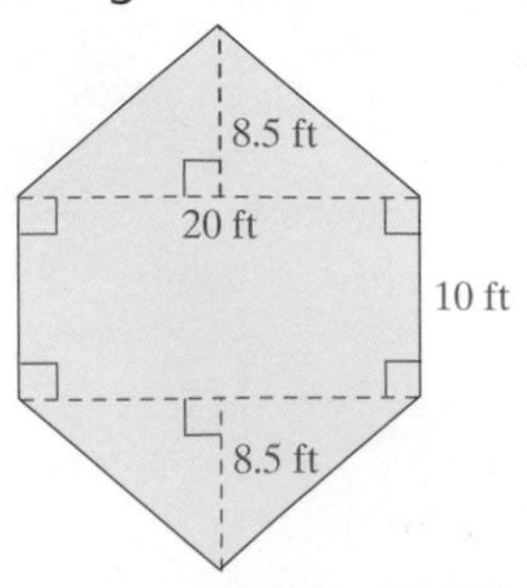

Quick Check

1. Find the area of the deck at the left.

Vocabulary Tip

The prefix *de-* means to do or make the opposite of. So *compose* is to join and ***de**compose* is to do the opposite or take apart.

To **compose** means to join together. To **decompose** means to take apart. Composing and decomposing figures into simpler shapes can sometimes help you find the total area of a polygon.

EXAMPLE Composing a Polygon to Find Area

2 Haley drew a diagram of the two sections of her garden. Find the total area of her garden.

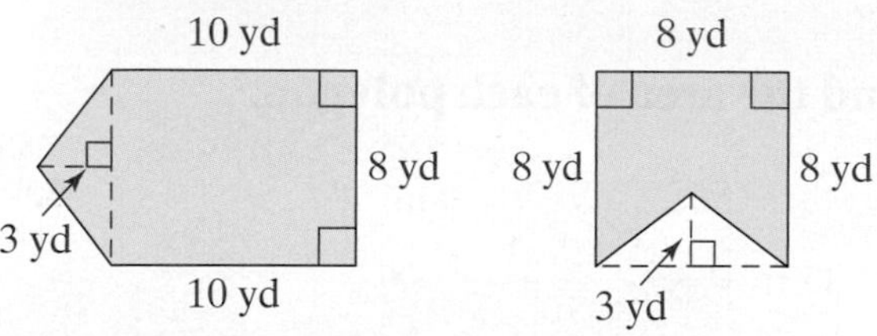

Step 1 Compose the two polygons into one rectangle.

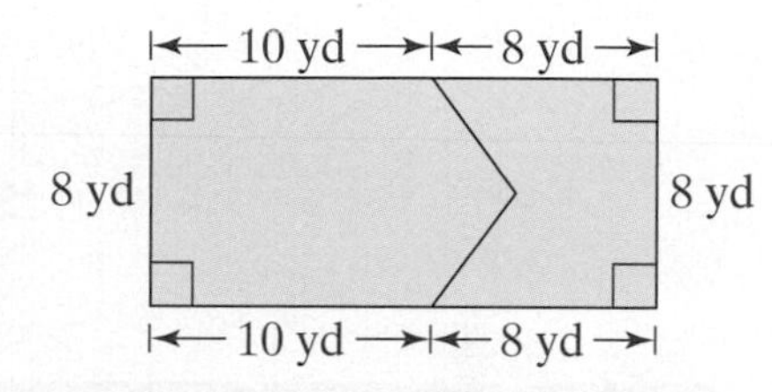

Step 2 Find the area of the new rectangle.

$A = b \times h$

$= (10 + 8) \times 8 = 18 \times 8 = 144$

The total area of Haley's garden is 144 square yards.

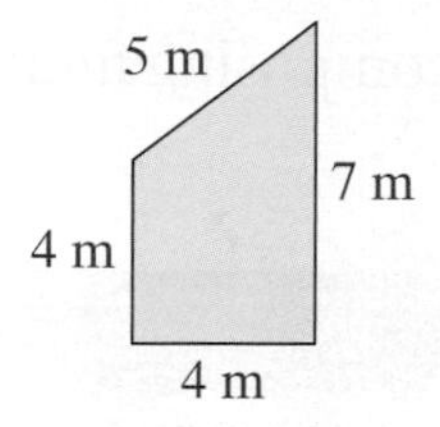

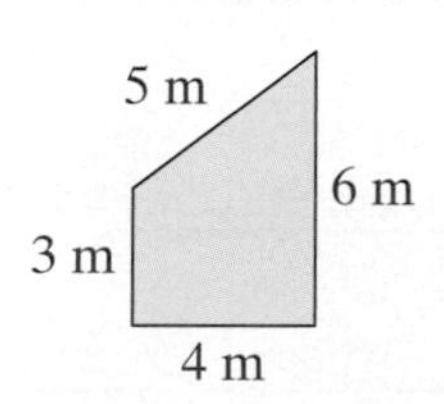

Quick Check

2. Tyler's garden has the two sections shown at the left. Find the total area of Tyler's garden.

EXAMPLE Decomposing a Polygon to Find Area

3 Find the area of the polygon.

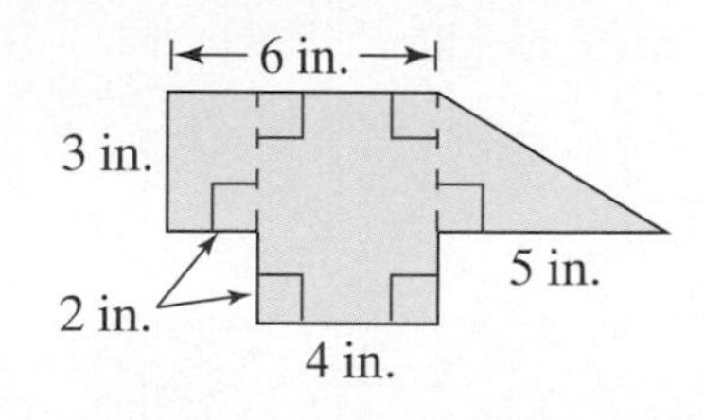

Decompose the polygon into two rectangles and a triangle.

Area of smaller rectangle: $b \times h = 2 \times 3$, or 6 in.^{2}

Area of larger rectangle: $b \times h = 4 \times 5$, or 20 in.^{2}

Area of triangle: $\frac{1}{2} \times b \times h = \frac{1}{2} \times 5 \times 3$, or 7.5 in.^{2}

The total area is $6 + 20 + 7.5$, or 33.5 in.^{2}.

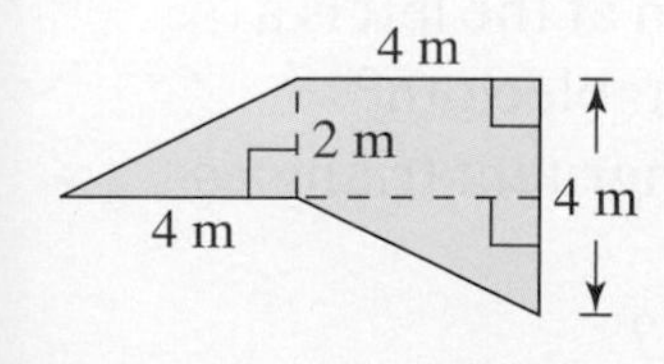

Quick Check

3. Find the area of the figure at the left.

Check Your Understanding

Vocabulary **Write *decomposing* or *composing* to describe what each diagram shows.**

1. 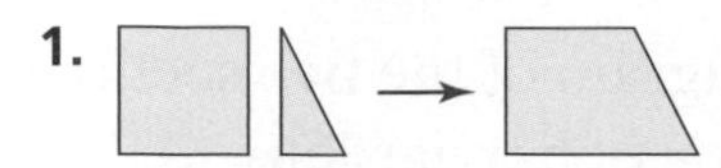

2. 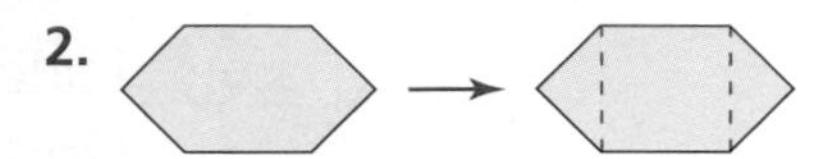

Find the area of each polygon.

3. 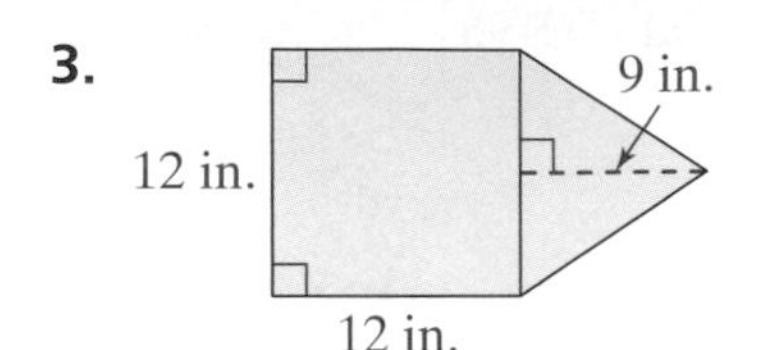

4. 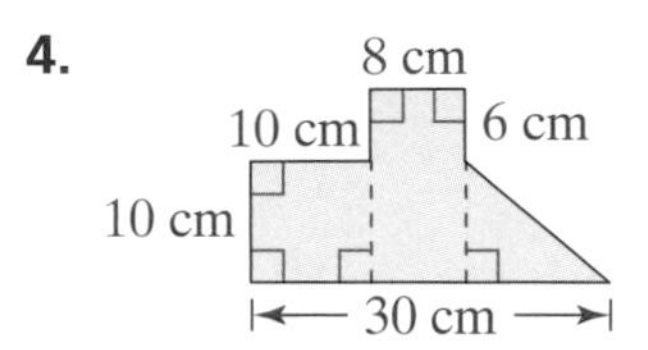

5. **Open ended** Explain how composing and decomposing figures can help you find the areas of polygons.

Homework Exercises

For more exercises, see Extra Skills and Word Problems.

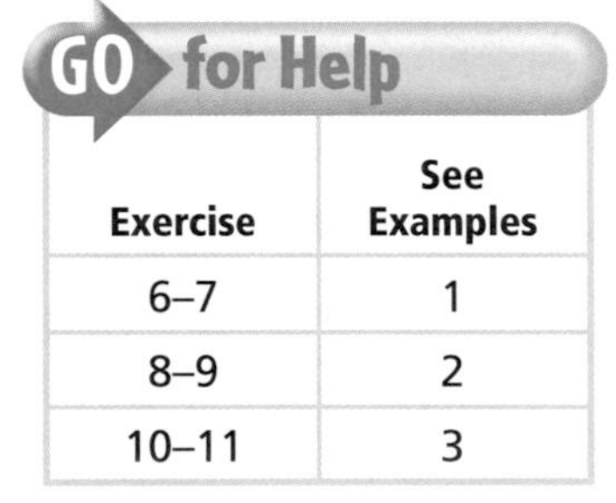

GO for Help

Exercise	See Examples
6–7	1
8–9	2
10–11	3

Find the area of the shaded polygon.

6. 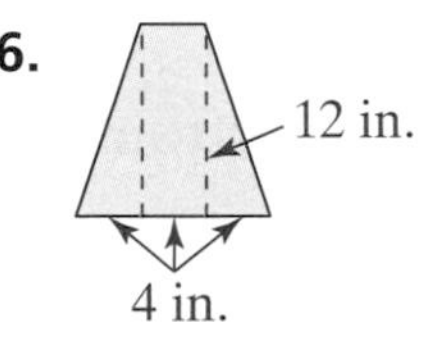

7. 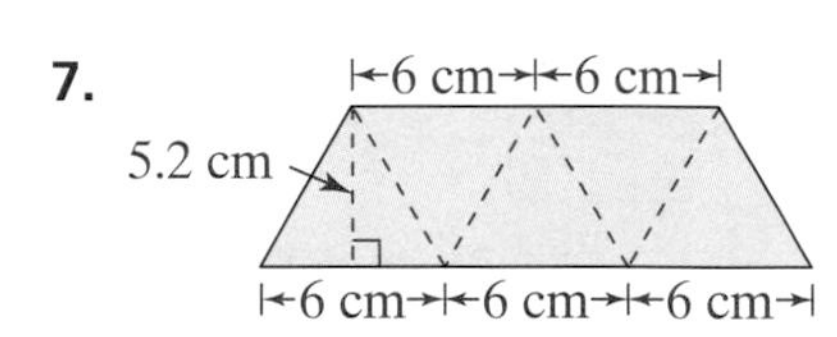

Find the total area of the shaded polygons.

8. 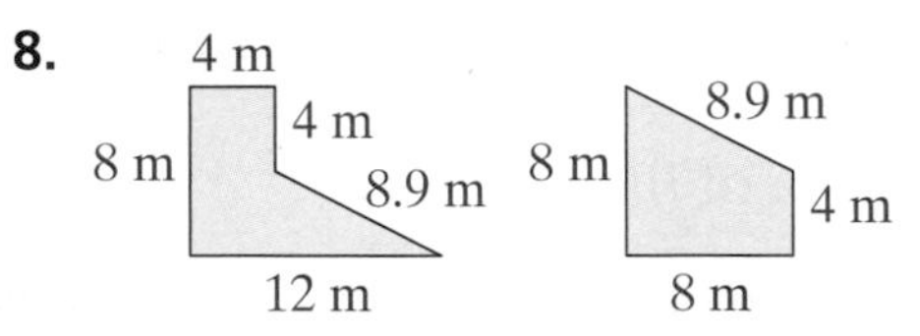

9. 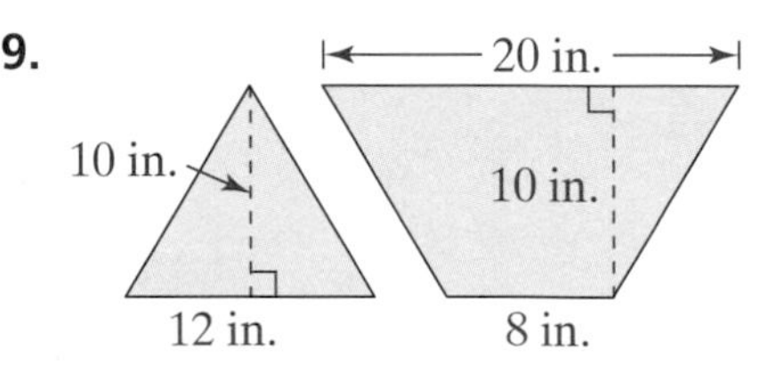

Find the area of the shaded polygon.

10. 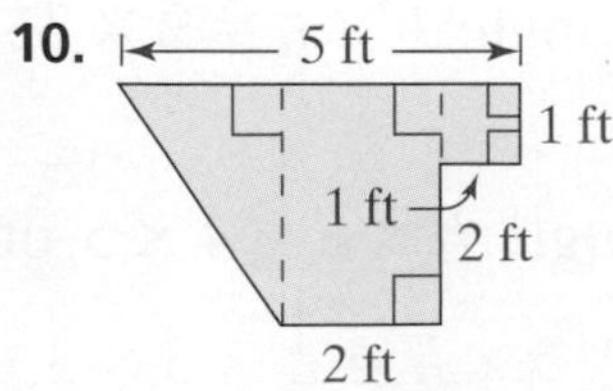

11. 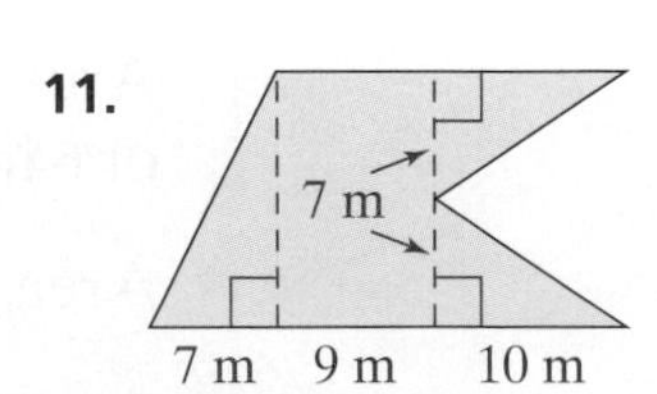

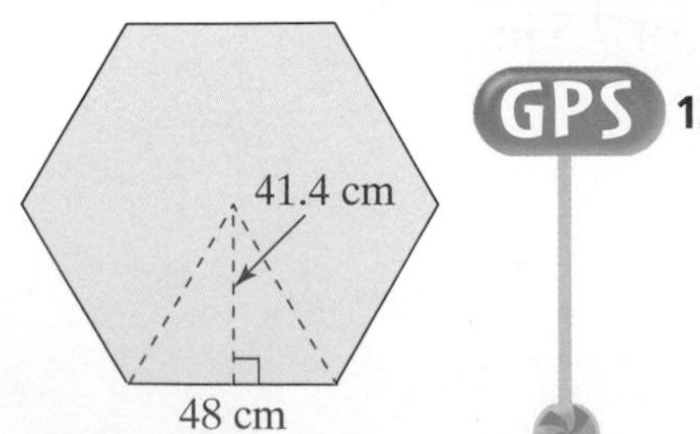

GPS 12. **Guided Problem Solving** Regular polygons can be decomposed into congruent triangles. The tablecloth shown at the left is a regular hexagon. What is the total area of the tablecloth?

- Decompose the regular pentagon into congruent triangles. How many triangles are there?
- How can you find the area of the hexagon?

13. **Writing in Math** Describe two ways to decompose the figure at the right. Find the area using both methods and compare your results.

Standard Sizes of Wood	
4' × 6'	5' × 6'
4' × 7'	5' × 8'
4' × 8'	5' × 10'
4' × 10'	5' × 12'
4' × 12'	5' × 14'

14. A carpenter knows she needs 5 rectangular pieces of wood for shelves and 10 triangular pieces for braces. Each shelf is 2 feet long and 1 foot wide. Each brace is a right triangle with a base of 1 foot and a height of 1 foot. Rather than buy many small pieces of wood, she can save money by cutting them from one large piece. What is the smallest standard size of wood, from the table at the left, that she could buy?

15. **Spatial Sense** The figures below can be composed into a rectangle. Sketch a possible rectangle and find the area.

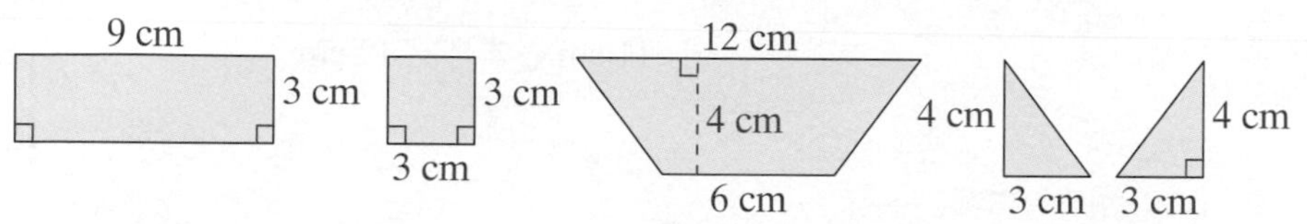

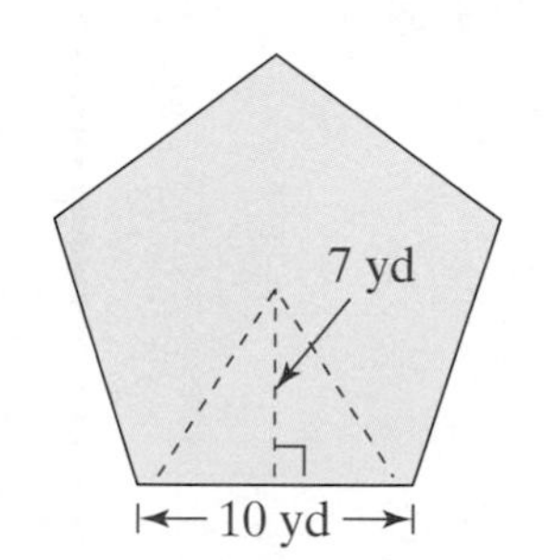

16. Joe is having a concrete patio installed in the shape of the regular pentagon shown at the left. The cost of the finished patio is $2.75 per square foot. How much will Joe pay for the patio?

17. **Challenge** Carla wants to plant a flower garden with an area of 28 square meters. The garden will be in the shape of a regular pentagon. If the height of each of the 6 congruent triangles is 2.8 meters, what is the length of each side of the pentagon?

Test Prep and Mixed Review

Practice

Multiple Choice

18. If you compose two polygons into a triangle, which formula could you use to find the area?
 - Ⓐ $A = l \times h$
 - Ⓑ $A = \frac{1}{2}b \times h$
 - Ⓒ $A = b \times h$
 - Ⓓ $A = \frac{1}{2}b \times (h_1 + h_2)$

19. A shirt that originally costs $20 is marked 30% off. What is the sale price of the shirt?
 - Ⓕ $6
 - Ⓖ $14
 - Ⓗ $26
 - Ⓙ $34

20. Jeremy got a raise from $7.80 per hour to $8.24 per hour. He works 36.5 hours each week. How much more will Jeremy earn each week?
 - Ⓐ $300.76
 - Ⓑ $150.38
 - Ⓒ $16.06
 - Ⓓ $0.44

GO for Help

For Exercise	See Lesson
21–23	1–2

Find the value of each expression.

21. $(3 - 2) \times 5 + 4$ 22. $6 + 4 \times 3 - 5$ 23. $4 \times (3 + 6) \div 2$

Checkpoint Quiz 1

Lessons 8-1 through 8-2

1. Write a formula for finding the area of a parallelogram.
2. Write a formula for finding the area of a triangle.
3. Write *composing* or *decomposing* to describe what the diagram below shows.

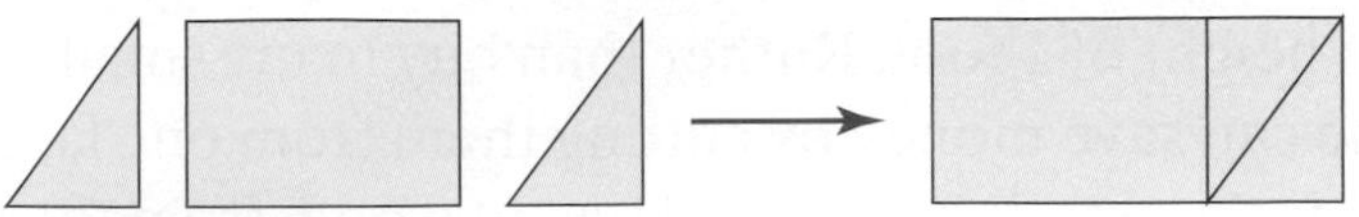

Find the area of each figure.

4. 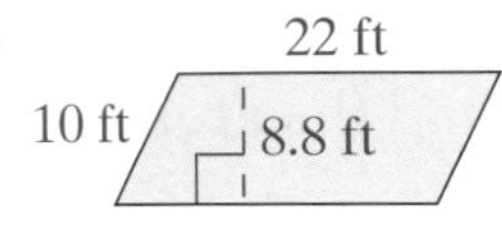

5. 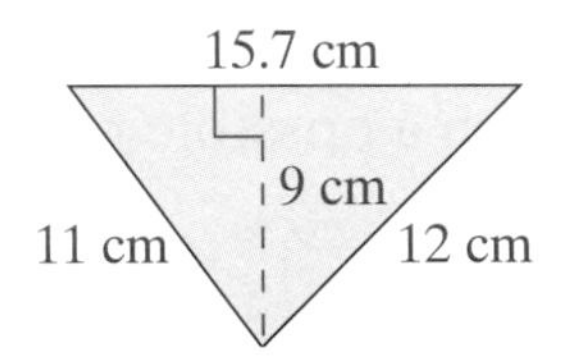

6. 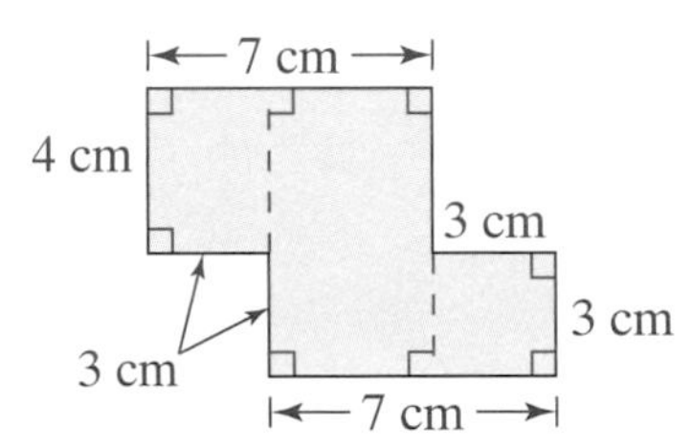

7. 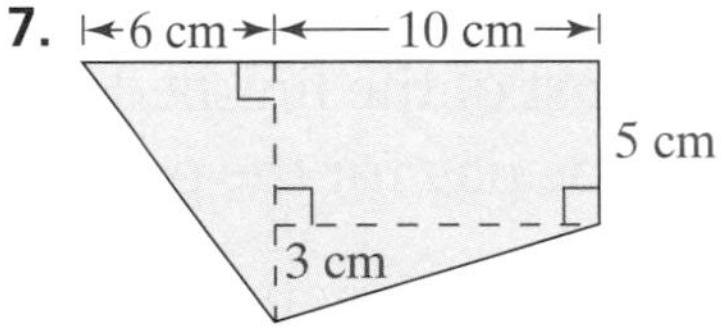

8. 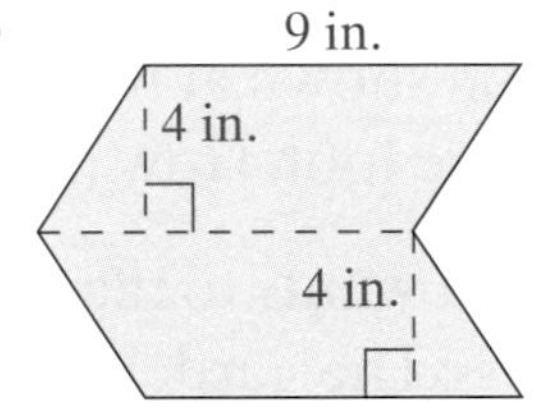

9. 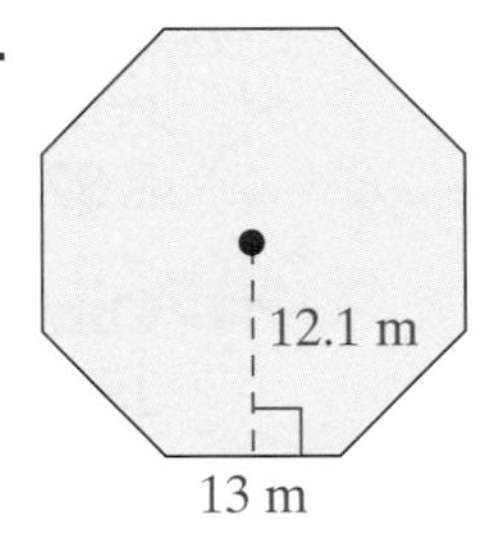

MATH AT WORK

Event Planner

Event planners organize and arrange all the details for parties, business meetings, and other group activities. Their responsibilities include finding the meeting place, choosing the menu, and arranging the decorations for an event.

Geometry is useful to event planners as they determine dimensions for room sizes, arrange rectangular or circular tables, and plan serving areas.

For information on event planners
PearsonSuccessNet.com

Hands On

Three-Dimensional Views

You can draw three-dimensional objects so that they appear to have length, width, and height. You can also draw different views of the blocks.

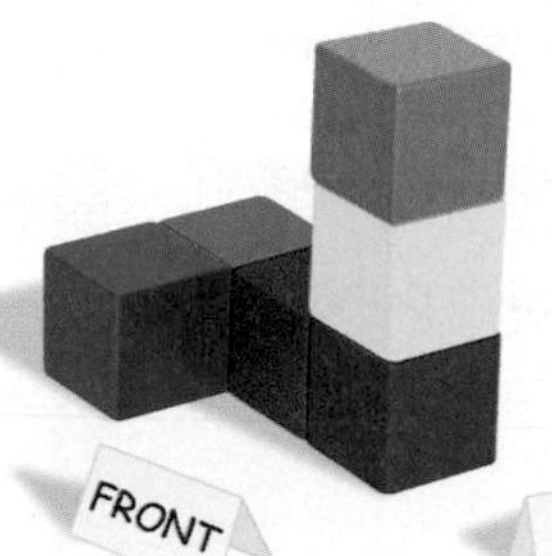

1. Stack 6 blocks as shown at the right.
2. Make three different drawings. Draw a view from the:

   a. top b. front c. right side

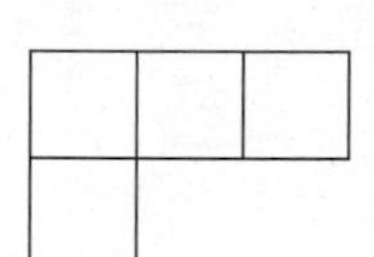

Top View

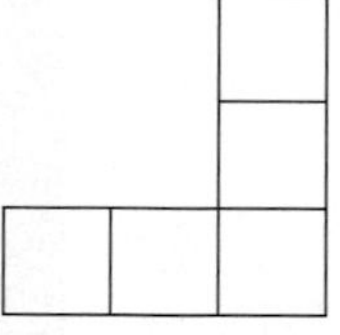

Front View

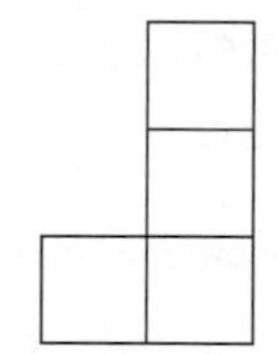

Right Side View

Exercises

Use blocks or centimeter cubes to build the figures below. Then draw the top, front, and right side views of each figure.

1. 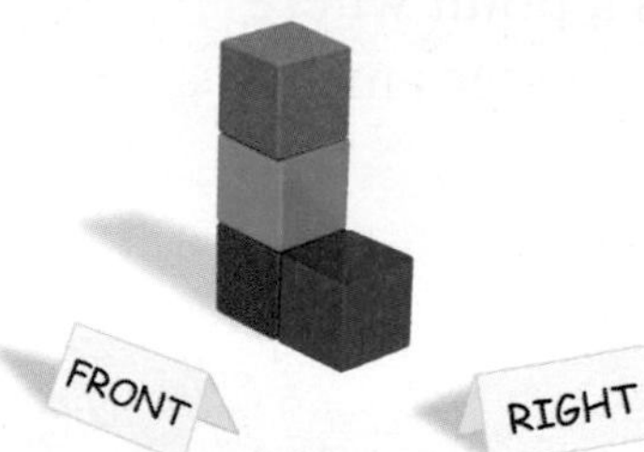

2. 

3. 

Reasoning **Use the drawings below. Make a figure of blocks for each set of views.**

4. 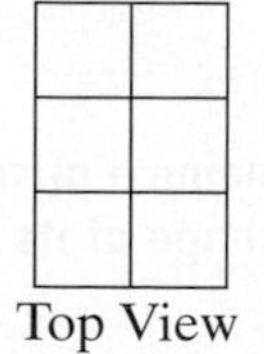

Top View

Front View

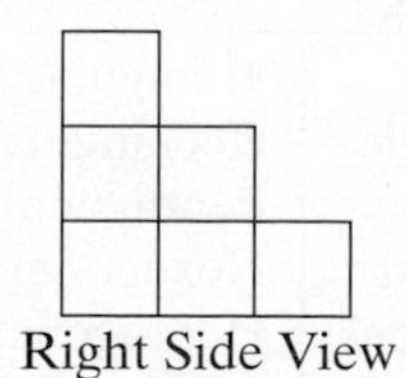

Right Side View

5. 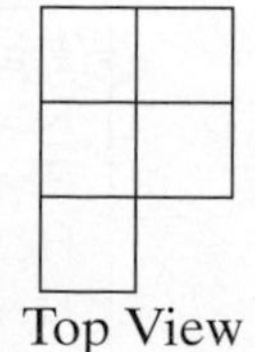

Top View

Front View

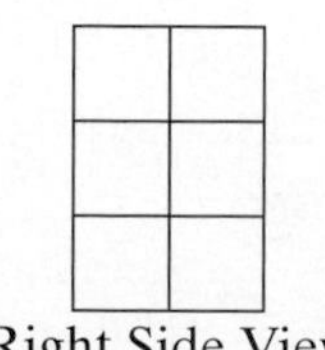

Right Side View

8-3 Three-Dimensional Figures and Spatial Reasoning

1. **Vocabulary Review** What is the least number of sides a *polygon* must have?

Name each polygon.

2. 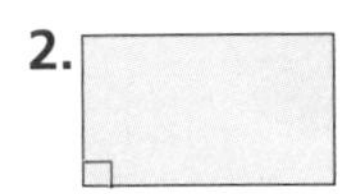

3.

4. 

5. 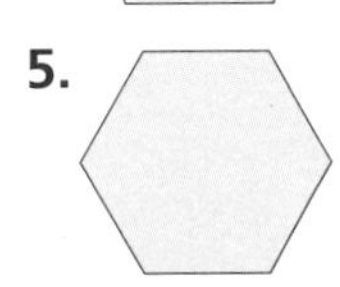

Lesson 8-2

CONTENT STANDARD
Essential for understanding 6.G.2

Vocabulary Tip

Three-dimensional is often abbreviated as 3-D.

What You'll Learn

To identify three-dimensional figures

New Vocabulary three-dimensional figure, faces, edge, vertex, prism, cube, pyramid, cylinder, cone, sphere

Why Learn This?

Architects use shapes to design buildings. To identify these figures, you need to understand how they differ.

A **three-dimensional figure** is a figure that does not lie in a plane. It has three dimensions: length, width, and height.

The flat surfaces of a three-dimensional figure are called **faces**.

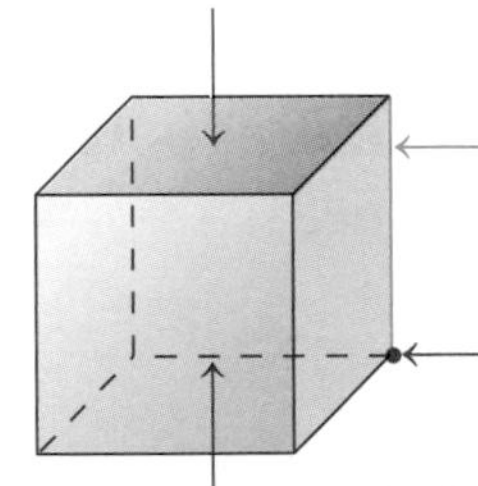

An **edge** is a segment where two faces meet.

A **vertex** is a point where two or more edges meet.

When you draw three-dimensional figures, use dashed lines to indicate "hidden" edges.

A **prism** is a three-dimensional figure with two parallel and congruent faces that are polygons. These faces are called bases. The prism above is a **cube**. All of its faces are congruent.

Base Shape	Name of Prism
Triangle	Triangular Prism
Rectangle	Rectangular Prism
Pentagon	Pentagonal Prism
Hexagon	Hexagonal Prism
Heptagon	Heptagonal Prism
Octagon	Octagonal Prism

You name a prism by the shape of its bases.

Test Prep Tip

When naming a 3-D figure, identify the shape of its base. Then determine whether the faces meet at one vertex.

EXAMPLE Naming Prisms

1 Name the prism shown.

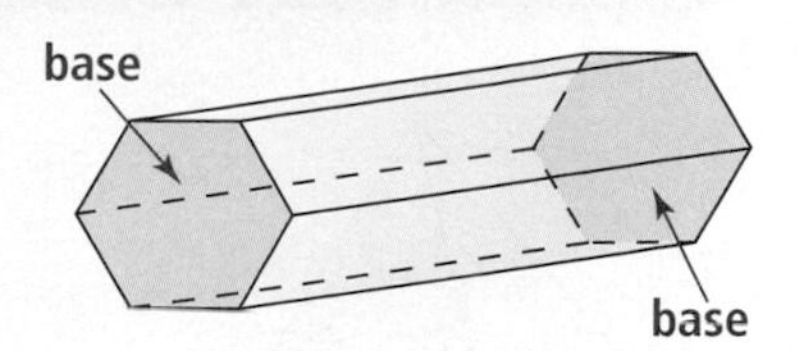

Each base is a hexagon. So the figure is a hexagonal prism.

Quick Check

1. Name each prism.

a. 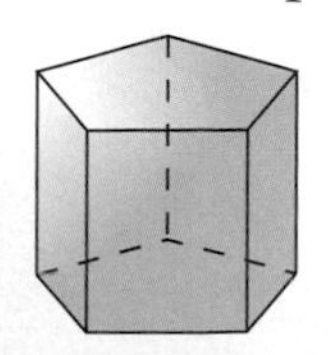

b. 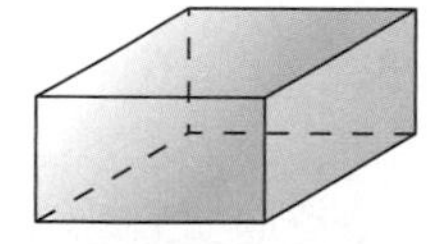

c. 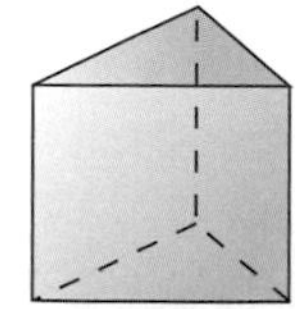

A **pyramid** is a three-dimensional figure with one polygon for a base. All of the other faces are triangles. The faces all meet at one vertex. You name a pyramid by its base.

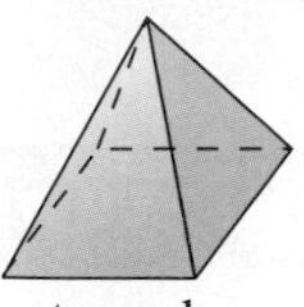
rectangular pyramid

Some three-dimensional figures do not have polygons for bases.

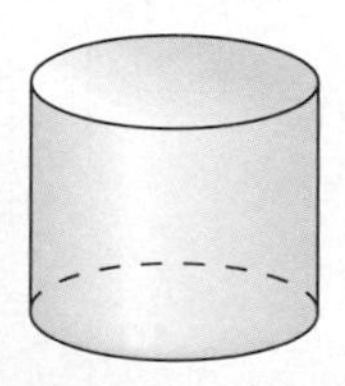

A **cylinder** has two congruent parallel bases that are circles.

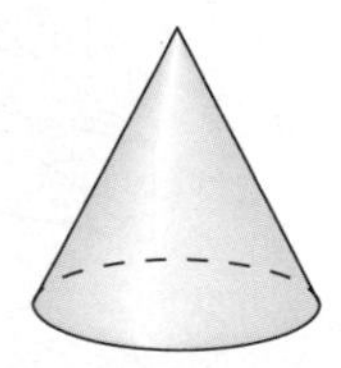

A **cone** has one circular base and one vertex.

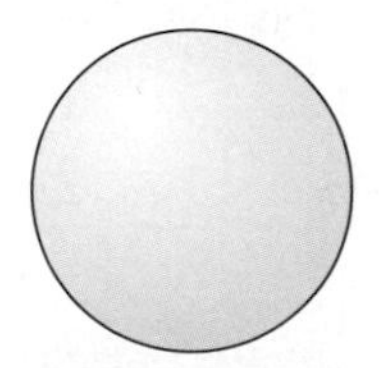

A **sphere** has no base.

EXAMPLE Identifying Three-Dimensional Figures

2 **Museum** The American Museum of Natural History in New York City is shown at the right. Name a three-dimensional figure in the photo.

The sphere in the photo is a three-dimensional figure without a base.

Quick Check

2. Name another three-dimensional figure in the photo.

Check Your Understanding

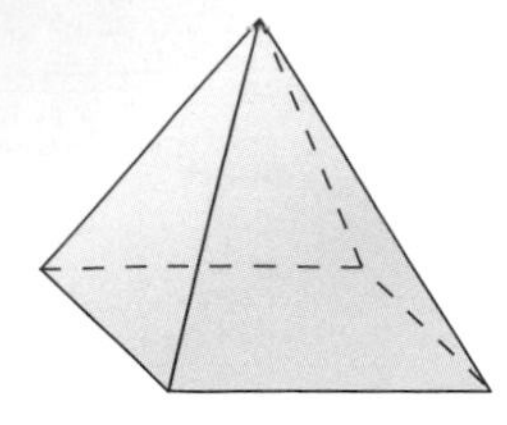

1. **Vocabulary** How are a prism and a pyramid alike? How are they different?
2. **Writing in Math** Describe the shape of the square pyramid at the left.

Label each figure as a *cylinder*, *cone*, or *sphere*.

3. 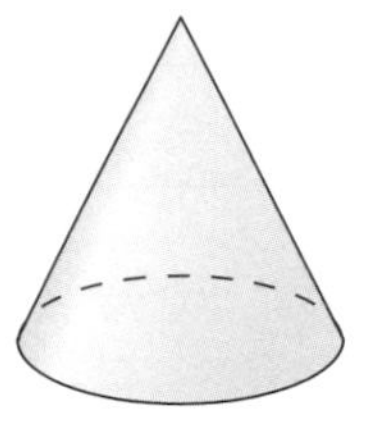
4. 
5. 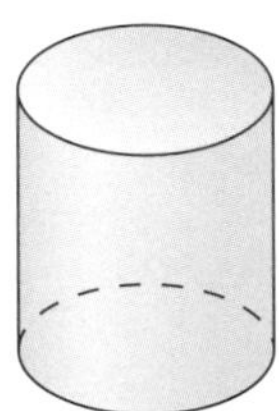

Homework Exercises

For more exercises, see Extra Skills and Word Problems.

GO for Help

For Exercises	See Examples
6–11	1
12–15	2

Name each prism.

6. 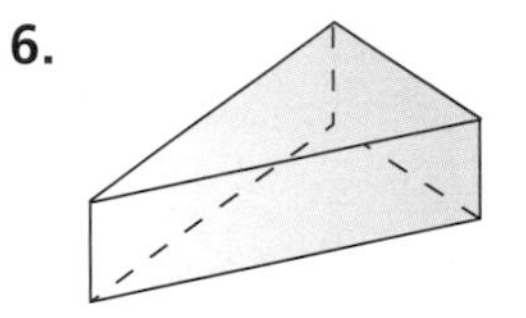
7. 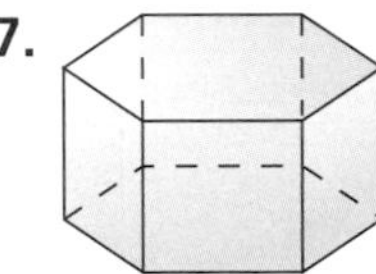
8. 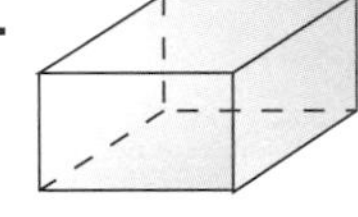
9. 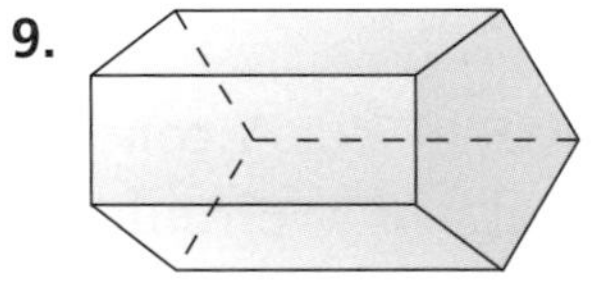
10. 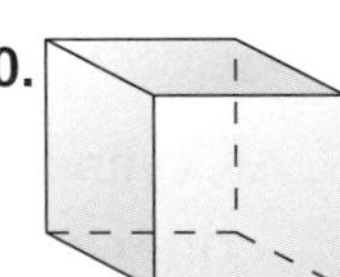
11. 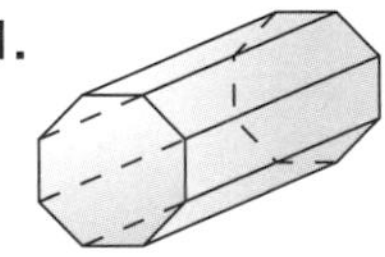

Structures **Name a three-dimensional figure in each photo.**

12. 
13. 
14. 
15. 

16. **Guided Problem Solving** Name the figure at the right. Find the number of faces, vertices, and edges in the figure.
    - What is the shape of the base in the figure?
    - How many faces does the figure have?

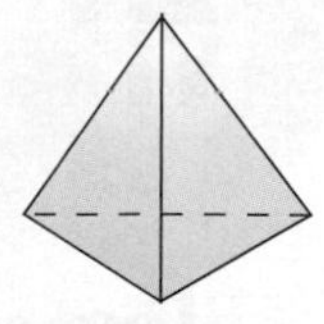

17. Name the figure. Then find the number of faces, vertices, and edges in the figure.

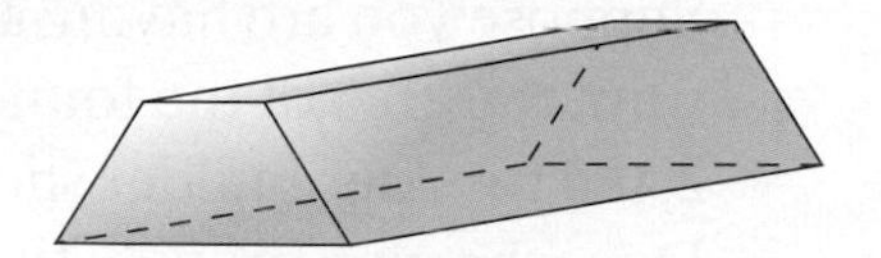

18. **Reasoning** In a prism, what shape are the faces that are not the base?

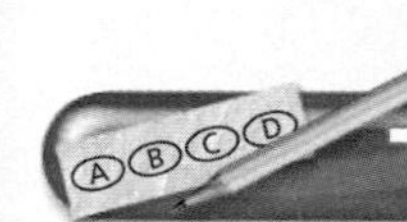

Homework Video Tutor
PearsonSuccessNet.com

Art You can use translations to draw three-dimensional figures.

Step 1	Step 2	Step 3	Step 4
Draw a figure on graph paper.	Translate the figure.	Connect each vertex with its image.	Use dashes for hidden lines.

19. Start with a triangle. Draw a three-dimensional figure.
20. Start with a pentagon. Draw a three-dimensional figure.
21. **Challenge** Describe the translation used in Steps 1–4. Redraw the rectangle. Use a different translation to draw the figure.

Test Prep and Mixed Review — Practice

Multiple Choice

22. A meteorologist listed the high temperatures for one week as 74°F, 70°F, 72°F, 75°F, 79°F, 80°F, and 82°F. What was the range of high temperatures?
    (A) 82°F (B) 70°F (C) 12°F (D) 8°F
23. Brittany drank one gallon of water in one weekend. Which measurement could NOT be expressed as one gallon?
    (F) 4 quarts (G) 8 pints (H) 16 cups (J) 32 ounces
24. You have $25. You buy a cap for $13.79. Write and solve an inequality to find how much more money you can spend.

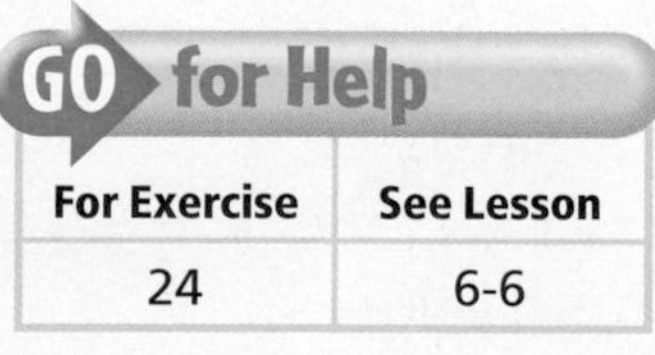
GO for Help

For Exercise	See Lesson
24	6-6

GPS Guided Problem Solving

Practice Solving Problems

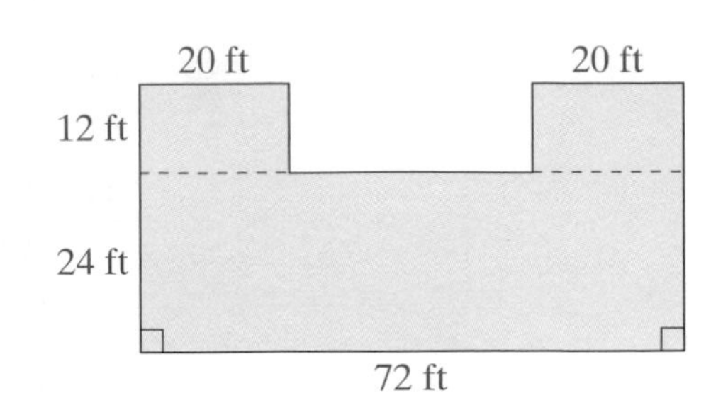

Suppose you are having a new home built. You want the area of the foundation to be greater than 2,100 ft^2. Your builder shows you the plan at the right. Does the plan provide the area that you want?

What You Might Think	What You Might Write
What do I know? What do I want to find?	• I know the shape and the dimensions of the foundation. • I want to find the area of the foundation.
What is my plan?	I'll decompose the figure into two rectangles where the smaller rectangle has been cut out of the larger rectangle. I'll find the area of each rectangle and then subtract to find the total area.
What is the area of the larger rectangle?	The width of the larger rectangle is 12 ft + 24 ft, or 36 ft, so the area is 72 ft × 36 ft, or 2,592 ft^2.
What is the area of the smaller rectangle?	The length of the smaller rectangle is 72 ft − (20 ft + 20 ft), or 32 ft, so the area is 12 ft × 32 ft, or 384 ft^2.
What is the area of the foundation?	The area of the foundation is 2,592 ft^2 − 384 ft^2, or 2,208 ft^2.
Does the plan provide the area that you want?	Since 2,208 > 2,100, the plan provides the area that I want.

Think It Through

1. Suppose you ask the builder to remove one of the 20 ft by 12 ft rectangles from the plan. Will the total area still be greater than 2,100 ft^2? Explain.
2. **Reasoning** Is there another way to find the area of the foundation? Explain.

Exercises

3. A swimming pool cover has the shape shown. Find the area of the cover.
   a. What do you know?
   b. What do you want to find?
   c. Find the area of the cover by finding the sum of the areas of two rectangles.

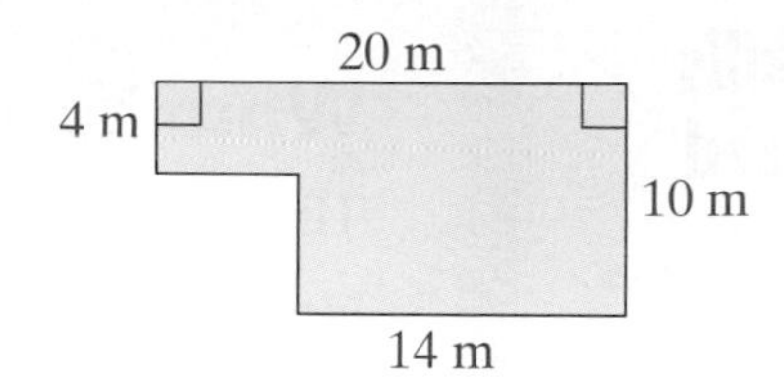

4. What will it cost to tile the floor shown below with 1-foot square tiles costing $3.75 each? Assume that you can buy the exact number of tiles you need.

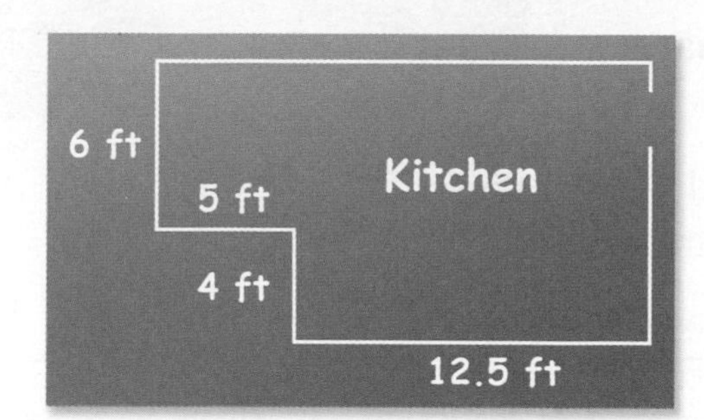

5. The area of a rectangular figure is 9 times the area of the figure shown below. Draw the larger figure showing its dimensions. Explain how you decided on the dimensions.

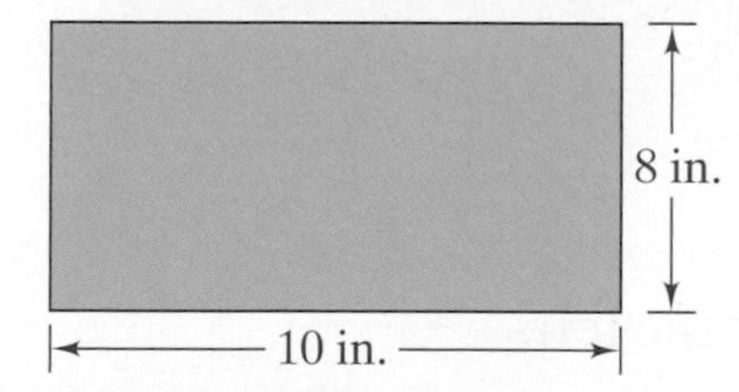

6. Tomas wants to buy a new laptop computer. The laptop is on sale at Store A for 20% off the regular price of $450. The price of the laptop at Store B is 30% off the regular price of $500. At which store will Tomas pay less for the laptop?

8-4 Surface Areas of Prisms and Pyramids

1. Vocabulary Review Describe the *area* of a piece of paper.

Find the area of each rectangle.

2. $\ell = 7$ m, $w = 3$ m

3. $\ell = 10$ m, $w = 3$ m

Lesson 8-1

CONTENT STANDARD
6.G.4

What You'll Learn

To use nets and to find the surface areas of prisms and pyramids

New Vocabulary net, surface area

Why Learn This?

Package designers make creative labels. The surface area of an object is the space designers have to work with.

A **net** is a pattern you can fold to form a three-dimensional figure.

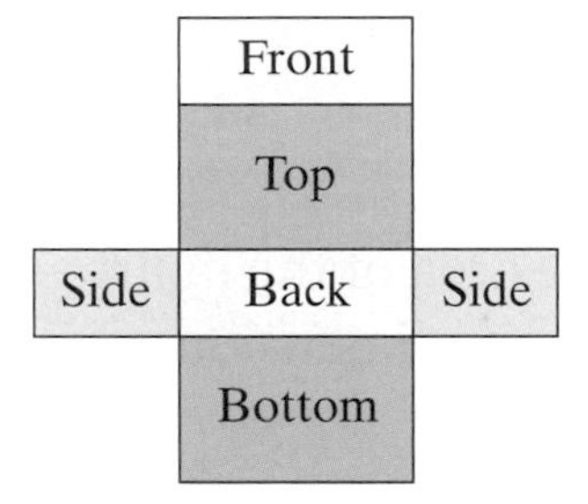

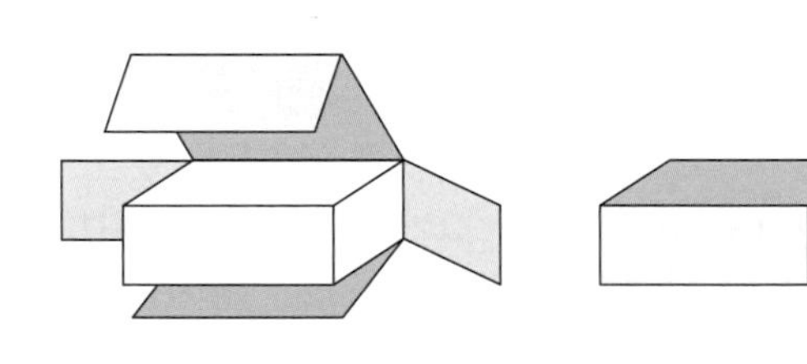

EXAMPLE Drawing a Net

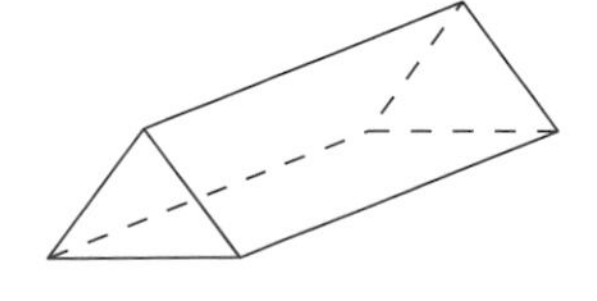

1 Draw a net for the triangular prism at the left.

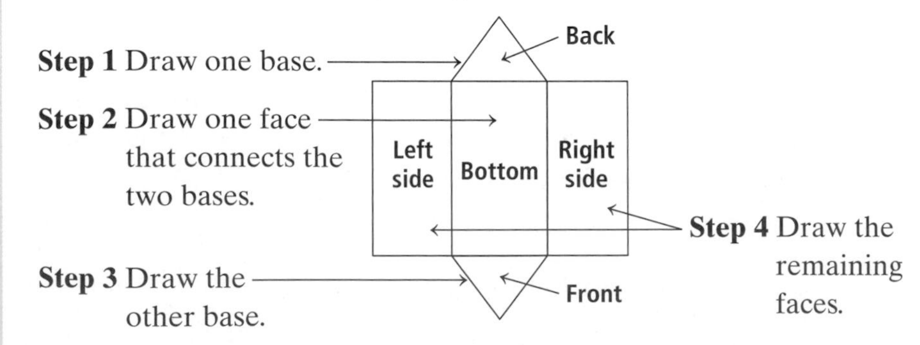

Quick Check

1. Draw a net for a cube.

The **surface area** of a three-dimensional figure is the sum of the areas of its surfaces.

EXAMPLE Finding the Surface Area of a Prism

$h = 10$ cm

$w = 3$ cm

$\ell = 6$ cm

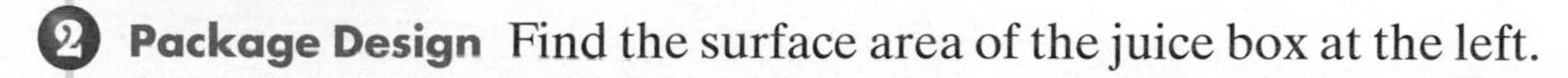

2 **Package Design** Find the surface area of the juice box at the left.

Step 1 Draw and label a net for the prism.

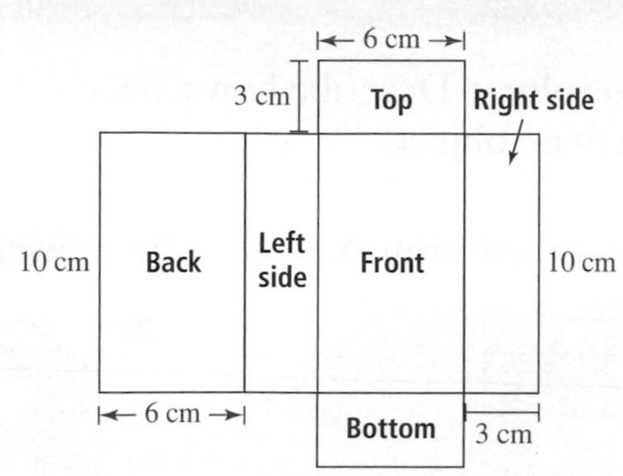

Step 2 Find and add the areas of all the rectangles.

Top		Back		Left		Front		Right		Bottom
3×6	+	10×6	+	10×3	+	10×6	+	10×3	+	3×6
= 18	+	60	+	30	+	60	+	30	+	18

$= 216$

The surface area of the juice box is 216 square centimeters.

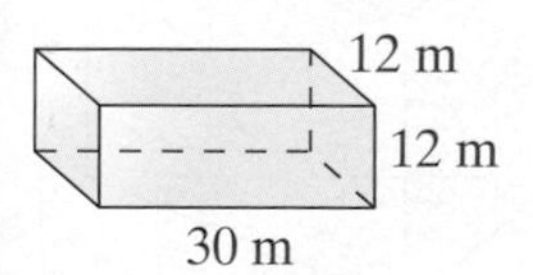

Quick Check

2. Find the surface area of the prism.

EXAMPLE Finding the Surface Area of a Pyramid

20 in.

25 in.

25 in.

3 Find the surface area of the square pyramid at the left.

Step 1 Draw and label a net for the pyramid.

Step 2 Find and add the areas of the square and the triangles. Since the base is a square, the triangular faces are congruent.

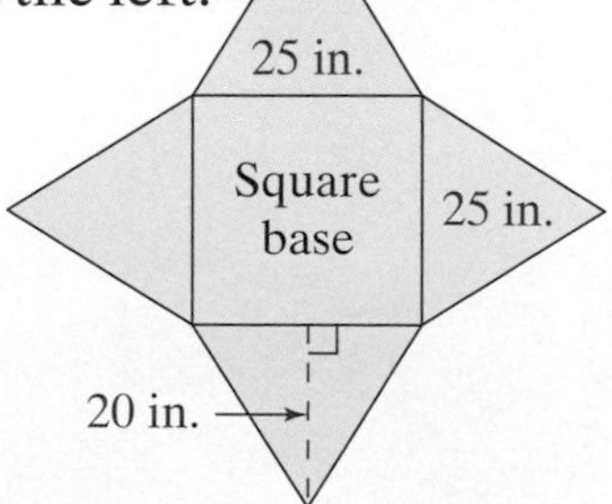

Square		Triangle		Triangle		Triangle		Triangle
25×25	+	$\frac{1}{2}(25 \times 20)$	+	$\frac{1}{2}(25 \times 20)$	+	$\frac{1}{2}(25 \times 20)$	+	$\frac{1}{2}(25 \times 20)$
= 625	+	250	+	250	+	250	+	250

$= 1{,}625$

The surface area of the pyramid is 1,625 square inches.

Quick Check

3. Find the surface area of the square pyramid at the right.

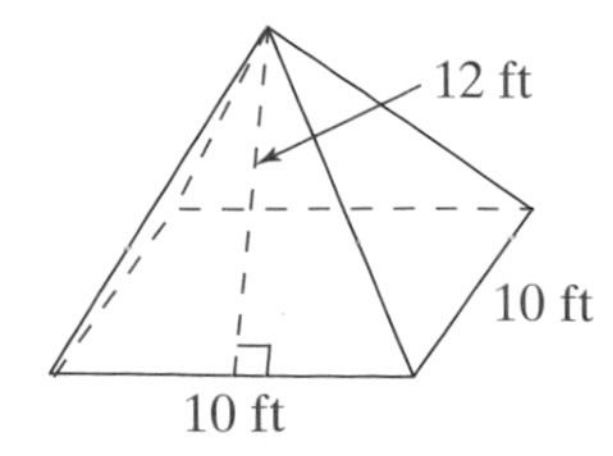

Check Your Understanding

1. **Vocabulary** Describe how a net can help you find the surface area of an object.

Find the surface area. A small cube measures 1 cm on a side.

2.  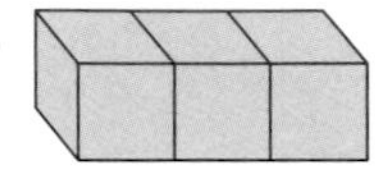

3. 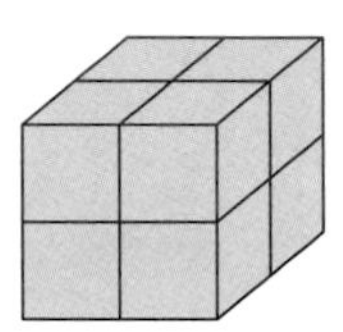

Homework Exercises

For more exercises, see Extra Skills and Word Problems.

GO for Help

For Exercises	See Examples
4–6	1
7–9	2
10–12	3

Draw a net for each three-dimensional figure.

4. 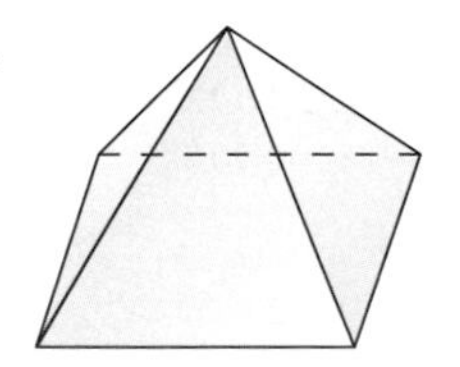

5. 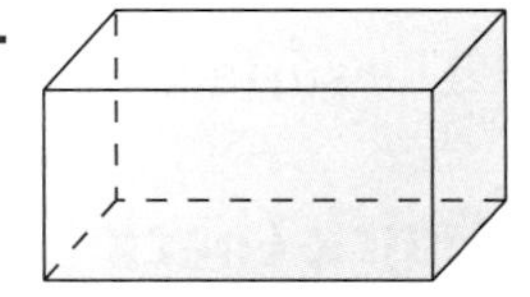

6. 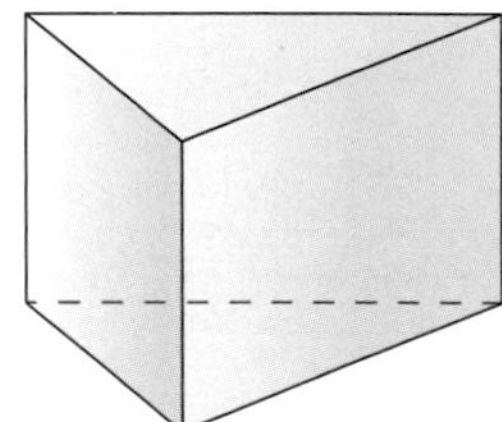

Find the surface area of each prism or pyramid.

7. 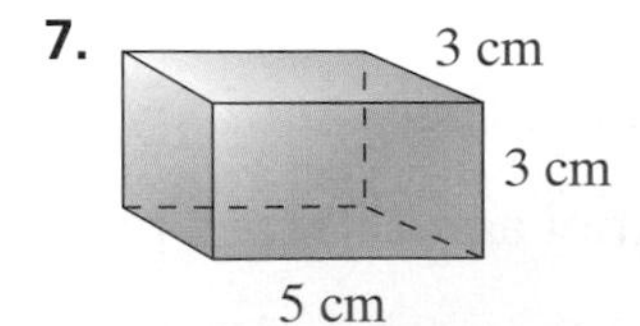

8. 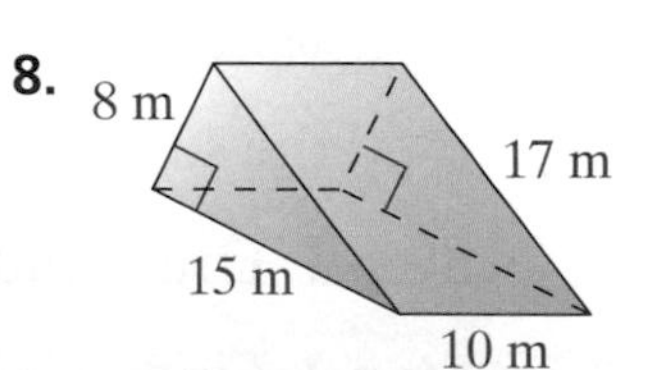

9. 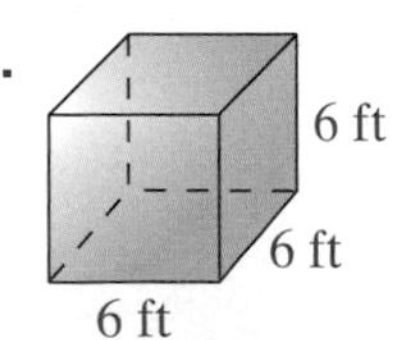

10. 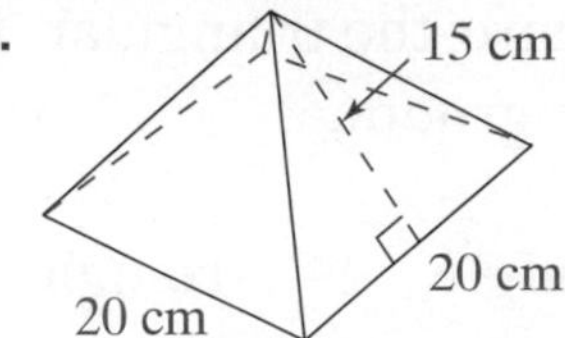

11. 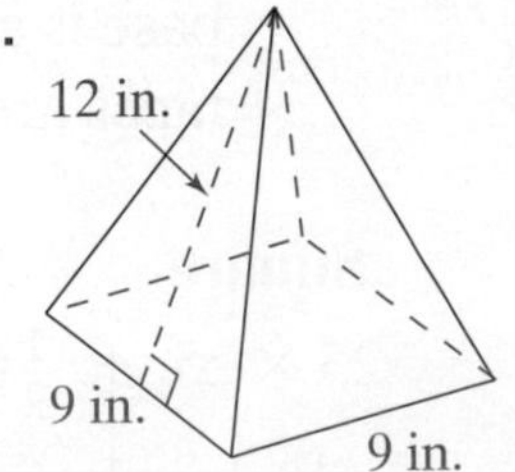

12. 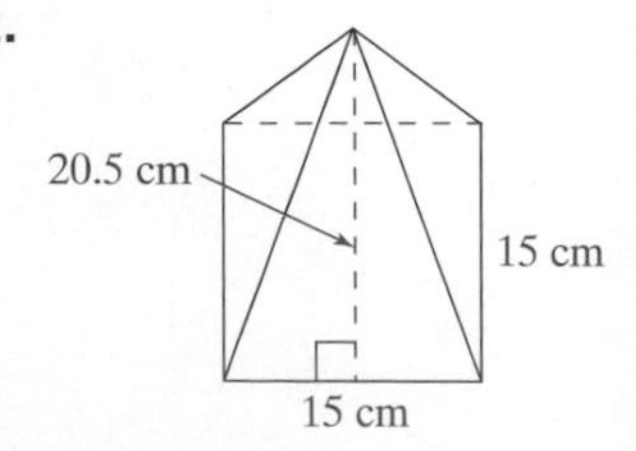

13. **Guided Problem Solving**
Find the surface area of the spaghetti box.

- **Understand the Problem** Draw a net of the figure, and label all sides.
- **Make a Plan** Find the area of each surface of the box. Then add the areas to find the total surface area.

14. **Writing in Math** Suppose each dimension of a square pyramid is doubled. How is the surface area affected?

15. Which of the following cannot be the dimensions of the piece of wrapping paper used to wrap the box?

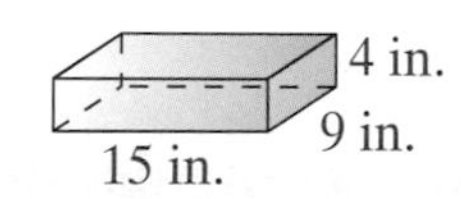

Ⓐ 20 in. by 28 in.
Ⓑ 36 in. by 18 in.
Ⓒ 40 in. by 10 in.
Ⓓ 24 in. by 24 in.

Homework Video Tutor
PearsonSuccessNet.com

16. **Reasoning** The surface area of a cube is 54 square inches. What is the length of each edge?

17. **Algebra** A net for a triangular pyramid is made of 4 congruent equilateral triangles. If the height of each triangle is x and the base of each triangle is y, what is the surface area of the pyramid?

18. **Challenge** Suppose each dimension of a cube is increased. What happens to the surface area when each dimension is doubled? Tripled? Quadrupled?

Test Prep and Mixed Review

Practice

Multiple Choice

19. What is the surface area of the square pyramid?

Ⓐ 252 square centimeters
Ⓑ 576 square centimeters
Ⓒ 1,008 square centimeters
Ⓓ 1,296 square centimeters

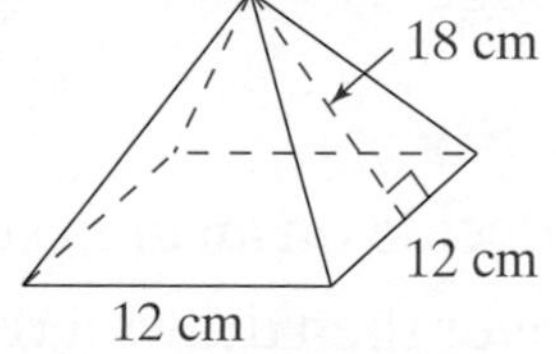

20. Carly buys 8 books that cost \$3 each and 8 books that cost \$4 each. Which expression shows the total amount Carly pays for the books?

Ⓕ $8 \times \$3 \times \$4$
Ⓖ $\$8 + \$3 + \$4$
Ⓗ $(8 \times \$3) + (8 \times \$4)$
Ⓙ $(8 \times \$3) - (8 \times \$4)$

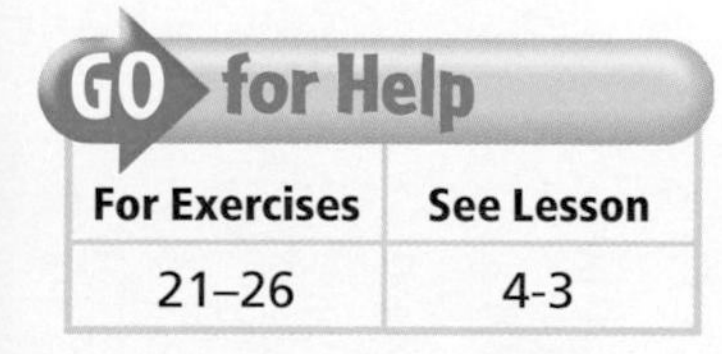

For Exercises	See Lesson
21–26	4-3

Find each quotient.

21. $\frac{1}{3} \div \frac{1}{2}$
22. $\frac{2}{5} \div \frac{1}{5}$
23. $4 \div \frac{2}{3}$
24. $\frac{5}{8} \div \frac{1}{3}$
25. $\frac{8}{9} \div \frac{2}{5}$
26. $5 \div \frac{2}{3}$

Checkpoint Quiz 2

Lessons 8-3 through 8-4

Name each figure.

1. 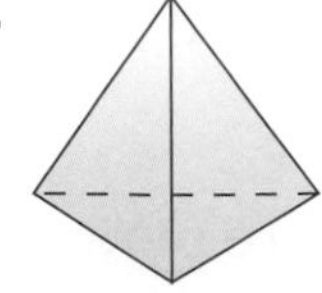

2. 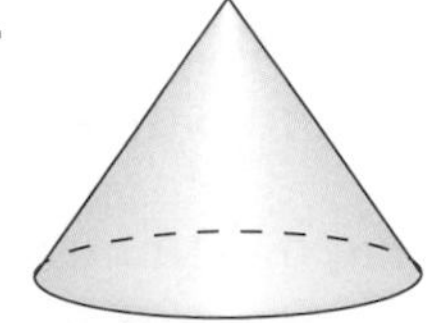

3. 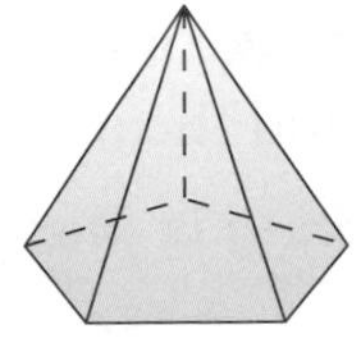

4. 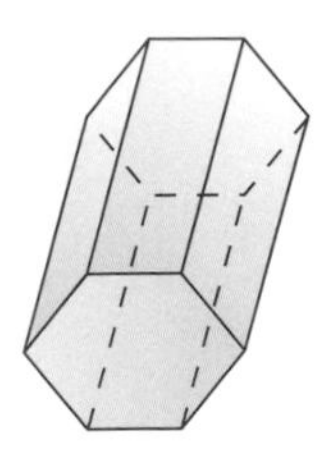

Use the rectangular prism and the pyramid at the right for Exercises 5 and 6.

5. Find the surface area of the rectangular prism.

6. Find the surface area of the pyramid.

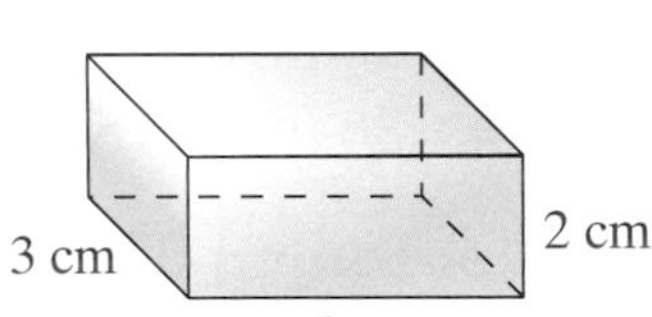

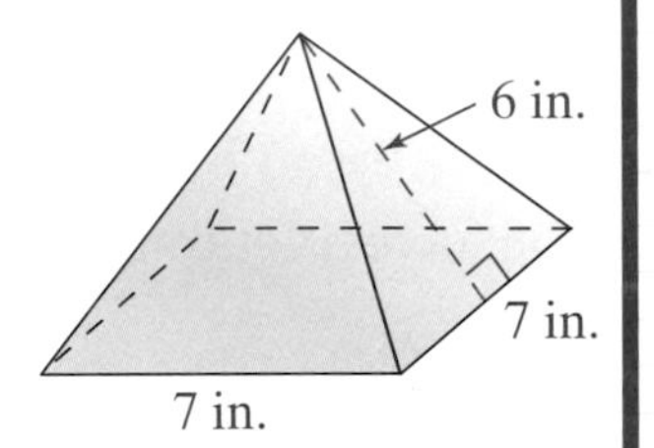

MATH GAMES

Drawing the Area

What You'll Need

- 1-centimeter graph paper
- straightedge

How to Play

- Players decide on an area such as 20 cm^2, 45 cm^2, or 80 cm^2.
- Each player then draws a rectangle, square, or triangle with that area.
- Players exchange drawings and check the areas of the figures.
- If an area is incorrect, the player loses a number of points equal to the difference in the area of his or her drawing and the correct area. If an area is correct, the player wins a number of points equal to the correct area.
- After several rounds of play, the player with the most points wins.

8-5a Activity Lab

Exploring Volume

Volume is the space inside a three-dimensional figure. The number of unit cubes that can fill the space inside a figure shows its volume. You can use cubes with side lengths other than 1 to fill the space. The edges on the cube at the right are $\frac{1}{2}$-centimeter long.

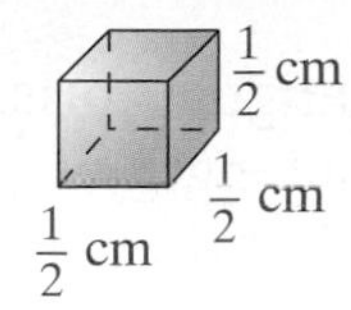

ACTIVITY

1. Use cubes to build the rectangular prism. Assume that each side of each cube has a length of $\frac{1}{2}$-centimeter. How many $\frac{1}{2}$-centimeter cubes did you use to make the base of the prism?

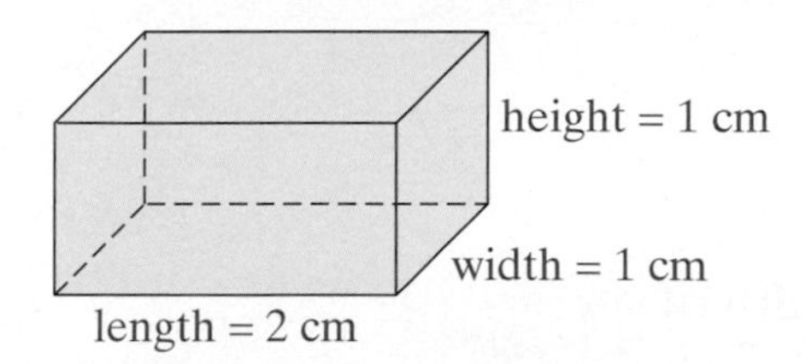

2. How many 1 centimeter cubes would you need to build the base?
3. How many layers high is your prism built with $\frac{1}{2}$-centimeter cubes?
4. How many layers high would the prism be if you built it with 1-centimeter cubes?
5. How many $\frac{1}{2}$-centimeter cubes did you use to build the entire prism?
6. What is the volume of one $\frac{1}{2}$-centimeter cube?
7. What is the total volume of the $\frac{1}{2}$-centimeter cubes you used to build the entire prism?
8. Use the formula $V = Bh$ to find the volume of the prism.
9. How does the formula $V = Bh$ relate to the total volume of the $\frac{1}{2}$-centimeter cubes you used to build the entire prism?

ACTIVITY

1. Use cubes to build the rectangular prism. Assume that each side of each cube has a length of $\frac{1}{3}$-centimeter. How many $\frac{1}{3}$-centimeter cubes do you place along the length of your prism?

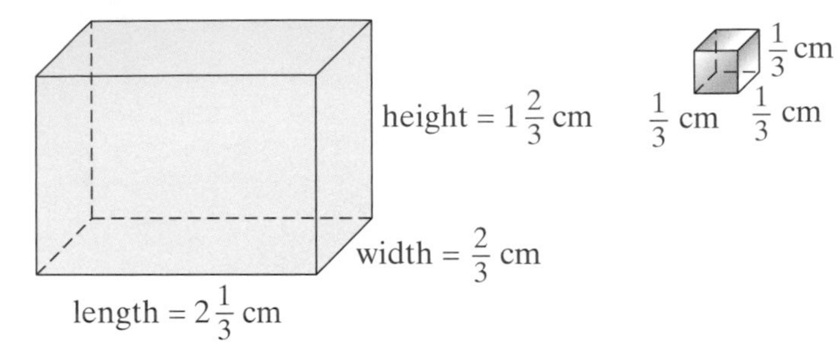

2. How many cubes are along the width?
3. Use multiplication to find the number of cubes you used to build the base of the prism.
4. How is this related to multiplying the length and the width of the prism to finding the area of the base?
5. How many layers high is your prism built with $\frac{1}{3}$-centimeter cubes?
6. How many $\frac{1}{3}$-centimeter cubes did you use to build the prism?
7. What is the volume of one $\frac{1}{3}$-centimeter cube?
8. What is the total volume of the $\frac{1}{3}$-centimeter cubes you used to build the prism?
9. Use the formula $V = lwh$ to find the volume of the prism.
10. How is the solution you found using the formula $V = lwh$ prism related to the total volume of the $\frac{1}{3}$-centimeter cubes you used to build the prism?
11. **Writing in Math** You have cubes with edge lengths of $\frac{1}{4}$ inch, $\frac{1}{3}$ inch, and $\frac{1}{2}$ inch. If you only use one size of cube, which can you use to fill the box at the right? Explain.

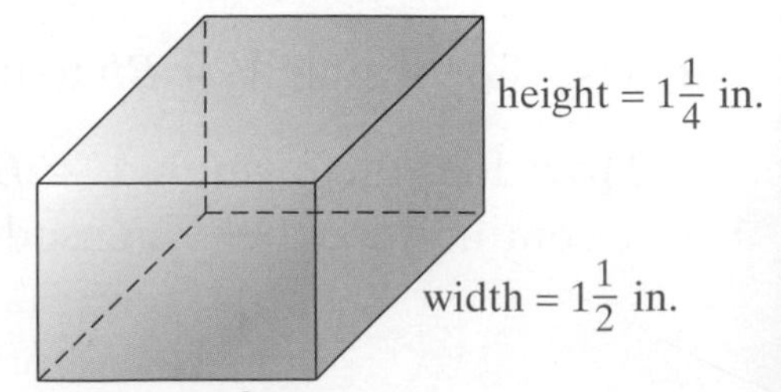

8-5 Volumes of Rectangular Prisms

1. Vocabulary Review Any side can be considered the __?__ of a parallelogram.

Find the area of a triangle with the given dimensions.

2. $b = 17$, $h = 13$

3. $b = 1.2$, $h = 4.5$

for Help Lesson 8-1

CONTENT STANDARD 6.G.2

What You'll Learn

To find the volume of rectangular prisms with fractional edge lengths

New Vocabulary volume

Why Learn This?

The volume of a fish tank tells you how much water the tank can hold. The **volume** of a three-dimensional figure is the number of cubic units needed to fill the space inside the figure.

EXAMPLE Counting Cubes to Find Volume

1 Find the volume of the rectangular prism.

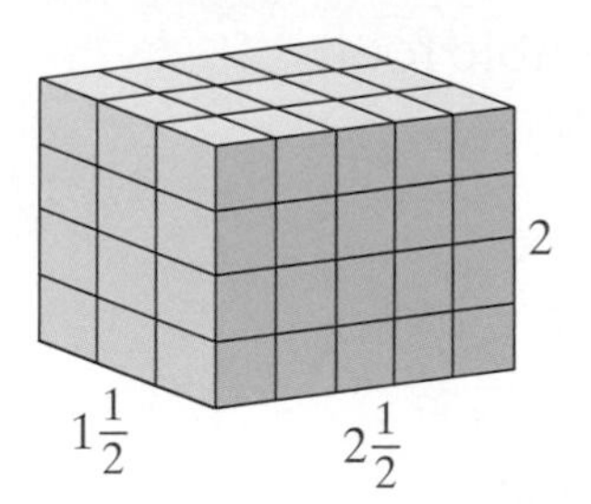

Step 1 Choose an appropriate cube. Two of the mixed numbers have fractions with denominators of 2. Use a $\frac{1}{2}$-unit cube.

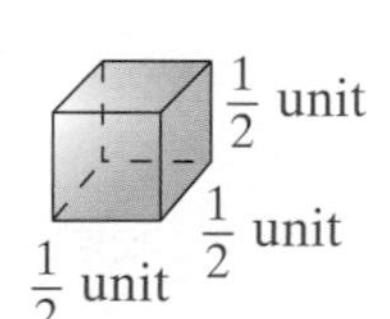

Step 2 Count the number of cubes in the prism.

$2\frac{1}{2} = \frac{5}{2}$ or $5 \times \frac{1}{2}$ ← **There are 5 cubes across the front.**

$1\frac{1}{2} = \frac{3}{2}$ or $3 \times \frac{1}{2}$ ← **There are 3 cubes along the side.**

$2 = \frac{4}{2}$ or $4 \times \frac{1}{2}$ ← **There are 4 cubes up.**

So the prism has a total of $5 \times 3 \times 4$, or 60 cubes.

Step 3 Find the volume of one cube.

The volume of one cube is $\frac{1}{2} \times \frac{1}{2} \times \frac{1}{2}$, or $\frac{1}{8}$ cubic unit.

Step 4 Multiply the number of cubes by the volume of each cube.

$60 \times \frac{1}{8} = \frac{60}{8} = \frac{15}{2} = 7\frac{1}{2}$

The volume of the prism is $7\frac{1}{2}$ cubic units.

Quick Check

1. Choose an appropriate sized cube and then count the cubes to find the volume of the prism.

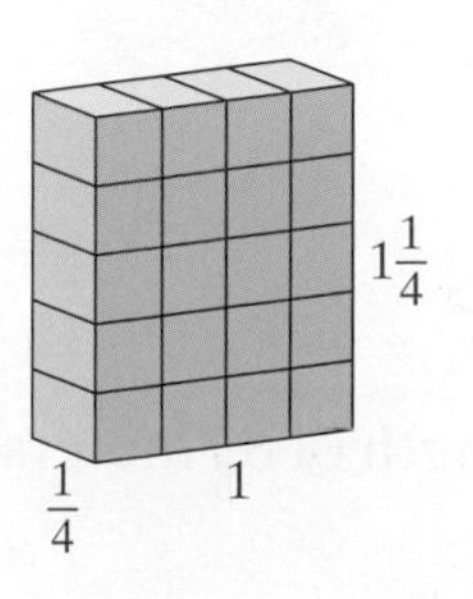

You have used formulas to find the volume of prisms whose edges have whole number lengths.

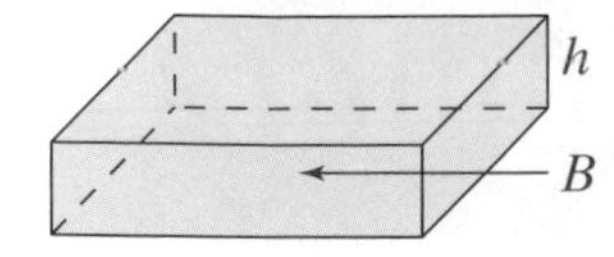

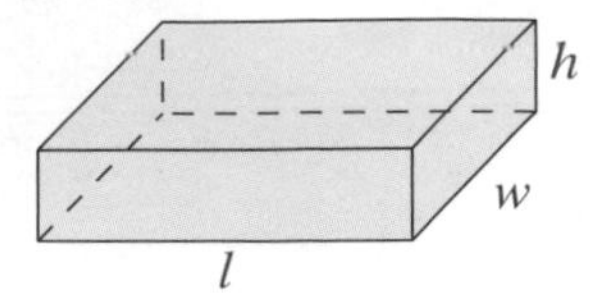

volume = area of base × height
$V = Bh$

volume = length × width × height
$V = lwh$

You can use the same formulas when the lengths of the prism edges are fractions or mixed numbers.

EXAMPLE Finding the Volume of a Prism

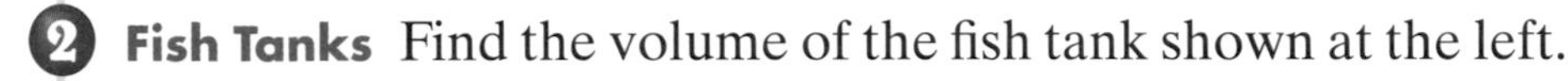

2 **Fish Tanks** Find the volume of the fish tank shown at the left.

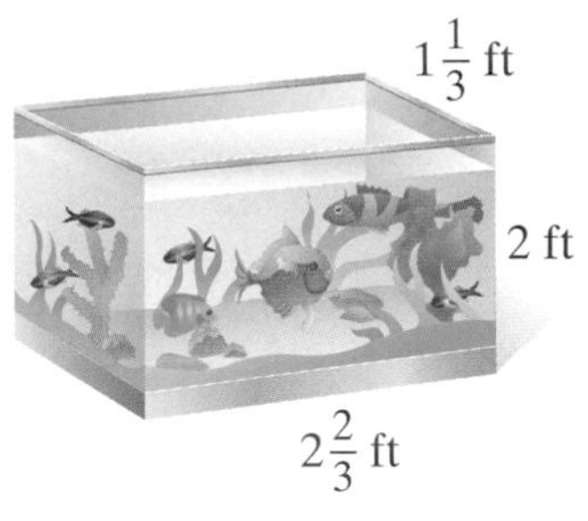

Method 1 Count the cubes.

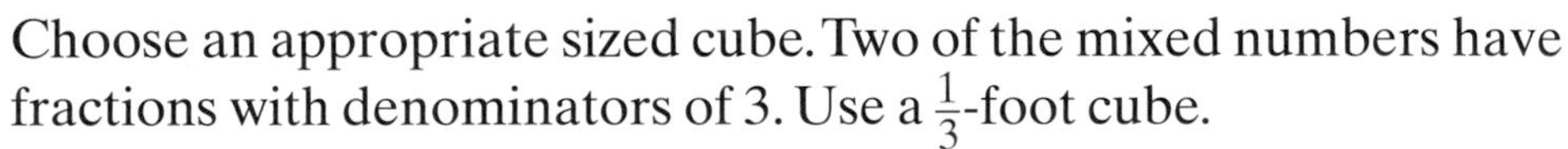

Choose an appropriate sized cube. Two of the mixed numbers have fractions with denominators of 3. Use a $\frac{1}{3}$-foot cube.

$2\frac{2}{3} = \frac{8}{3}$ ← **There are 8 cubes across the front.**

$1\frac{1}{3} = \frac{4}{3}$ ← **There are 4 cubes along the side.**

$2 = \frac{6}{3}$ ← **There are 6 cubes up.**

So the prism has a total of $8 \times 4 \times 6$, or 192 cubes.

The volume of a $\frac{1}{3}$-foot cube is $\frac{1}{3} \times \frac{1}{3} \times \frac{1}{3}$, or $\frac{1}{27}$ cubic foot.

$192 \times \frac{1}{27} = \frac{192}{27} = \frac{64}{9} = 7\frac{1}{9}$

The volume of the prism is $7\frac{1}{9}$ cubic feet.

Method 2 Use a formula.

$V = l \times w \times h$ ← **Use the formula for the volume of a rectangular prism.**

$= 2\frac{2}{3} \times 1\frac{1}{3} \times 2$ ← **Substitute $2\frac{2}{3}$ for l, $1\frac{1}{3}$ for w, and 2 for h.**

$= \frac{8}{3} \times \frac{4}{3} \times \frac{2}{1}$ ← **Multiply.**

$= \frac{64}{9} = 7\frac{1}{9}$

The volume is $7\frac{1}{9}$ cubic feet, or $7\frac{1}{9}$ ft³.

Quick Check

2. Find the volume of a rectangular prism with a length of $8\frac{1}{5}$ meters, a width of 7 meters, and a height of $10\frac{2}{5}$ meters.

Check Your Understanding

1. **Vocabulary** How are volume and area different?
2. **Number Sense** How does the volume of a cube change if its dimensions are doubled?
3. What is the volume of a $\frac{1}{5}$-cm cube?

Find the volume of each rectangular prism.

4. $l = 6\frac{3}{4}$ m, $w = 4$ m, $h = 11$ m
5. $l = 3$ ft, $w = 2$ ft, $h = 9\frac{1}{2}$ ft
6. **Estimation** Estimate the volume of a rectangular prism with a length of $4\frac{1}{8}$ yd, a width of 3 yd, and a height of $5\frac{7}{8}$ yd.

Homework Exercises

For more exercises, see Extra Skills and Word Problems.

GO for Help

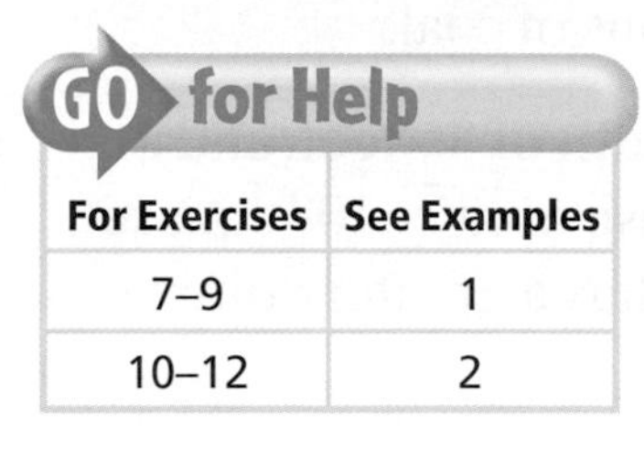

For Exercises	See Examples
7–9	1
10–12	2

Choose an appropriate sized cube. Then count the cubes to find the volume of each rectangular prism.

7.

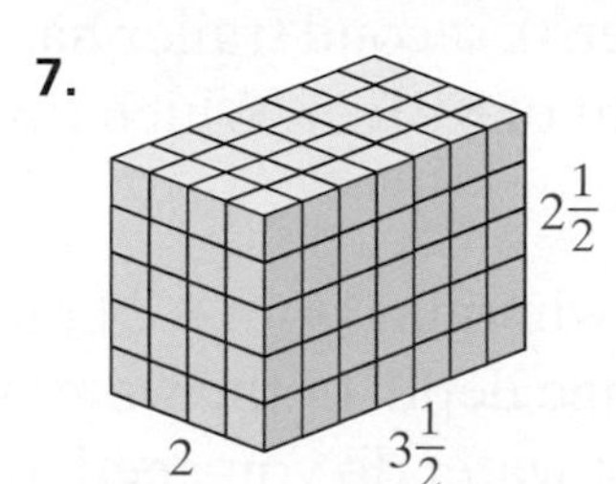

8.

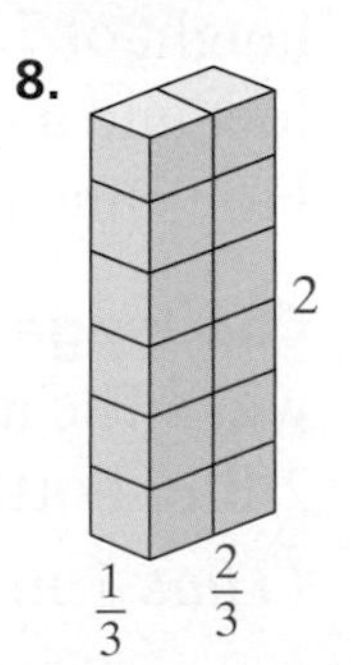

9.

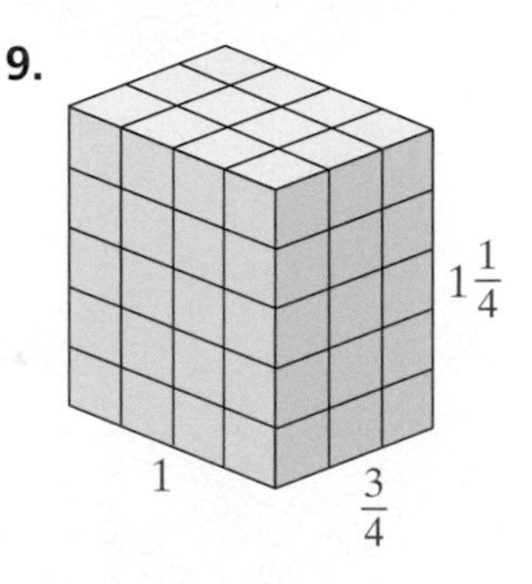

Find the volume of each rectangular prism.

GO Online
Homework Video Tutor
PearsonSuccessNet.com

10.

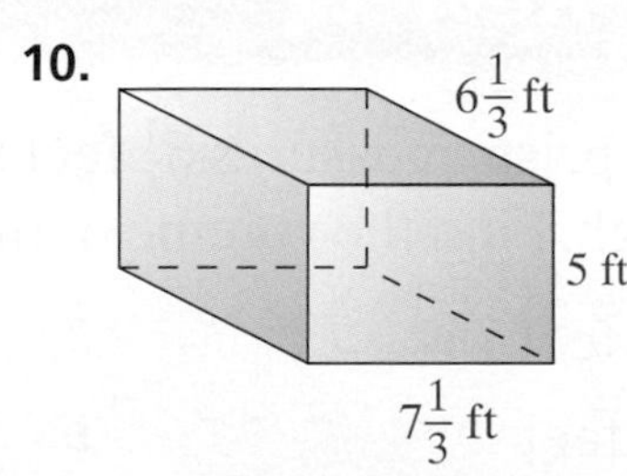

11.

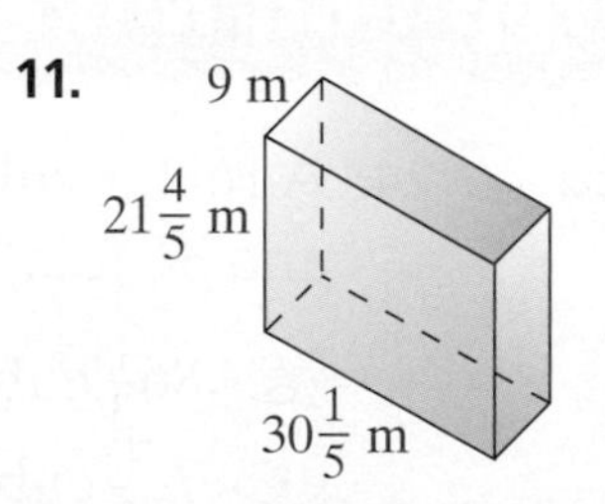

12.

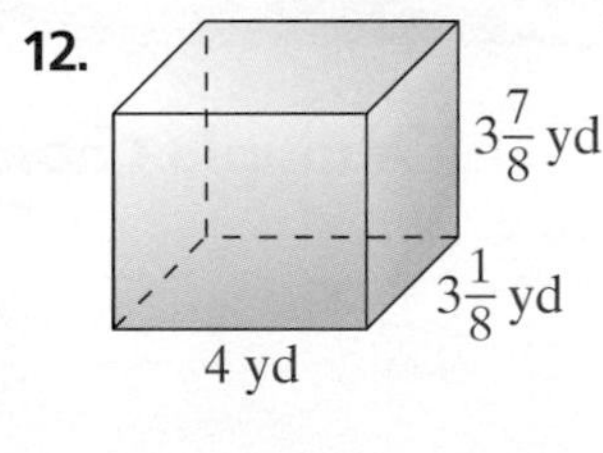

GPS 13. **Guided Problem Solving** The shape of a monument is a rectangular prism. The length is $1\frac{2}{3}$ feet, the width is $\frac{1}{2}$ foot, and the height is 3 feet. Count the cubes to find the volume of the monument.

- What are the denominators of the fractions in the mixed numbers?
- How would rewriting the fractions help you determine what sized cube to use?
- What sized cube should you use to find the volume? Why?
- Find the volume by counting cubes. Then check your answer by using the formula.

14. **Algebra** A rectangular prism has a volume of 70 m^3, a height of $2\frac{1}{2}$ m and a width of $3\frac{1}{2}$ m. What is the length of the prism?

Find the volume of each rectangular prism.

15. $l = 5\frac{1}{3}$ yd, $w = 6$ yd, $h = 2\frac{1}{4}$ yd

16. $l = 1\frac{1}{2}$ ft, $w = \frac{7}{8}$ ft, $h = 4$ ft

17. $l = 6$ in., $w = 4.3$ in., $h = 1\frac{3}{5}$ in.

18. $l = 3.2$ m, $w = 2$ m, $h = 9.45$ m

19. As part of a community project, a sixth grade class cleans up a neighborhood park and builds a sand box for the young children. The sand box is 5 feet long, 4 feet 6 inches wide, and $\frac{2}{3}$ foot tall. What volume of sand will fit in the sand box?

20. **Writing in Math** Two rectangular prisms have the same base area. The height of the second prism is twice the height of the first prism. How do their volumes compare? Explain.

21. **Reasoning** One ton of coal fills a bin that is $1\frac{2}{3}$ yd by $1\frac{1}{3}$ yd by $\frac{2}{3}$ yd Find the dimensions of a bin that holds 2 tons of coal.

22. A truck trailer has a length of 20 feet, a width of $8\frac{1}{2}$ feet, and a height of $7\frac{1}{2}$ feet. A second trailer has a base area of 108 square feet and a height of $8\frac{1}{2}$ feet. Which trailer has a greater volume? How much greater is it?

23. **Challenge** A swimming pool is 24 meters long and 16 meters wide. The average depth of the water is $2\frac{1}{2}$ meters. How many 2-liter bottles of water do you need to fill the pool? (*Hint*: $1 \text{ m}^3 = 1{,}000$ L)

Test Prep and Mixed Review

Practice

Multiple Choice

24. A rectangular prism measures $6\frac{1}{6}$ feet long, 4 inches wide, and $3\frac{1}{2}$ feet high. Find the volume of the prism.

Ⓐ $86\frac{1}{3}$ cubic feet

Ⓑ $7\frac{7}{36}$ cubic feet

Ⓒ 10 cubic feet

Ⓓ $18\frac{1}{36}$ cubic feet

25. What missing piece of information is needed to find the area of the parallelogram?

4 in.

5 in.

Ⓕ Side length

Ⓖ Base length

Ⓗ Height

Ⓙ Perimeter

GO for Help

For Exercises	See Lesson
26–27	8-1

Find the area of each polygon.

26. parallelogram: base 12 m, height 6.5 m

27. triangle: base 9 ft, height 14 ft

Test-Taking Strategies

Measuring to Solve

Some test questions ask you to measure with a ruler to solve a problem.

EXAMPLE

Emily used aluminum to make this pin in art class.

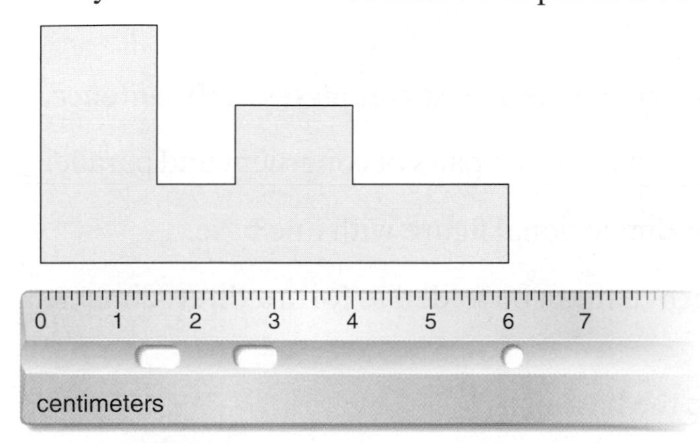

Use a ruler to find how many square centimeters of aluminum she used for the pin.

Ⓐ 9 cm^2 Ⓑ 10.5 cm^2 Ⓒ 16.5 cm^2 Ⓓ 21 cm^2

The shape can be decomposed into these 3 rectangles: 3 cm by 1.5 cm, 1.5 cm by 1 cm, and 1 cm by 4.5 cm. The areas of the 3 rectangles are 4.5 cm^2, 1.5 cm^2, and 4.5 cm^2. The sum of the areas is 10.5 cm^2.

Emily used 10.5 cm^2 of aluminum for the pin. The correct answer is choice B.

Exercises

1. A pentagon is shown. Use a ruler to find the area of the pentagon in square millimeters.
   Ⓐ 580 mm^2 Ⓒ 1,010 mm^2
   Ⓑ 860 mm^2 Ⓓ 1,160 mm^2

2. One face of a cube is shown. Use a ruler to find the dimensions of the face. What is the volume of the cube?
   Ⓕ 54 cm^3 Ⓗ 18 cm^3
   Ⓖ 27 cm^3 Ⓙ 9 cm^3

Chapter 8 Review

Vocabulary Review

area (p. 275)
base of a parallelogram (p. 275)
base of a triangle (p. 276)
compose (p. 281)
cone (p. 287)
cube (p. 286)
cylinder (p. 287)
decompose (p. 281)
edge (p. 286)
faces (p. 286)
height of a parallelogram (p. 275)
height of a triangle (p. 276)
net (p. 292)
prism (p. 286)
pyramid (p. 287)
sphere (p. 287)
surface area (p. 293)
three-dimensional figure (p. 286)
vertex (p. 286)
volume (p. 299)

Choose the vocabulary term that best completes each sentence.

1. A rectangular prism has three pairs of congruent and parallel __?__.
2. A __?__ is a three-dimensional figure with one base.
3. A __?__ is a pattern that can be folded to form a three-dimensional figure.
4. Any side can be the base of a __?__.
5. The number of cubic units needed to fill the space inside a figure is the __?__.

Go Online
For vocabulary quiz
PearsonSuccessNet.com

Skills and Concepts

Lessons 8-1 and 8-2

- To solve problems involving areas of parallelograms, triangles, and complex figures
- To compose and decompose polygons to solve problems involving area

The **area** of a figure is the number of square units inside the figure. The formula for the area of a parallelogram is $A = b \times h$. The formula for the area of a triangle is $A = \frac{1}{2}b \times h$.

Find the area of each figure or set of figures.

6. 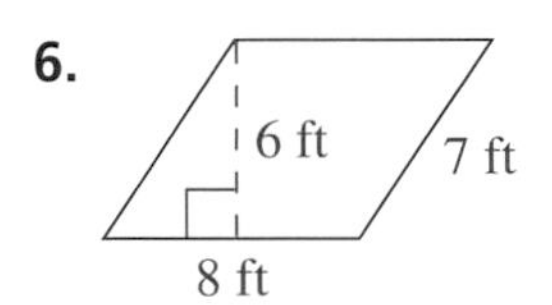

7. 15.2 m, 29 m, 24.7 m

8. 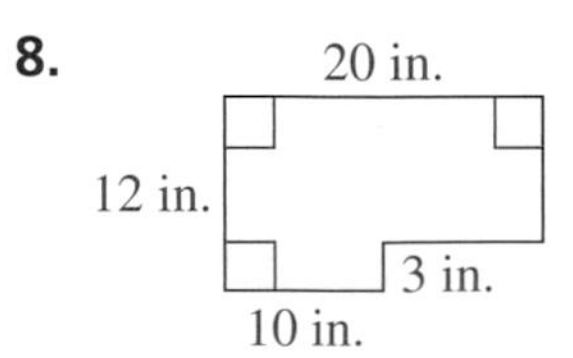

9. 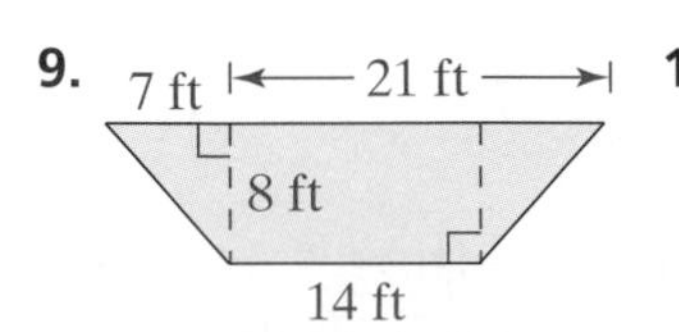

10. 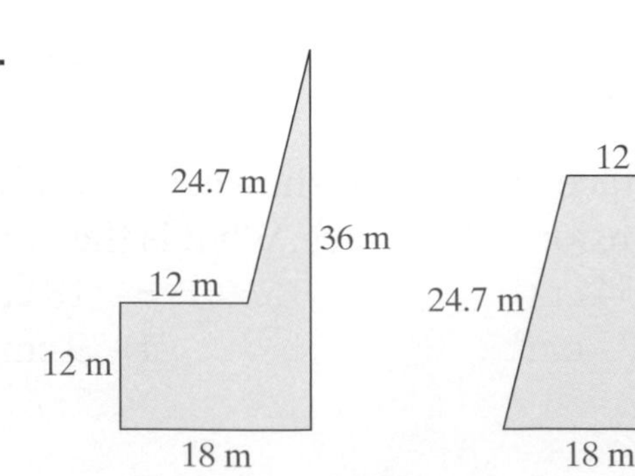

Lesson 8-3

- To identify three-dimensional figures

A **prism** is a **three-dimensional figure** with two parallel and congruent **faces** that are polygons. A **pyramid** has triangular faces and one base that is a polygon. You name a prism or a pyramid by the shape of its base or bases.

Name each figure.

11.

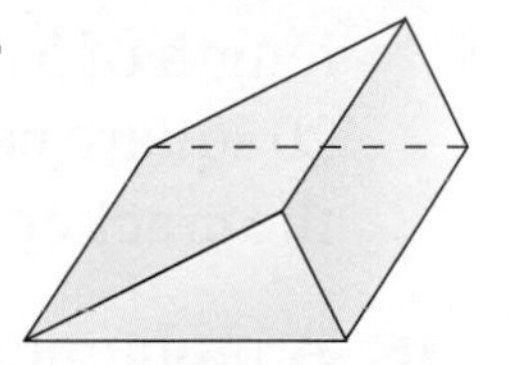

12.

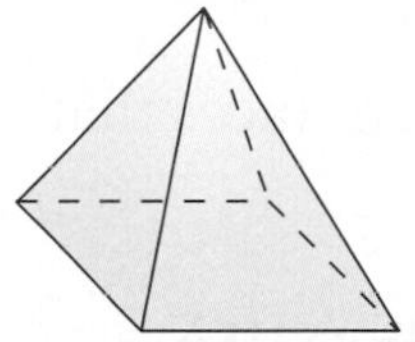

13.

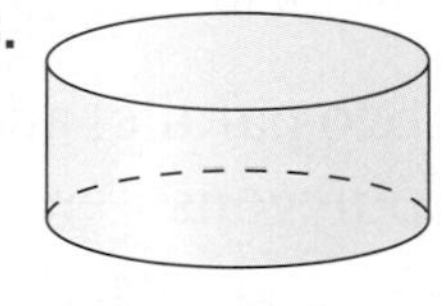

Lesson 8-4

- To use nets and to find the surface areas of rectangular prisms and pyramids

The **surface area** of a three-dimensional figure is the sum of the areas of all its faces.

Find the surface area of each figure.

14.

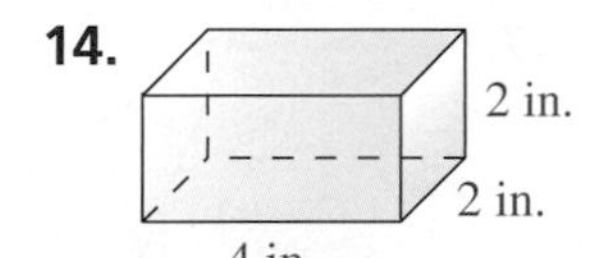

15.

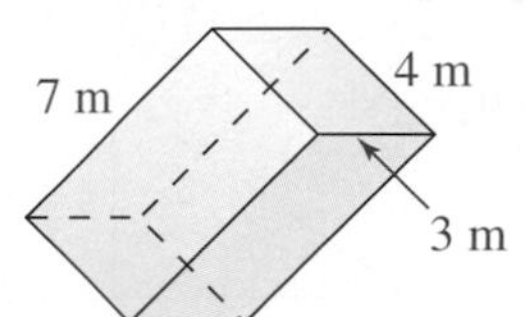

16.

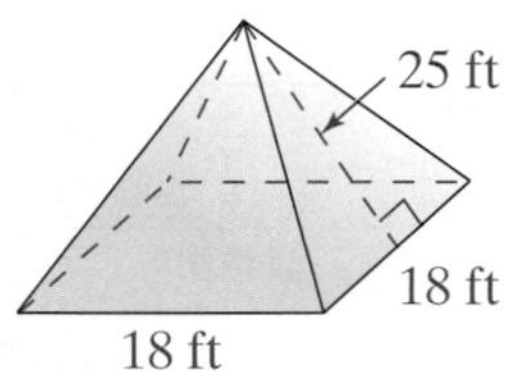

Lesson 8-5

- To find the volume of rectangular prisms with fractional edge lengths

The **volume** of a three-dimensional figure is the number of cubic units needed to fill the space inside the figure. The formula for the volume of a prism is $V = lwh$ or $V = B \times h$, where B is the area of the base.

Find the volume of each prism.

17.

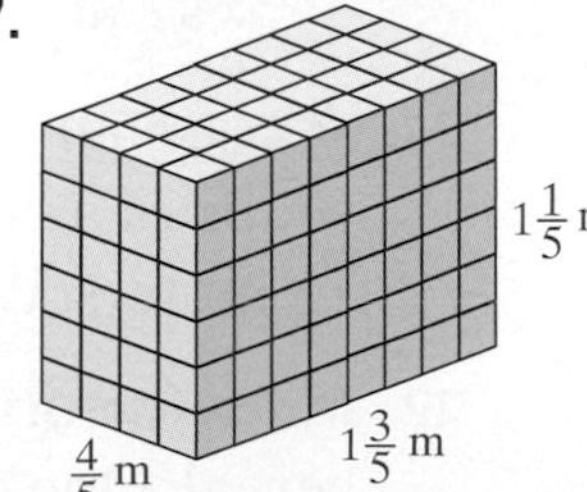

18.

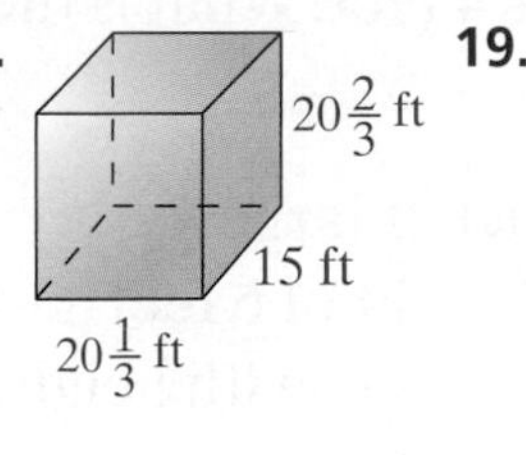

19.

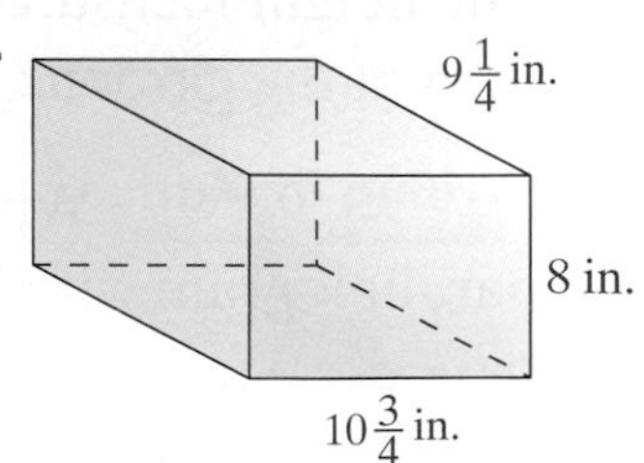

20. Julia is filling a crate with wood chips. The crate is $2\frac{1}{2}$ feet long, $3\frac{3}{4}$ feet wide, and $2\frac{2}{3}$ feet high. How many cubic feet of wood chips will she need to completely fill the crate?

Chapter 8 Test

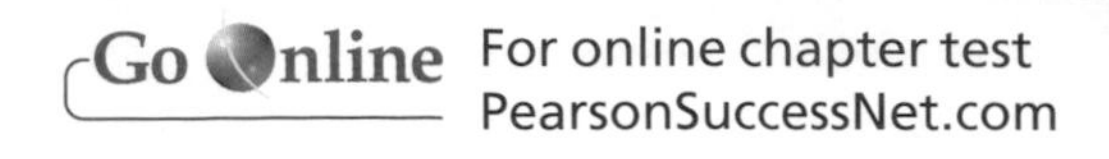

For online chapter test PearsonSuccessNet.com

Name the three-dimensional figure that fits each description.

1. two circular bases
2. faces that are triangles and one base that is a polygon
3. no base
4. two parallel and congruent faces that are polygons
5. one circular base and one vertex
6. a prism with congruent sides
7. two parallel and congruent faces that are triangles

Find the area of each figure.

8. 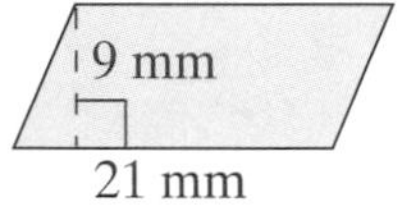

9. 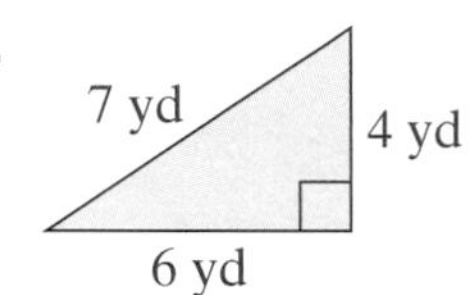

10. 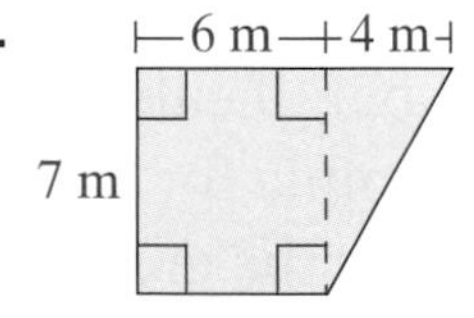

11. 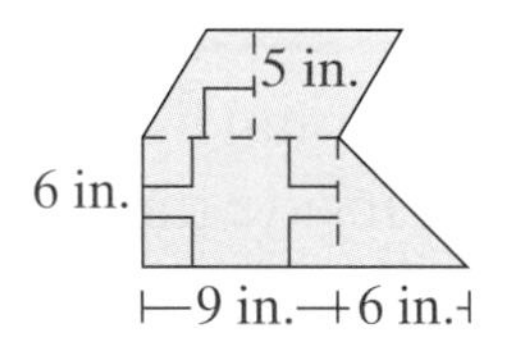

12. A garden is in the shape of a right triangle. The base of the triangle measures 8 feet. The height measures 4 feet. What is the area of the garden?

13. **Writing in Math** Which is larger, a parallelogram with height of 6 feet and base of 10 feet or a triangle with height of 6 feet and base of 20 feet? Explain.

Find the total area of the shaded polygons.

14. 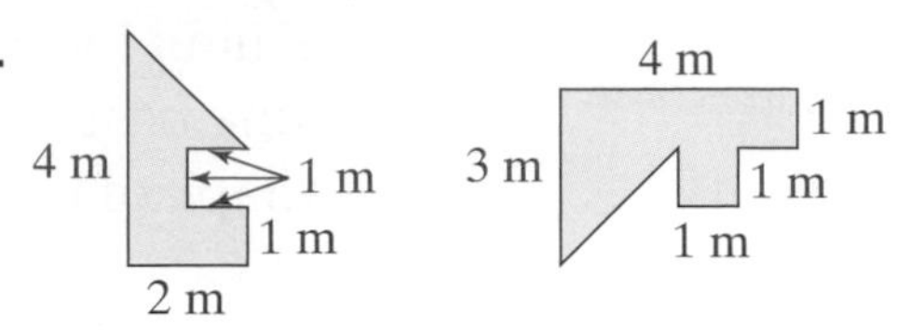

15. **Food** A rectangular cracker has a length of 5 centimeters and an area of 20 square centimeters. Find the height of the cracker.

16. A monument has the shape of square pyramid. The base has a length of 6 ft. The height of a face is 13 ft. What is the surface area of the pyramid?

Find the surface area of each figure.

17. 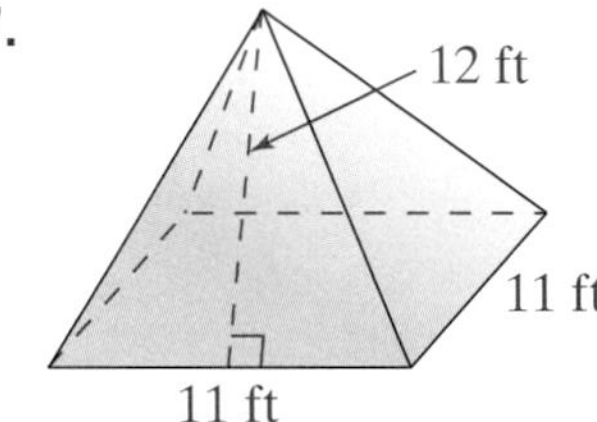

18. 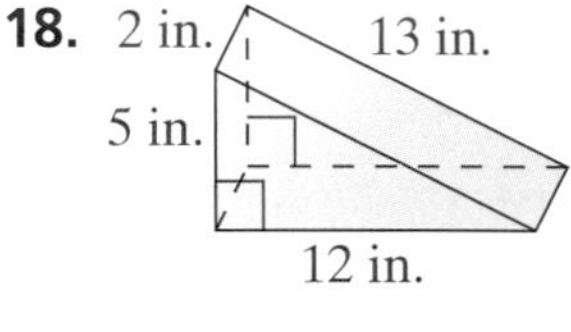

Find the volume of each figure.

19. 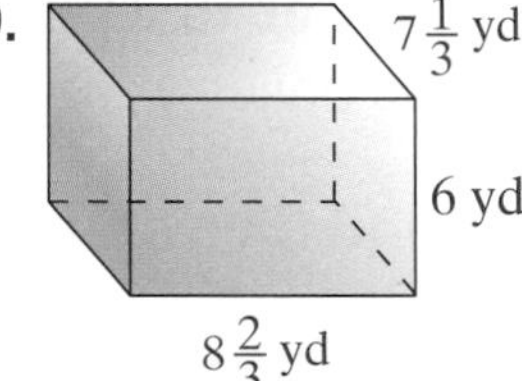

20. 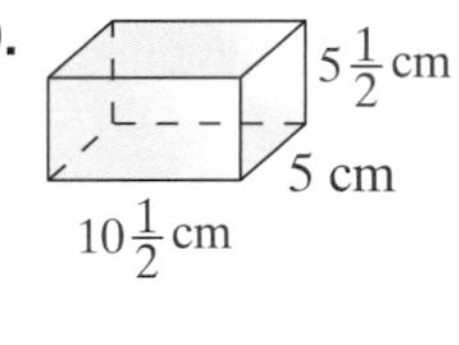

21. A company makes compost bins in the shape of a cube. The height of each bin is $1\frac{1}{2}$ meters. What is the volume of each bin?

22. **Manufacturing** A factory fills boxes with cereal. One cereal box is $9\frac{1}{2}$ inches high, $6\frac{1}{2}$ inches long, and $2\frac{3}{4}$ inches wide. A second cereal box has a base area of $16\frac{1}{4}$ square inches and a height of $10\frac{1}{4}$ inches. Find the volume of each cereal box. Which has a greater volume?

Test Prep Practice

Reading Comprehension

Read each passage and answer the questions that follow.

Baseballs A company that makes baseballs packs each baseball in a paperboard box that is a cube. The length of each side of the box is $3\frac{1}{8}$ inches. The baseball boxes are then packed in cardboard shipping cartons that are $2\frac{1}{6}$ feet long, $1\frac{2}{3}$ feet tall, and $1\frac{1}{6}$ feet wide. The company ships out about 10,000 baseballs each day.

1. What is the least amount of paperboard that can be used to make a baseball box?

   (A) $18\frac{3}{4}$ in.^{2} (B) $37\frac{1}{2}$ in.^{2} (C) $58\frac{19}{32}$ in.^{2} (D) 75 in.^{2}

2. About how many shipping cartons can be made from 100 square feet of cardboard?

   (F) 5 cartons (G) 10 cartons (H) 15 cartons (J) 100 cartons

3. Which expression represents the volume of one shipping carton?

   (A) $3\frac{1}{8} \times 3\frac{1}{8} \times 3\frac{1}{8}$

   (B) $2\frac{1}{6} \times 1\frac{2}{3} \times 1\frac{1}{6}$

   (C) $\frac{1}{2}(2\frac{1}{6} \times 1\frac{2}{3} \times 1\frac{1}{6})$

   (D) $3\frac{1}{8}(2\frac{1}{6} + 1\frac{2}{3} + 1\frac{1}{6})$

4. How many baseball boxes will there be in one layer of a packed shipping carton?

   (F) 12 boxes (G) 48 boxes (H) 32 boxes (J) 192 boxes

Mountain Math It takes about $1\frac{1}{2}$ hours to get from Al's house to Mount Monadnock. First you go west 40 miles on a state highway. Then you turn right and go north another 30 miles, and you're there. On a clear day you can see the tallest buildings in Al's hometown from the top of the mountain.

5. Which choice does NOT correctly identify a point in this diagram?

   (A) Q is Al's house.

   (B) R is Al's house.

   (C) P is at the right turn.

   (D) Q is the mountain.

   Q
   30 mi
   P
   R
   40 mi

6. How long will it take Al to drive to Mount Monadnock if he averages a rate of 56 miles per hour for the whole trip?

   (F) 1 h (G) 1.25 h (H) 1.5 h (J) 1.8 h

7. How many miles is the trip from Al's house to Mount Monadnock?

   (A) 30 miles (B) 40 miles (C) 50 miles (D) 70 miles

8. The odometer on Al's car shows how many miles the car travels. If the odometer shows 12,350 miles as Al leaves home, what will it show after a round trip to the mountain?

   (F) 12,000 miles (G) 12,490 miles (H) 12,520 miles (J) 12,900 miles

CHAPTER 9 Data and Graphs

What You've Learned

- In Chapter 1, you compared and ordered decimals.
- You used addition, subtraction, multiplication, and division to solve problems involving decimals.
- You used order of operations to simplify expressions.

GO for Help

For Exercises	See Lesson
1–2	1-2
3–9	1-4
10–12	1-6

Using Order of Operations

Find the value of each expression.

1. $16 + 12 \div 4 - 1$
2. $6 \times (4 + 3) - 2$

Adding Decimals

Find each sum.

3. $13.2 + 23.6 + 26.3$
4. $152.3 + 143.6 + 128$
5. $49.0 + 22.2 + 11.22 + 23.4$
6. $6.09 + 1.5 + 4.68 + 13.6$

Subtracting Decimals

Find each difference.

7. $109.55 - 89.34$
8. $10.42 - 9.36$
9. $75 - 73.2$

Dividing Decimals

Find each quotient.

10. $142.03 \div 10$
11. $361.6 \div 16$
12. $100.75 \div 25$

What You'll Learn Next

- In this chapter, you will find the mean, median, mode, and range of a set of data.
- You will select and use different types of data graphs such as dot plots, box-and-whisker plots, and histograms.
- You will solve problems by collecting, organizing, displaying, and interpreting data.

Key Vocabulary

- box-and-whisker plot (p. 323)
- dot plot (p. 320)
- frequency table (p. 319)
- histogram (p. 328)
- interquartile range (IQR) (p. 335)
- lower quartile (p. 323)
- mean (p. 311)
- mean absolute deviation (MAD) (p. 334)
- measure of center (p. 334)
- measure of variability (p. 334)
- median (p. 315)
- mode (p. 316)
- outlier (p. 312)
- range (p. 320)
- statistical question (p. 345)
- upper quartile (p. 323)

9-1a Activity Lab

Exploring the Mean

Three friends went apple picking. The friends want to make sure that each person has the same number of apples.

1. The diagram below shows the number of apples picked by each friend. Use objects to represent the apples. Make a pile of "apples" for each of the friends.

2. Describe a method you can use to even out the number of apples so that each person has the same number. What is this number?

3. Graph the number of apples each friend picked on the number line. Then draw a small star on the number of apples each friend will get after sharing.

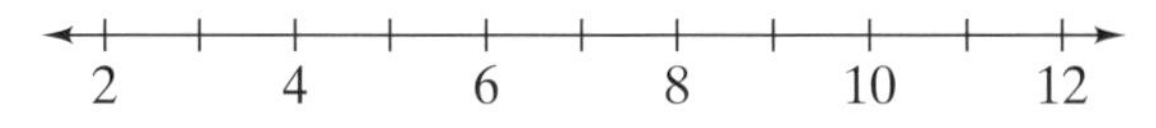

4. **Writing in Math** The value indicated by the star on your number line is called "the mean." Use what you have learned to write a definition for the word *mean*.

5. Make four piles with 13, 16, 18, and 19 "apples." Use the method you described in Step 2 to create four equal piles. What problem did you encounter? How can you solve this problem?

6. A dance committee is inflating balloons for a dance. The mean number of balloons inflated by each person is 9. Use objects to represent the number of balloons in the table at the right. How many balloons did Eric inflate?

Dance Committee

Name	Number of Balloons
Jamil	12
Ashley	10
Hoshi	4
Eric	■

9-1 Finding the Mean

Check Skills You'll Need

1. **Vocabulary Review** When dividing, the result other than the remainder is the _?_.

Find each quotient.

2. $330 \div 12$
3. $6\overline{)256.5}$
4. $237.4 \div 4$

for Help Lesson 1-6

CONTENT STANDARDS
6.SP.3, 6.SP.5, 6.SP.5.c

What You'll Learn

To find and analyze the mean of a data set using models and calculations

New Vocabulary mean, outlier

Why Learn This?

Meteorologists analyze data. They often use a measure, such as the mean, to help describe a set of data.

The **mean** of a set of data is the sum of the data divided by the number of data items. To find the mean of a set of data, you can adjust all of the values so the values are the same.

EXAMPLE Using a Model to Find the Mean

1 On four days it rained 2 inches, 4 inches, 5 inches, and 1 inch. Find the mean amount of rain.

You can draw a picture or use objects to model the situation.

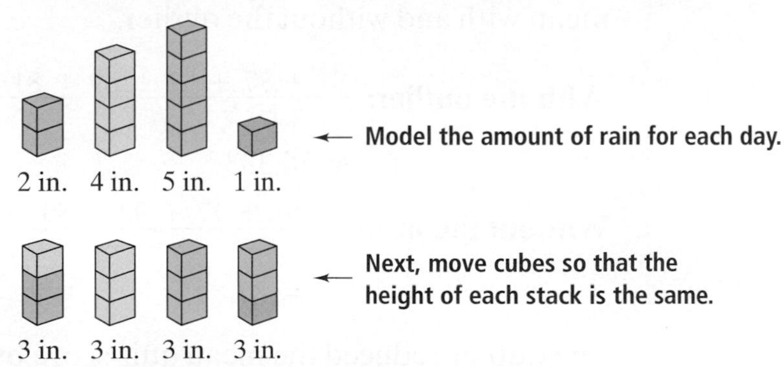
2 in.
4 in.
5 in.
1 in.
Model the amount of rain for each day.
3 in.
3 in.
3 in.
3 in.
Next, move cubes so that the height of each stack is the same.

The mean amount of rain is 3 inches.

Quick Check

1. Use a model to find the mean of 3, 6, 3, 4, 2, and 6.

EXAMPLE Calculating the Mean

The thorny lizard survives high temperatures by using its spikes to collect moisture at night.

2 You measure the temperature outside each day during the week. The temperatures are 95°, 96°, 103°, 99°, and 96°. Find the mean temperature.

$95 + 96 + 103 + 99 + 96 = 489$ ← **Add the temperatures.**

$\frac{489}{5} = 97.8$ ← **Divide by the number of readings.**

The mean temperature is 97.8°.

Check for Reasonableness The mean is between the lowest value, 95, and the greatest value, 103. So, the answer 97.8 is reasonable.

Quick Check

2. You play a word game. Your scores are 12, 23, 13, 32, and 20. Find your mean score.

An **outlier** is a data item that is much greater or less than the other data items. If a data set has an outlier, then the mean may not describe the data very well.

EXAMPLE Analyzing the Mean

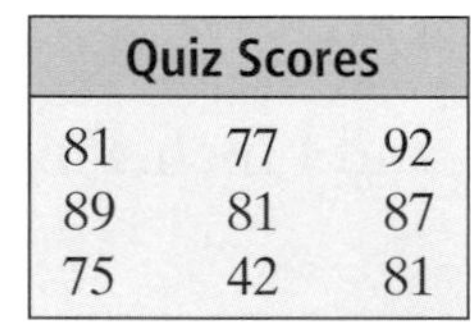

Quiz Scores		
81	77	92
89	81	87
75	42	81

3 Your quiz scores in science are listed at the left. Find the mean test score with and without the outlier. What effect does the outlier have on the mean?

Since 42 is much less than the other scores, the outlier is 42. Find the mean with and without the outlier.

With the outlier: $\frac{81 + 77 + 92 + 89 + 81 + 87 + 75 + 42 + 81}{9}$

≈ 78.333

Without the outlier: $\frac{81 + 77 + 92 + 89 + 81 + 87 + 75 + 81}{8}$

$= 82.875$

The outlier reduced the mean quiz score by about 5 points.

Quick Check

3. You keep track of the number of hours you baby-sit for six days: 1.25, 1.50, 1.50, 1.75, 2.0, 5.5. What effect does the outlier have on the mean?

Check Your Understanding

1. **Vocabulary** Explain how to find the mean of five test scores.

Use a model to find the mean of each data set.

2. 3, 2, 8, 4, 3

3. 5, 3, 7, 10, 6, 5

4. **Open-Ended** Explain why the mean might not be a good measure for a set of data when the set includes outliers. Write a set of data items that supports your explanation.

Homework Exercises

For more exercises, see Extra Skills and Word Problems.

GO for Help

For Exercises	See Example
5–13	1–2
14–16	3

Find the mean of each data set. You may find a model helpful.

5. 3, 4, 7, 2, 5, 9

6. 6, 4, 5, 9, 7, 6, 8, 3

7. 12, 9, 11, 8, 9, 12, 9

8. 14, 16, 28, 17, 20

9. 121, 95, 115, 92, 113, 108, 91

10. 2.4, 1.8, 3.5, 2.3, 6.5

11. 500, 450, 475, 450, 500

12. 23, 24, 27, 25, 26, 22, 21

13. You keep track of the time you spend doing homework each evening. You spend 58 minutes, 36 minutes, 44 minutes, and 37 minutes. Find the mean of these times.

For each set of data, identify any outliers. Then determine the effect that the outlier has on the mean.

14. 95, 90, 87, 85, 79, 82, 87, 40, 90, 80

15. 8, 7, 10, 12, 8, 11, 8, 6, 9, 50, 8, 10, 7, 7

16. 200; 225; 3,000; 500; 325; 311; 295; 485; 359; 325

17. **Guided Problem Solving** The prices for a gallon of milk at four stores are \$1.99, \$2.29, \$2.19, and \$1.88. Is the mean a good measure of the price of milk in the four stores? Explain.
    - **Understand the Problem** You have to determine whether any outliers affect the mean.
    - **Make a Plan** How will you find the mean?

18. **Data Collection** Measure the height, in inches, of five different cups in your home. Find the mean height.

GO Online
Homework Video Tutor
PearsonSuccessNet.com

Find the mean of each data set.

19. 10, 4, 11.7, 30, 7.9, 11, 8.2, 3, 8, 9.2, 14.2, 5.2

20. 2.4, 5.3, 3.5, 2.6, 2.3, 3.5, 2.8, 4.3, 4.5, 3.8

Dense rain forests are found in Hawaii because of its wet, tropical climate.

21. The table shows the monthly rainfall for one year in Hilo, Hawaii.
   a. Find the mean amount of rain to the nearest inch.
   b. **Writing in Math** Why are most of the data items less than the mean?

Rainfall in Hilo, Hawaii

Month	Rainfall (in.)
January	5
February	1
March	15
April	43
May	9
June	9
July	11
August	11
September	14
October	12
November	36
December	6

SOURCE: *The Weather Almanac*

22. (Algebra) The mean of 22, 19, 25, and x is 23. Find x.

23. Shelby made a list of her test scores: 88, 100, 92, 80, 85, 94, and 90. What is the lowest score she can get on her next test to have a mean score of 90?

24. **Challenge** The mean of 22.3, 19.7, 25.4, and another number is 23.4. Find the missing number.

Test Prep and Mixed Review

Practice

Multiple Choice

25. Which number is between the two points graphed on the number line?

Ⓐ 1.44 Ⓑ 1.55 Ⓒ 1.63 Ⓓ 1.72

26. Kristi received scores of 5.2 and 2.3 on her two ice-skating routines. What is the difference between these scores?

Ⓕ 2.1 Ⓖ 2.9 Ⓗ 3.1 Ⓙ 3.9

27. Duke has football practice for 2 hours after school every day. If he goes to practice 5 days, which method can be used to find the total number of hours Duke practices?

Ⓐ Add 2 and 5.
Ⓑ Subtract 2 from 5.
Ⓒ Multiply 5 by 2.
Ⓓ Divide 5 by 2.

GO for Help

For Exercises	See Lesson
28–30	1-5

Find each product.

28. 4.2×9.6 **29.** 3.07×6.3 **30.** 4.25×1.04

9-2 Median and Mode

1. Vocabulary Review To find the mean of 1, 2, 3, 4, and 5, you add the numbers and divide by __?__.

Find the mean of each set of data.

2. 4, 16, 20, 40

3. 12, 23, 19, 32, 26

4. 5, 15, 75, 105, 85

Lesson 9-1

CONTENT STANDARDS
6.SP.3, 6.SP.5, 6.SP.5.c

What You'll Learn

To find and analyze the median and mode of a data set

New Vocabulary median, mode

Why Learn This?

Scientists use the mean, median, and mode to describe sets of data, including fish populations.

The **median** is the middle number in a set of ordered data. The median gives a good description of numerical data with outliers.

4 7 9 13 25
↑
median

For an even number of data items, you can find the median by adding the two middle numbers and dividing by 2.

Test Prep Tip

A griddable answer is not always a decimal.

		2	1

EXAMPLE Finding the Median

1 **Gridded Response** A biologist studying the ecology of a river makes a weekly fish count. The results are 19, 18, 22, 23, 20, 24, 23, 20, 34, and 19. Find the median number of fish.

18, 19, 19, 20, 20, 22, 23, 23, 24, 34 ← **Order the data. Since there are 10 items, use the two middle values.**

$\frac{20 + 22}{2} = \frac{42}{2}$, or 21 ← **Find the mean of 20 and 22.**

The median number of fish is 21.

Quick Check

1. Weekly sales of comics at a store are 39, 19, 28, 9, 32, 35, and 17 comics. What is the median number of comics sold?

The **mode** is the data item(s) that appears most often. A data set may have more than one mode. If all data items occur the same number of times, there is no mode. The mode is useful when the data items are repeated or not numerical.

EXAMPLE Finding the Mode

2 The list shows the favorite lunches of 15 students. Find the mode.

Favorite Lunch
hamburger, pizza, taco, pizza, spaghetti, taco, spaghetti, hamburger, hamburger, pizza, taco, pizza, pizza, spaghetti, taco

Group the data.

pizza, pizza, pizza, pizza, pizza
hamburger, hamburger, hamburger
taco, taco, taco, taco
spaghetti, spaghetti, spaghetti

Pizza occurs the most. It is the mode.

GO Online

Video Tutor Help
PearsonSuccessNet.com

Quick Check

2. How many students would have to switch from hamburger to taco as their favorite lunch for taco to be the only mode?

EXAMPLE Analyzing Data

Amount of Time Spent on Internet (minutes)			
50	276	57	50
62	53	72	71
63	60	22	

3 Find the mean, median, and mode for the number of minutes spent on the Internet. Does the mean, median, or mode best describe the typical amount of time spent on the Internet?

mean $\frac{50 + 276 + 57 + 50 + 62 + 53 + 72 + 71 + 63 + 60 + 22}{11} = \frac{836}{11}$

$= 76$

median 22 50 50 53 57 60 62 63 71 72 276: 60

mode 50

The mode and mean are close to only a few data points. The median is close to most of the data items. So the median best describes the typical amount of time spent on the Internet.

Quick Check

3. The top five women's 1-meter diving scores are 288.75, 261.83, 254.85, 254.1, and 246.8. Does the mean, median, or mode best describe these data? Explain.

Check Your Understanding

1. **Vocabulary** The (mean, median, mode) of the following data is 4: 1, 2, 2, 4, 7, 9, 20.
2. **Open-Ended** Create a set of data with more than one mode.

Vocabulary Tip

The word *median* means "middle."

Find the median and mode(s) of each data set.

3. 5, 7, 8, 8, 8, 10, 12
4. 1, 1, 1, 2, 3, 4, 5, 5, 5

5. Add two data items to 40, 20, and 60 so that the median and mode are 60.

Homework Exercises

For more exercises, see Extra Skills and Word Problems.

GO for Help

For Exercises	See Example
6–12	1
13–16	2
17	3

Find the median of each data set.

6. 8, 42, 13, 7, 50, 91
7. 0, 1, 1, 1, 0, 1, 1, 0, 0, 0
8. 14.1, 20.7, 24.3, 16.0, 20.8
9. 500, 450, 475, 450, 500
10. 60.2, 63.5, 62, 62.2, 63.4, 61.1, 60.8
11. 1,205; 1,190; 1,225; 1,239; 1,187; 1,763

12. **Birds** Here are the numbers of birds spotted by a bird watcher: 2, 7, 3, 8, 10, and 2. What is the median number of birds?

Find the mode(s) of each data set.

13. 8, 7, 8, 9, 8, 7
14. sad, glad, glad, mad, sad
15. 15, 12, 17, 13, 20, 19
16. 23, 24, 27, 25, 26, 23, 21

17. **Fitness** For a week you keep track of the number of push-ups you do each morning: 9, 9, 4, 12, 11, 12, and 12. Does the mean, median, or mode best describe the set of data?

18. **Guided Problem Solving** Your homework grades are 92, 87, 74, 96, 83, 88, 91, 82, and 85. What score on your next homework will make the median and the mode equal?
    - List the scores in order from least to greatest.
    - You can use the strategy *Systematic Guess and Check* to help you find the solution.

Find the mean, median, and mode of each data set.

19. 13.5, 15, 13.5, 11, 13

20. 32, 28.3, 26.8, 31, 24.4

21. Number Sense The median of four numbers is 48. Three of the numbers are 42, 51, and 52. What is the other number?

22. Writing in Math Your scores on five math tests are 96, 88, 96, 85, and 30. Write a letter to your teacher stating which measure—mean, median, or mode—you think your teacher should use to determine your grade.

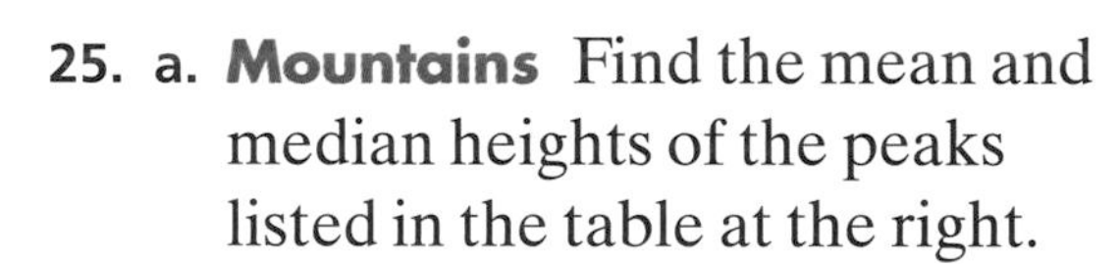

23. A company is asking students which types of shoe designs they prefer. Which is the best measure for describing the selections, the mean, the median, or the mode? Explain.

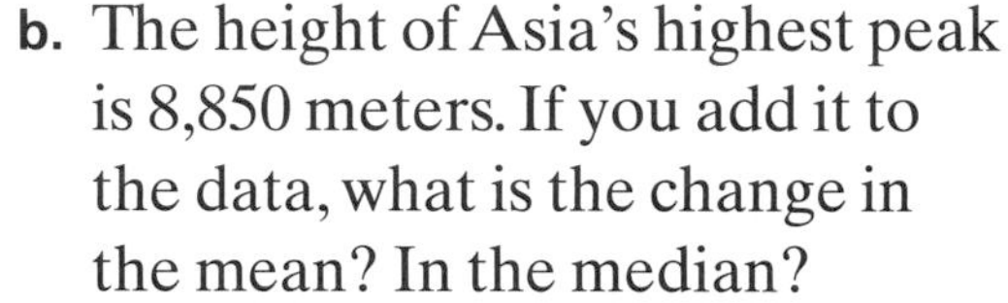

Careers Shoe designers use survey and research data to decide what features to include in a shoe.

24. Books The page lengths of five books are 198, 240, 153, 410, and 374. What is the median?

25. a. Mountains Find the mean and median heights of the peaks listed in the table at the right.

b. The height of Asia's highest peak is 8,850 meters. If you add it to the data, what is the change in the mean? In the median?

Highest Peaks

Continent	Altitude (meters)
Africa	5,895
Europe	5,642
North America	6,194
South America	6,960

SOURCE: *Time Almanac*

26. Challenge Use an example to explain why teachers do not use the median to calculate final grades.

Test Prep and Mixed Review

Practice

Gridded Response

27. A shoe store recorded the sale of the following shoe sizes: 5, 7, 5, 11, 8, 11, 7, 6, 5, 8, 9, 10, 7, 6, and 7. What is the mode?

28. The height of a tree is 2.7 meters. The height of a second tree is 1.8 meters. What is the difference of the heights in meters?

29. A lilac bush is 1 foot tall when you buy it. The bush will grow about 1.5 feet each year. What will be the height of the bush in feet after 6 years?

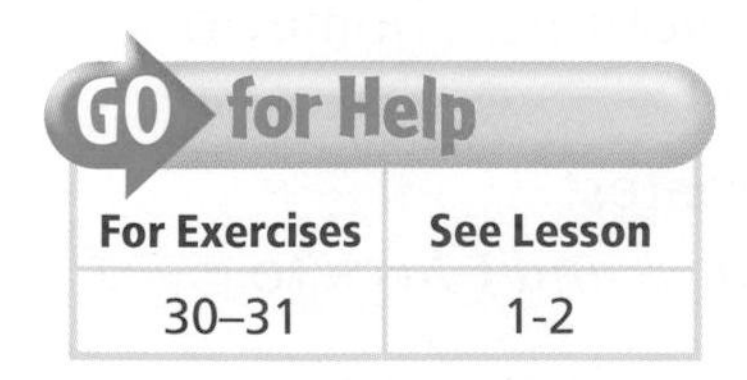

For Exercises	See Lesson
30–31	1-2

Find the value of each expression.

30. $10 - 2 \times 4 - 1$

31. $200 \div (32 - 12) + 5$

9-3 Frequency Tables and Dot Plots

1. Vocabulary Review What is the *mode* of a set of data?

Find the mean, median, and mode of each data set.

2. 6, 4, 6, 7, 4, 3, 8, 4

3. 1.5, 0, 3, 0, 2, 8.5, 1

Lesson 9-2

CONTENT STANDARD
6.SP.4

What You'll Learn

To analyze a set of data by finding the range and by making frequency tables and dot plots

New Vocabulary frequency table, dot plot, range

Why Learn This?

Data, such as your classmates' favorite colors, are easier to read in a table or graph than in a list.

A **frequency table** is a table that lists each item in a data set with the number of times the item occurs.

Favorite Colors

Blue	Blue
Purple	Red
Red	Orange
Blue	Yellow
Blue	Green
Yellow	Blue
Green	Yellow
Purple	Blue

EXAMPLE Frequency Table

1 Your classmates' favorite colors are shown above. Organize the data in a frequency table. Find the mode.

Favorite Color

Color	Tally	Frequency
Blue	~~IIII~~ I	6
Green	II	2
Orange	I	1
Purple	II	2
Red	II	2
Yellow	III	3

Make a tally mark for each color chosen.

The number of tally marks in each row is the frequency.

Students selected blue most often. So the mode is blue.

Quick Check

1. The first initials of the names of 15 students are listed below. Organize the data in a frequency table. Find the mode.
   A J B K L C K D L S T D V P L

A **dot plot** is a graph that shows the shape of a data set by stacking dots above each data value on a number line. This type of graph is also known as a *line plot*.

Online active math

For: Dot Plots Activity
Use: Interactive Textbook, 9-3

EXAMPLE Using a Dot Plot

2 **Movies** The number of DVDs each customer rents when he or she visits a video store are 3, 5, 1, 2, 2, 1, 2, 3, 3, 4, 1, 2, 6, 2, 2, 4, 3, 1. Use a dot plot to interpret the data.

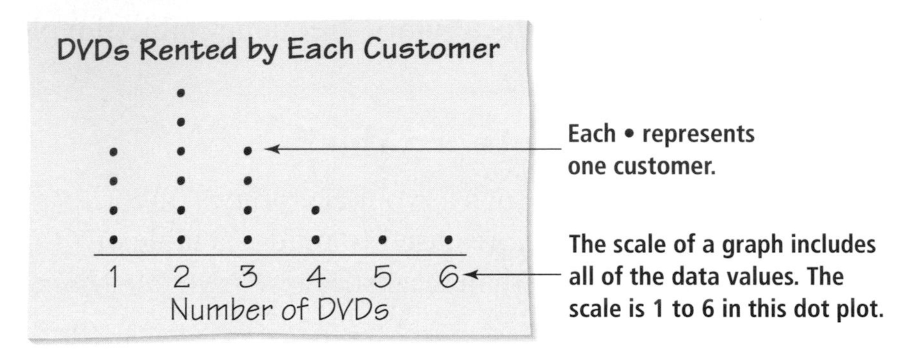
DVDs Rented by Each Customer
1 2 3 4 5 6
Number of DVDs
Each • represents one customer.
The scale of a graph includes all of the data values. The scale is 1 to 6 in this dot plot.

Customers usually rent between one and three DVDs. Most customers rent two DVDs.

Quick Check

2. Use a dot plot to interpret the number of sales calls made each hour: 2, 3, 0, 7, 1, 1, 9, 8, 2, 8, 1, 2, 8, 7, 1, 8, 6, 1.

The **range** of a data set is the difference between the least and greatest values.

EXAMPLE Finding the Range

3 **Geography** In 1849 and 1850, six different surveyors made the following measurements of the height of Mount Everest.

28,990 ft; 28,992 ft; 28,999 ft; 29,002 ft; 29,005 ft; 29,026 ft

What is the range of the measurements?

$29{,}026 - 28{,}990 = 36$ ← **Subtract the least from the greatest value.**

The range of the measurements is 36 feet.

Quick Check

3. The numbers of pottery items made by students are 36, 21, 9, 34, 36, 10, 4, 35, 30, 7, 5, and 10. Find the range of the data.

Check Your Understanding

1. **Vocabulary** How is a dot plot similar to a frequency table?

The ages for required school attendance in ten states are 6, 7, 6, 5, 7, 6, 8, 6, 5, and 7. Use the data for Exercises 2–5.

2. Make a frequency table.
3. Make a dot plot.
4. What is the range of the data? Is this a data point? Explain.
5. **Reasoning** Describe an advantage of using a dot plot rather than a frequency table.

Homework Exercises

For more exercises, see Extra Skills and Word Problems.

GO for Help

For Exercises	See Example
6–7	1
8–9	2
10–11	3

Organize each set of data in a frequency table. Find the mode.

6. days in each month: 31, 28, 31, 30, 31, 30, 31, 31, 30, 31, 30, 31
7. vehicles in a parking lot:

pickup	compact	compact	mid-size
compact	SUV	mid-size	SUV
mid-size	compact	station wagon	pickup

Use a dot plot to interpret each set of data.

8. lengths of baseball bats (inches):
30 29 31 28 29 29 30 32 30 29 28 30 30
9. word lengths (letters): 7 2 6 1 7 6 9 1 8 4 2 3 10

Find the range for each set of data.

10. the ages of the first ten U.S. presidents when they took office:
57, 61, 57, 57, 58, 57, 61, 54, 68, 51
11. heights of trees (meters): 2.3, 1.8, 3.4, 2.5, 2.9, 3.1, 3.2, 3.5, 2.8

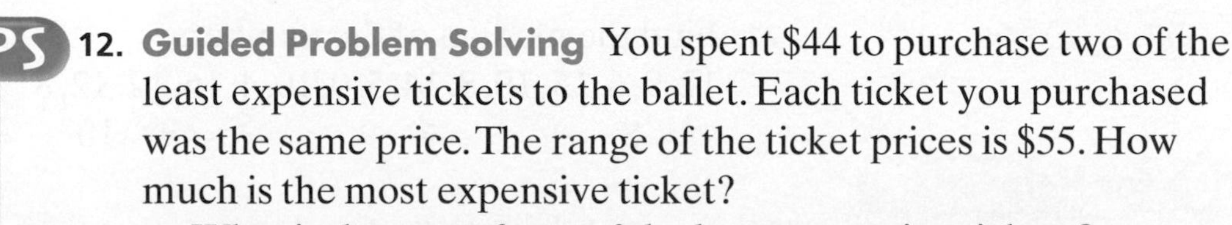

GPS 12. **Guided Problem Solving** You spent $44 to purchase two of the least expensive tickets to the ballet. Each ticket you purchased was the same price. The range of the ticket prices is $55. How much is the most expensive ticket?

- What is the cost of one of the least expensive tickets?
- How can you use the range to find the cost of the most expensive ticket?

13. **Speed Limits** On a highway, the minimum speed allowed is 40 miles per hour. The maximum speed is 65 miles per hour. What is the range of speeds allowed on the highway?

14. **Social Studies** A town in Wales, United Kingdom, is named Llanfairpwllgwyngyllgogerychwyrndrobwllllantysiliogogogoch.
   a. Make a frequency table for the letters in the town's name.
   b. **Writing in Math** Use the mean, median, or mode to describe the data in your table. Explain your choice.

Nineteen water samples were taken from a river. The number of organisms counted in each sample is shown in the dot plot.

0 1 2 3 4

15. What do the numbers represent?

16. Find the median and mode.

17. Why might you not want to use the mean to describe the data?

18. a. Make a frequency table and a dot plot of the quiz scores.
   b. Use either the frequency table or dot plot to identify any outliers. Which display did you use? Explain your choice.

Quiz Scores		
8	2	9
7	8	6
10	10	8
8	7	10

19. **Challenge** Make two sets of data with the same range but different means.

Test Prep and Mixed Review

Practice

Multiple Choice

20. Which statement is supported by the graph?
   (A) More students received a D than a B.
   (B) Six students received a C or better.
   (C) Most students received an A or a D.
   (D) Two more students received a C than the number who received a B.

Semester Science Grades

A B C D
Letter Grades

21. Find the median of the numbers.
12, 9, 6, 15, 10, 8, 14, 5, 0, 10, 4, 16, 12, 12, 8
   (F) 8 (G) 9 (H) 10 (J) 12

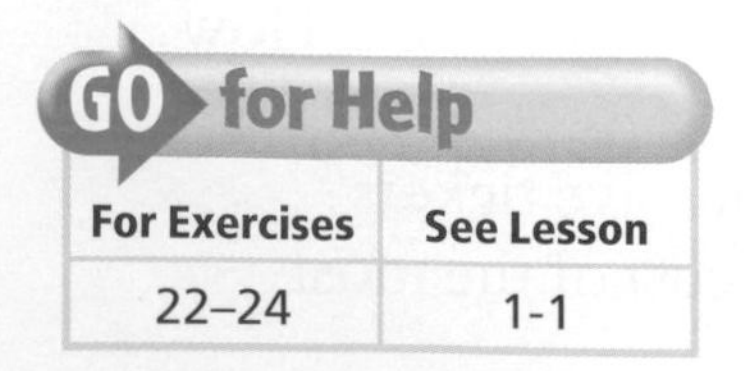

GO for Help

For Exercises	See Lesson
22–24	1-1

Use mental math to find each sum.

22. 17 + 23

23. 46 + 0 + 14

24. 5 + 32 + 15

9-4 Box-and-Whisker Plots

1. **Vocabulary Review** The middle number in an ordered set of data is called the __?__.
2. The ages of eight students in the math club are 11, 12, 11, 13, 11, 12, 12, 11, and 10. Use the dot plot to interpret the data.

Students in Math Club

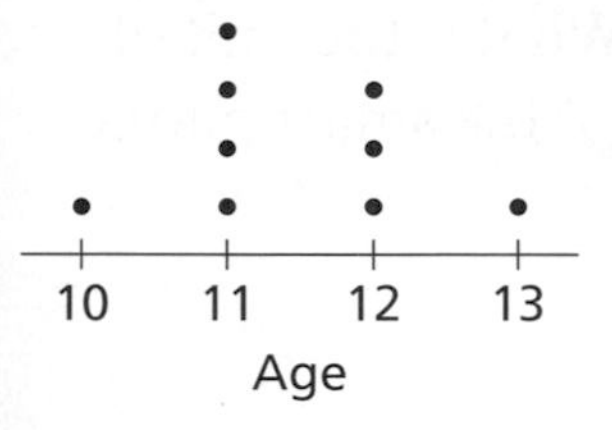

CONTENT STANDARDS

6.SP.4, 6.SP.5.a, 6.SP.5.b

What You'll Learn

To analyze a set of data by creating a box-and-whisker plot

New Vocabulary box-and-whisker plot, lower quartile, upper quartile

Why Learn This?

You can observe how data values, such as basketball scores, are distributed by displaying the data in a graph.

A **box-and-whisker plot**, or *box plot*, shows how a set of data is distributed. The plot uses five key values to represent an ordered set of data: the least value, the lower quartile, the median, the upper quartile, and the greatest value. The **lower quartile** is the median of the lower half of the data. **The upper quartile** is the median of the upper half of the data.

EXAMPLE Constructing a Box-and-Whisker Plot

1 A girls' basketball team had the following scores: 7, 10, 16, 18, 20, 22, 22, 25, 30, 37, 43. Construct a box-and-whisker plot to represent the data.

There are 11 observations in the data set. List the data in order to identify the five key values. The unit of measurement for this data set is points per game.

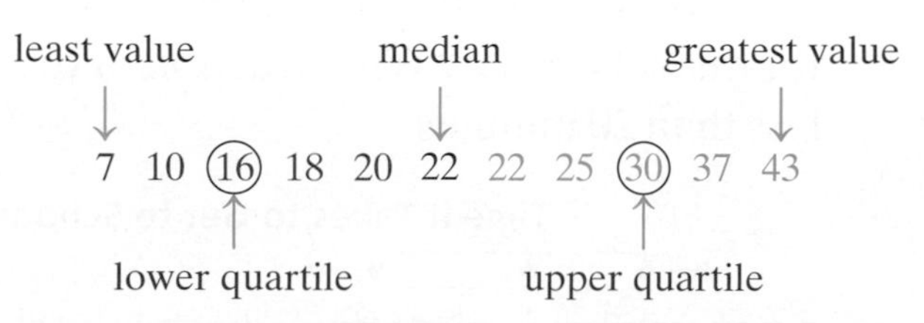

Graph the five key values above a number line. Label the number line with the unit of measurement. Draw a box from the lower to the upper quartile. Draw a vertical line inside at the median. Connect the least and greatest values to the box for the "whiskers."

Test Prep Tip

When making a box plot, include a title and the unit of measurement of the data.

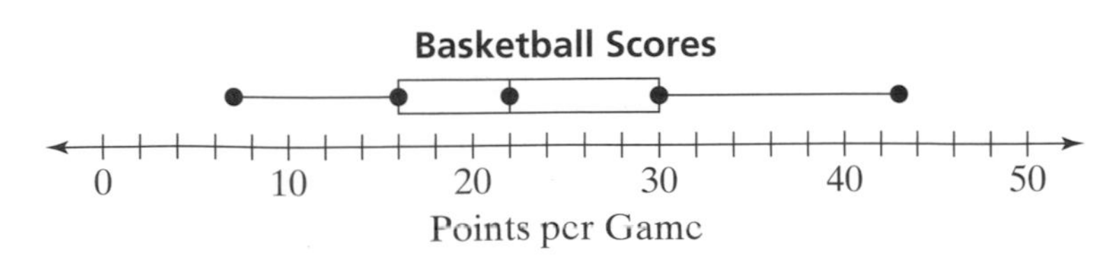

Quick Check

1. The basketball team scored 40 points in a playoff game. Add the value 40 to the list of data. What are the five key values for a box-and-whisker plot that includes this game?

The lower quartile, median, and upper quartile of a box-and-whisker plot divide the data into four parts. Each part represents about one quarter of the data.

Vocabulary Tip

Quartile and quarter both start with the prefix *quart-*, which means four.

EXAMPLE Analyzing a Box-and-Whisker Plot

2 A store sells 16 different smart phone cases. The prices are represented in the box-and-whisker plot below. What is the unit of measurement for this set of data? What fraction of the smart phone cases are between $12 and $23?

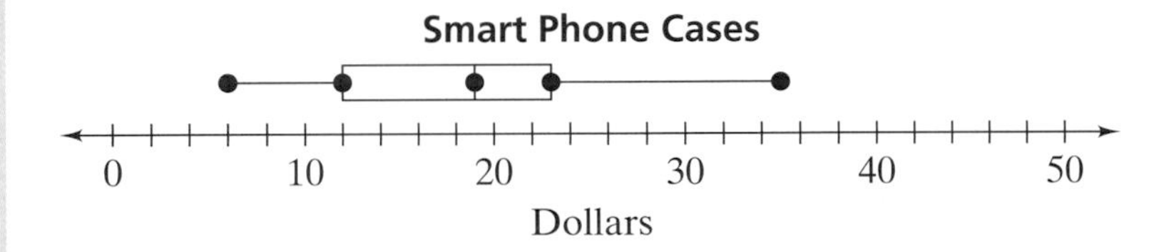

The unit of measurement for the data is dollars. The lower quartile is $12 and the upper quartile is $23. Since each of the four parts of the box-and-whisker plot represents about one quarter of the data, about half of the data fall between $12 and $23.

Quick Check

2. The box-and-whisker plot represents the number of minutes it takes 10 students to get to school. What is the unit of measurement for this set of data? What fraction of the students get to school in less than 20 minutes?

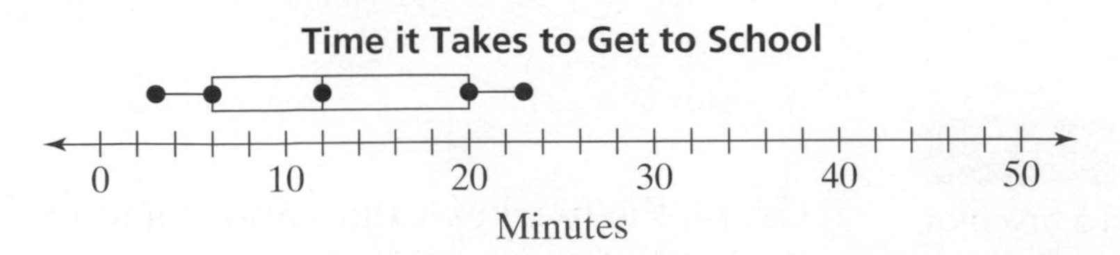

Check Your Understanding

1. **Vocabulary** What is the upper quartile of a data set?
2. What fraction of the data is inside the box of a box plot?
3. What fraction of the data is represented by each whisker of a box plot?

Homework Exercises

For more exercises, see Extra Skills and Word Problems.

GO for Help

For Exercises	See Example
4–6	1
7–8	2

Tell how many observations are in the data set. Then construct a box-and-whisker plot to represent the data.

4. Cost of a haircut (in dollars) at local hair salons: 42, 14, 26, 55, 60, 35, 45, 28, 40.
5. Number of items in different grocery carts: 18, 49, 5, 9, 26, 56, 38, 35, 9, 10, 12, 35, 41, 50.
6. The height in feet of the 10 demonstration trees in the arboretum are 17, 16.3, 8.5, 12, 16.5, 18.9, 19.1, 10.2, 11.4, 19.1. What five numbers need to be graphed above the number line?
7. The box-and-whisker plot represents the number of ice cream flavors at 15 different creameries.

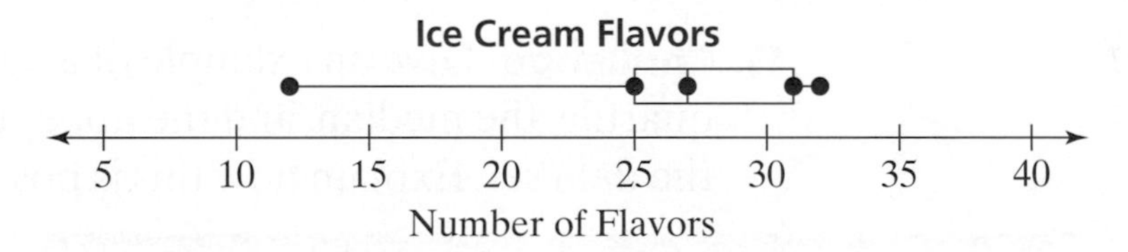

   a. What fraction of the creameries have at least 25 flavors?
   b. What is the unit of measurement for this set of data?

8. The box-and-whisker plot represents the cost of a large cheese pizza at 12 different pizzerias.

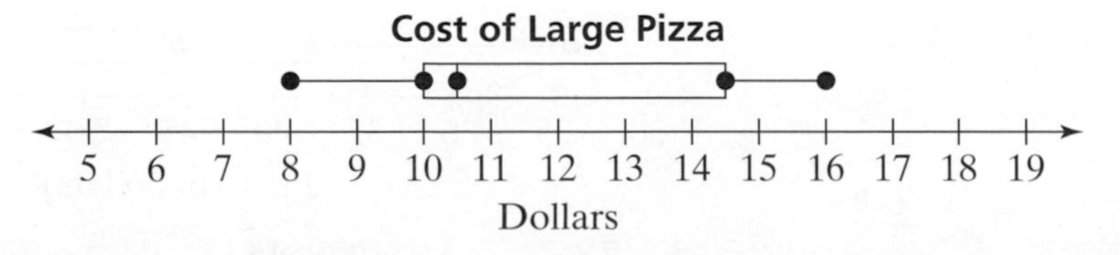

   a. What fraction of the pizzerias charge between $14.50 and $16?
   b. What fraction of the pizzerias charge less than $10.50?

9. **Guided Problem Solving** The heights of the 11 girls and 9 boys in a class are given below.

Heights (in inches)

Girls: 68, 56, 57, 67, 65, 58, 60, 60, 65, 63, 62
Boys: 60, 68, 70, 62, 63, 66, 63, 64, 66

   a. Construct a box-and-whisker plot to represent the heights of the boys. Above that, using the same number line, construct a box-and-whisker plot to represent the heights of the girls.
   b. How do the two data sets compare?

Go Online
Homework Video Tutor
PearsonSuccessNet.com

10. **Reasoning** Why might the boxed part of a box-and-whisker plot not represent *exactly* half of the data?

11. The number of words per minute that students can type at the end of the first semester are shown in the dot plot.

Semester 1 Keyboarding Class

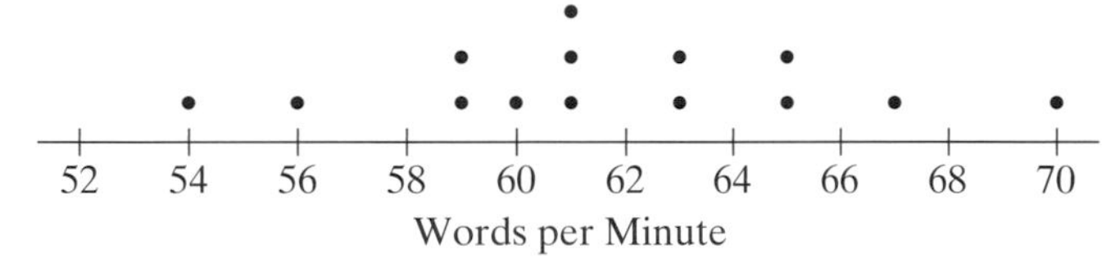

   a. How many observations are in the data set?
   b. Construct a box-and-whisker plot to represent the data.

12. **Writing in Math** If you were a teacher looking at a box plot of the math scores on a test for one grade 6 class, what might you find out about the class? How would this information help you?

13. **Challenge** Give an example of a data set in which the lower quartile, the median, and the upper quartile are not values in the data set. Explain how this is possible.

Test Prep and Mixed Review

Practice

Multiple Choice

14. The box-and-whisker plot represents the prices of 50 pairs of sneakers. What is the upper quartile of the data?

Pairs of Sneakers

20 25 30 35 40 45 50 55 60 65 70

Price (in dollars)

Ⓐ 38 Ⓑ 45 Ⓒ 56 Ⓓ 62

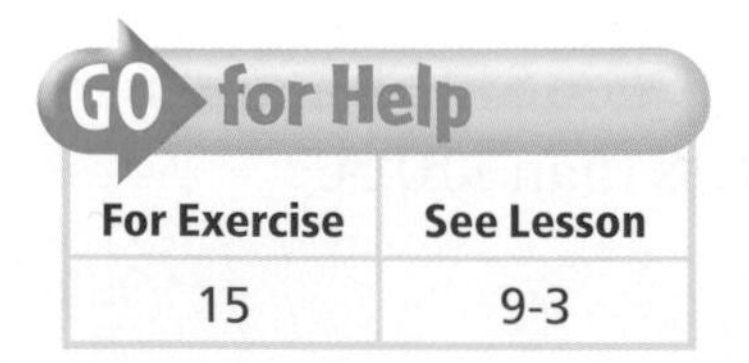

GO for Help

For Exercise	See Lesson
15	9-3

15. The number of minutes spent on homework each night by a student are: 35, 25, 25, 45, 60, 45, 35, 25, 45, and 20. Make a frequency table for the data.

Checkpoint Quiz 1

Lessons 9-1 through 9-4

Use the dot plot for Exercises 1–4.

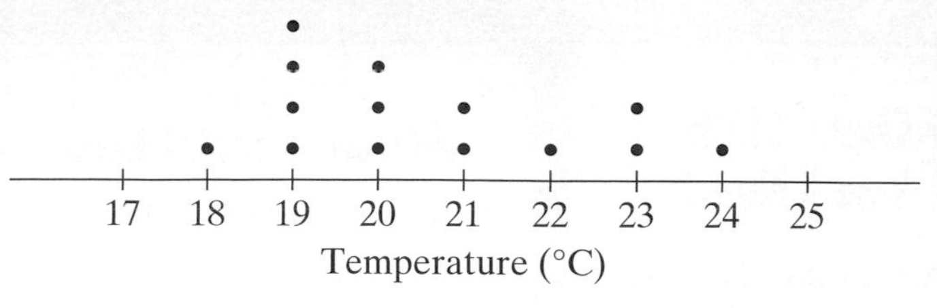

1. Find the mean, the median, and the mode of the data.
2. Find the range of temperatures.
3. Are there any outliers? Explain.
4. Does the mean, median, or mode best describe these data? Explain.
5. **Nutrition** The grams of fat per serving for 24 breakfast cereals are 0, 1, 3, 1, 1, 2, 2, 0, 3, 1, 3, 2, 0, 1, 0, 2, 1, 1, 0, 0, 0, 2, 1, and 0. Make a frequency table for the data.

Use the box-and-whisker plot for Exercises 6–8.

Events in Which Swimmers Qualified

0 1 2 3 4 5 6 7 8 9 10

Number of Events

6. What is the lower quartile of the data? What is the upper quartile of the data?
7. What fraction of the data falls between the lower and upper quartiles?
8. Do you think the median is one of the data values? Explain why or why not.

MATH AT WORK

Park Ranger

Do you enjoy working outdoors? Are you interested in history? If so, maybe a career as a park ranger is for you. Park rangers use mathematics to predict the number of visitors, measure rainfall and tree growth, plan trails, solve problems involving acid rain or deforestation, and construct timelines.

Go Online For information on park rangers PearsonSuccessNet.com

9-5 Histograms

Check Skills You'll Need

1. **Vocabulary Review** A _?_ can help you organize a set of data by tallying numbers of data items.

Divide.

2. $9 \div 1.5$
3. $15.75 \div 7$

GO for Help Lesson 1-6

CONTENT STANDARDS
6.SP.4, 6.SP.5, 6.SP.5.b, 6.SP.5.c

What You'll Learn

To construct and interpret a histogram

New Vocabulary histogram

Why Learn This?

You can obtain an overall impression of data from a data display such as a histogram. An online shopping site may view patterns of data to determine how much time most people spend shopping at online sites.

A **histogram** is a type of bar graph that shows the frequency of data within given intervals. The height of each bar shows the frequency within that interval. There is no space between the bars of a histogram.

EXAMPLE Interpreting a Histogram

1 **Shopping Online** A department store survey asked customers the number of minutes in an hour they would typically spend shopping online. The results are in the frequency table.

Time (in Minutes) Spent Shopping Online						
Interval	0–9	10–19	20–29	30–39	40–49	50–59
Frequency	10	12	13	4	9	2

The interval tells how the data are grouped.

The frequency is the number of people whose answers fell within each interval.

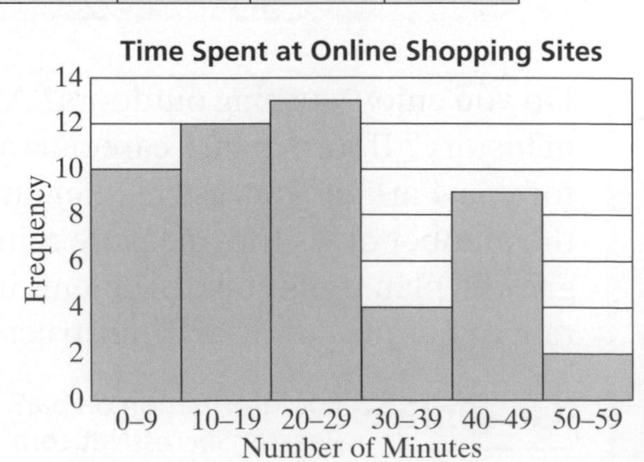

a. How many observations (customer responses) are in this data set? Add the frequencies or the heights of the bars to find the total number of observations: $10 + 12 + 13 + 4 + 9 + 2 = 50$
b. What does each observation represent?
c. Which interval had the fewest number of customer responses?

Quick Check

1. Interpret the histogram to answer.
   a. Which interval had the greatest number of customer responses?
   b. Did most customers spend less than 30 minutes or more than 30 minutes on shopping sites?

EXAMPLE Constructing a Histogram

Interval	Frequency
76–80	4
81–85	5
86–90	2
91–95	8
96–100	6

2 The frequency table shows the scores for a test that Mr. Warren gave his English class. Construct a histogram to display the data.

- Label the intervals on the horizontal axis.
- Find the range of the data. Choose an appropriate scale for the vertical axis. The frequencies vary from 2 to 8. Use 0 to 10 for the vertical scale.

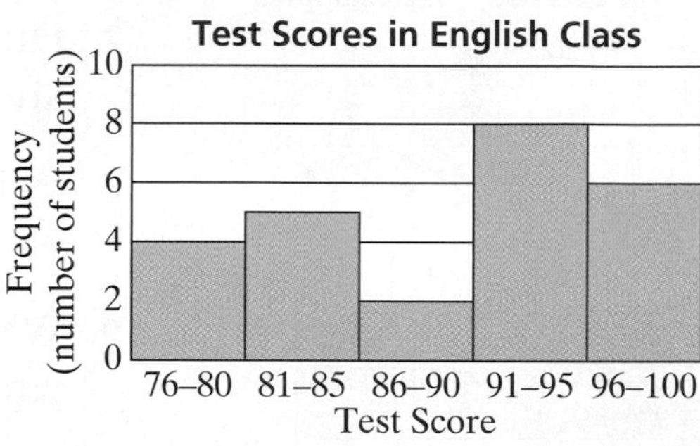

- Draw a bar for each interval. The bar heights should correspond to the frequencies, and the bars should have no spaces between them.

Quick Check

Interval	Frequency
0–19	10
20–29	2
30–39	6
40–49	8

2. Which histogram matches the data in the table?

A.

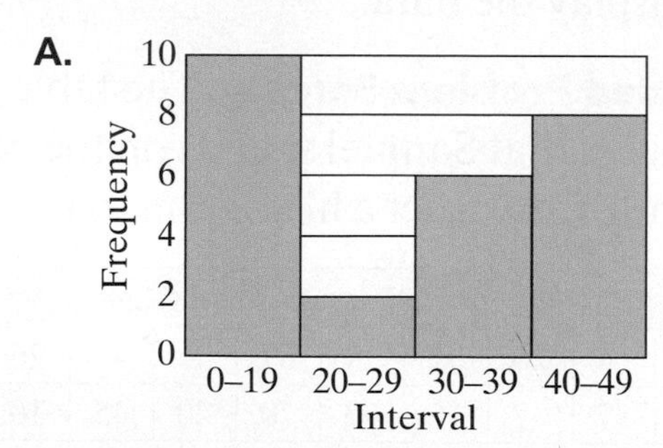

B.

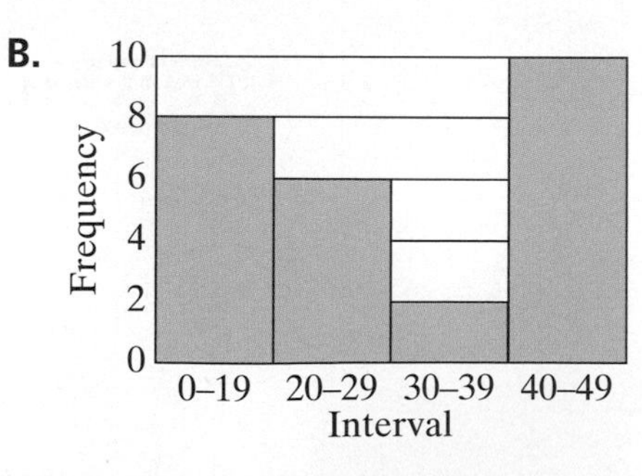

Check Your Understanding

1. **Vocabulary** A histogram is a type of bar graph that shows [ ] of data within given intervals.
2. **Reasoning** Why are there no gaps between the bars in a histogram?

The frequency table shows the daily miles traveled by a car. Use the table for Exercises 3–6.

Interval	Frequency
0–9	2
10–19	3
20–29	8
30–39	6
40–49	2
50–59	4

3. How many observations were made in this data set?
4. What does each observation represent?
5. Construct a histogram to represent the data.
6. Can you conclude from the histogram that the car traveled between 20 and 39 miles on more than half of the days? Explain.

Homework Exercises

For more exercises, see Extra Skills and Word Problems.

GO for Help

For Exercise	See Examples
7–9	1
10	2

The histogram represents the money made during a car wash fundraiser. Use the histogram for Exercises 7–9.

7. How many observations are in this data set?
8. What does each observation represent?
9. What conclusions can you make?

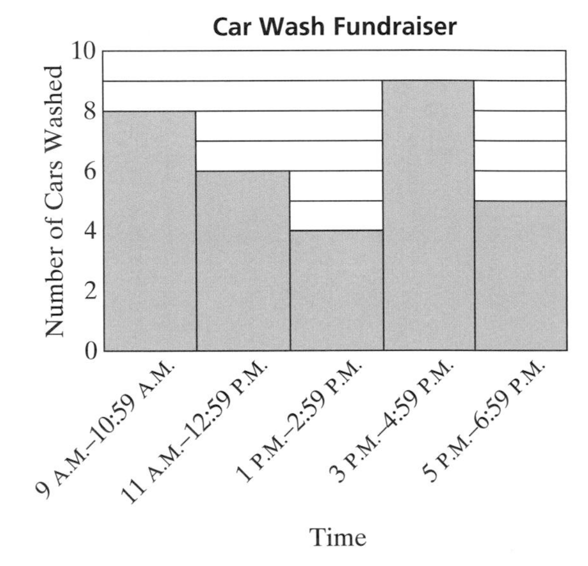

10. The frequency table shows the daily water temperature, in a pool during the summer. Construct a histogram to display the data.

Interval (Degrees Fahrenheit)	Frequency
61–65	3
66–70	16
71–75	22
76–80	23
81–85	19
86–90	11

11. **Guided Problem Solving** The table shows the number of minutes that Samuel spends on the computer each day for a month. Construct a histogram to represent the data.

Samuel's Computer Time														
95	4	26	95	4	87	36	47	26	51	23	18	45	81	76
24	57	7	16	63	70	20	45	16	32	37	64	8	28	44

- What is the range of the data?
- Would an interval size of 5, 20, or 50 be the most appropriate to display the data?
- Use your intervals to make a frequency table.
- Complete your histogram. Which interval will have the highest bar in your histogram?

12. The table shows the number of songs Owen purchased online during each of 20 weeks. Construct a histogram for the data.

Songs Purchased Each Week									
0	4	1	7	2	0	0	5	9	1
3	2	1	0	8	5	5	0	1	6

a. Explain how you chose your intervals.

b. Describe any patterns you see in the data.

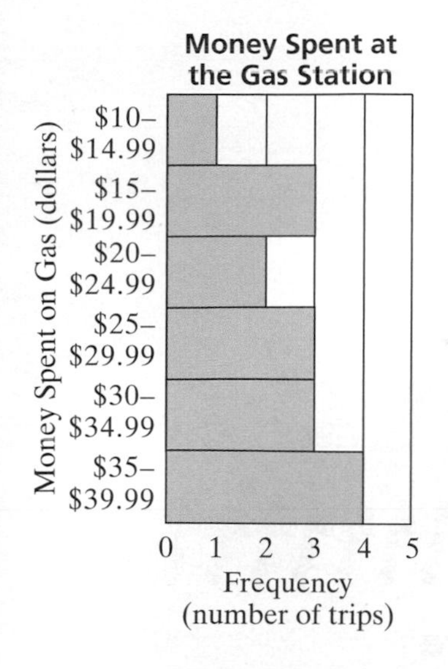

13. **Writing in Math** How can you determine the median in a set of data displayed in a histogram?

14. What is different about the histogram on the left? Explain how you read and interpret that histogram.

15. **Challenge** The histogram shows the amount of money Mr. Sanchez spent on trips to the gas station. In six months, what is the least amount Mr. Sanchez could have spent at the gas station in total? What is the greatest amount? Explain your reasoning.

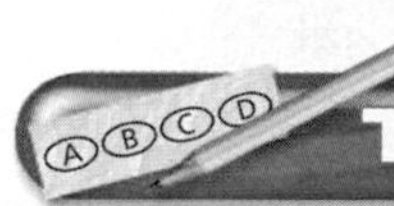

Test Prep and Mixed Review

Practice

Multiple Choice

16. The histogram shows the number of goals scored in one season by the players on a lacrosse team. Which of the following is NOT possible to determine from the histogram?

Ⓐ The number of players who scored at least 10 goals

Ⓑ The number of players who scored more than 4 goals

Ⓒ The number of players who scored less than 20 goals

Ⓓ The number of players who scored less than 8 goals

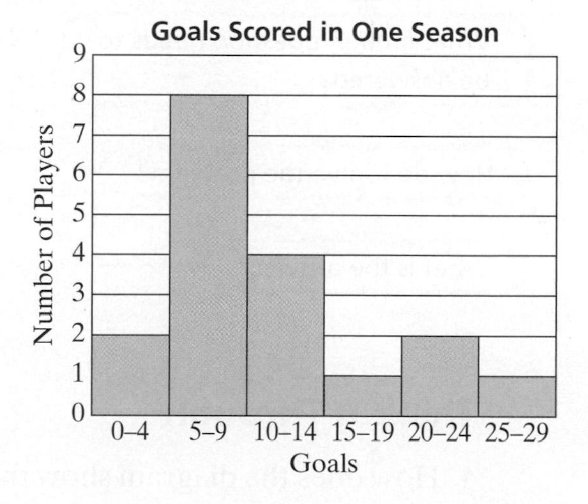

Find the mean of each data set.

17. 4, 3, 8, 4, 1, 2, 2, 4

18. 12, 13, 12, 10, 15, 26, 18, 9, 11

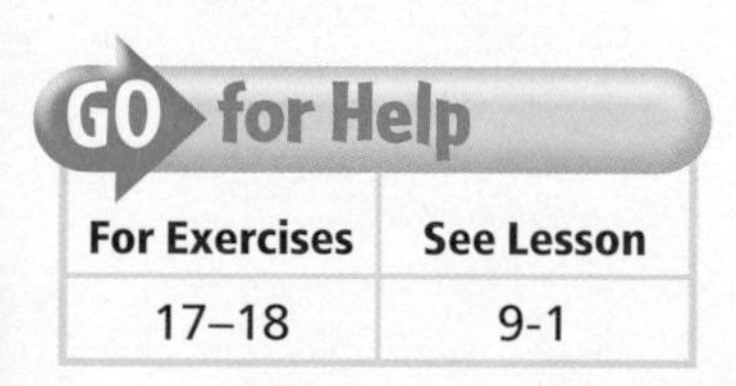

For Exercises	See Lesson
17–18	9-1

GPS Guided Problem Solving

Solving Multiple-Step Problems

The table below shows some gasoline prices. At those prices, how much more would it cost to fill a 22-gallon gas tank in Hawaii than in Georgia?

Gas Prices (dollars per gallon)

Higher Prices		Lower Prices	
Hawaii	2.416	New Jersey	1.872
California	2.302	Texas	1.935
Oregon	2.130	Georgia	1.951

SOURCE: AAA Fuel Gauge Report

What You Might Think	What You Might Write
What do I know?	Hawaii: $2.416 per gal *Georgia:* $1.951 per gal
What am I trying to find out?	I want to know how much more it costs to fill a 22-gallon tank in Hawaii than in Georgia.
What diagram can I draw to show the situation?	Cost of gas in Hawaii / Cost in Georgia, ?
What *hidden question* needs to be answered?	How much more does 1 gallon cost in Hawaii than in Georgia?
How do I solve the problem?	$2.416 − $1.951 = $0.465. This is the additional cost per gallon in Hawaii. $0.465 per gal × 22 gal = $10.23
What is the answer?	It costs $10.23 more to fill a 22-gallon tank in Hawaii than in Georgia.

Think It Through

1. How does the diagram show that subtraction is the operation needed to find how much more gas costs in Hawaii?
2. **Check for Reasonableness** How can you use rounding to decide whether the answer is reasonable? Check the answer.
3. **Reasoning** Is there another way to solve the problem? Explain. (*Hint:* Use the total cost to fill a 22-gallon tank.)

Exercises

4. How much less does it cost to fill an 18-gallon tank than a 23-gallon tank in Texas?
   a. What do you know?
   b. What hidden question needs to be answered?
   c. Solve the problem. Decide if the answer is reasonable. Tell how you decided.

5. Use the graph at the right. How much more did a gallon of gas cost in Week 11 than in Week 1?

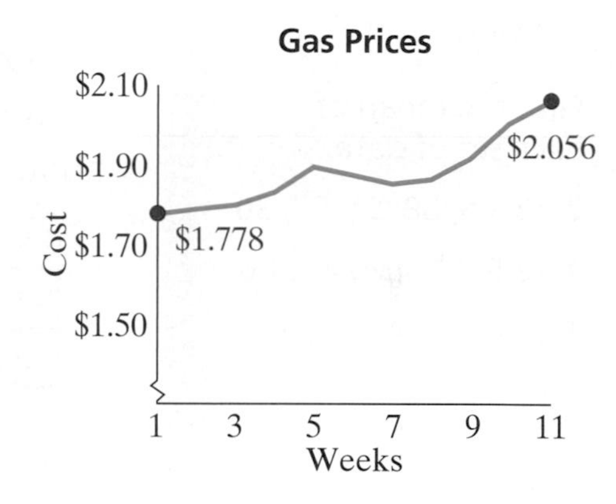

6. A cab driver filled his car with 15.5 gallons of gasoline at $2.45 per gallon. He then bought snacks for $7.85. Use the diagram below to help you find the total cost. Is your answer reasonable? Explain.

Total cost	
Cost of gas	Cost of snacks

7. The tax on a gallon of gasoline in Texas is $.20. If there were no tax on gasoline, what would it cost to fill an 18.5 gallon tank in Texas? Use the diagram below to help answer the hidden question.

$1.935	
$0.20	Cost per gallon without tax

8. Find the mean, median, and mode of the neighborhood gas prices shown. What would you use for a newspaper headline about the typical gasoline price at these neighborhood stations? Explain your reasoning.

Neighborhood Gas Prices

$2.78, $2.94, $2.70, $2.72, $2.65, $2.91, $2.87, $2.89, $2.89, $2.93, $2.95, $2.98, $2.80, $2.68, $2.35, $2.80, $2.80, $2.87, $2.72, $2.78, $2.67

9. Airlines measure the amount of fuel in an airplane in pounds. One gallon of fuel weighs 6.1 pounds. One gallon of water weighs 8.3 pounds. How much less does the fuel in a 5-gallon can weigh than the water in a 5-gallon bucket?

9-6 Variability of Data

Check Skills You'll Need

1. **Vocabulary Review** The median of the upper half of an ordered set of data is called the __?__.

Find the mean of each set of data.

2. 33, 45, 38, 51, 37, 30
3. 12.5, 17.9, 20.4, 11.6
4. 3, 3, 3, 2, 4, 4, 3, 2

for Help
Lesson 9-1

CONTENT STANDARDS
6.SP.2, 6.SP.3, 6.SP.5.c

What You'll Learn

To find and use measures of variability to describe and compare data sets

New Vocabulary measure of center, measure of variability, mean absolute deviation (MAD), interquartile range (IQR)

Why Learn This?

Farmers can use growth patterns in plants to make predictions about future crop yields.

Big Boy Tomato Plant Yields										
Plant	1	2	3	4	5	6	7	8	9	10
Number of Tomatoes	17	22	16	45	18	24	30	22	27	19

You can describe a data set by studying its center, spread, and overall shape. A value that describes how data is centered is called a **measure of center**. The mean, median, and mode are measures of center.

A value that describes how data is spread out, such as the range, is called a **measure of variability**. One measure of variability is mean absolute deviation. **Mean absolute deviation (MAD)** is the average amount that the data values vary from the mean.

EXAMPLE Using Variability of Data: Mean Absolute Deviation

Vocabulary Tip

To *deviate* means to move away from something. You can think of the MAD as average amount by which the data move away from the mean.

1 A scientist investigated the yield of his Big Boy tomato plants, displayed above. How can you describe the variability in the yields?

One way to describe the variability is to find the mean absolute deviation (MAD) of the tomato data.

Step 1: Find the mean number of tomatoes over 10 days. Record the mean as shown in the table below.

$$\text{Mean} = \frac{17+22+16+45+18+24+30+22+29+19}{10} = 24$$

Big Boy Tomato Yields										
Plant	1	2	3	4	5	6	7	8	9	10
Number of Tomatoes	17	22	16	45	18	24	30	22	27	19
Mean	24	24	24	24	24	24	24	24	24	24
Distance from Mean	7	2	8	21	6	0	6	2	3	5

Step 2: Find the distance between the number of tomatoes on each plant and the mean. Write each distance as a positive number.

Step 3: Calculate the mean of all the distances in the bottom row.

$$\frac{7+2+8+21+6+0+6+2+3+5}{10} = \frac{60}{10} = 6$$

The MAD is 6. So, the average difference between the data values and the mean is 6.

Quick Check

1. Suppose that Plant 1 grows 5 more tomatoes for a total of 22 tomatoes instead of 17.
   a. What is the new mean absolute deviation for the data?
   b. What does the change in MAD for the new data set tell you about the data set? Explain.

Another measure of variability is the **interquartile range (IQR).** This measure gives the spread of the middle half of the data. To find the IQR, subtract the lower quartile of the data from the upper quartile of the data.

The mean absolute deviation and the interquartile range give you information about the variability of a data set using a single number. This is helpful when comparing the variability of two data sets.

For help with quartiles, go to Lesson 9-4.

EXAMPLE Using Variability of Data: Interquartile Range

2 Describe the variability of the the Big Boy tomato data in Example 1 in a different way.

Another way to describe the variability is to find the interquartile range for the data.

Order the data to determine the mean, lower quartile, and upper quartile.

Median 22 ↓ (between 22 and 22)

16 17 18 19 22 22 24 27 30 45

Lower quartile: 18 ↑ — Upper quartile: 27 ↑

The IQR = upper quartile − lower quartile = 27 − 18 = 9.

You can say that the interquartile range of the data values is 9.

2. Suppose that two more Big Boy tomato plants produced 20 and 25 tomatoes.
   a. What is the interquartile range for the 12 data values?
   b. How does this result affect your conclusion about the variability of the data?

1. **Vocabulary** How is the interquartile range different from the range for a set of data?
2. The table shows the daily rainfall in a rainforest for ten days in June.

June Rainfall

Day	1	2	3	4	5	6	7	8	9	10
Rainfall (cm)	5	6	8	16	7	6	1	5	9	7

   a. Find the mean absolute deviation for the June rainfall data.
   b. How can you use the MAD to describe the variability in the data?
3. Use the June Rainfall data.
   a. Find the interquartile range for the June rainfall data.
   b. What does the IQR tell you about the variability in the June rainfall data?
4. The table below shows the daily rainfall in a rainforest for ten days in July.

July Rainfall

Day	1	2	3	4	5	6	7	8	9	10
Rain (cm)	3	6	1	0	10	14	8	10	7	11

   a. Find the mean absolute deviation for the July rainfall data.
   b. Find the interquartile range for the July rainfall data.
5. Compare the MAD for the June and July rainfall. Which month's rainfall shows more more variability?
6. Compare the IQR for June and July rainfall. What does it tell you about the variability tell you about the data for June rainfall compared to the data for July rainfall?

Homework Exercises

For more exercises, see Extra Skills and Word Problems.

GO for Help

For Exercise	See Example
15–17, 7–10	1
11–16	2

Find the mean absolute deviation for the data set. Round your answer to the nearest tenth if necessary.

7. 10, 12, 9, 14, 15, 11, 6

8. 1, 3, 3, 5, 5, 2, 1, 4

9. 15, 20, 23, 14, 9, 30, 7, 10

10. 50, 43, 33, 45, 45, 60

Find the interquartile range for the data set.

11. 21, 22, 31, 40, 25, 19, 17, 18

12. 10, 8, 8, 7, 5, 9, 7, 9, 12

13. 30, 28, 30, 24, 25, 36

14. 50, 55, 50, 34, 45, 45, 43

Find the mean absolute deviation and the interquartile range for each data set. Then compare the variability of the two sets. Round your answer to the nearest tenth if necessary.

15. Set A: 23, 22, 28, 22, 31, 30
Set B: 11, 20, 8, 24, 33, 24, 27

16. Set A: 10, 2, 8, 2, 15, 23, 13, 7
Set B: 50, 48, 53, 54, 50

17. The table below shows the weekly spending of Marcus and his brother, Darren.

Weekly Spending					
Week	1	2	3	4	5
Marcus	15	5	18	20	32
Darren	40	10	7	8	10

a. What is the mean of each data set?

b. For each data set, what is the difference between the mean and each data value?

c. What is the mean of the differences for each set?

d. What does the MAD comparison tell you about Marcus and Darren's spending habits?

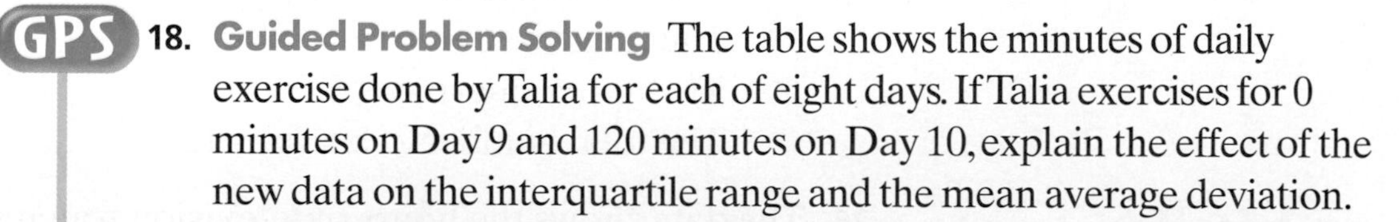

GPS **18. Guided Problem Solving** The table shows the minutes of daily exercise done by Talia for each of eight days. If Talia exercises for 0 minutes on Day 9 and 120 minutes on Day 10, explain the effect of the new data on the interquartile range and the mean average deviation.

Daily Exercise								
Day	1	2	3	4	5	6	7	8
Talia's Exercise (min)	40	60	45	40	20	32	30	45

- What is the IQR for each data set? How do the values compare?
- What is the MAD for each data set. How do the values compare?
- What effect do outliers have on a data set?

19. **Reasoning** Using Talia's 8-Day exercise schedule, what effect would it have if the value for Day 4 changed from 4 to 0? Explain.

20. **Writing in Math** How are the mean absolute deviation and the interquartile range similar? How are they different?

21. **Mental Math** Consider the data set 3, 3, 3, 3, 3, and 3. What is the mean absolute deviation? What is the interquartile range?

22. **Challenge** Consider two data sets, A and B. Is it possible for B to have a greater mean absolute value than A, and A to have a greater interquartile range than B? If so, give an example. If not, explain why not.

Test Prep and Mixed Review

Practice

Multiple Choice

23. Which of the following statements is NOT true about the following data set?

5, 2, 3, 2, 7, 10, 7, 4

Ⓐ The mean absolute deviation is 18.
Ⓑ The interquartile range is 4.5.
Ⓒ The range is 8.
Ⓓ The mean is 5.

24. What is the sum of forty-five hundredths and eight hundred nine thousandths?

Ⓕ 0.854
Ⓖ 1.259
Ⓗ 8.54
Ⓙ 12.59

25. The data shows the number of books read over the summer by each student. Which statement about the data set is true?

5, 3, 6, 0, 1, 10, 8, 5, 4, 4, 7, 2

Ⓐ The median is 4.
Ⓑ The range is 9.
Ⓒ The upper quartile is 6.5.
Ⓓ The total number of books is 12.

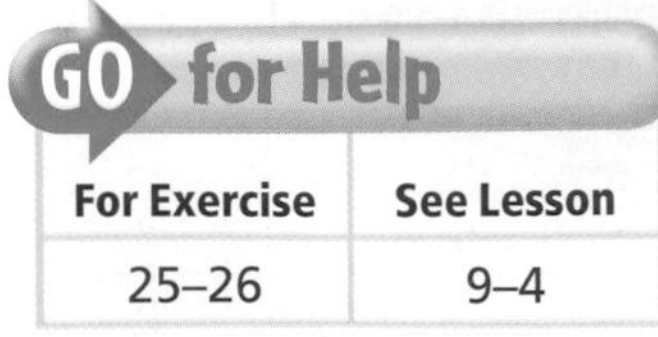
GO for Help

For Exercise	See Lesson
25–26	9–4

26. The data shows the hours of television watched in one week by 12 sixth graders. Construct a box-and-whisker plot to represent the data.

Hours of TV Watched in One Week											
10	15	4	22	8	16	6	10	11	15	7	9

9-7 Shape of Distributions

Check Skills You'll Need

1. **Vocabulary Review** The average amount by which the data values differ from the mean is called the _?_.

Identify the lower quartile, the median, and the upper quartile for each data set.

2. 13, 20, 38, 44, 37, 35
3. 25, 17, 20, 11, 13
4. 6, 5, 6, 7, 5, 5, 3, 2

GO for Help Lesson 9-4

CONTENT STANDARDS

6.SP.2, 6.SP.5.d

What You'll Learn

To relate the shape of a data display to how the data is distributed

Why Learn This?

The shape of data, such as the daily mileage of a cyclist, can give you information about how the data are grouped.

You can describe data by its overall shape or by how it is distributed. Some data shapes are symmetrical; others are higher on the right or on the left. Some data values are grouped around a certain value.

KEY CONCEPTS

Definition	Sample
Several data points that lie close together within a small interval **cluster**	
In an ordered set of data, a value that is greater than its neighboring values on either side **peak**	
A large space where there is no data between sets of data values **gap**	6 7 8 9 10
Distribution of data that have the same shape on either side of the center **symmetry**	

EXAMPLE

1 Describe the shape of each distribution using the terms *gap*, *peak*, and *symmetry*.

For help with box-and-whisker plots, go to Lesson 9-4.

a. 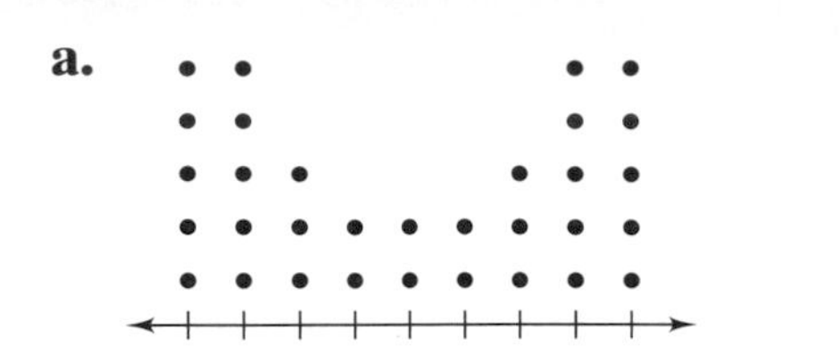

2 peaks; symmetric around the midpoint; no gaps between the data values

b. 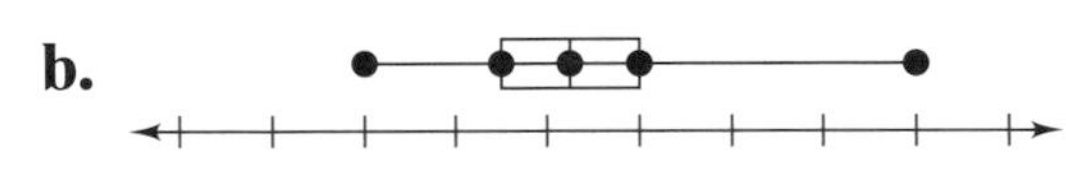

Clustered around the median, no symmetry

c. 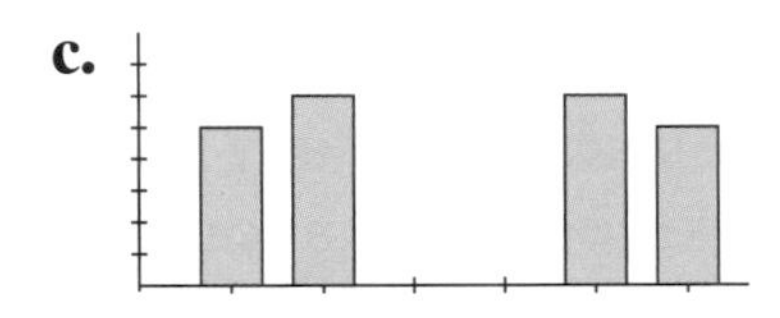

Gap between the two middle data values and symmetric around the middle value

Quick Check

1. Match the shape of each distribution with the description that best fits it.

S

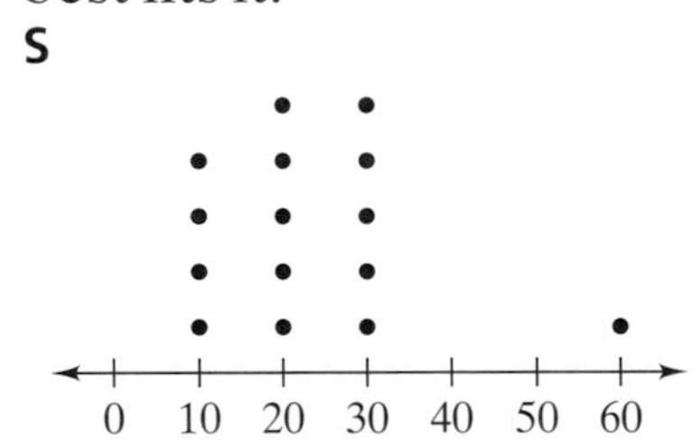

T

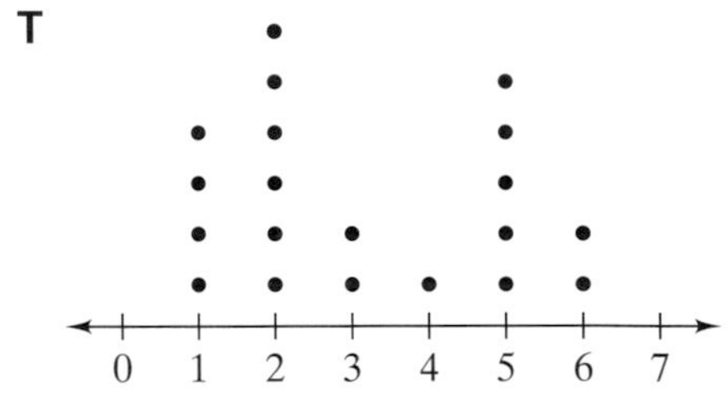

x. a gap and 2 peaks **y.** cluster and a gap **z.** no gap and 2 peaks

EXAMPLE Relating Distribution Shape to Measures

2 What can the shape of this dot plot tell you about its measures of center and variability?

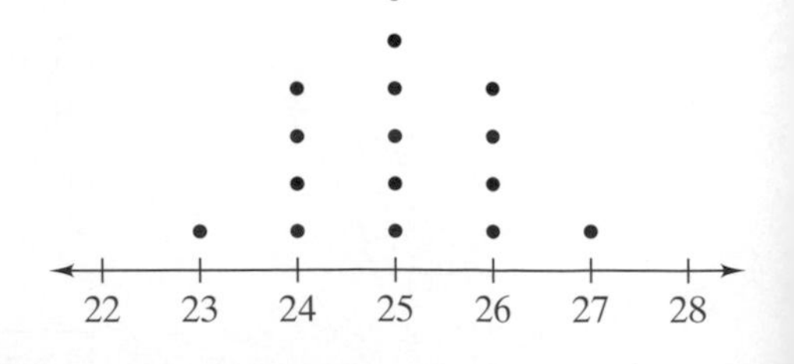

The distribution is symmetrical. It has a peak at 25, and values are clustered around the peak. There are no gaps.

The distribution is symmetrical and has a peak at 25, so the median, mean, and mode will be the same value, 25. Since the values are clustered close together rather than spread out, the interquartile range will be small.

GO Online

Video Tutor Help
PearsonSuccessNet.com

Quick Check

2. Compare the dot plot to the one above.

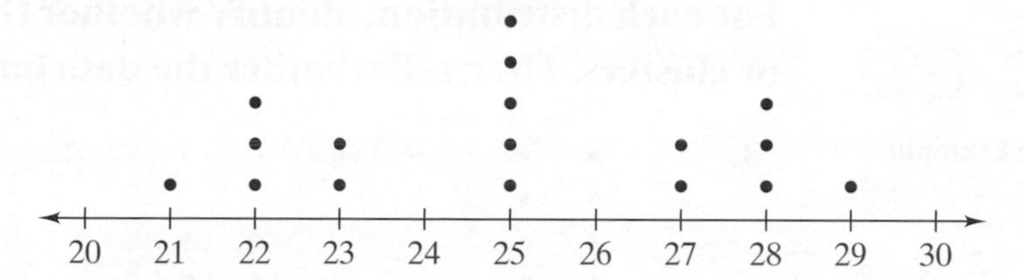

a. What similarities and differences are there between the two dot plots?

b. What do your observations tell you about variability and center?

c. What if there were 6 more dots at 21 and 29? How would your answer change?

Check Your Understanding

1. **Vocabulary** What term describes a distribution of data that has the same shape on either side of the center?

2. Match the shape of each distribution with the description that best fits it.

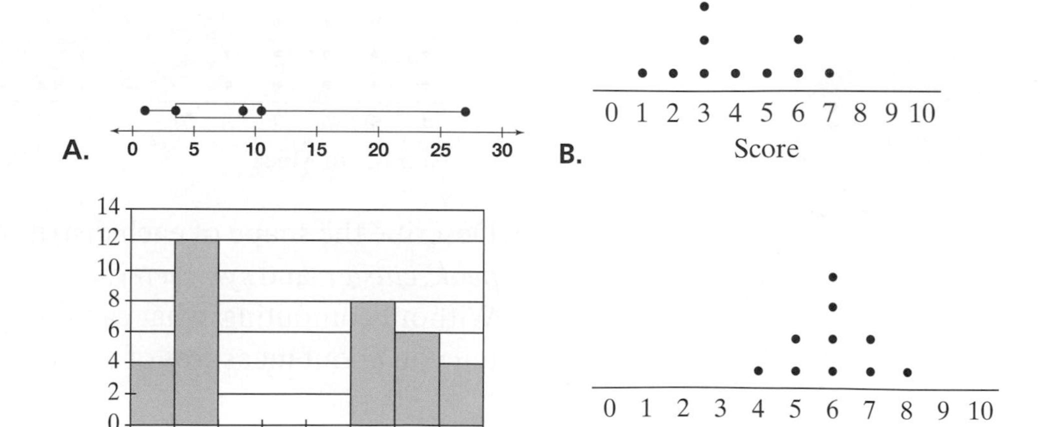

a. Data has an outlier, not symmetrical
b. Data clustered around a peak of 6, symmetrical around the peak
c. Data has 2 peaks, not symmetric
d. Data has a gap, no symmetry

Homework Exercises

For more exercises, see Extra Skills and Word Problems.

GO for Help

For Exercises	See Example
3–4	1
5	2

For each distribution, identify whether the data has any peaks, gaps, or clusters. Then tell whether the data have symmetry.

3.

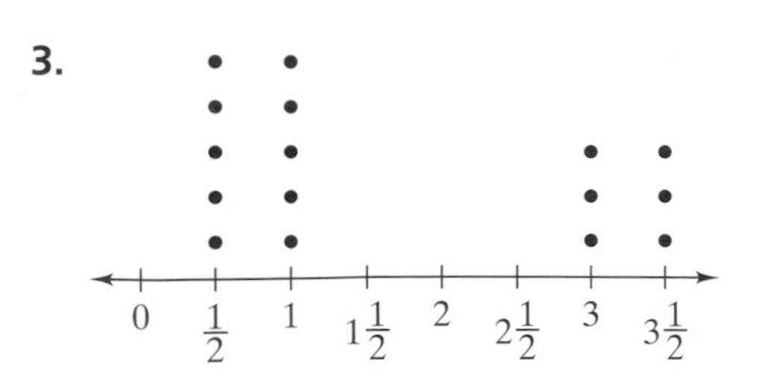

4.

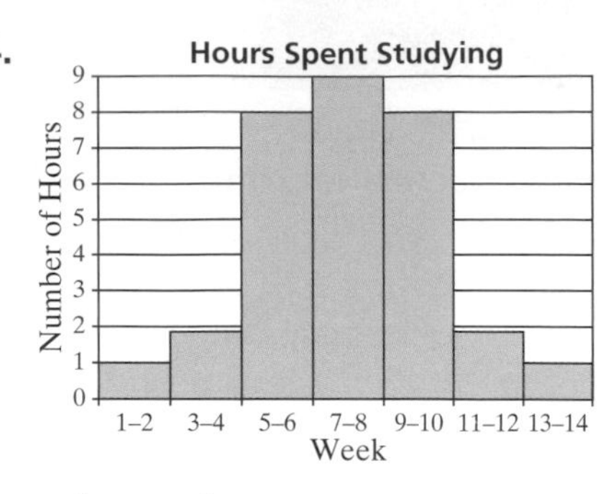

5. Carlos determined that a set of data about time spent on homework by boys has a mean of 10 and a MAD of 3. A set of data about time spent on homework by girls has a mean of 12 and a MAD of 8. Describe the shapes of the data. How are the measures related to the shape of the distribution?

6. Guided Problem Solving

Bicycling The dot plots show the number of miles two cyclists traveled during a training period. Compare the distributions.

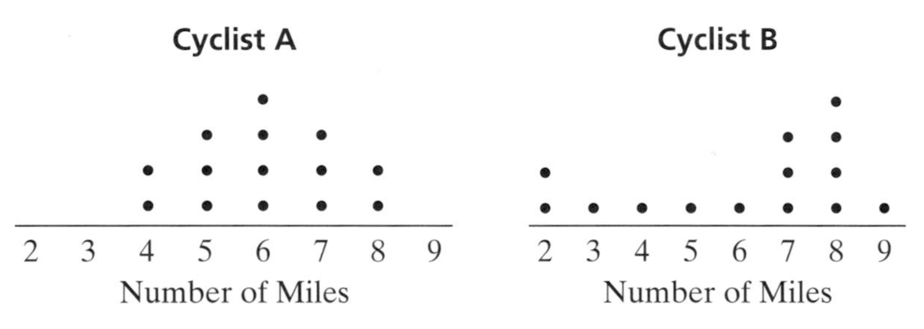

- Describe the shape of each distribution using the terms *gap*, *peak*, *cluster*, and *symmetry*.
- Without computing, what can the shape of the distributions tell you about measures of center and variability?

7. Gas Mileage The box-and-whisker plot below shows the average gas mileage of two vehicles. Compare the shapes of the distributions. What can you tell about measures of variability without computing any measures? Explain how the shapes are related to variability.

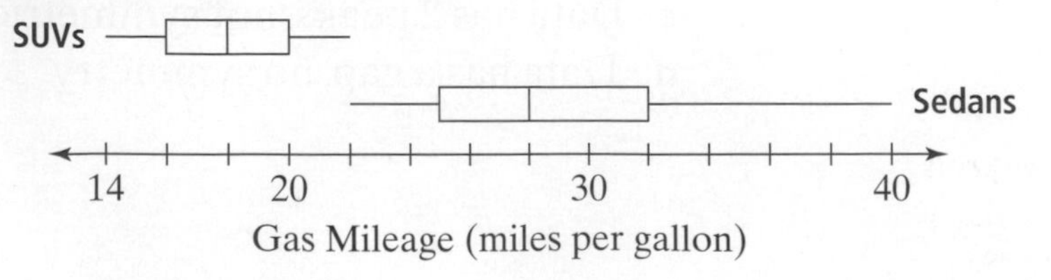

8. Two age groups were surveyed about the hours per week they spend of the internet. The histograms show the results.

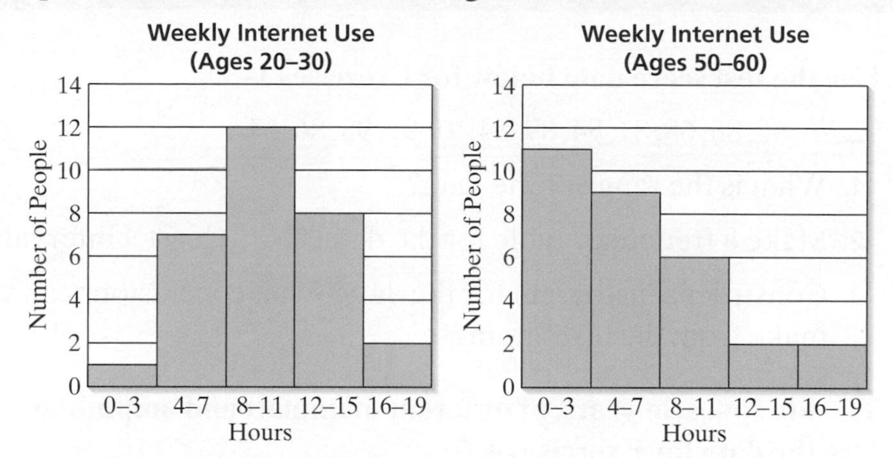

GO Online
Homework Video Tutor
PearsonSuccessNet.com

a. Describe the shape of each distribution.

b. In which range of hours would you expect to find the median for each distribution?

9. **Writing in Math** What explanation could you give for the differences in the two sets of data in Exercise 8?

10. **Challenge** Suppose a box-and-whisker plot is symmetrical with the median at 10. Give two examples of data that could have resulted in that plot: one with a large IQR and one with a small IQR, having the same lowest and greatest values. Explain what each would look like and what it shows about the data.

Test Prep and Mixed Review

Practice

Multiple Choice

11. Which of the following statements best describes the shape of the data in the dot plot?

Ⓐ The data has a peak at 4.

Ⓑ The data has a gap at 1.

Ⓒ The data is symmetric.

Ⓓ The data is clustered around 3.

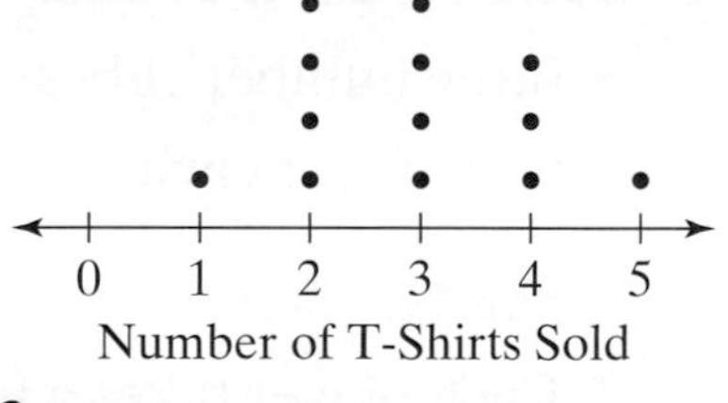

Use the data table for Exercises 12 and 13.

Campers Signed up for Activities									
10	5	7	8	12	18	11	18	12	7
4	9	8	11	12	17	13	21	25	10

GO for Help

For Exercises	See Lesson
12–13	9-3

12. What is the range of the data?

13. Make a frequency table for the data using at least 5 equal-sized intervals. Then construct a histogram to represent the data.

Checkpoint Quiz 2

Lessons 9-5 through 9-7

Use the test score data below for Exercises 1–3.

92, 76, 85, 85, 68, 81, 84, 89, 84, 91, 97, 95, 86, 64

1. What is the range of the data?
2. Make a frequency table for the data. Use at least 4 intervals.
3. Construct a histogram for the data. What conclusions can you make from the histogram?

The life spans, in years, of different mammals and amphibians are given below. Use the data for Exercises 4–7.

Mammals: 32, 3, 15, 54, 10, 44, 110, 28
Amphibians: 9, 18, 22, 18, 20, 24, 15, 26

4. Calculate the mean average deviation for each data set.
5. Calculate the interquartile range for each data set.
6. How does the variability of the mammal lifespans compare with the variability of the amphibian lifespans?
7. Construct a box-and-whisker plot for each data set. Explain how the shape of the data relates to the variability of the data.

MATH GAMES

Histogram Race

What You'll Need

- three number cubes
- a graph for each player, labeled as shown

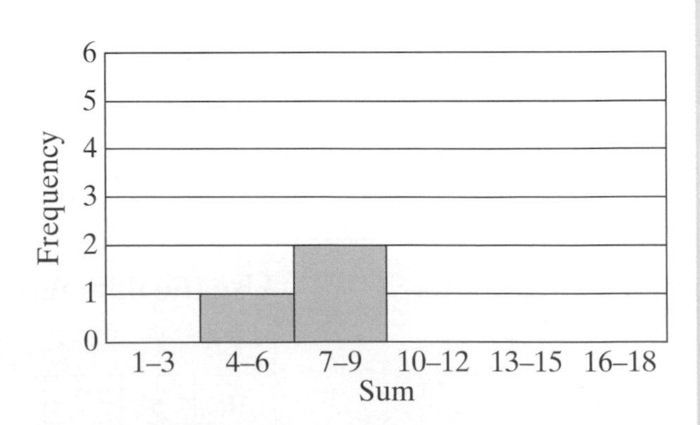

How to Play

- Each player takes a turn rolling the three number cubes. The player then chooses one, two, or three of the numbers rolled and adds them.
- The player fills in one square on the graph in the column labeled with the sum.
- Once any player fills a column completely, no other players may play in the column on their own graphs.
- If a player cannot fill a square, then the player loses a turn.
- The first player to fill in three columns wins.

9-8 Statistical Questions

Check Skills You'll Need

1. **Vocabulary Review** Mean absolute deviation and interquartile range are measures of __?__.

Find the interquartile range for each data set.

2. 1, 1, 2, 2, 0, 3, 3, 5
3. 100, 770, 150, 80
4. 9, 3, 5, 1, 7, 1, 11

for Help Lesson 9-6

CONTENT STANDARDS
6.SP.1, 6.SP.2

What You'll Learn

To identify a statistical question and to recognize and remove bias from statistical questions

New Vocabulary statistical question

Why Learn This?

Surveys can give us valuable information. In order to gather valid data, we need to ask appropriate questions.

A **statistical question** is one for which you expect to get a variety of different answers. You can analyze the distribution and tendency of those answers using statistical measures.

Questions that have only one answer are not statistical questions.

Before you ask a question on a survey, you should know the types of answers you expect.

EXAMPLE Identifying Statistical Questions

1 Tell whether the question is a statistical question. If it is, identify possible answers. If not, explain why not.

a. How many states are in the United States?
This is not a statistical question because there is just one answer: 50. A statistical question might ask a group of people: How many states have you visited?

b. What is the favorite vegetable of sixth graders in your school?
This is a statistical question because it can have many different answers depending on whom you ask. Possible favorites: corn, peas, spinach, broccoli, etc.

c. How many siblings do I have?
This is not a statistical question. There is only one factual answer. A statistical question might ask of an entire class or school: How many siblings do you have?

Vocabulary Tip

The purpose of a statistical question is to gather data that has variability. If there is just one answer, there is no variability.

Quick Check

1. Tell whether the question is a statistical question. If it is, identify possible answers. If not, explain why not.
   a. How many students are taller than 6 feet?
   b. What size shoe do you wear?

A good survey question can have few answers or it may have many possible answers. However, the question should avoid words that influence the answer.

Vocabulary Tip

A biased question leads a person to a particular answer.

EXAMPLE Identifying Bias

2 Emelio and Leila want to create a survey about preferred vacation spots. Which question is likely to give biased results? Why?

- Emelio's question: Would you prefer to vacation in sunny Bermuda or rainy London?
- Leila's question: Would you prefer to vacation in Bermuda or London?

Emelio's question is biased. He uses words that could influence the answers. The word "sunny" makes Bermuda seem more inviting than "rainy" London.

Quick Check

2. Determine if the survey question is biased and explain your answer. If it is biased, rewrite the question so it is unbiased.
   a. Rolondo wrote the survey question: Do you prefer delicious sweet red grapes or bitter strawberries?
   b. Eliana wants to find out which internet service people in her area people think is best. She asks: Which is the fastest internet service in your area?

Check Your Understanding

1. **Vocabulary** A question that has one answer regardless of who answers it is _____ a statistical question.
2. Which is NOT a statistical question?
   a. How tall are you?
   b. How high is an NBA basketball hoop?
   c. What time do you eat dinner?
   d. What is your favorite food?

3. Aaron conducted a survey about how much TV students watch. He asked: How many hours a night do you watch television?
   a. Did Aaron ask a statistical question?
   b. Did Aaron ask a biased question?

4. **Open-ended** Give an example of a biased question. Explain how the question is biased and how responders are likely to answer.

Homework Exercises

For more exercises, see Extra Skills and Word Problems.

GO for Help

For Exercise	See Example
5–9, 15	1
10–14	2

Tell whether the question is a statistical question. If it is, identify likely answers. If not, explain why not.

5. How many hours a week do you practice a musical instrument?

6. How many blocks is the library from the school?

7. Do I have red hair?

8. Do you have brown eyes?

9. What is your favorite type of music to listen to?

Is the survey question biased? If so, explain why. Then rewrite the question so it is unbiased.

10. Do you prefer healthy fruit, unhealthy sweets, or salty chips as a snack?

11. Would you prefer to live in the city or in the country?

12. Which flavor of ice cream do you like the best: chocolate, strawberry, or vanilla?

13. How many hours of sleep do you get a night?

14. Do you agree with most people that playing the guitar is cooler than playing the clarinet?

Test Prep Tip

When writing survey questions, be careful not to use words that give an opinion about the topic.

15. Which is NOT a statistical question?
   a. How old are the students in your school?
   b. Have you ever had a pet dog or cat?
   c. Are you taller or shorter than I am?
   d. How long are the sentences on this page?

GPS 16. **Guided Problem Solving** Jason and Kate conducted a survey about favorite sports. The results are shown below.
Jason asked: Which sport do you prefer to play: baseball or soccer?

Kate asked: Do you prefer to play baseball or the fast-paced game of soccer?

Survey Results								
Jason	soccer	baseball	soccer	soccer	baseball	baseball	soccer	baseball
Kate	soccer	soccer	soccer	baseball	soccer	soccer	soccer	soccer

- Does either question contain words that could influence how people respond?
- Compare the survey results. Does one set of results seem noticeably different from the other?

17. Pauline collects the following results from a survey.

Survey Results				
	12 miles	28 miles	15 miles	48 miles
	10 miles	6 miles	2 miles	36 miles

a. Is it likely that Pauline asked a statistical question? Explain.
b. What question might Pauline have asked?

18. Reasoning What kind of results would you expect to get from a survey question that asks "Would you rather play the latest cool videogame or read a required book for school?" Explain your reasoning.

19. Writing in Math Do you think a bar graph or a histogram would best represent the results of a survey that asks "What is your favorite sport?" Explain your reasoning.

20. Challenge Jack asked 10 people his survey question and they all gave the same answer. Can you determine if Jack's question is a statistical question? Explain.

Test Prep and Mixed Review — Practice

Multiple Choice

21. Which question is biased?
(A) How many pets have you had in your lifetime?
(B) Do you prefer jazz or soulful country music?
(C) Which is your favorite season of the year?
(D) Do you prefer peanuts, popcorn, or pretzels?

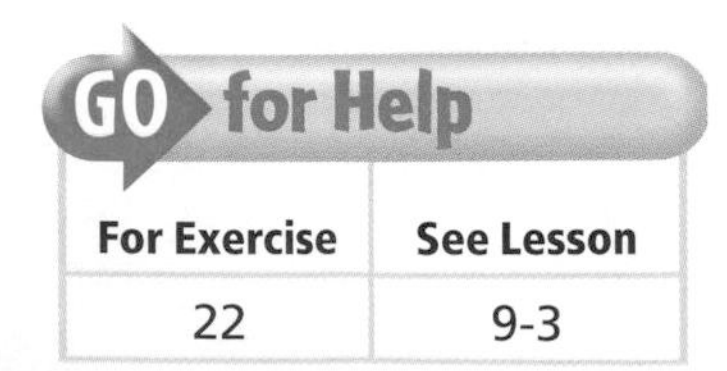

For Exercise	See Lesson
22	9-3

22. The dot plot shows the number of slices in loaves of bread. Which statement is NOT supported by the plot?
(F) 24 different loaves of bread were counted.
(G) The median value is 18.
(H) The range of slices is 5.
(J) The most frequent number of slices is 20.

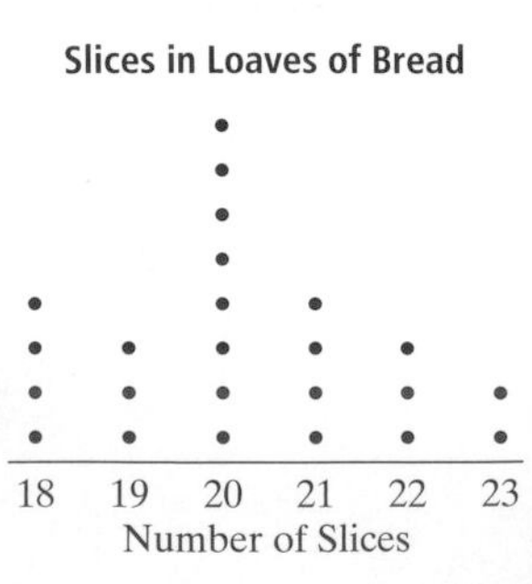

Test-Taking Strategies

Answering the Question Asked

When answering a question, be sure to answer the question that is asked. Read the question carefully and identify the answer that you are asked to find. Some answer choices are answers to related questions, so you have to be careful.

EXAMPLE

1 In Mrs. Sanchez's class, students received the scores shown in the line plot. How many students took thc test?

(A) 9 (B) 19 (C) 20 (D) 28

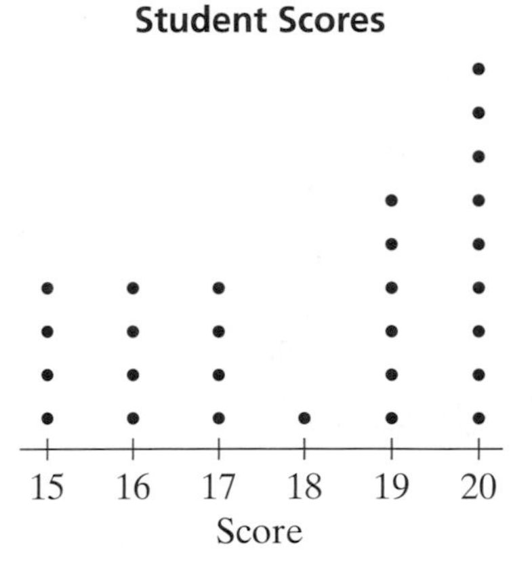

The question asks for the number of students who took the test. The total number of scores is $4 + 4 + 4 + 1 + 6 + 9 = 28$. The correct answer is choice D.

The number of students who scored 20 points is 9. The mode is 20. The median is 19. But none of these is what is asked for.

EXAMPLE

2 The list provides the heights of 11 students in inches. What is the median height?

(F) 60 in. (G) 62 in. (H) 63 in. (J) 64 in.

Heights of Students (in inches)

61, 71, 57, 60, 63, 67, 70, 62, 58, 60, 64

The question asks for the median height. For eleven data items, the sixth is the median. The sixth height is 62 in. The correct answer is choice G.

The mode is 60 in. The mean is 63 in. Answer J is the average of 57 in. and 71 in., or 64 in. But none of these is what is asked for.

Exercises

1. In Example 2, how tall is the tallest student who is less than 70 in. tall?

   (A) 60 in. (B) 67 in. (C) 70 in. (D) 71 in.

2. In Example 2, what is the range of data?

   (F) 14 in. (G) 57 in. (H) 64 in. (J) 71 in.

Chapter 9 Review

Vocabulary Review

box-and-whisker plot (p. 323)
dot plot (p. 320)
frequency table (p. 319)
histogram (p. 328)
interquartile range (IQR) (p. 335)
lower quartile (p. 323)
mean (p. 311)
mean absolute deviation (MAD) (p. 334)
measure of center (p. 334)
measure of variability (p. 334)
median (p. 315)
mode (p. 316)
outlier (p. 312)
range (p. 320)
statistical question (p. 345)
upper quartile (p. 323)

Go Online

For vocabulary quiz
PearsonSuccessNet.com

Choose the correct vocabulary term to complete each sentence.

1. A(n) __?__ lists each item in a data set with the number of times it occurs.
2. The __?__ of a data set is the sum of the values divided by the number of values.
3. A(n) __?__ of a data set is much greater or much less than the other data values.
4. You can construct a(n) __?__ to represent a data set if you know the least value, the lower quartile, the median, the upper quartile, and the greatest value.
5. The range, interquartile range, and mean absolute deviation are all types of __?__.

A. mean
B. measure(s) of variability
C. frequency table
D. median
E. box-and-whisker plot
F. histogram
G. outlier

Skills and Concepts

Lessons 9-1 and 9-2

- To find and analyze the mean of a data set using models and calculations
- To find and analyze the median and mode of a data set

The **mean** of a set of data is the sum of the values divided by the number of data items. The **median** is the middle value when the data are arranged in numerical order. The **mode** is the value or item that appears most often.

Find the mean, median, and mode of each data set.

6. 34, 49, 63, 43, 50, 50, 26
7. 3, 7, 1, 9, 9, 5, 8

Lesson 9-3

- To analyze a set of data by finding the range and by making frequency tables and dot plots

A **frequency table** lists each item in a data set with the number of times the item occurs. A **dot plot** displays a data set by stacking dots above each data value on a number line.

8. Make a dot plot showing the number of times the words *the*, *and*, *a*, and *of* appear in the paragraph above.

Lesson 9-4

- To construct and analyze box-and-whisker plots

To make a **box-and-whisker plot**, order the data and identify the least value, the greatest value, the median, the **lower quartile** and the **upper quartile**.

9. Make a box-and-whisker plot to represent the following heights (in inches) of players on a basketball team: 60, 72, 75, 66, 60, 68, 64, 70.

Lesson 9-5

- To construct and analyze histograms

A **histogram** is a type of bar graph that shows the frequency of data within given intervals.

10. Make a histogram to represent the following test scores: 100, 84, 75, 95, 92, 80, 64, 100, 88, 85, 90.

Lessons 9-6 through 9-8

- To analyze the variability of data using the MAD and IQR
- To relate the shape of data to its variability
- To recognize statistical questions and bias in questions

Measures of variability describe how data are spread out. To find the **mean absolute deviation (MAD)**, first find the mean of the data. Then find the difference between each data value and the mean and calculate the mean of these differences. To find the **interquartile range (IQR)**, subtract the lower quartile from the upper quartile. The shape of the data can also indicate the variability of the data.

The dot plot represents the ages of children at a summer camp. Use the dot plot in Exercises 11–12.

8 9 10 11 12 13 14
Age

11. Find the mean absolute deviation and the interquartile range for the data.

12. Describe the shape of the graph. How does the shape relate to the variability of the data?

13. Tell whether or not the following question is a statistical question: "What is my middle name?"

14. Is the following question biased? Explain. "Which would you rather eat: greasy chicken or fresh stir-fried vegetables?"

Chapter 9 Test

Go Online For online chapter test PearsonSuccessNet.com

1. Find the mean, median, mode, and range of the data set: 31, 20, 31, 51, 27.

The numbers of children in 15 families are 1, 3, 2, 1, 3, 1, 2, 6, 2, 3, 3, 4, 3, 4, and 5.

2. Find the median, mode, and range.
3. Make a frequency table of the data.
4. Make a dot plot of the data.
5. **Profits** A business has weekly profits of $5,000, $3,000, $2,000, $2,500, and $5,000. Why is using the mode to describe this data set misleading?
6. The spreadsheet below shows three quiz scores for two students. Write formulas for cells E2 and E3.

	A	B	C	D	E
1	Student	Q 1	Q 2	Q 3	Mean
2	Yori	81	95	88	■
3	Sarah	78	81	87	■

7. Make a box-and-whisker plot for these state-fair pumpkin weights (pounds): 288, 207, 210, 212, 226, 233, 212, 218, 247, 262, 269, 203, 271.

Reading **Twelve people estimated the time, in minutes, they spend reading each day.**

Their responses are below.
20, 5, 45, 90, 60, 45, 30, 10, 30, 45, 15, 25

8. Find the mean, median, mode, and range of the data.
9. Which would you use to describe the data—the mean, median, or mode?
10. **Writing in Math** What type of data display would you use for the data? Explain.

The weights (in pounds) of 16 pumpkins at a farm are 10, 8, 12, 16, 20, 5, 8, 10, 24, 13, 9, 26, 7, 14, 20, 22.

11. Make a histogram to represent the data. Use at least 4 intervals.
12. What conclusions can you make about the data?

The dot plots show the number of pets owned by girls and boys in a 6th grade class.

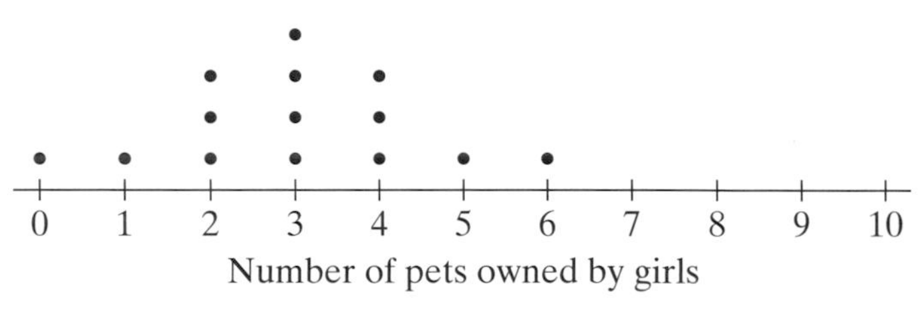

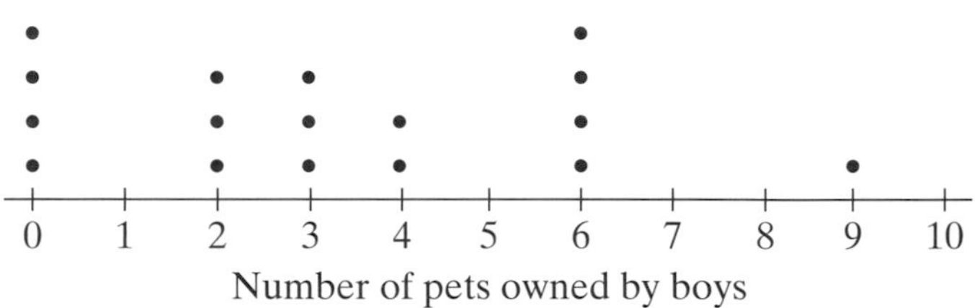

13. Find the mean absolute deviation for each data set.
14. Find the interquartile range for each data set.
15. For each dot plot, identify whether the data has any peaks, gaps, or clusters. Then tell whether the data have symmetry.
16. Which data set shows more variability? Explain.
17. Tell whether the following question is a statistical question. Explain your reasoning. How tall are you?
18. Tell whether the question is biased. Explain your reasoning. Do you exercise daily as is recommended or do you mostly sit around and watch TV?

Multiple Choice

Choose the correct letter.

1. What operation would you perform first in the expression $3.9 + 4.1 \times 16 - 6 \div 4.8$?
   - (A) Add 3.9 and 4.1.
   - (B) Multiply 4.1 and 16.
   - (C) Subtract 6 from 16.
   - (D) Divide 10 by 4.8.

2. Four servers at a restaurant equally share \$87.44 in tips. How much does each server receive?
   - (F) 20.68 (H) 21.86
   - (G) 20.86 (J) 22.86

3. Simplify the expression. $(4 + 2)^2$
   - (A) 8 (C) 36
   - (B) 12 (D) 42

4. Solve the equation $0.2x = 46$.
   - (F) 2.3 (H) 23
   - (G) 9.2 (J) 230

5. Find the quotient $0.317 \div 0.08$.
   - (A) 0.039625 (C) 39.625
   - (B) 3.9625 (D) 396.25

6. Simplify the expression $4 + 6 \times (-3) - (-10) \div (-2)$.
   - (F) −19 (G) −10 (H) 10 (J) 19

7. Solve the equation $c + 3\frac{2}{3} = 7\frac{4}{5}$.
   - (A) $3\frac{2}{15}$ (B) $3\frac{7}{15}$ (C) $4\frac{2}{15}$ (D) $4\frac{7}{15}$

8. Estimate the product $7\frac{5}{6} \times 5\frac{3}{4}$.
   - (F) 35 (G) 40 (H) 42 (J) 48

9. Find the reciprocal of $4\frac{2}{5}$.
   - (A) $\frac{5}{22}$ (B) $\frac{1}{4}$ (C) $\frac{5}{2}$ (D) $2\frac{4}{5}$

10. What is the ordered pair for P?
    - (F) (3, 2)
    - (G) (−2, −3)
    - (H) (2, −2)
    - (J) (−3, 2)

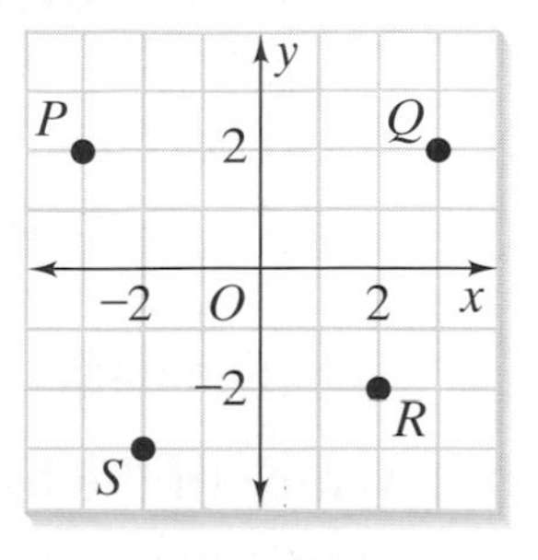

11. Find the unit rate.
    84 students in 4 classrooms
    - (A) 21 classes per student
    - (B) 24 classrooms per school
    - (C) 21 students per classroom
    - (D) 24 students per classroom

12. Which of the following is NOT equivalent to 48%?
    - (F) $\frac{48}{100}$ (G) $\frac{24}{50}$ (H) 0.048 (J) 0.48

13. Solve $6a = 120$.
    - (A) −20 (B) −2 (C) 2 (D) 20

14. You collect 9 new coins over the holidays. At the end of the holidays, you have 47 coins in your collection. How many coins did you have before the holidays?
    - (F) 36 (G) 38 (H) 40 (J) 56

15. Find the LCM of 20, 35, and 100.
    - (A) 5 (B) 10 (C) 100 (D) 700

16. Simplify the expression. $7x - 2 + 3x$
    - (F) $10x - 2$ (H) $21x + 2$
    - (G) $4x - 2$ (J) $10x + 2$

17. You buy tape and seven boxes for \$18.55. If the tape costs \$2.10, how much is each box?
    - (A) \$.70 (B) \$2.35 (C) \$2.65 (D) \$2.95

18. The dot plot shows student absences over a five-day period. Which of the following statements best describes the shape of the data?

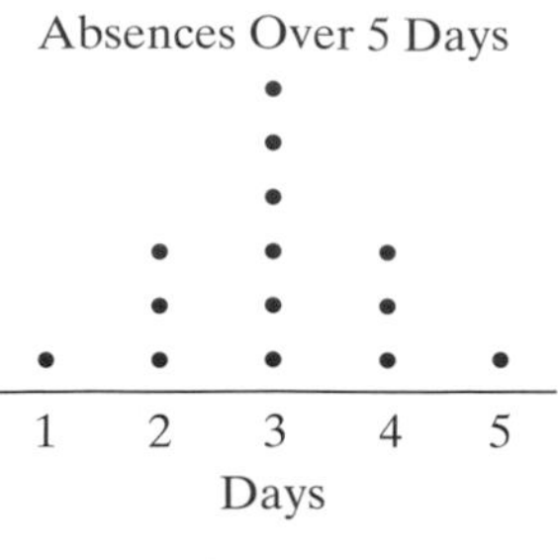

Ⓕ There are no clusters in the data.
Ⓖ The data is symmetric.
Ⓗ There are no peaks in the data.
Ⓙ The data has a gap at 2.

19. Which of the following is a statistical question?
Ⓐ Where is my home?
Ⓑ How many months are in a year?
Ⓒ Do I have long fingernails?
Ⓓ How many days a month do you do aerobic exercise?

20. A veterinarian weighed the puppies at the local animal shelter. Based on the histogram, which of the following statements is NOT true?

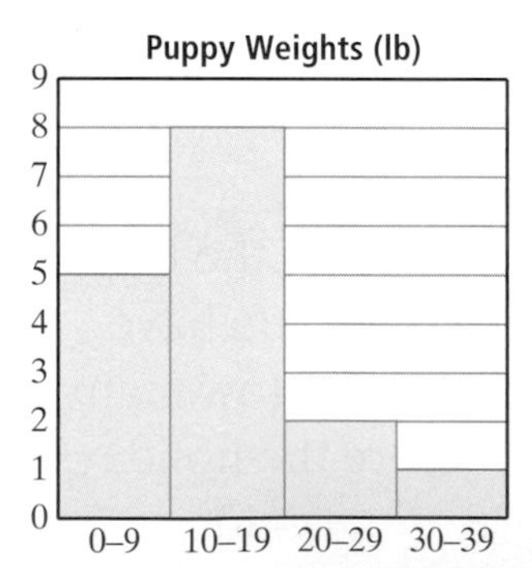

Ⓕ Most of the puppies weighed between 10 and 19 pounds.
Ⓖ More puppies weighed less than 10 pounds than over 30 pounds.
Ⓗ Only two puppies weighed between 20 and 29 pounds.
Ⓙ The biggest puppy weighed less than 30 pounds.

21. Which set of numbers is ordered from least to greatest?
Ⓐ $\frac{1}{5}, -0.4, 1.4, -\frac{15}{75}$
Ⓑ $-0.4, \frac{1}{5}, -\frac{15}{75}, 1.4$
Ⓒ $-0.4, -\frac{15}{75}, \frac{1}{5}, 1.4$
Ⓓ $1.4, \frac{1}{5}, -0.4, -\frac{15}{75}$

Gridded Response

Record your answer in a grid.

22. A gardener plants 121 marigolds in a square garden. Each row has the same number of plants. How many plants are in each row?

23. The equation $y = 15x$ represents the amount of money Elton saves each week. How much will Elton have saved in 14 weeks?

24. Find the surface area in square feet of the figure below.

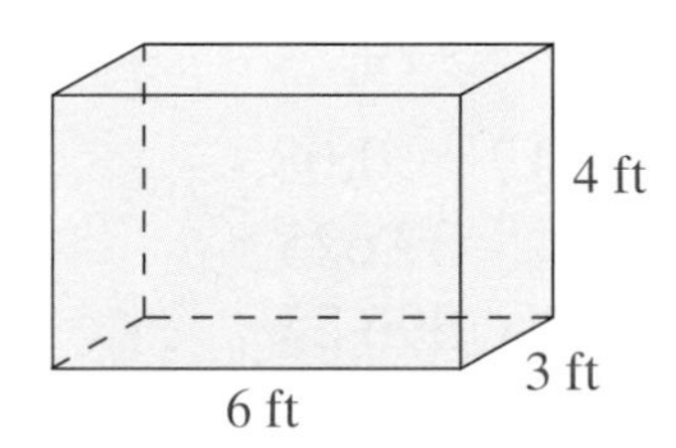

25. Trae wants to put sod on a path in his backyard. Each strip of sod is $1\frac{1}{3}$ feet wide. The path is 5 feet wide. How many strips of sod will he need?

26. Solve the equation $4j = 12$ for j.

27. How many yards is 93 feet?

28. Simplify the expression $(16 - 8) \times 2 + (10 \div 100)$.

29. Find 35% of 240.

30. Simplify the expression $3 \times 8 - 4 + 5$.

Short Response

31. No more than 12 students volunteered to work at the local food pantry.
   a. Write an inequality for this situation.
   b. Graph the solution on a number line.

32. Identify each three-dimensional figure.

a. 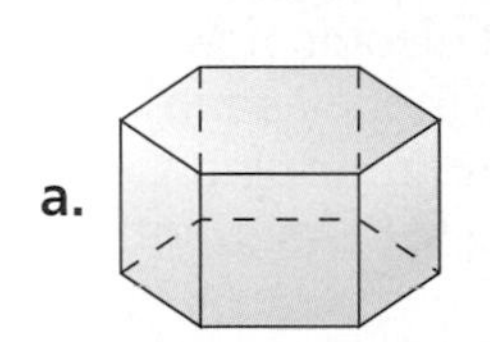

b. 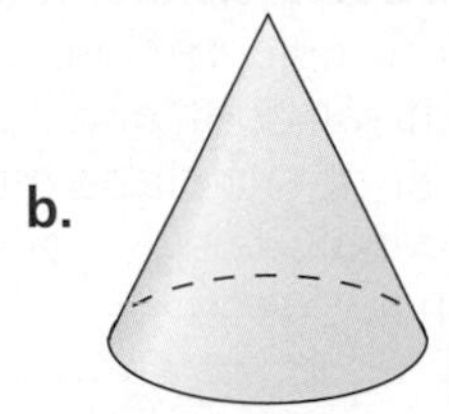

c. 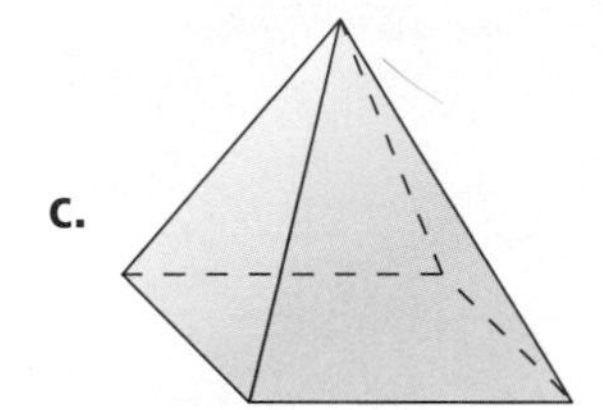

d. 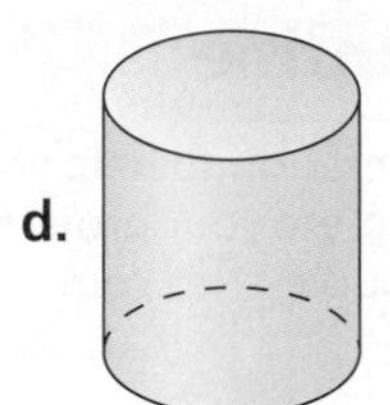

33. Complete the function table using the rule.
Output = Input · 8

Input	Output
−4	■
7	■
9	■

34. Find the mean, median, and mode of the data set.
2, 3, 7, 4, 1, 4, 9, 3, 3

35. Solve $0.5b = 24$.

36. Solve $n + 9 \geq 17$.

37. Find the prime factorization of 98 by using a factor tree.

38. Andrew jogs 3 miles in an hour. How many minutes will it take him to jog 5 miles?

Extended Response

39. The sum of a number t and 7 is greater than 20.
   a. Write an inequality for this situation.
   b. Solve the inequality.
   c. Graph the solution on a number line.

40. A rectangle measures 5 inches by 7 inches.
   a. What is the area of the rectangle?
   b. A 1 inch-by-1 inch square is cut from each corner of the rectangle. What is the area of the new figure? Explain.

41. An open box is made by folding the sides of the net below.

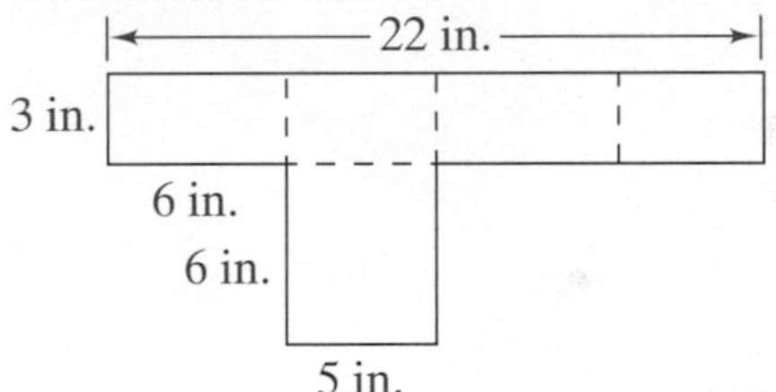

   a. Find the surface area of the open box.
   b. Now find the volume of the box.

42. The cost of your dinner is $18.64. You want to leave a 15% tip for the server.
   a. How much is the tip?
   b. What is the total cost of dinner, excluding any tax?

43. Use the graph to answer the questions.

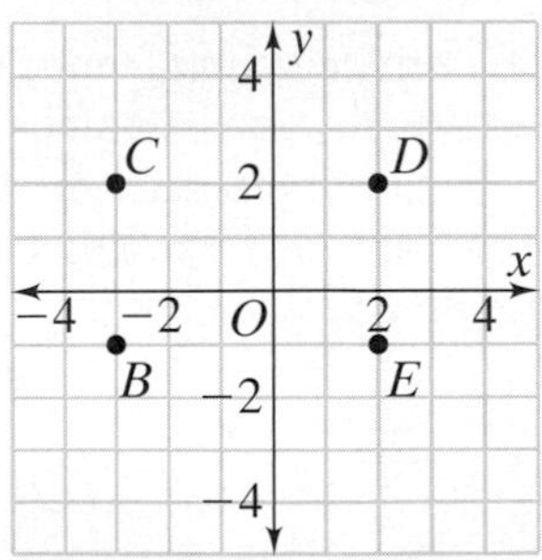

   a. Find the length of the line segment joining points C and D.
   b. The given points are connected to form a rectangle. Find the perimeter of the rectangle.

Chapter Projects

Chapter 1 *Number Properties and Decimals*

Suppose your class is planning to honor someone special in the community or to congratulate a winning team. You need to decide when and where you will hold the event, how you will decorate, and what entertainment and refreshments you will provide. You may also need to decide how to raise funds for the celebration.

Plan a Celebration Your chapter project is to plan a celebration. You must decide how much it will cost and how much money each member of the class must raise. Your plan should include a list of supplies for the event and their costs.

Go Online

For Information to help you complete your project
PearsonSuccessNet.com

making THE measure

Chapter 2 *Expressions and Equations*

In the high jump, as in most sports, a consistent system of measurement allows athletes to make comparisons. It took the decree of a king to create one such system!

Back in the 12th century, King Henry I of England decided that a yard was the distance from the tip of his nose to the end of his thumb. How far is it from the tip of your nose to the end of your thumb? Is it more than a yard or less? Is it the same distance for everyone?

Invent Your Own Ruler For the chapter project, you will design a new system for measuring distance. Your final project will be a new ruler, together with a report on its usefulness. Don't forget to include equations that show how your new tool relates to other familiar measuring tools.

Go Online

For Information to help you complete your project
PearsonSuccessNet.com

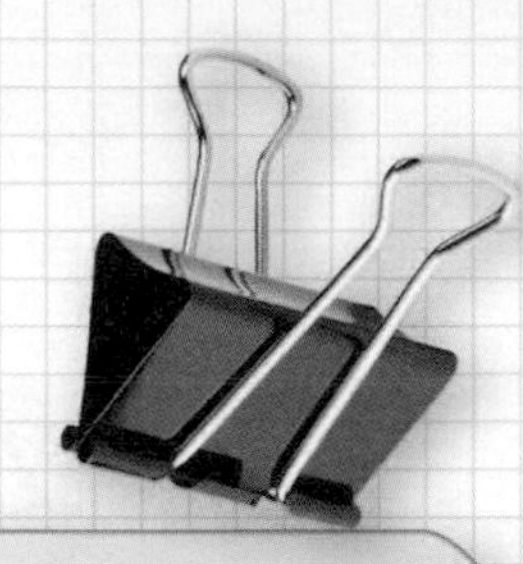

STEPPING STONES

Chapter 3 Number Theory

Think about a historic building, such as one of the ancient pyramids or the Eiffel Tower. How many pieces of stone do you think were needed for the bottom of a pyramid compared to the top? Many buildings use mathematical patterns in their designs.

Building a Fort For this project, you will build a model of a simple fort. You will record the amounts of materials needed for each course, or layer of blocks. How high can you go? Evaluate expressions for different layers. You will look for patterns and write equations to describe the patterns.

Go Online

For Information to help you complete your project PearsonSuccessNet.com

Toss and Turn

Chapter 4 Fraction Operations

Did you ever make pancakes? The recipe can be pretty simple—an egg, some pancake mix, milk, and maybe some oil. Or forget the mix and start from scratch! Either way, you can vary the ingredients to suit your tastes. Do you want to include some wheat germ? How about some pecans, or maybe some blueberries.

Write Your Own Recipe For the chapter project, you will write your own recipe for pancakes. Your final project will be a recipe that will feed everyone in your class. Also include instructions for how to adapt the recipe to make fewer servings.

Go Online

For Information to help you complete your project PearsonSuccessNet.com

Chapter 5 Ratios and Percents

When you look up at the stars in the sky, you may not think about how far away they are. Stars appear a lot closer than they really are. The same is true of planets. The huge distances between planets make it impossible for books to show how vast our solar system really is.

Make a Scale Model In this chapter project, you will make scale models of two planets. You will compare their sizes and distances from the sun and calculate the ratios involved in your scale model.

Go Online

For Information to help you complete your project PearsonSuccessNet.com

Board Walk

Chapter 6 Integers and Rational Numbers

What makes a board game so much fun? You have challenges like road blocks or false paths that make you backtrack. Then you land on a lucky square that lets you leap forward past your opponent. Best of all, you are with your friends as you play!

Create a Board Game For this chapter project, you will use integers to create a game. Then you will play your game with friends or family for a trial run. Finally you will decorate your game and bring it to class to play.

Go Online

For Information to help you complete your project PearsonSuccessNet.com

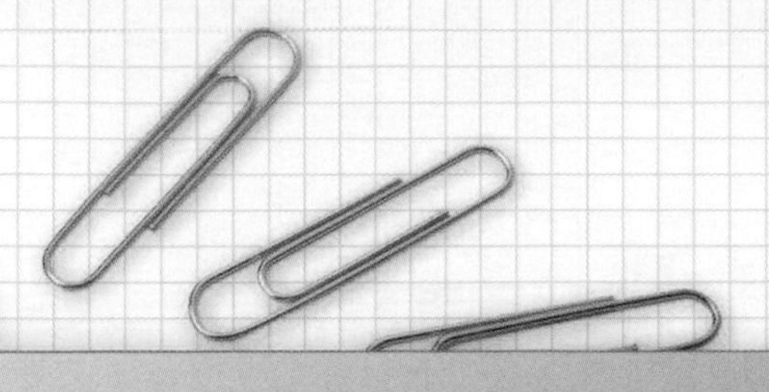

happy *landings*

Chapter 7 The Coordinate Plane

Imagine this—you have just opened your parachute and you are floating through the air. Exciting, huh? You can calculate how long it takes you to parachute to the ground, because the change in height versus time occurs in a predictable pattern. Many other events change in a predictable pattern, for instance, the height of a burning candle and the growth of money in a bank account.

Graphing Data For the chapter project, you will find how fast a container of water empties when there is a hole in it. Your final project will be a graph of the data you collect.

Go Online

For Information to help you complete your project
PearsonSuccessNet.com

Puzzling Pictures

Chapter 8 Geometry and Measurement

Do you remember putting together simple puzzles when you were younger? Puzzles designed for young children are often made of wood and have large pieces. Many of the pieces have corners or straight sides so that a child can put the puzzle together easily.

Create a Puzzle Think about one of your favorite pictures. How can you make it into a puzzle using various geometric shapes? Does your puzzle have to be a rectangle or square? Your project is to make an attractive but challenging puzzle for your classmates. Include as many geometric shapes as you can.

Go Online

For Information to help you complete your project PearsonSuccessNet.com

ON YOUR OWN TIME

Chapter 9 Data and Graphs

RING!!! The last bell of the day has rung. You and your classmates will soon head in different directions. Some of your classmates are on the same team or in the same club as you. Some of them are not. Do you know how much time your classmates spend on their favorite activities? You could guess the answers to the last question, but a more accurate method of finding the answers would be to collect real data.

Conduct a Survey For this chapter project, you will survey 25 of your friends and classmates. You can choose the survey subject, such as how much time your classmates spend on sports. You will organize, graph, and interpret the data. Then you will present your findings to your class.

Go Online

For Information to help you complete your project PearsonSuccessNet.com

CHAPTER 1 Extra Practice

Skills

Lesson 1-1 **Tell whether each equation is true or false.**

1. $65 = 10 + 65$
2. $8 \times 0 = 8$
3. $1 \times 9.8 = 9.8$
4. $4 + 5 + 7 = 4 + 11$

Lesson 1-2 **Find the value of each expression.**

5. $2 + 6 \times 3 + 1$
6. $(14 + 44) \div 2$
7. $3 + 64 \div 4 - 10$
8. $144 + 56 \div 4$

Lesson 1-3 **Write each number in expanded form.**

9. two hundred sixteen
10. two hundred twenty-two thousandths

Write each number in words.

11. 0.26
12. 0.3481
13. 72.053
14. 691.4

Lesson 1-4 **First estimate and then find each sum or difference.**

15. $1.14 + 9.3$
16. $3.541 + 1.333$
17. $5.45 - 2.8$
18. $4.11 - 2.621$
19. $15.348 - 7.92$
20. $1.925 + 3.085$
21. $18 - 5.3619$
22. $728.6 + 36.09$

Lesson 1-5 **Find each product.**

23. 1.8×4.302
24. $0.29(0.43)$
25. $7.4(930)$
26. $0.617 \cdot 0.09$
27. 5.32×2.01
28. 9.4×0.94
29. 24.3×8.5
30. 3.7×48.043

Lesson 1-6 **Find each quotient.**

31. $23 \div 25$
32. $348 \div 60$
33. $0.672 \div 3$
34. $228.2 \div 7$
35. $1.428 \div 2.1$
36. $91.2 \div 7.6$
37. $22.932 \div 3.6$
38. $233.445 \div 23.7$

Word Problems

Lessons 1-1 and 1-2

39. Music What is the total number of instruments in the orchestra shown in the table at the right?

Orchestra

Instrument	Number
Violin	29
Viola	13
Bass	2
Cello	12

40. A group of 28 students and 3 teachers goes to the theater. Each student pays $12. The school pays an additional $4 per student and $16 per adult. Find the total cost of the trip.

Lesson 1-3

41. Currency The rupee and the paisa are units of money in India. One paisa is equal to $\frac{1}{100}$ of an Indian rupee. Using decimals, write 256 paisas as a number of rupees.

Lesson 1-4

42. Animals The table shows typical weights regularly reached by some adult animals. Suppose a truck carried a gorilla and a bear in separate cages. How many tons of animals would the truck carry?

Animal	Weight (tons)
American bison	1.5
Anaconda	0.23
Gorilla	0.35
Kodiak bear	0.74
Leatherback turtle	0.8

43. At a bicycle store, an 18-speed bicycle costs $174.99. At another store, the same bicycle costs $222.98. What is the difference in prices?

Lesson 1-5

44. Malia was 55.5 inches tall last year. What is the Malia's height in inches if she is 1.08 times as tall this year as last year?

45. Money There are 40 coins in a roll of nickels. Find the value of 25 rolls of nickels.

Lesson 1-6

46. You spend $585 on school lunches for the school year. There are about 180 days of school in the school year. How much do you spend on lunch each day?

47. Regular unleaded gasoline costs $2.359 per gallon. You spend $10 on gasoline. About how many gallons do you buy?

CHAPTER 2 Extra Practice

Skills

Lesson 2-1 **Evaluate each expression for $n = 9$.**

1. $n - 7$
2. $3n - 5$
3. $22 - 2n$
4. $4n \div 6$

Lesson 2-2 **Write an expression for each word phrase.**

5. 1 less than b
6. p times 2
7. 4 more than b
8. n divided by 2

Lesson 2-3 **Solve each equation. Use mental math or the strategy, *Guess, Check, and Revise.***

9. $x + 6 = 8$
10. $5x = 40$
11. $36 = 36 - x$
12. $x + 2 = 8.3$

Use mental math to solve each equation.

13. $c + 3 = 7$
14. $8 = d - 6$
15. $3m = 15$
16. $5 = 30 \div n$
17. $20 = y + 1$
18. $t - 10 = 24$
19. $a \div 3 = 3$
20. $178 = 10b$

Lessons 2-4 and 2-5 **Solve each equation. Then check the solution.**

21. $b + 4 = 7.7$
22. $c + 3.5 = 7.5$
23. $n - 1.7 = 8$
24. $8.4 = s - 0.2$

Lesson 2-6 **Solve each equation. Then check the solution.**

25. $15t = 600$
26. $62 = 2b$
27. $x \div 5 = 2.5$
28. $a \div 0.05 = 140$
29. $5f = 75$
30. $121 = 11d$
31. $32.1 = g \div 3$
32. $n \div 7.5 = 4$

Word Problems

Lesson 2-1

33. The formula $A = l \times w$ gives the area of a rectangle with length l and width w. Find the area of a rectangle with length 8.5 cm and width 3.2 cm.
34. A company selling T-shirts charges $45 to create a design it will print on shirts. Each T-shirt costs $3. You can use the expression $3x + 45$ to find the cost of an order, where x stands for the number of T-shirts. How much does it cost to order 350 T-shirts?

Lesson 2-2

35. **Boating** A paddleboat rents for $10 plus $8 per hour. How much does it cost to rent a paddleboat for h hours? Draw a model and write an expression for the situation.

Lesson 2-3

36. **Sports** A hockey team spends $75 on chin straps. Each strap costs $5. Solve the equation $5n = 75$ to find how many straps the team buys.

Lesson 2-4

37. **Biology** The height of the female giraffe in a zoo is 14.1 feet. The female is 3.2 feet shorter than the male giraffe. Write and solve an equation to find the male's height.

Lesson 2-5

38. In a class of 26 students, 15 students have birthdays in the first half of the year. Write and solve an equation to find how many students have birthdays in the last half of the year.

39. Your family buys carpeting for the two rooms shown at the right. How many square feet of carpeting does your family buy?

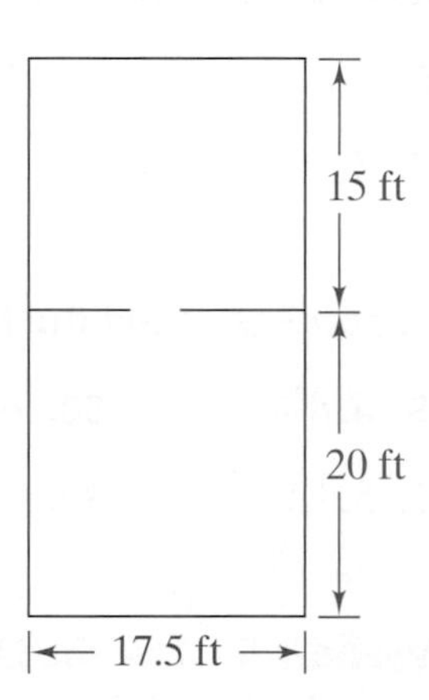

Lesson 2-6

40. **Geography** The area of the Pacific Ocean is about 64,000,000 square miles. This area is about twice the area of the Atlantic Ocean. Find the approximate area of the Atlantic Ocean.

CHAPTER 3 Extra Practice

Skills

Lesson 3-1 **Test each number for divisibility by 2, 3, 5, 9, or 10.**

1. 324 **2.** 2,685 **3.** 540 **4.** 114 **5.** 31 **6.** 981

Lesson 3-2 **Simplify each expression.**

7. $7 + 5^2$ **8.** $(6 - 2)^3 \times 3$ **9.** 8^3 **10.** $9^2 + 2^2$

Lesson 3-3 **Tell whether each number is prime or composite.**

11. 24 **12.** 49 **13.** 7 **14.** 81 **15.** 37 **16.** 29

Lesson 3-4 **Find the GCF of each set of numbers.**

17. 10, 30 **18.** 15, 18 **19.** 25, 35 **20.** 28, 36 **21.** 45, 72 **22.** 8, 12

23. 24, 42 **24.** 4, 24 **25.** 22, 121 **26.** 35, 49 **27.** 6, 12, 15 **28.** 14, 42, 84

Lesson 3-5 **Find the LCM of each set of numbers.**

29. 4, 8 **30.** 6, 14 **31.** 15, 25 **32.** 20, 36 **33.** 3, 4, 12 **34.** 8, 15

35. 5, 12 **36.** 4, 18 **37.** 22, 121 **38.** 7, 49 **39.** 6, 12, 15 **40.** 6, 10, 15

Lesson 3-6 **Use the Distributive Property to write an equivalent expression for each of the following.**

41. $5(y + 6)$ **42.** $(r + 6) \times 11$ **43.** $7(w + 4y - 8)$ **44.** $(9 + 3s) \times 13$

Lesson 3-7 **Find an equivalent expression for each expression by simplifying.**

45. $3a + 5a - a$ **46.** $(r + 6) \times 11$ **47.** $7(w + 4y - 8)$

48. $9b + 5 - b$ **49.** $(q - 12) \times 6$ **50.** $11(z - 5y - 11)$

51. $12c - 9 - c + 9$ **52.** $(p - t) \times 2$ **53.** $6(x + 2y - 2y)$

Word Problems

Lesson 3-1

54. You and three friends eat lunch at a restaurant. The bill totals $18.21. Can you and your friends split the bill evenly? Explain.

55. One hundred twenty-three people showed up for a hike through a river canyon. The leader wants to make groups of 9 to walk together. Can everyone who showed up be in a group of 9? Explain your thinking.

56. Jake said, "The way to find the smallest number that is divisible by 2, 3, 5, and 10 is to multiply $2 \times 3 \times 5 \times 10$." Is this true? Why or why not?

Lessons 3-2 through 3-4

57. The table shows the number of rectangles you make each time you fold a piece of paper in half. After 6 folds, how many rectangles have you made? Write your answer using an exponent.

Number of Folds	Number of Rectangles
1	2
2	4
3	8
4	16

58. A photographer arranges 126 students for a class picture. Each row has the same number of students. What numbers of rows can he make?

59. On a field day, 84 girls and 78 boys are divided into teams. Each team has the same number of girls and the same number of boys. At most, how many teams are possible?

Lesson 3-5

60. Use the table. Find the least number of folders, stickers, and pens you can buy so that you have the same number of each.

Item	Number in Pack
Folders	6
Stickers	10
Pens	12

61. Joan goes to the gym every 2 days, Ruth goes every 3 days, and Leah goes every 4 days. They were all there today. In how many days will all three be at the gym together again?

Lesson 3-6

62. Roger and five friends plan to attend a concert. The tickets cost $19.50. How much will it cost for the tickets for Roger and his friends?

Lesson 3-7

63. Sam simplified the expression $5z + 13 - 2z + 1$ as shown. Explain and correct Sam's error.

$$\begin{aligned} 5z + 13 - 2z + 1 &= 5z - 2z + 13 + 1 \\ &= 3 + 14 \\ &= 17 \end{aligned}$$

CHAPTER 4 Extra Practice

Skills

Lesson 4-1 **Find each product.**

1. $\frac{1}{2}$ of $\frac{2}{3}$
2. $\frac{1}{3}$ of $\frac{1}{5}$
3. $\frac{7}{8} \times \frac{3}{4}$
4. $\frac{7}{6} \times 42$
5. $7\frac{1}{2} \times 2\frac{2}{3}$
6. $6\frac{2}{3} \times 7\frac{1}{5}$
7. $5\frac{5}{8} \times 2\frac{1}{3}$
8. $12\frac{1}{4} \times 6\frac{2}{7}$

Lesson 4-2 **Draw a model to find each quotient.**

9. $4 \div \frac{1}{4}$
10. $3 \div \frac{3}{4}$
11. $7 \div \frac{1}{5}$
12. $6 \div \frac{2}{3}$

Lesson 4-3 **Write the reciprocal of each fraction.**

13. $\frac{5}{6}$
14. 8
15. $\frac{2}{3}$
16. 15

Find each quotient.

17. $2 \div \frac{4}{5}$
18. $\frac{2}{3} \div \frac{2}{5}$
19. $\frac{1}{4} \div \frac{1}{5}$
20. $\frac{4}{11} \div 8$

Lesson 4-4 **Estimate each quotient.**

21. $12 \div 3\frac{1}{5}$
22. $7\frac{3}{7} \div 1\frac{2}{5}$
23. $41\frac{8}{10} \div 6\frac{1}{3}$
24. $36\frac{2}{7} \div 4\frac{3}{9}$

Find each quotient.

25. $2\frac{1}{4} \div \frac{2}{3}$
26. $4\frac{1}{2} \div 3\frac{1}{3}$
27. $2\frac{2}{5} \div \frac{2}{25}$
28. $5\frac{2}{3} \div 1\frac{1}{2}$

Lesson 4-5 **Solve each equation. Check the solution.**

29. $a + 9 = 12\frac{7}{9}$
30. $4\frac{5}{7} = b - 3\frac{1}{2}$
31. $c - 11\frac{2}{3} = 15$
32. $n + 4\frac{1}{2} = 5$
33. $\frac{x}{4} = 8$
34. $\frac{a}{3} = 9$
35. $\frac{c}{7} = 24$
36. $\frac{m}{2} = 14$
37. $\frac{r}{4} = 3.5$
38. $\frac{t}{12} = 3$
39. $\frac{1}{3}y = 15$
40. $\frac{3}{4}w = 12$

Word Problems

Lesson 4-1

Item	Full Price
Shirt	$21.00
Jeans	$40.00
Shoes	$27.00

41. To save money, you buy some clothes on sale. You buy a shirt for $\frac{4}{5}$ of the full price, a pair of jeans for $\frac{3}{4}$ of the full price, and a pair of shoes for $\frac{9}{10}$ of the full price. How much money do you save by buying these clothes on sale?

42. Carpentry A carpenter needs 6 pieces of wood that are $3\frac{1}{2}$ feet long. She has two 10-foot boards. Does she have enough wood? Explain.

Lesson 4-2

43. Sylvia has 3 cups of strawberries. She wants to give $\frac{2}{3}$ cup of strawberries each to three friends. Does she have enough strawberries for herself and three friends? She drew the model at the right to solve $3 \div \frac{2}{3}$. Will this model help her find the answer? Explain.

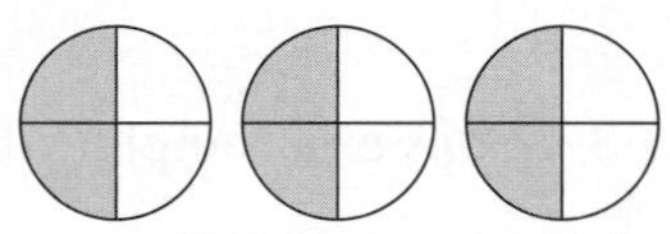

44. Lance bicycled $2\frac{1}{2}$ miles in $\frac{1}{6}$ hour. How fast is he bicycling in miles per hour? Solve by using a fraction division model.

Lesson 4-3

45. Baking You bake an apple pie. The recipe calls for eight sliced apples. You cut the apples into eighths. How many pieces of apple do you have?

Lesson 4-4

46. Stock Market The price of one technology stock rises $71\frac{5}{8}$ points in $7\frac{1}{2}$ hours. Find the number of points gained per hour during that time.

Lesson 4-5

47. Rainfall During the first week of January, a rain gauge collected $\frac{1}{2}$ inch of rain. By the end of January, the total rainfall was $2\frac{3}{5}$ inches. How much rain fell after the first week of January?

48. Reading A book has 8 chapters. You read $\frac{3}{8}$ of the book in a week. How much do you have left to read?

49. Pedro bikes $3\frac{1}{3}$ times as far as Pat, and Pat bikes $\frac{1}{5}$ as far as Jen. If Pedro rides 8 miles a day, how far does Jen ride?

CHAPTER 5 Extra Practice

Skills

Lesson 5-1 **Write each ratio in two other ways.**

1. $\frac{30}{60}$
2. 5 : 15
3. 13 to 52
4. 7 : 77
5. 18 to 72

Lesson 5-2 **Find each unit price. Round to the nearest cent. Then determine the better buy.**

6. cereal: 12 ounces for $2.99
   16 ounces for $3.59
7. rice: 8 ounces for $1.95
   15 ounces for $2.99

Lesson 5-3 **Copy and complete the equivalent ratio tables.**

8.

1	2	3	4
5	■	■	■

9.

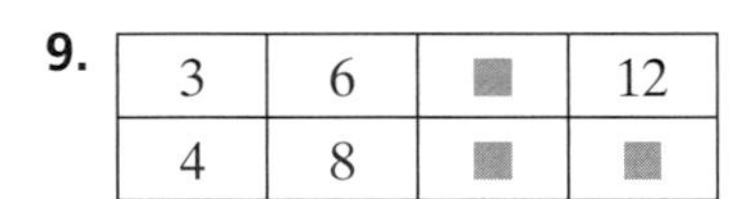

3	6	■	12
4	8	■	■

10.

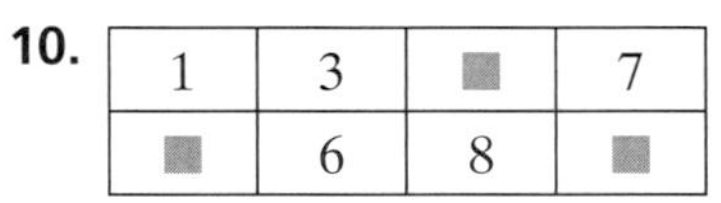

1	3	■	7
■	6	8	■

Lesson 5-4 **Convert each measurement.**

11. 36 inches to feet
12. 6 quarts to cups
13. 12 meters to centimeters
14. 500 milliliters to liters
15. 4 miles to yards
16. 5 grams to milligrams

Lesson 5-5 **Write each ratio as a percent.**

17. $\frac{1}{4}$
18. $\frac{3}{10}$
19. $\frac{8}{25}$
20. $\frac{41}{50}$
21. $\frac{2}{5}$

Lesson 5-6 **Write each percent as a decimal and as a fraction in simplest form.**

22. 42%
23. 96%
24. 80%
25. 1%
26. 87%
27. 88%

Lesson 5-7 **Find each answer.**

28. 20% of 80
29. 15% of 22.5
30. 50% of 86
31. 90% of 100

Lesson 5-8 **Solve each problem.**

32. 50 is 20% of what number?
33. 120 is 75% of what number?
34. 42 is 15% of what number?
35. 9 is 60% of what number?

Word Problems

Lessons 5-1 and 5-2

36. Eight out of 21 students at a school do not like horror movies. Write the ratio, in three different ways, of students who like horror movies to students who dislike horror movies.

37. You baby-sit for four hours and earn $22.00. How much money do you make each hour?

Lesson 5-3

38. For every 5 hot dogs sold at a carnival, 8 hamburgers were sold. If 78 hot dogs and hamburgers were sold in all, how many hamburgers were sold?

Lesson 5-4

39. Linda can run 1 mile in 9 minutes. How many miles can she run in 1 hour?

Lesson 5-5

40. Thirty-two out of 50 sixth-graders said they have flown on an airplane. What percent of the sixth-graders have *not* flown?

Lesson 5-6

41. You answer 39 out of 50 questions on a test correctly. Write your score as a fraction and as a decimal.

Lesson 5-7

42. **Basketball** Hector made 80% of his free throws. He attempted 200 free throws. How many free throws did Hector make?

Lesson 5-8

43. You buy a camera for $72 after a 20% discount. What was the original price of the camera?

CHAPTER 6 Extra Practice

Skills

Lesson 6-1 **Use an integer to represent each situation.**

1. 1,000 ft above　**2.** in debt \$125　**3.** 17° below 0°C　**4.** gaining 11 lb

Lesson 6-2 **Order from least to greatest.**

5. $3, -1, 0, -2$　**6.** $4, -8, -5, 2$　**7.** $-6, 8, 7, -8$　**8.** $-1, -8, 0, 1$

Lesson 6-3 **Show that each number is a rational number by writing it as the quotient of two integers.**

9. 12　**10.** $-\frac{1}{2}$　**11.** 3.56　**12.** -9.1

Plot each rational number on a vertical number line.

13. -3.5　**14.** $\frac{3}{4}$　**15.** 0.3　**16.** -1

Lesson 6-4 **Compare the numbers. Write < or >.**

17. -0.1 ■ -1.9　**18.** -0.4 ■ $-\frac{1}{2}$　**19.** -0.7 ■ $-\frac{2}{5}$

Order the numbers from least to greatest.

20. $0.3, -1.4, -2$　**21.** $-0.5, -1\frac{2}{3}, -3.6$　**22.** $-1.74, -\frac{7}{8}, -\frac{2}{3}$

Lesson 6-5 **Write an inequality for each graph.**

23.
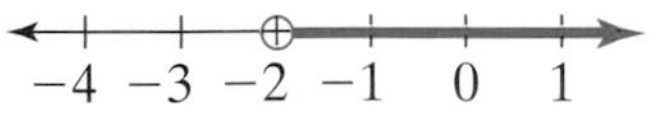

24.
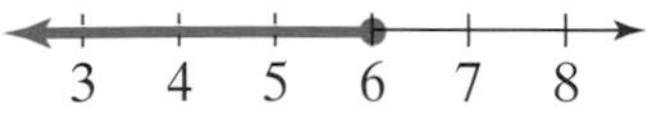

25.
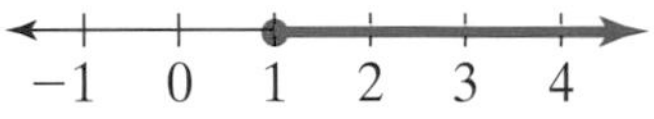

Write an inequality to represent each situation. Then graph the inequality.

26. The temperature stayed below 0°.

27. You must bring at least \$5 to cover the cost of lunch.

28. The paintings for display can be a maximum of 12 inches wide.

Lesson 6-6 **Solve each inequality.**

29. $m + 8 < 14$　**30.** $n - 16 \geq 3$　**31.** $p + 9 \leq -5$　**32.** $q - 8 > 7$

Word Problems

Lesson 6-1

33. Thoma dives to 6 feet below sea level. Sandy dives to 15 feet below sea level. Use absolute value to find who dives farther below sea level.

34. On a thermometer, the air temperature reads $-10°F$. It rises $2°F$. What is the final air temperature?

Lesson 6-2

35. The temperature on Monday was $-5°C$. The temperature on Wednesday was $-9°C$. Which temperature was greater?

36. Use the table on the right. The average high temperatures in December for four cities in Alaska are listed in the table. Order the temperatures from least to greatest.

Average High Temperatures in December

City	Temperature
Seward	1°C
Haines	−4°C
Bethel	−8°C
Anchorage	−5°C

Lesson 6-3

37. The weight of a bag of tomatoes is $6\frac{1}{3}$ lb. Explain how you know that $6\frac{1}{3}$ is a rational number.

38. Aaron owes his dad \$3.50. This debt is represented by -3.5. Draw a number line that includes positive and negative numbers and 0. Plot the decimal on the number line.

Lesson 6-4

39. The town measures the water level in the reservoir and considers the average depth of the reservoir to be 0 ft. After Week 1, the water level was -3.2 ft. In Week 2, the water level was measured again and was at $-3\frac{3}{4}$ ft. Compare the numbers. In which week was the water level lower?

Lesson 6-5

Use the table on the right.

40. Careers Officers in local law enforcement must meet certain requirements at the time of hire. Write and graph an inequality showing the usual age requirement for local law enforcement officers.

41. The requirements for federal law enforcement officers are different from those for local law enforcement officers. Write and graph an inequality showing the maximum age for federal law enforcement officers.

Law Enforcement Hiring Requirements

Level	Federal	Local
U.S. Citizen	Yes	Yes
Age (years)		
Minimum	21	20
Maximum	36	None

SOURCE: *Occupational Outlook Handbook*

Lesson 6-6

42. Angelica sells magazines. She earns \$30 a day plus \$2 for each magazine subscription sold. Angelica would like to earn a minimum of \$65 each day. How many magazine subscriptions must she sell per day to earn the minimum?

CHAPTER 7

Extra Practice

Skills

Lesson 7-1 **Use the coordinate grid at the right for Exercises 1–12. Find the coordinates of each point.**

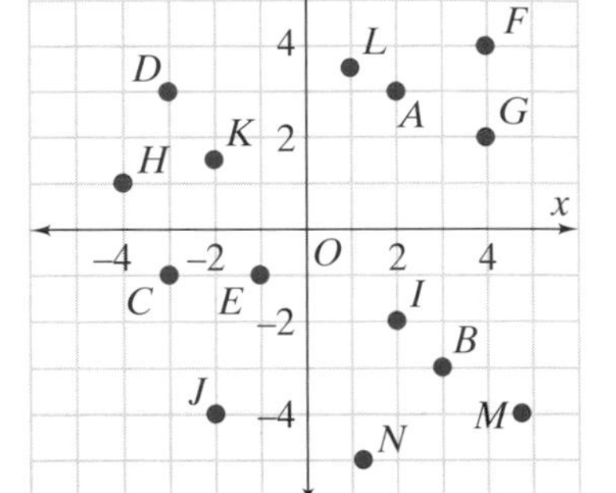

1. A **2.** B **3.** C **4.** D

Name the point with the given coordinates.

5. $(4.75, -4)$ **6.** $(-2, 1.5)$ **7.** $\left(1\frac{1}{4}, -5\right)$ **8.** $\left(1, 3\frac{1}{2}\right)$

9. $(4, 2)$ **10.** $(2, -2)$ **11.** $(-4, 1)$ **12.** $(-2, -4)$

Lesson 7-2 **Find the distance between the two points.**

13. $A(-2, -7)$ and $B(-10, -7)$ **14.** $C(1, -5)$ and $D(1, 9)$ **15.** $E(3, -8)$ and $F(20, -8)$

Lesson 7-3 **Complete each function table.**

16. Output = Input ÷ (−5)

Input	Output
–10	
0	
20	
50	

17. Output = Input + (−2)

Input	Output
–5	
–1	
3	
9	

Lesson 7-4 **Make a table and graph some points for each function. Use −2, −1, 0, 1, and 2 for x.**

18. $y = x + 5$ **19.** $y = x - 5$ **20.** $y = \frac{x}{5}$

Lesson 7-5 **Write an equation showing the relationship between the two variables. Then solve the problem.**

21. A company loses $3 per day. How much do they lose in 4 days?

22. Carrie works 4 fewer hours a week than Jane. How many hours does Carrie work if Jane works 23 hours?

Word Problems

Lesson 7-1

23. An ambulance begins at $(-2, -9)$ where the hospital is located. When it gets a call, it travels 12 blocks north and 3 blocks west to the house. In what quadrant is the house?

24. Your cousin is at $(-5, -2)$. He walks 3 blocks west and 1 block south to the park. Find the coordinates of the park.

Lesson 7-2

25. On a floor plan, Ms. Willis uses a rectangle that has coordinates $(1, 8)$, $(1, 4)$, $(-5, 4)$, and $(-5, 8)$ to represent the location of the computer lab in her room. What is the perimeter of the computer lab? Each unit of length represents one yard.

Lesson 7-3

26. Franco records how many pages he has read in his book after different lengths of time. Write an equation for how many pages he has read.

Number of Hours	Pages Read
2	90
3	135
5	225
8	360

Lesson 7-4

27. Sales A uniform company sells name patches for uniforms. The company charges \$2 per patch plus a handling fee of \$5 for each order. The function $p = 2n + 5$ shows how price p relates to the number of patches n. Make a table and graph the function.

Lesson 7-5

28. Biking Katie rides her bike at 13 miles per hour. Write a function equation showing the relationship between hours and distance. How far does Katie ride her bike in 4 hours?

CHAPTER 8 Extra Practice

Skills

Lessons 8-1 and 8-2 **Find the area of each figure.**

1\.

5.5 ft

9.5 ft

2\. 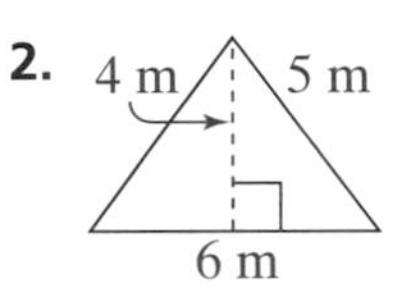

3\. 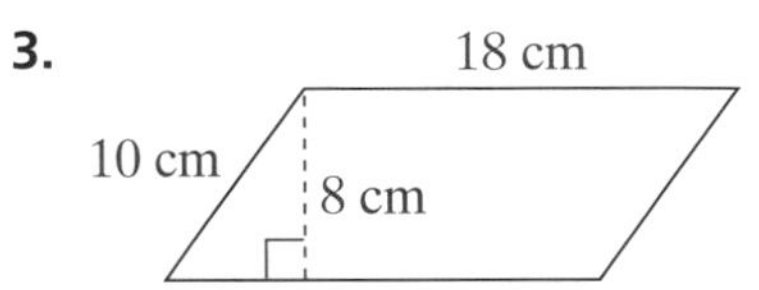

4\. 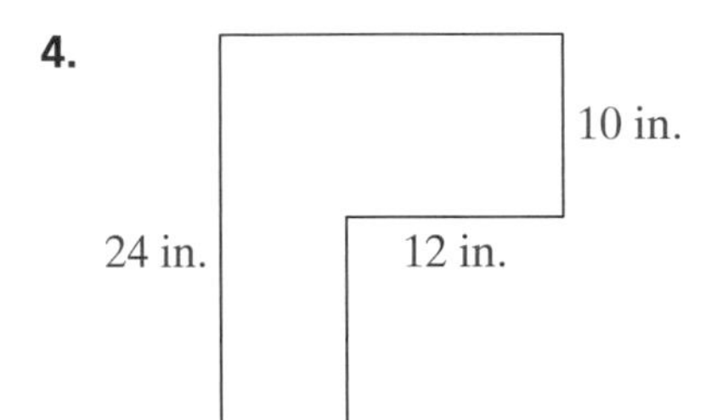

5\. 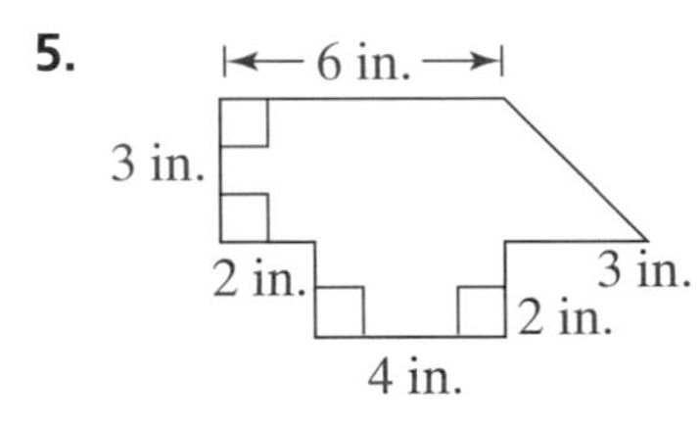

6\. 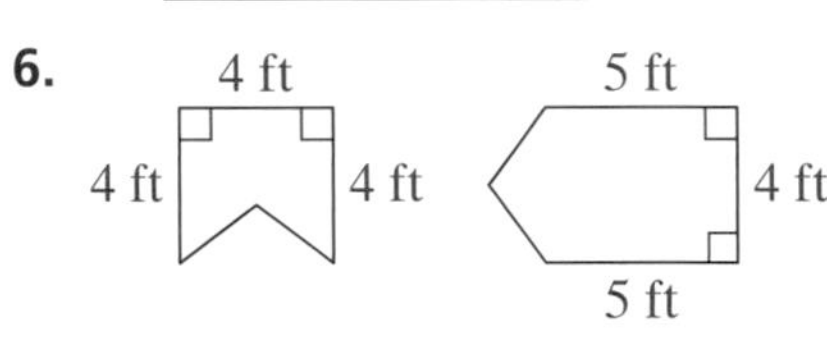

Lesson 8-3 **Name each figure.**

7\. 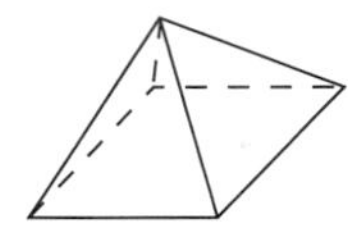

8\. 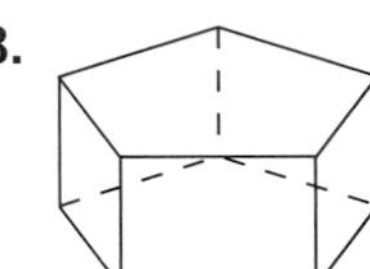

9\. 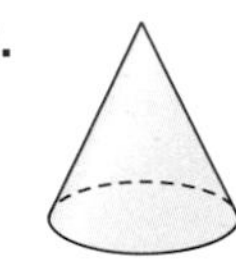

Lesson 8-4 **Find the surface area of each rectangular prism with the given dimensions.**

10\. $\ell = 10$ ft, $w = 5$ ft, $h = 8$ ft

11\. $\ell = 12$ m, $w = 16$ m, $h = 12$ m

Find the surface area of each figure.

12\. 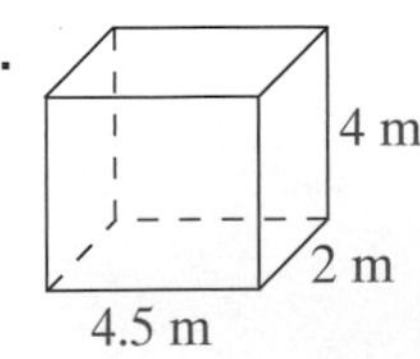

13\. 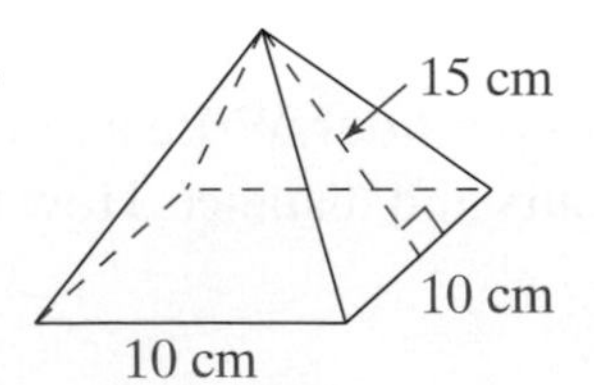

14\. 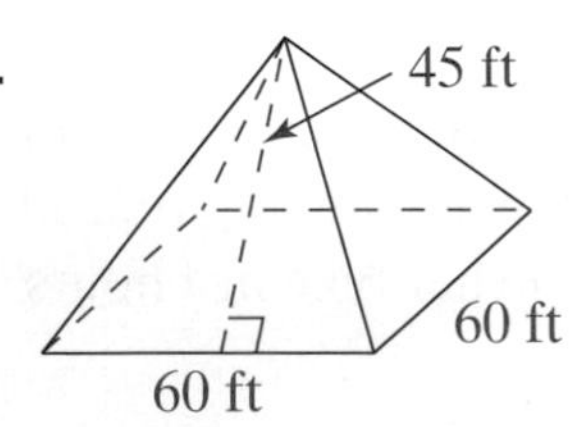

Lesson 8-5 **Find the volume of each figure.**

15\. 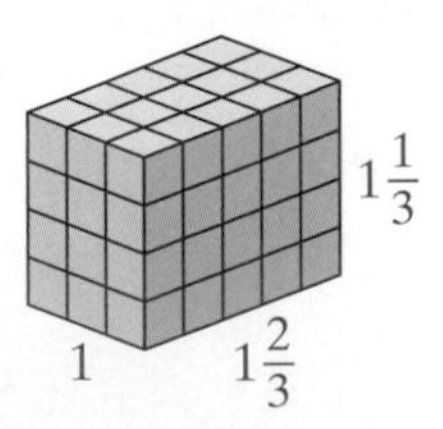

16\. 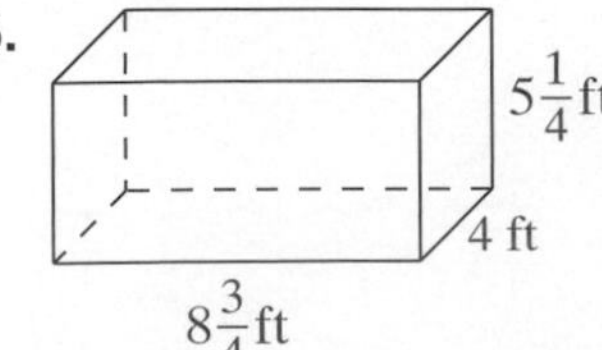

17\. 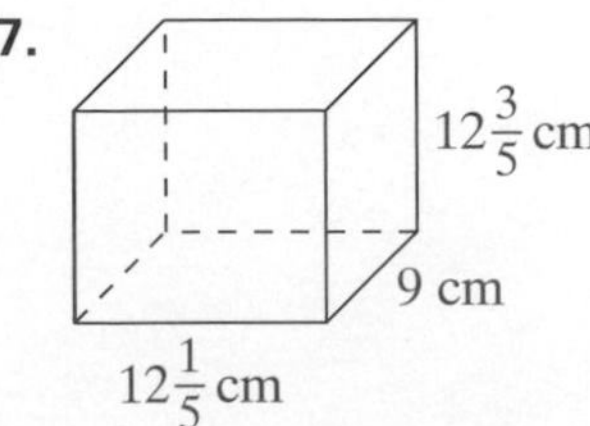

Word Problems

Lesson 8-1

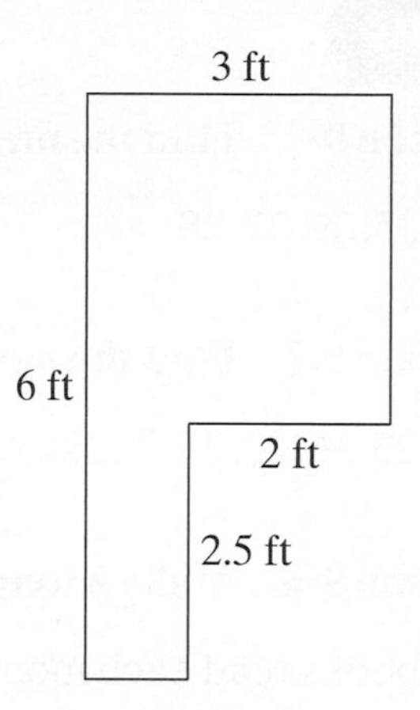

18. **Construction** Find the area of the sheet of plywood in the drawing at the right.

19. A parallelogram has an area of 96 square inches and a base length of 12 inches. What is the height of the parallelogram?

Lesson 8-2

20. An architect is building a stained-glass window and corner tiles into a rectangular wall opening. The opening is 3 feet wide by 5 feet high. The two tiles that fit in the corners are in the shape of right triangles, and each have a base of 1 foot and a height of 2 foot. What is the area of the stained-glass window?

Lesson 8-3

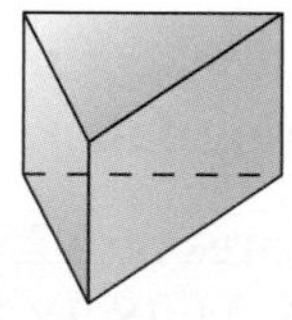

21. Name the figure at the right. Then find the number of faces, vertices, and edges.

22. Lisa plans to cover a pentagonal pyramid with fabric. How many faces will she have to cover?

Lesson 8-4

23. Suppose each dimension of a rectangular prism is tripled. How much larger is the surface area of the prism?

24. While he was on a trip, Luis bought a gift for his brother. The gift has the shape of a square pyramid. Its base has an edge length of 5 inches and the height is 8 inches. Find the surface area of the gift.

Lesson 8-5

25. A packing crate has a length of $8\frac{1}{3}$ feet, a width of 6 feet, and a height of $4\frac{2}{3}$ feet. What is the volume of the packing crate?

26. A storage unit has a floor area of $15\frac{3}{4}$ square meters. The height of the unit from floor to ceiling is $6\frac{1}{2}$ meters. Which formula should you use, $V = Bh$ or $V = lwh$? Find the volume of the storage unit.

CHAPTER 9

Extra Practice

Skills

Lesson 9-1 Find the mean of each data set.

1. 35, 39, 27, 28
2. 253, 277, 249, 279, 265
3. 7.5, 3.8, 12.4, 11.7, 12.4

Lesson 9-2 Find the median and mode of each data set.

4. 23, 26, 22, 25, 22, 28, 22, 10
5. 14.2, 11.3, 12.0, 11.1, 13.0, 13.3
6. 36, 42, 58, 29, 45, 63, 57, 29

Lesson 9-3 Make a frequency table and a dot plot for each set of data.

7. books read each month:
   3, 1, 4, 2, 4, 1, 3, 2, 4, 4, 2, 1
8. words typed per minute:
   65, 35, 40, 65, 40, 40, 55, 35, 35, 70, 35, 55

Lesson 9-4 Make a box-and whisker plot for the set of data below.

9. test scores (percents): 86, 76, 72, 85, 69, 85, 78, 91, 77

Lesson 9-5 Construct a histogram with at least three intervals for the following data.

10. scores on a 25-item test: 23, 15, 20, 17, 21, 24,12, 15, 25, 25, 25, 25, 11, 23, 22, 16, 24, 18, 18, 21
11. ages of students in a night school class: 23, 25, 38, 23, 53, 46, 51, 29, 22, 35, 41, 38

Lesson 9-6 Find the mean absolute deviation (MAD) and the interquartile range (IQR) for each data set.

12. Data Set A: 5, 10, 12, 2, 1, 8, 10, 12, 12, 18
13. Data Set B: 10, 4, 5, 9, 8, 9, 8, 3

Lesson 9-7 Use Data Sets A and B above.

14. Which set shows gaps? Explain.
15. Which set has less overall spread? Explain the relationship between the measures of variability and the shape of that data.

Lesson 9-8

16. In a survey, which is NOT a statistical question? Explain.
    a. How many hours did you spend on homework yesterday?
    b. How tall is the Empire State Building?

Word Problems

Lessons 9-1 and 9-2

17. Biology The weights, in pounds, of 5 adult coyotes are 36, 25, 28, 39, and 30. What is the mean weight of the adult coyotes?

18. Weather The daily high temperatures (°F) for one week are 86°, 78°, 92°, 79°, 87°, 77°, and 91°. Find the median and the mode of the high temperatures.

Lesson 9-3

19. The frequency table at the right shows the number of correct answers each student wrote on a 24-question quiz. What is the range of the number of correct answers?

Number	Tally	Frequency
15	|	1
17	|	1
18	|	1
19	||	2
20	||||	4
21	||	2
22	||	2
24	|	1

Lesson 9-4

20. Make a box-and-whiskers plot for the number of calories eaten in the three meals listed in the table. List the five key values.

Day	Breakfast	Lunch	Dinner
Monday	550	730	920
Tuesday	420	660	750
Wednesday	250	880	1200

Lesson 9-5

21. Animals Elaine wants to make a histogram for the data in the table at the right showing the speeds of animals. She chooses intervals of 20-30, 31-39, and 40-45. Is that a good choice? If not, explain and give the intervals you would use.

Animal Speeds

Animal	Miles per hour
Coyote	43
Hyena	40
Rabbit	35
Giraffe	32
Grizzly bear	30
Elephant	25

SOURCE: *World Almanac*

Lesson 9-6 through 9-8

22. Find the interquartile range for the MPG (miles per gallon) listed below for various new cars. Then explain the effect on the IQR it would have if every car had an increase of 5 MPG.

28 32 42 37 30 25 57 38 33 44 38 34
30 44 31 28 39 29 32 29 31 29 24 32

23. Does the graph of languages spoken show symmetry? Explain.

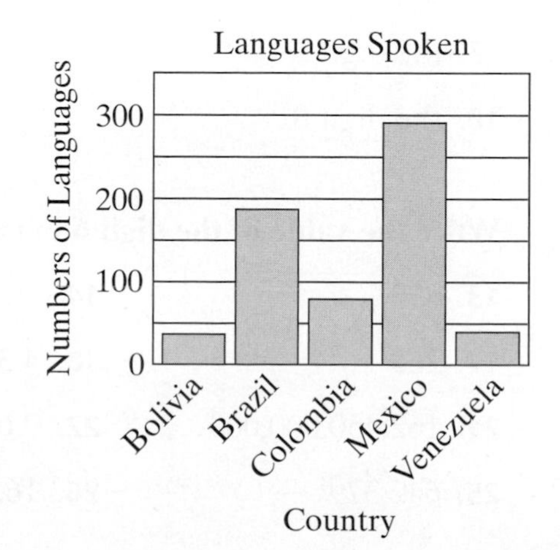

24. Marti asked "Would you rather live in a crowded, noisy city or in the country?" Is her question biased? If so, explain why and rewrite the question to be unbiased.

Place Value of Whole Numbers

The digits in a whole number are grouped into periods. A period has three digits, and each period has a name. Each digit in a whole number has both a place and a value.

Billions Period			Millions Period			Thousands Period			Ones Period		
Hundred billions	Ten billions	Billions	Hundred millions	Ten millions	Millions	Hundred thousands	Ten thousands	Thousands	Hundreds	Tens	Ones
9	5	1,	6	3	7,	0	4	1,	1	8	2

The digit 5 is in the ten billions place. So its value is 5 ten billions, or 50 billion.

EXAMPLE

a. In what place is the digit 7?

millions

b. What is the value of the digit 7?

7 million

Exercises

Use the chart above. Write the place of each digit.

1. the digit 3
2. the digit 4
3. the digit 6
4. the digit 8
5. the digit 9
6. the digit 0

Use the chart above. Write the value of each digit.

7. the digit 3
8. the digit 4
9. the digit 6
10. the digit 8
11. the digit 9
12. the digit 0

Write the value of the digit 6 in each number.

13. 633
14. 761,523
15. 163,500,000
16. 165,417
17. 265
18. 4,396
19. 618,920
20. 204,602
21. 162,450,000,000
22. 7,682
23. 358,026,113
24. 76,030,100
25. 642,379
26. 16,403
27. 45,060
28. 401,601,001

Rounding Whole Numbers

Number lines can help you round numbers. On a number line, 5 is halfway between 0 and 10, 50 is halfway between 0 and 100, and 500 is halfway between 1 and 1,000. The accepted method of rounding is to round 5 up to 10, 50 up to 100, and 500 up to 1,000.

EXAMPLE

1 Round 2,462 to the nearest ten.

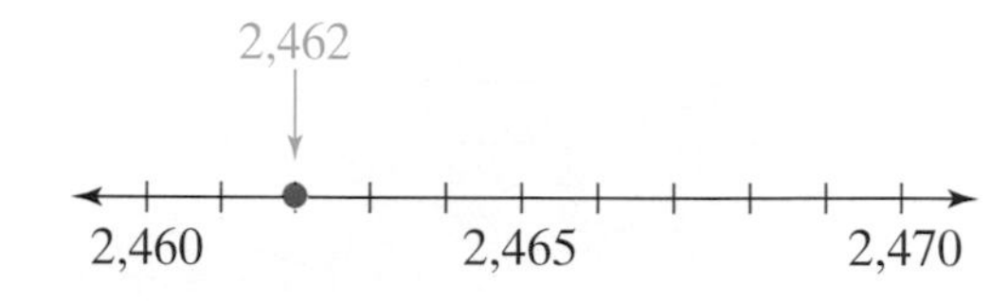

2,462 is closer to 2,460 than to 2,470.

2,462 rounded to the nearest ten is 2,460.

EXAMPLE

2 Round 247,451 to the nearest hundred.

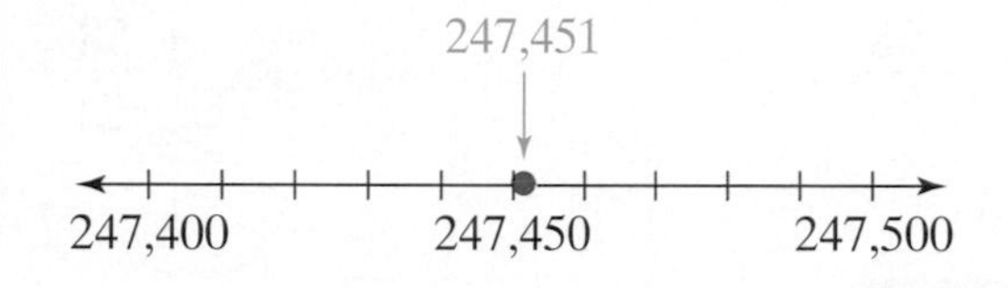

247,451 is closer to 247,500 than to 247,400.

247,451 rounded to the nearest hundred is 247,500.

Exercises

Round each number to the nearest ten.

1. 65 **2.** 832 **3.** 4,437 **4.** 21,024 **5.** 3,545

Round each number to the nearest hundred.

6. 889 **7.** 344 **8.** 2,861 **9.** 1,138 **10.** 50,549

11. 6,411 **12.** 88,894 **13.** 13,735 **14.** 17,459 **15.** 6,059

Round each number to the nearest thousand.

16. 2,400 **17.** 16,218 **18.** 7,430 **19.** 89,375 **20.** 9,821

21. 15,631 **22.** 76,900 **23.** 163,875 **24.** 38,295 **25.** 102,359

26. Describe a situation in which it is helpful to round data.

27. Explain how to round number 17 in the exercises above to the nearest ten thousand.

28. Suppose you round 31 to the nearest hundred. Is 0 the correct response? Explain your answer.

Adding Whole Numbers

When you add, line up the digits in the correct columns. Begin by adding the ones. You may need to regroup from one column to the next.

EXAMPLE

1 Add 463 + 58.

Step 1	**Step 2**	**Step 3**
1	11	11
463	463	463
+ 58	+ 58	+ 58
1	21	521

EXAMPLE

2 Find each sum.

a. 962 + 120	**b.** 25 + 9 + 143	**c.** 3,887 + 1,201
	1	1
962	25	3,887
+ 120	9	+ 1,201
1,082	+ 143	5,088
	177	

Exercises

Find each sum.

1. 45 + 31	**2.** 56 + 80	**3.** 25 + 16	**4.** 43 + 29	**5.** 66 + 78	**6.** 87 + 35
7. 81 + 312	**8.** 406 + 123	**9.** 207 + 72	**10.** 480 + 365	**11.** 217 + 347	**12.** 675 + 329
13. 2,051 + 843	**14.** 786 + 4,109	**15.** 5,227 + 1,527	**16.** 3,104 + 2,698	**17.** 5,337 + 1,812	**18.** 4,282 + 7,518

19. 78 + 56 **20.** 35 + 96 **21.** 105 + 71 **22.** 29 + 342 **23.** 654 + 103

24. 286 + 42 **25.** 55 + 77 **26.** 242 + 83 **27.** 32 + 68 **28.** 108 + 13

29. 589 + 318 **30.** 642 + 975 **31.** 2,308 + 451 **32.** 976 + 4,035

33. 8,228 + 1,024 **34.** 5,417 + 2,391 **35.** 6,470 + 9,828 **36.** 7,121 + 5,359

Subtracting Whole Numbers

When you subtract, line up the digits in the correct columns. Begin by subtracting the ones. Rename if the bottom digit is greater than the top digit. You may need to rename more than once.

EXAMPLE

1 **Subtract 725 − 86.**

Step 1	**Step 2**	**Step 3**
115	11	11
725	6115	6115
− 86	725	725
9	− 86	− 86
	39	639

EXAMPLE

2 **Find each difference.**

a. 602 − 174	**b.** 625 − 273	**c.** 5,002 − 1,247
9	512	9 9
51012	625	4101012
602	− 273	5,002
− 174	352	− 1,247
428		3,755

Exercises

Find each difference.

1. 81 − 37 **2.** 59 − 23 **3.** 41 − 19 **4.** 83 − 25 **5.** 99 − 78 **6.** 87 − 31

7. 707 − 361 **8.** 680 − 47 **9.** 240 − 63 **10.** 881 − 391 **11.** 517 − 287 **12.** 973 − 529

13. 7,411 − 583 **14.** 3,789 − 809 **15.** 6,508 − 2,147 **16.** 8,000 − 5,274 **17.** 3,003 − 1,998 **18.** 8,282 − 4,118

19. 78 − 19 **20.** 231 − 99 **21.** 901 − 65 **22.** 629 − 382 **23.** 918 − 133

24. 800 − 435 **25.** 403 − 122 **26.** 973 − 228 **27.** 721 − 119 **28.** 522 − 146

29. 642 − 223 **30.** 427 − 193 **31.** 444 − 345 **32.** 988 − 489 **33.** 601 − 425

Multiplying Whole Numbers

When you multiply by a one-digit number, multiply the one-digit number by each digit in the other number.

EXAMPLE

1 Multiply 294 × 7.

Step 1 Multiply 7 by the ones digit.

$$\begin{array}{r} {\scriptstyle 2} \\ 294 \\ \times\ 7 \\ \hline 8 \end{array}$$

Step 2 Multiply 7 by the tens digit.

$$\begin{array}{r} {\scriptstyle 62} \\ 294 \\ \times\ 7 \\ \hline 58 \end{array}$$

Step 3 Multiply 7 by the hundreds digit.

$$\begin{array}{r} {\scriptstyle 62} \\ 294 \\ \times\ \ 7 \\ \hline 2{,}058 \end{array}$$

When you multiply by a two-digit number, first multiply by the ones. Then multiply by the tens. Add the products. Remember, 0 times any number is equal to 0.

EXAMPLE

2 Multiply 48 × 327.

Step 1 Multiply the ones.

$$\begin{array}{r} {\scriptstyle 25} \\ 327 \\ \times\ 48 \\ \hline 2{,}616 \end{array}$$

Step 2 Multiply the tens.

$$\begin{array}{r} {\scriptstyle 12} \\ 327 \\ \times\ 48 \\ \hline 2616 \\ +\ 1308 \\ \hline \end{array}$$

Step 3 Add the products.

$$\begin{array}{r} 327 \\ \times\ 48 \\ \hline 2616 \\ +\ 1308\ \\ \hline 15696 \end{array}$$

Exercises

Find each product.

1. $\begin{array}{r} 81 \\ \times\ 3 \\ \hline \end{array}$ **2.** $\begin{array}{r} 47 \\ \times\ 2 \\ \hline \end{array}$ **3.** $\begin{array}{r} 58 \\ \times\ 6 \\ \hline \end{array}$ **4.** $\begin{array}{r} 678 \\ \times\ 5 \\ \hline \end{array}$ **5.** $\begin{array}{r} 412 \\ \times\ 7 \\ \hline \end{array}$ **6.** $\begin{array}{r} 326 \\ \times\ 4 \\ \hline \end{array}$

7. 7 × 45 **8.** 62 × 3 **9.** 213 × 4 **10.** 8 × 177 **11.** 673 × 9

12. $\begin{array}{r} 25 \\ \times\ 46 \\ \hline \end{array}$ **13.** $\begin{array}{r} 62 \\ \times\ 88 \\ \hline \end{array}$ **14.** $\begin{array}{r} 808 \\ \times\ 60 \\ \hline \end{array}$ **15.** $\begin{array}{r} 409 \\ \times\ 70 \\ \hline \end{array}$ **16.** $\begin{array}{r} 915 \\ \times\ 27 \\ \hline \end{array}$ **17.** $\begin{array}{r} 312 \\ \times\ 53 \\ \hline \end{array}$

18. 415 × 76 **19.** 500 × 80 **20.** 320 × 47 **21.** 562 × 18 **22.** 946 × 37

23. 76 × 103 **24.** 32 × 558 **25.** 371 × 84 **26.** 505 × 40 **27.** 620 × 19

Multiplying and Dividing Whole Numbers by 10, 100, and 1,000

Basic facts and patterns can help you when multiplying and dividing whole numbers by 10, 100, and 1,000.

$8 \times 1 = 8$
$8 \times 10 = 80$
$8 \times 100 = 800$
$8 \times 1{,}000 = 8{,}000$

Count the number of ending zeros.

The product will have this many zeros.

$5{,}000 \div 1 = 5{,}000$
$5{,}000 \div 10 = 500$
$5{,}000 \div 100 = 50$
$5{,}000 \div 1{,}000 = 5$

Count the zeros in the divisor.

If possible, remove this many zeros from the dividend. This number will be the quotient.

EXAMPLE

Multiply or divide.

a. $77 \times 1{,}000$

77,000 ← **Insert three zeros.**

b. $430 \div 10$

43 ← **Remove one zero.**

Exercises

Multiply.

1. 85×10 **2.** 85×100 **3.** $85 \times 1{,}000$ **4.** $420 \times 1{,}000$ **5.** 420×100

6. 420×10 **7.** 603×100 **8.** 97×10 **9.** 31×100 **10.** 10×17

11. 100×56 **12.** $1{,}000 \times 4$ **13.** 13×10 **14.** 68×100 **15.** $19 \times 1{,}000$

Divide.

16. $3{,}200 \div 10$ **17.** $3{,}200 \div 100$ **18.** $32{,}000 \div 1{,}000$ **19.** $8{,}000 \div 100$ **20.** $8{,}000 \div 10$

21. $170 \div 10$ **22.** $45{,}000 \div 1{,}000$ **23.** $9{,}300 \div 10$ **24.** $90 \div 10$ **25.** $6{,}100 \div 100$

26. $7{,}900 \div 100$ **27.** $2{,}400 \div 10$ **28.** $240 \div 10$ **29.** $78{,}000 \div 1{,}000$ **30.** $9{,}900 \div 10$

Multiply or divide.

31. 76×100 **32.** $52 \times 1{,}000$ **33.** $370 \div 10$ **34.** 505×10 **35.** $6{,}200 \div 100$

36. $340 \div 10$ **37.** $14{,}000 \div 1{,}000$ **38.** 253×100 **39.** $3{,}700 \div 10$ **40.** 418×10

Dividing Whole Numbers

Division is the opposite of multiplication. So you multiply the divisor by your estimate for each digit in the quotient. Then subtract. You repeat this step until you have a remainder that is less than the divisor.

EXAMPLE

Divide $23\overline{)1{,}178}$.

Step 1 Estimate the quotient.

$1{,}178 \div 23$ ← **The dividend is 1,178. The divisor is 23.**

$\downarrow \quad \downarrow$

$1{,}200 \div 20 = 60$ ← **Round 1,178 to the nearest hundred. Round 23 to the nearest ten.**

Step 2

$$\begin{array}{r} 6 \\ 23\overline{)1178} \\ -138 \\ \hline \end{array}$$

← **Try 6 tens.**

← **6 × 23 = 138 You cannot subtract, so 6 tens is too much.**

Step 3

$$\begin{array}{r} 5 \\ 23\overline{)1178} \\ -115 \\ \hline 2 \end{array}$$

← **Try 5 tens.**

← **5 × 23 = 115**

← **Subtract.**

Step 4

$$\begin{array}{r} 51 \text{ R5} \\ 23\overline{)1178} \\ -115\downarrow \\ \hline 28 \\ -23 \\ \hline 5 \end{array}$$

← **Bring down 8.**

← **1 × 23 = 23**

← **Subtract. The remainder is 5.**

Step 5 Check your answer.

First compare your answer to the estimate. Since 51 R5 is close to 60, the answer is reasonable.

Then find $51 \times 23 + 5$.

Exercises

Find each quotient. Check your answer.

1. $9\overline{)659}$	**2.** $9\overline{)376}$	**3.** $3\overline{)280}$	**4.** $8\overline{)541}$	**5.** $8\overline{)232}$
6. $1{,}058 \div 5$	**7.** $3{,}591 \div 3$	**8.** $5{,}072 \div 7$	**9.** $1{,}718 \div 4$	**10.** $3{,}767 \div 6$
11. $3{,}872 \div 17$	**12.** $19\overline{)1{,}373}$	**13.** $27\overline{)1{,}853}$	**14.** $4{,}195 \div 59$	**15.** $41\overline{)4{,}038}$
16. $2{,}612 \div 31$	**17.** $34\overline{)1{,}609}$	**18.** $1{,}937 \div 40$	**19.** $54\overline{)1{,}350}$	**20.** $1{,}824 \div 32$

21. **Writing in Math** Describe how to estimate a quotient. Use the words *dividend* and *divisor* in your description.

Zeros in Quotients

When you divide, after you bring down a digit you must write a digit in the quotient. In this example, the second digit in the quotient is 0.

EXAMPLE

Find $19\overline{)5{,}823}$.

Step 1

Estimate the quotient.

$$\begin{array}{ccccc} 5{,}823 & \div & 19 & & \\ \downarrow & & \downarrow & & \\ 5{,}800 & \div & 20 & = & 290 \end{array}$$

Step 2

$$\begin{array}{r} 3 \\ 19\overline{)5{,}823} \\ -5\,7 \\ \hline 1 \end{array}$$

Step 3

$$\begin{array}{r} 30 \\ 19\overline{)5{,}823} \\ -5\,7 \\ \hline 12 \\ -\ 0 \\ \hline 12 \end{array}$$

Step 4

$$\begin{array}{r} 306 \text{ R9} \\ 19\overline{)5{,}823} \\ -5\,7 \\ \hline 12 \\ -\ 0 \\ \hline 123 \\ -114 \\ \hline 9 \end{array}$$

Step 5

Check your answer.
Since 306 is close to 290, the answer is reasonable.
Find $306 \times 19 + 9$.

Exercises

Find each quotient.

1. $7\overline{)212}$ **2.** $9\overline{)367}$ **3.** $3\overline{)271}$ **4.** $8\overline{)485}$ **5.** $6\overline{)483}$

6. $34\overline{)1{,}371}$ **7.** $19\overline{)1{,}335}$ **8.** $62\overline{)1{,}881}$ **9.** $54\overline{)1{,}094}$ **10.** $41\overline{)3{,}710}$

11. $282 \div 4$ **12.** $143 \div 7$ **13.** $181 \div 3$ **14.** $400 \div 8$ **15.** $365 \div 9$

16. $1{,}008 \div 5$ **17.** $3{,}018 \div 6$ **18.** $4{,}939 \div 7$ **19.** $1{,}682 \div 4$ **20.** $3{,}647 \div 6$

21. $2{,}488 \div 31$ **22.** $3{,}372 \div 67$ **23.** $1{,}937 \div 48$ **24.** $4{,}165 \div 59$ **25.** $1{,}686 \div 82$

Reading Thermometer Scales

The thermometer at the right shows temperature in degrees Celsius (°C) and degrees Fahrenheit (°F).

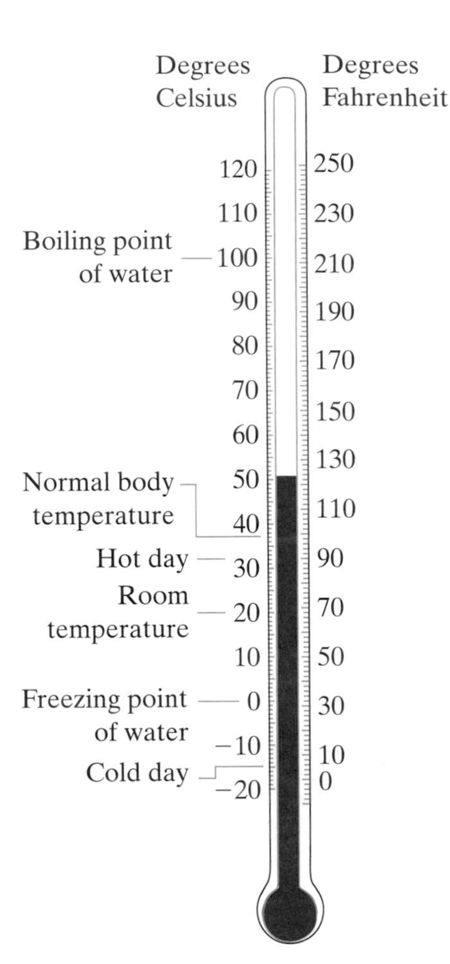

EXAMPLE

1 How do you read point A on the Celsius thermometer below?

Each 1-degree interval is divided into 10 smaller intervals of 0.1 degree each. The reading at point A is 36.2°C.

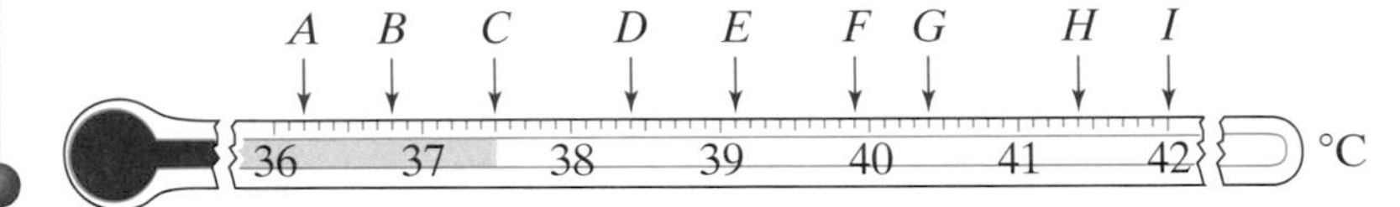

EXAMPLE

2 How do you read point V on the Fahrenheit thermometer below?

Each 1-degree interval is divided into 5 smaller intervals. Since $10 \div 5 = 2$, each smaller interval represents 0.2 degree. Count by 0.2, beginning with 98.0. The reading at point V is 98.6°F.

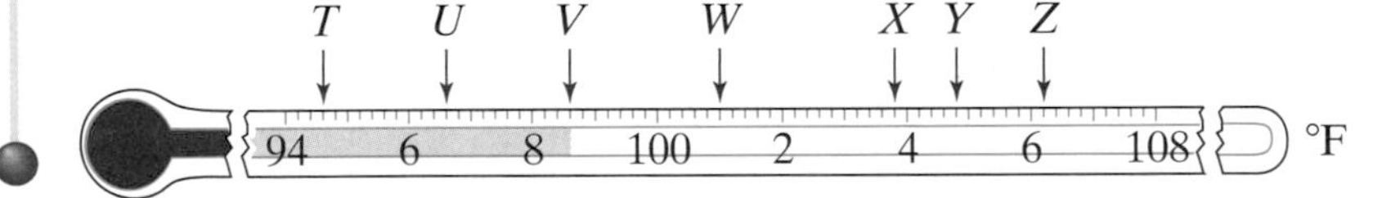

Exercises

Use the thermometers above to write the temperature reading for each point. Tell whether the reading is in degrees Celsius (°C) or degrees Fahrenheit (°F).

1. B **2.** C **3.** D **4.** T **5.** U **6.** Z

Use the thermometers above to name the point that relates to each temperature reading.

7. 40.4°C **8.** 42.0°C **9.** 39.9°C **10.** 104.8°F **11.** 101°F **12.** 103.8°F

Roman Numerals

The ancient Romans used letters to represent numerals. The table below shows the value of each Roman numeral.

I	V	X	L	C	D	M
1	5	10	50	100	500	1,000

Here are the Roman numerals from 1 to 10.

1	2	3	4	5	6	7	8	9	10
I	II	III	IV	V	VI	VII	VIII	IX	X

Roman numerals are read in groups from left to right.

If the value of the second numeral is the same as or less than the first numeral, add the values. The Roman numerals II, III, VI, VII, and VIII are examples in which you use addition.

If the value of the second numeral is greater than the first numeral, subtract the values. The Roman numerals IV and IX are examples in which you use subtraction.

EXAMPLE

Find the value of each Roman numeral.

a. CD

$500 - 100$

400

b. MXXVI

$1{,}000 + 10 + 10 + 5 + 1$

1,026

c. XCIV

$(100 - 10) + (5 - 1)$

$90 + 4 = 94$

Exercises

Find the value of each Roman numeral.

1. XI **2.** DIII **3.** XCV **4.** CMX **5.** XXIX

6. DLIX **7.** MLVI **8.** LX **9.** CDIV **10.** DCV

Write each number as a Roman numeral.

11. 15 **12.** 35 **13.** 1,632 **14.** 222 **15.** 159

16. 67 **17.** 92 **18.** 403 **19.** 1,990 **20.** 64

Estimating Lengths Using Nonstandard Units

Jan wanted to find a way to estimate lengths when she did not have any measuring tools. She measured her hand in several ways, the length of her foot, and the length of her walking stride. Then she used these "natural units" as measuring tools.

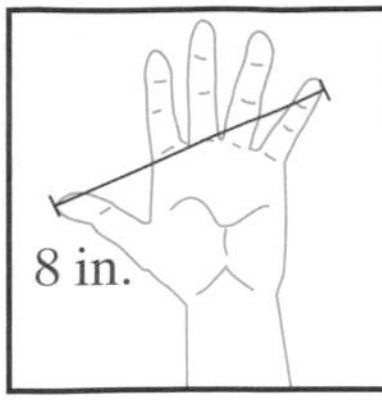

Span

$\frac{1}{2}$ in.
Finger width

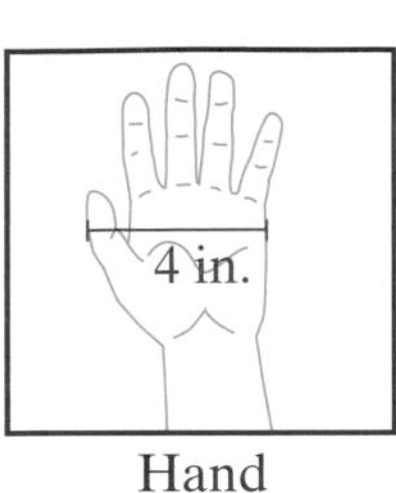

Hand

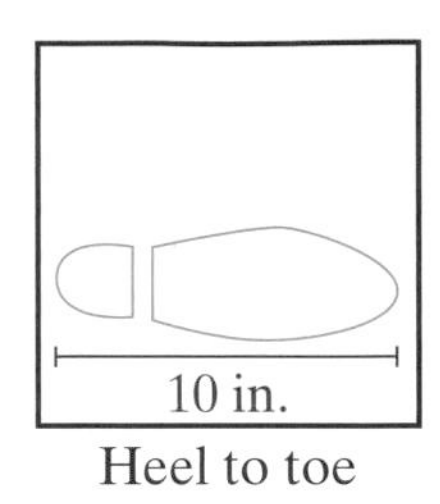

Heel to toe

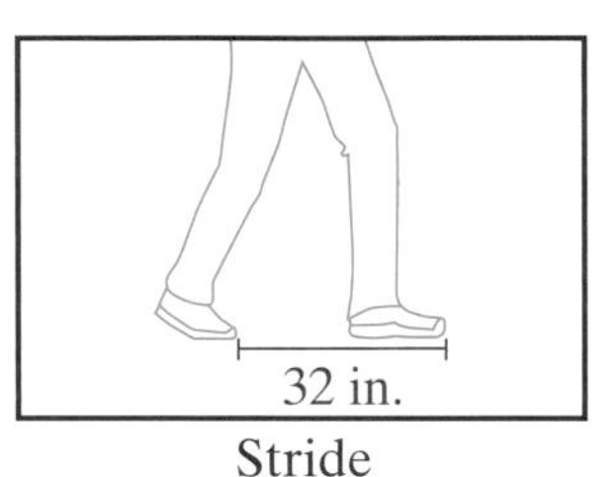

Stride

EXAMPLE

Jan used strides to measure the length of her room. She counted about 5 strides. What is the approximate length of the room?

$1 \text{ stride} \approx 32 \text{ in.}$	← **Write the relationship between strides and inches.**
$5 \times 1 \text{ stride} \approx 5 \times 32 \text{ in.}$	← **Multiply both sides by 5.**
$5 \text{ strides} \approx 160 \text{ in.}$	← **Change strides to inches.**
$160 \text{ in.} = (160 \div 12) \text{ ft}$	← **Change inches to feet.**
$160 \text{ in.} \approx 13 \text{ ft}$	

The approximate length of the room is 13 feet.

Exercises

Measure your "finger width," "hand," "span," and "heel to toe." Use these natural units to find the indicated measure for each object. Then give the approximate measure in inches, feet, or yards.

1. thickness of a math book
2. height of a chair
3. height of a door
4. length of an eraser
5. height of your desk
6. length of a new pencil
7. distance across a room
8. thickness of a door
9. length of a chalkboard
10. **Open-Ended** Measure your stride. Then measure something such as a hallway in strides, and approximate the length in feet or yards. Tell what distance you measured.

Writing Equivalent Times

The standard unit of time is the second (s). You use equivalent units to change from one unit of time to another.

Units of Time
1 minute (min) = 60 s
1 hour (h) = 60 min = 3,600 s
1 day (d) = 24 h = 1,440 min
1 week (wk) = 7 d = 168 h

EXAMPLE

How many seconds are equivalent to 1 minute 20 seconds?

1 minute 20 seconds = 60 s + 20 s ← **One minute is equivalent to 60 seconds.**

= 80 s ← **Simplify.**

So 1 minute 20 seconds is equivalent to 80 seconds.

Exercises

For each time, write an equivalent time using only the smaller unit.

1. 4 wk 3 days
2. 1 h 30 min
3. 2 min 59 s
4. 8 h 2 min
5. 5 min 36 s
6. 3 wk 5 days
7. 2 days 17 h
8. 2 h 15 min
9. 1 yr 2 wk
10. 12 min 4 s
11. 2 wk 1 day
12. 4 days 14 h
13. 3 yr 14 wk
14. 23 min 32 s
15. 3 h 47 min
16. 7 min 46 s
17. 5 wk 3 days
18. 1 yr 8 wk
19. 12 h 12 min
20. 3 days 4 h
21. 9 min 9 s
22. 5 yr 40 wk
23. 4 h 52 min
24. 7 wk 1 day

Estimating with Whole Numbers

Sometimes you do not need an exact answer to compute with whole numbers. To estimate sums and differences, round each number to the same place before you add or subtract.

To estimate products and quotients, you can use compatible numbers.

Compatible numbers are numbers that are easy to compute mentally.

$38 \div 6$
$\downarrow \quad \downarrow$
$36 \div 6$ ← **Since you can divide 36 by 6 mentally, 36 and 6 are compatible.**

6×78
$\downarrow \quad \downarrow$
5×80 ← **5 and 80 are compatible because 5 and 80 can be multiplied mentally.**

EXAMPLES

Estimate $298 \div 16$ using compatible numbers.

$298 \div 16$
$\downarrow \quad \downarrow$
$300 \div 16$ ← **Change 298 to 300 because 300 is easier to use mentally.**
$\downarrow \quad \downarrow$
$300 \div 15 = 20$ ← **Change 16 to 15 because 15 is compatible with 300.**

So $298 \div 16 \approx 20$.

Exercises

Estimate. Round each number first.

1. $47 + 228 + 23$
2. $653 - 295$
3. $34 + 68 + 93$
4. $59 + 26 - 23$
5. $6{,}963 - 3{,}098$
6. $8{,}043 + 5{,}983$
7. $42 + 86 + 51 + 38$
8. $257 - 109 - 46 - 21$

Estimate using compatible numbers.

9. $2 \times 3{,}978$
10. $102 \div 25$
11. $611 \div 58$
12. 997×5
13. $1{,}089 \div 521$
14. $4{,}978 \div 983$
15. 48×41
16. $207 \div 51$
17. $69 \div 7$

Table 1 Measures

Metric	Customary
Length	**Length**
10 millimeters (mm) = 1 centimeter (cm)	12 inches (in.) = 1 foot (ft)
100 cm = 1 meter (m)	36 in. = 1 yard (yd)
1,000 mm = 1 meter	3 ft = 1 yard
1,000 m = 1 kilometer (km)	5,280 ft = 1 mile (mi)
	1,760 yd = 1 mile
Area	**Area**
100 square millimeters (mm^2) = 1 square centimeter (cm^2)	144 square inches ($in.^2$) = 1 square foot (ft^2)
10,000 cm^2 = 1 square meter (m^2)	9 ft^2 = 1 square yard (yd^2)
	4,840 yd^2 = 1 acre
Volume	**Volume**
1,000 cubic millimeters (mm^3) = 1 cubic centimeter (cm^3)	1,728 cubic inches ($in.^3$) = 1 cubic foot (ft^3)
1,000,000 cm^3 = 1 cubic meter (m^3)	27 ft^3 = 1 cubic yard (yd^3)
Mass	**Mass**
1,000 milligrams (mg) = 1 gram (g)	16 ounces (oz) = 1 pound (lb)
1,000 g = 1 kilogram (kg)	2,000 lb = 1 ton (t)
Liquid Capacity	**Liquid Capacity**
1,000 milliliters (mL) = 1 liter (L)	8 fluid ounces (fl oz) = 1 cup (c)
1,000 L = 1 kiloliter (kL)	2 c = 1 pint (pt)
	2 pt = 1 quart (qt)
	4 qt = 1 gallon (gal)

Time
60 seconds (s) = 1 minute (min)
60 min = 1 hour (h)
24 h = 1 day
7 days = 1 week (wk)
365 days ≈ 52 wk ≈ 1 year (yr)

Table 2 Reading Math Symbols

Symbol	Meaning	Page
$+$	plus (addition)	p. 2
$-$	minus (subtraction)	p. 2
$\times, \cdot$	times (multiplication)	p. 2
$\div, \overline{)}$	divide (division)	p. 2
$=$	is equal to	p. 5
$>$	is greater than	p. 5
$<$	is less than	p. 5
$\approx$	is approximately equal to	p. 8
$()$	parentheses for grouping	p. 16
$*$	multiply (in a spreadsheet formula)	p. 81
$\ldots$	and so on	p. 108
$\neq$	is not equal to	p. 124
$\stackrel{?}{=}$	Is the statement true?	p. 124
3^4	3 to the power 4	p. 162
$\frac{1}{4}$	reciprocal of 4	p. 272
$3:5$	ratio of 3 to 5	p. 306
$\%$	percent	p. 331
$\overline{AB}$	segment AB	p. 362
$\overrightarrow{AB}$	ray AB	p. 362
$\overleftrightarrow{AB}$	line AB	p. 362
$\angle ABC$	angle with sides BA and BC	p. 367
$\angle A$	angle with vertex A	p. 367
$^\circ$	degree(s)	p. 367
∟	right angle (90°)	p. 368

Symbol	Meaning	Page
P	perimeter	p. 426
ℓ	length	p. 426
w	width	p. 426
A	area	p. 426
s	side	p. 427
b	base	p. 432
h	height	p. 432
C	circumference	p. 439
d	diameter	p. 439
π	pi; ≈ 3.14	p. 439
r	radius	p. 439
S.A.	surface area	p. 454
V	volume	p. 458
B	area of base	p. 458
$P(\text{event})$	probability of event	p. 482
-6	opposite of 6	p. 516
$\lvert 5 \rvert$	absolute value of 5	p. 517
$(2, 3)$	ordered pair with x-coordinate 2 and y-coordinate 3	p. 548
$\geq$	is greater than or equal to	p. 578
$\leq$	is less than or equal to	p. 578
$\sqrt{9}$	square root of 9	p. 578

Formulas and Properties

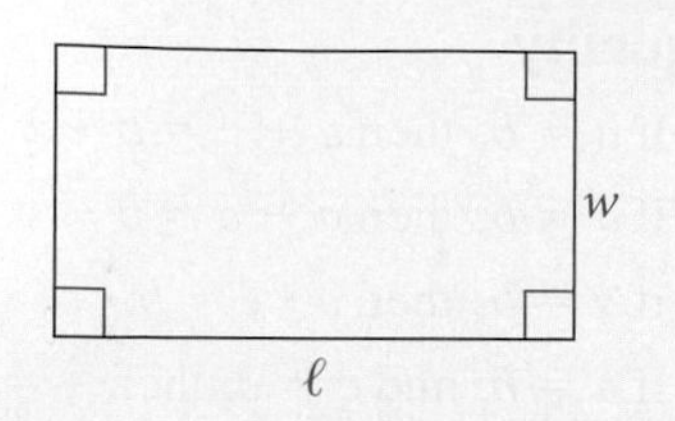

$P = 2\ell + 2w$, or $P = 2(\ell + w)$

$A = \ell \times w$

Rectangle

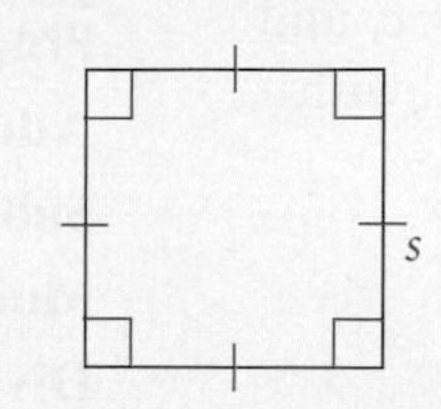

$P = s + s + s + s$, or $P = 4s$

$A = s \times s$, or $A = s^2$

Square

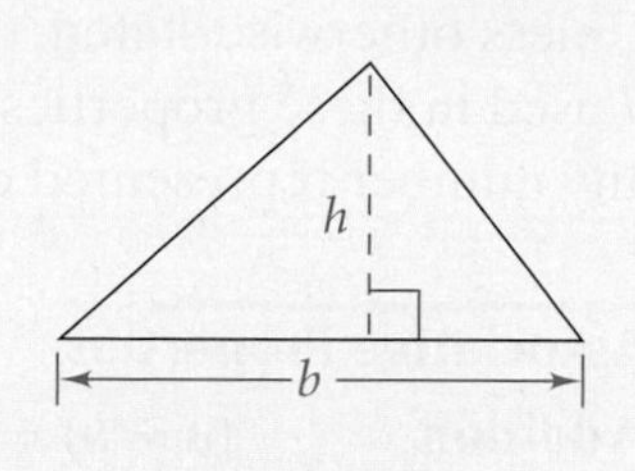

$A = \frac{1}{2}b \times h$

Triangle

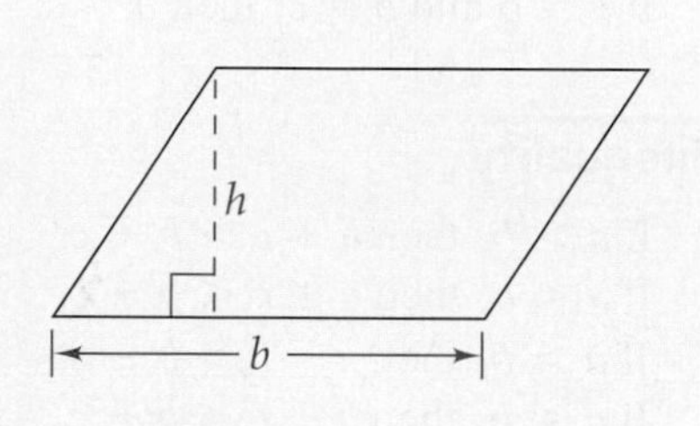

$A = b \times h$

Parallelogram

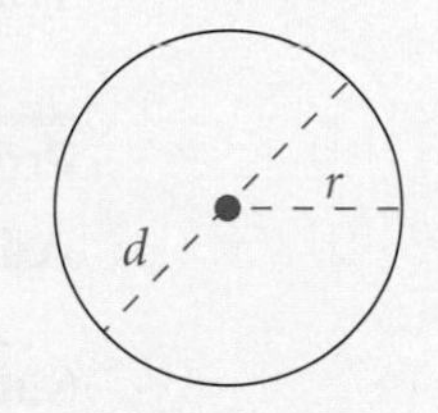

$C = 2\pi r$, or $C = \pi d$

$A = \pi r^2$

Circle

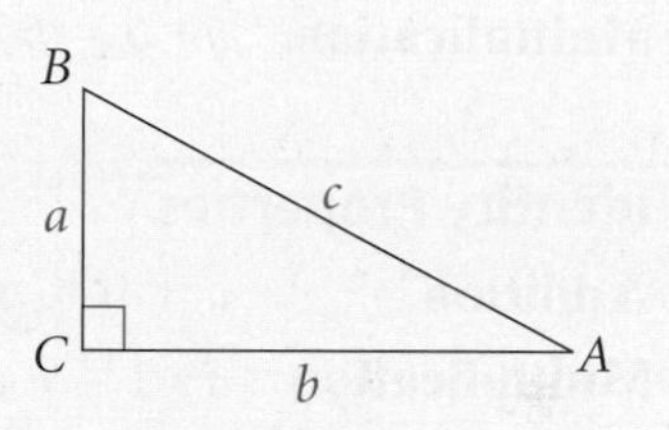

$a^2 + b^2 = c^2$

Pythagorean Theorem

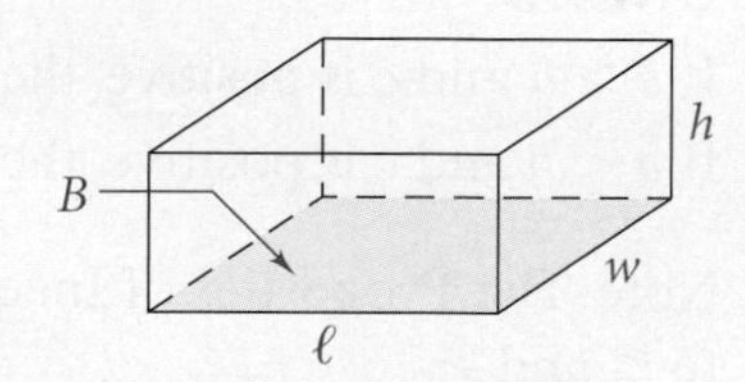

$V = B \times h$, or $V = \ell \times w \times h$

Surface Area (S.A.) =

$2(\ell \times w) + 2(\ell \times h) + 2(w \times h)$

Rectangular Prism

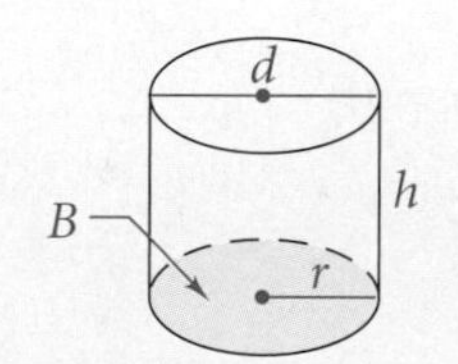

$V = B \times h$, or $V = \pi r^2 \times h$

Surface Area (S.A.) =

$2\pi r^2 + C \times h$

Cylinder

Properties of Numbers

Unless otherwise stated, the variables a, b, c, and d used in these properties can be replaced with any number represented on a number line.

Associative Properties

Addition $(a + b) + c = a + (b + c)$

Multiplication $(a \cdot b) \cdot c = a \cdot (b \cdot c)$

Commutative Properties

Addition $a + b = b + a$

Multiplication $a \cdot b = b \cdot a$

Identity Properties

Addition $a + 0 = a$ and $0 + a = a$

Multiplication $a \cdot 1 = a$ and $1 \cdot a = a$

Inverse Properties

Addition

$a + (-a) = 0$ and $-a + a = 0$

Multiplication

$a \cdot \frac{1}{a} = 1$ and $\frac{1}{a} \cdot a = 1 (a \neq 0)$

Distributive Properties

$a(b + c) = ab + ac$

$a(b - c) = ab - ac$

Cross Products Property

If $\frac{a}{c} = \frac{b}{d}$, then $ad = bc$ $(c \neq 0, d \neq 0)$.

Zero-Product Property

If $ab = 0$, then $a = 0$ or $b = 0$.

Properties of Equality

Addition If $a = b$, then $a + c = b + c$.

Subtraction If $a = b$, then $a - c = b - c$.

Multiplication If $a = b$, then $a \cdot c = b \cdot c$.

Division If $a = b$, and $c \neq 0$, then $\frac{a}{c} = \frac{b}{c}$.

Substitution If $a = b$, then b can replace a in any expression.

Reflexive $a = a$

Symmetric If $a = b$, then $b = a$.

Transitive If $a = b$ and $b = c$, then $a = c$.

Properties of Inequality

Addition If $a > b$, then $a + c > b + c$.
If $a < b$, then $a + c < b + c$.

Subtraction If $a > b$, then $a - c > b - c$.
If $a < b$, then $a - c < b - c$.

Multiplication

If $a > b$ and c is positive, then $ac > bc$.

If $a < b$ and c is positive, then $ac < bc$.

Division

If $a > b$ and c is positive, then $\frac{a}{c} > \frac{b}{c}$.

If $a < b$ and c is positive, then $\frac{a}{c} < \frac{b}{c}$.

Note: The Properties of Inequality apply also to $\leq$ and $\geq$.

English/Spanish Illustrated Glossary

EXAMPLES

Absolute value (p. 207) The absolute value of a number is its distance from 0 on a number line.

-7 is 7 units from 0, so $|-7| = 7$.

Valor absoluto (p. 207) El valor absoluto de un número es su distancia del 0 en una recta numérica.

Addition Property of Equality (p. 68) The Addition Property of Equality states that if the same value is added to each side of an equation, the results are equal.

Since $\frac{20}{2} = 10$, $\frac{20}{2} + 3 = 10 + 3$.
If $a = b$, then $a + c = b + c$.

Propiedad aditiva de la igualdad (p. 68) La propiedad aditiva de la igualdad establece que si se suma el mismo valor a cada lado de una ecuación, los resultados son iguales.

Algebraic expression (p. 47) An algebraic expression is a mathematical phrase that uses variables, numbers, and operation symbols.

$2x - 5$ is an algebraic expression.

Expresión algebraica (p. 47) Una expresión algebraica es un enunciado matemático que usa variables, números y símbolos de operaciones.

Area (p. 275) The area of a figure is the number of square units it encloses.

Área (p. 275) El área de una figura es el número de unidades cuadradas que contiene.

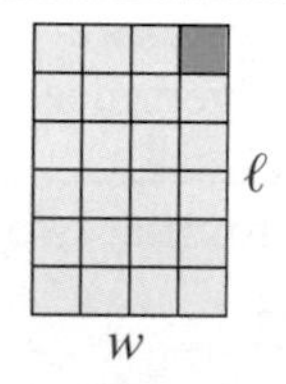

Each square equals 1 ft^2. With $\ell = 6$ ft and $w = 4$ ft, the area is 24 ft^2.

Associative Property of Addition (p. 4) The Associative Property of Addition states that changing the grouping of the addends does not change the sum.

$(2 + 3) + 7 = 2 + (3 + 7)$
$(a + b) + c = a + (b + c)$

Propiedad asociativa de la suma (p. 4) La propiedad asociativa de la suma establece que cambiar la agrupación de los sumandos no cambia la suma.

Associative Property of Multiplication (p. 5) The Associative Property of Multiplication states that changing the grouping of factors does not change the product.

$(3 \cdot 4) \cdot 5 = 3 \cdot (4 \cdot 5)$
$(a \cdot b) \cdot c = a \cdot (b \cdot c)$

Propiedad asociativa de la multiplicación (p. 5) La propiedad asociativa de la multiplicación establece que cambiar la agrupación de los factores no altera el producto.

B

EXAMPLES

Base (p. 90) When a number is written in exponential form, the number that is used as a factor is the base.

$5^4 = 5 \times 5 \times 5 \times 5$
↑ base

Base (p. 90) Cuando un número se escribe en forma exponencial, el número que se usa como factor es la base.

Bases of two-dimensional figures (pp. 275, 276) See *Parallelogram, Triangle, and Trapezoid*.

Bases de figuras bidimensionales (pp. 275, 276) Ver *Parallelogram, Triangle* y *Trapezoid.*

Box-and-whisker plot (p. 323) A box-and-whisker plot or *box plot*, shows how a set of data is distributed.

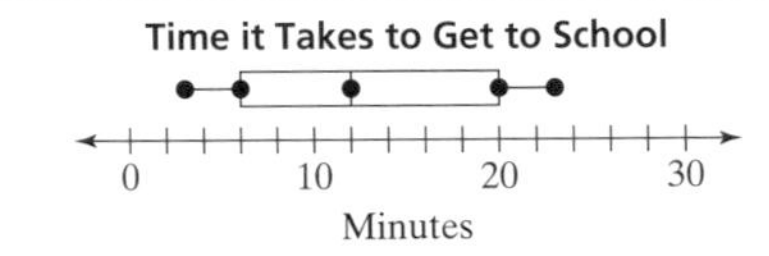

Gráfica de caja y bigotes (p. 323) Una gráfica de caja y bigotes o *gráfica de caja,* muestra cómo se distribuye un conjunto de datos.

C

Coefficient (p. 113) The coefficient is the number before a variable in an algebraic expression.

In the expression $4x^2$, the 4 is the coefficient.

Coeficiente (p. 113) El coeficiente es el número que aparece antes de una variable en una expresión algebraica.

Common factor (p. 99) A factor that two or more numbers share is a common factor.

4 is a common factor of 8 and 20.

Factor común (p. 99) Un número que es factor de dos o más números, es un factor común.

Common multiple (p. 103) A multiple shared by two or more numbers is a common multiple.

12 is a common multiple of 4 and 6.

Múltiplo común (p. 103) Un número que es múltiplo de dos o más números, es un múltiplo común.

Commutative Property of Addition (pp. 4, 126) The Commutative Property of Addition states that changing the order of the addends does not change the sum.

$3 + 1 = 1 + 3$
$a + b = b + a$

Propiedad conmutativa de la suma (pp. 4, 126) La propiedad conmutativa de la suma establece que al cambiar el orden de los sumandos no se altera la suma.

Commutative Property of Multiplication (pp. 5, 126) The Commutative Property of Multiplication states that changing the order of the factors does not change the product.

$6 \cdot 3 = 3 \cdot 6$
$a \cdot b = b \cdot a$

Propiedad conmutativa de la multiplicación (pp. 5, 126) La propiedad conmutativa de la multiplicación establece que al cambiar el orden de los factores no se altera el producto.

EXAMPLES

Complementary (p. 374) Two angles are complementary if the sum of their measures is 90°.

Complementario (p. 374) Dos ángulos son complementarios si la suma de sus medidas es 90°.

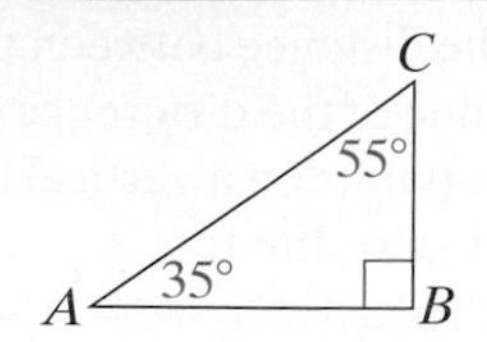

$\angle BCA$ and $\angle CAB$ are complementary angles.

Compose (p. 281) To compose two geometric figures, you join them together to make another shape.

Componer (p. 281) Para combinar dos figuras geométricas, las juntas para formar otra figura.

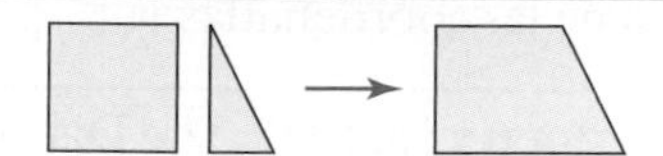

Composite number (p. 94) A composite number is a whole number greater than 1 with more than two factors.

Número compuesto (p. 94) Un número compuesto es un número entero mayor que 1, que tiene más de dos factores.

24 is a composite number that has 1, 2, 3, 4, 6, 8, 12, and 24 as factors.

Cone (p. 287) A cone is a three-dimensional figure with one circular base and one vertex.

Cono (p. 287) Un cono es una figura tridimensional con una base circular y un vértice.

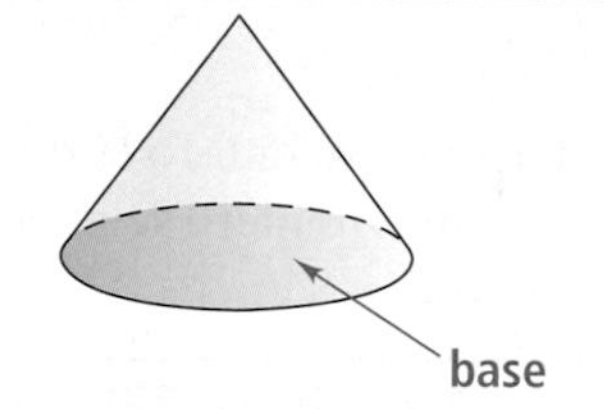

Coordinate plane (p. 241) A coordinate plane is a surface formed by the intersection of two number lines.

Plano de coordenadas (p. 241) Un plano de coordenadas está formado por una recta numérica horizontal llamada eje de x y por una recta numérica vertical llamada eje de y.

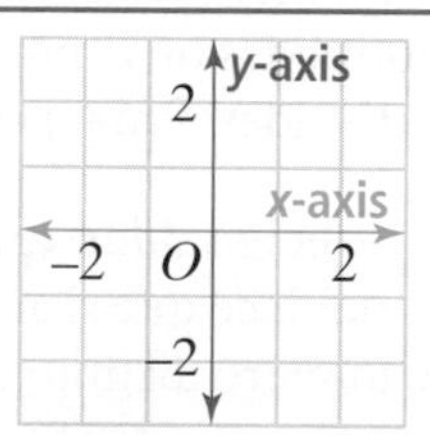

Cube (p. 286) A cube is a rectangular prism whose faces are all squares.

Cubo (p. 286) Un cubo es un prisma rectangular cuyas caras son todas cuadrados.

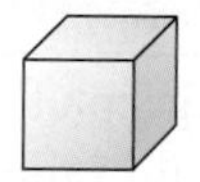

Cylinder (p. 287) A cylinder is a three-dimensional figure with two congruent parallel bases that are circles.

Cilindro (p. 287) Un cilindro es una figura tridimensional con dos bases congruentes paralelas que son círculos.

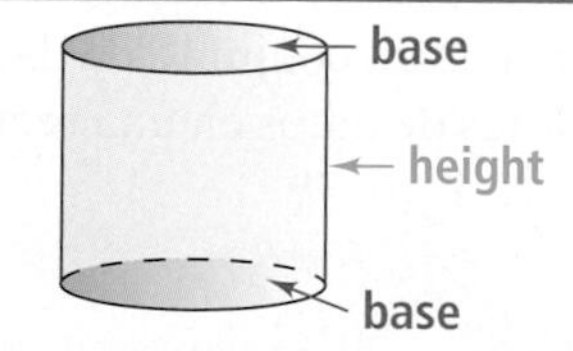

Decompose (p. 281) To decompose a geometric figure, you take it apart to make two or more smaller figures.

Descomponer (p. 281) Para descomponer una figura geométrica, la divides para formar dos o más figuras más pequeñas.

English/Spanish Glossary

EXAMPLES

Distance (p. 246) The distance between two points on a horizontal line is the absolute value of the difference of the x-coordinates. The distance between two points on a vertical line is the absolute value of the difference of the y-coordinates.

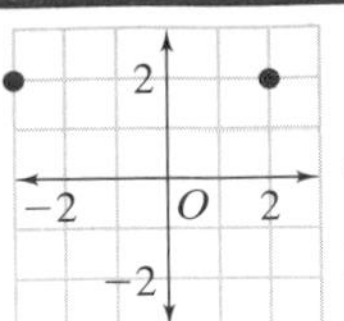

The distance between the points is $2 - (-3) = 5$.

Distancia (p. 246) La distancia entre dos puntos en una recta horizontal es el valor absoluto de la diferencia de las coordenadas x. La distancia entre dos puntos en una recta vertical es el valor absoluto de la diferencia de las coordenadas y.

Distributive Property (p. 107) The Distributive Property shows how multiplication affects an addition or subtraction: $a(b + c) = ab + ac$.

$2\left(3 + \frac{1}{2}\right) = 2 \cdot 3 + 2 \cdot \frac{1}{2}$

$8(5 - 3) = 8 \cdot 5 - 8 \cdot 3$

Propiedad distributiva (p. 107) La propiedad distributiva muestra cómo la multiplicación afecta a una suma o a una resta: $a(b + c) = ab + ac$.

Divisible (p. 86) A whole number is divisible by a second whole number if the first number can be divided by the second number with a remainder of 0.

16 is divisible by 1, 2, 4, 8, and 16.

Divisible (p. 86) Un número entero es divisible por un segundo número entero si el primer número se puede dividir por el segundo número y el residuo es 0.

Division Property of Equality (p. 72) The Division Property of Equality states that if both sides of an equation are divided by the same nonzero number, the sides remain equal.

Since $3(2) = 6$, $3(2) \div 2 = 6 \div 2$. If $a = b$ and $c \neq 0$, then $\frac{a}{c} = \frac{b}{c}$.

Propiedad de división de la igualdad (p. 72) La propiedad de división de la igualdad establece que si ambos lados de una ecuación se dividen por el mismo número distinto de cero, los des lados se mantienen iguales.

Dot plot (p. 320) A dot plot is a graph that shows the shape of a data set by stacking dots above each data value on a number line.

Diagrama de puntos (p. 320) Un diagrama de puntos es una gráfica que muestra la forma de un conjunto de datos apilando puntos sobre cada uno de los valores de datos en una recta numérica.

Science Grades

A B C D

Letter Grades

Double number line diagram (p. 161) A double number line diagram shows how two quantities in different units are related.

Diagrama de doble recta numérica (p. 161) Un diagrama de doble recta numérica muestra cómo se relacionan dos cantidades en diferentes unidades.

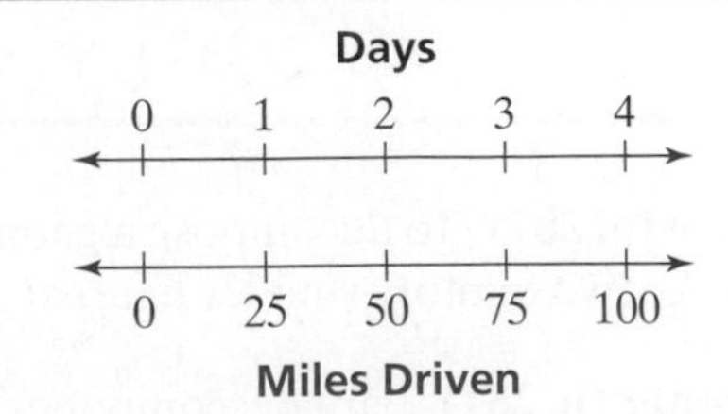

EXAMPLES

Edge (p. 286) An edge is a segment formed by the intersection of two faces of a three-dimensional figure.

Arista (p. 286) Una arista es un segmento formado por la intersección de dos caras de una figura tridimensional.

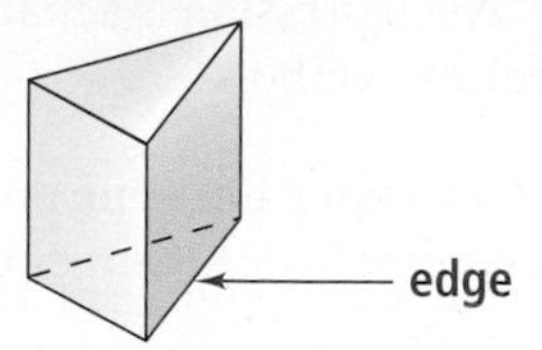

Equation (p. 58) An equation is a mathematical sentence with an equal sign.

Ecuación (p. 58) Una ecuación es una oración matemática con un signo igual.

$27 \div 9 = 3$ and $x + 10 = 8$ are examples of equations

Equivalent expression (p. 108) Equivalent expressions have the same value.

Expresión equivalente (p. 108) Las expresiones equivalentes tienen el mismo valor.

$2(n + 3)$ and $2n + 6$ are equivalent expressions

Equivalent ratios (p. 170) Equivalent ratios name the same number. Equivalent ratios written as fractions are equivalent fractions.

Razones equivalentes (p. 170) Las razones equivalentes indican el mismo número. Las razones equivalentes escritas como fracciones son fracciones equivalentes.

The ratios $\frac{4}{7}$ and $\frac{8}{14}$ are equivalent.

Evaluate an algebraic expression (p. 48) To evaluate an algebraic expression, replace each variable with a number. Then follow the order of operations.

Evaluación de una expresión algebraica (p. 48) Para evaluar una expresión algebraica se reemplaza cada variable con un número. Luego se sigue el orden de las operaciones.

To evaluate the expression $3x + 2$ for $x = 4$, substitute 4 for x.
$3x + 2 = 3(4) + 2 = 14$

Even number (p. 87) An even number is any whole number that ends with a 0, 2, 4, 6, or 8.

Número par (p. 87) Un número par es cualquier número entero que termina en 0, 2, 4, 6 u 8.

20 and 534 are even numbers.

Expanded form (p. 15) The expanded form of a number is the sum that shows the place and value of each digit. See also *Standard form*.

Forma desarrollada (p. 15) La forma desarrollada de un número es la suma que muestra el lugar y valor de cada dígito. Ver también *Standard form*.

4.85 can be written in expanded form as $4 + 0.8 + 0.05$.

Exponent (p. 90) An exponent tells how many times a number, or base, is used as a factor.

Exponente (p. 90) Un exponente dice cuántas veces se usa como factor un número o base.

exponent

$3^4 = 3 \times 3 \times 3 \times 3$

Read 3^4 as *three to the fourth power.*

English/Spanish Glossary

EXAMPLES

Expression (p. 8) An expression is a mathematical phrase containing numbers and operation symbols.

Expresión (p. 8) Una expresión es un enunciado matemático que contiene números y símbolos de operaciones.

The expression $24 - 6 \div 3$ contains two operations.

Face (p. 286) A face is a flat, polygon-shaped surface of a three-dimensional figure.

Cara (p. 286) Una cara es una superficie plana de una figura tridimensional que tiene la forma de un polígono.

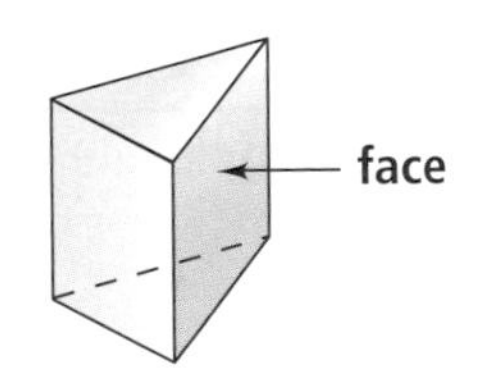

Factor (p. 94) A factor is a whole number that divides another whole number with a remainder of 0.

Divisor (p. 94) Un divisor es un número entero que divide a otro número entero y el residuo es 0.

1, 2, 3, 4, 6, 9, 12, 18, and 36 are factors of 36.

Frequency table (p. 319) A frequency table lists each item in a data set with the number of times the item occurs.

Tabla de frecuencia (p. 319) Una tabla de frecuencia es una tabla que registra todos los elementos de un conjunto de datos y el número de veces que ocurre cada uno.

Household Telephones

Phones	Tally	Frequency
1	卌 III	8
2	卌 I	6
3	IIII	4

This frequency table shows the number of household telephones for a class of students.

Front-end estimation (p. 19) To use front-end estimation to estimate sums, first add the front-end digits. Then adjust by estimating the sum of the remaining digits. Add the two values.

Estimación de entrada (p. 19) Para estimar usando la estimación de entrada, primero se suman los dígitos de entrada. Luego se ajustan estimando la cantidad de los dígitos restantes. Finalmente, se suman las dos cantidades.

Estimate \$3.09 + \$2.99.

\$**3**.09	→	\$3.**09**
+ \$**2**.99		\$2.**99**
\$5		**about \$1**

So \$3.09 + \$2.99 ≈ 5 + 1, or \$6.

Function (p. 251) A function is a relationship that assigns exactly one output value for each input value.

Función (p. 251) Una función es una relación que asigna exactamente un valor resultante a cada valor inicial.

Earned income i is a function of the number of hours worked h. If you earn \$6 per hour, then your income can be expressed by the function $i = 6h$.

Graph of an inequality (p. 224) The graph of an inequality shows all solutions of the inequality.

Gráfica de una desigualdad (p. 224) La gráfica de una desigualdad muestra todas las soluciones que satisfacen la desigualdad.

−6 −5 −4 −3 −2 −1 0

$x > -3$

EXAMPLES

Greatest common factor (GCF) (p. 99) The greatest common factor of two or more numbers is the greatest factor shared by all of the numbers.

The GCF of 12 and 30 is 6.

Máximo común divisor (MCD) (p. 99) El máximo común divisor de dos o más números es el mayor divisor que comparten todos los números.

Height of two-dimensional figures (pp. 275, 276) See *Parallelogram, Triangle,* and *Trapezoid.*

Altura de figuras bidimensionales (pp. 275, 276) Ver *Parallelogram, Triangle* y *Trapezoid.*

Histogram (p. 328) A histogram is a bar graph with no spaces between the bars. The height of each bar shows the frequency of data within that interval.

Histograma (p. 328) Un histograma es una gráfica de barras sin espacio entre las barras. La altura de cada barra muestra la frecuencia de los datos dentro del intervalo.

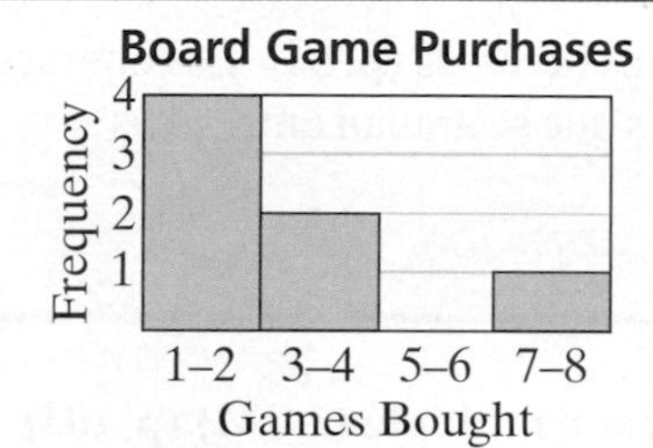

The histogram gives the frequency of board game purchases at a local toy store.

Horizontal line (p. 246) A horizontal line is a straight line that extends left and right.

A B

Recta horizontal (p. 246) Una recta horizontal es una recta que se extiende hacia la izquierda y hacia la derecha.

Identity Property of Addition (p. 4) The Identity Property of Addition states that the sum of 0 and a is a.

$0 + 7 = 7$
$a + 0 = a$

Propiedad de identidad de la suma (p. 4) La propiedad de identidad de la suma establece que la suma de 0 y a es a.

Identity Property of Multiplication (p. 5) The Identity Property of Multiplication states that the product of 1 and a is a.

$1 \cdot 7 = 7$
$a \cdot 1 = a$

Propiedad de identidad de la multiplicación (pp. 5) La propiedad de identidad de la multiplicación establece que el producto de 1 y a es a.

Inequality (p. 223) An inequality is a mathematical sentence that contains $<, >, \leq, \geq$, or $\neq$.

$x < -5$
$x > 8$
$x \leq 1$
$x \geq -11$
$x \neq 3$

Desigualdad (p. 223) Una desigualdad es una oración matemática que contiene los signos $<, >, \leq, \geq$ o $\neq$.

EXAMPLES

Integers (p. 206) Integers are the set of positive whole numbers, their opposites, and 0.

Enteros (p. 206) Los enteros son el conjunto de números enteros positivos, sus opuestos y el 0.

$\ldots -3, -2, -1, 0, 1, 2, 3, \ldots$

Interquartile range (p. 335) A measure of variability that gives the spread of the middle half of the data is the interquartile range.

Rango entre cuartiles (p. 335) El rango entre cuartiles es una medida de variabilidad que indica la dispersión de la mitad de los datos.

The IQR for the data 2, 3, 6, 9, 10, 12, 20 is $12 - 3 = 9$.

Inverse operations (p. 64) Inverse operations are operations that undo each other.

Operaciones inversas (p. 64) Las operaciones inversas son las operaciones que se anulan entre ellas.

Addition and subtraction are inverse operations.

Least common multiple (LCM) (p. 103) The least common multiple of two numbers is the smallest number that is a multiple of both numbers.

Mínimo común múltiplo (mcm) (p. 103) El mínimo común múltiplo de dos números es el menor número que es múltiplo de ambos números.

The LCM of 15 and 6 is 30

Line (p. 246) A line is a series of points that extends in two opposite directions without end.

Recta (p. 246) Una recta es una serie de puntos que se extiende indefinidamente en dos direcciones opuestas.

G

C

$\overleftrightarrow{CG}$ is shown.

Line of reflection (p. 245) A line of reflection is a line over which a figure is reflected.

Eje de reflexión (p. 245) Un eje de reflexión es una recta sobre la cual se refleja una figura.

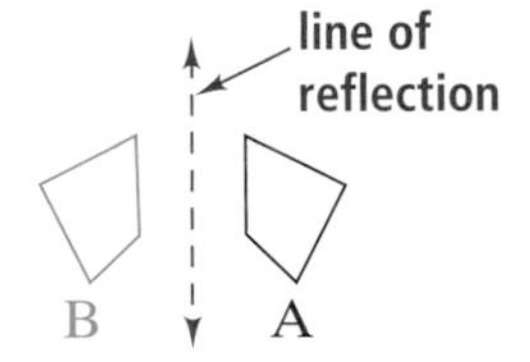

Figure B is a reflection of Figure A.

Linear function (p. 255) A function is a linear function if its graph is a line.

Función linear (p. 255) Una función es una función linear si su gráfica es una recta.

Hours Worked	Money Earned (dollars)
1	7
2	14
3	21
4	28

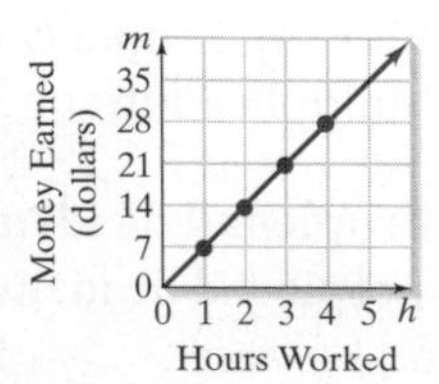

Money earned is a function of hours worked.

Lower quartile (p. 323) The median of the lower half of a data set is the lower quartile.

Cuartil inferior (p. 323) El cuartil inferior es la mediana de la mitad inferior de un conjunto de datos.

The lower quartile is 3 for the data below.
2, 3, 6, 9, 10, 12, 20

M

EXAMPLES

Mean (p. 311) The mean of a set of data values is the sum of the data divided by the number of data items.

Media (p. 311) La media de un conjunto de valores de datos es la suma de los datos dividida por el número de datos.

The mean temperature (°F) for the set of temperatures 44, 52, 48, 55, 61, and 67 is $\frac{44 + 52 + 48 + 55 + 61 + 67}{6} = 54.5$.

Mean absolute deviation (p. 334) Mean absolute deviation (MAD) is the average amount that the data values vary from the mean.

Desviación absoluta media (p. 334) La desviación absoluta media (MAD) es la cantidad promedio en la que varían los valores de datos en relación con la media.

The mean of the data 4, 5, 7, 8, is 6. The distances from the mean are 2, 1, 1, 2. The MAD is $\frac{2 + 1 + 1 + 2}{4} = 1.5$.

Measure of center (p. 334) A value that describes how data is centered is called a **measure of center.**

Medida de tendencia central (p. 334) Un valor que describe cómo están centrados los datos es una **medida de tendencia central.**

The mean, median, and mode are measures of center.

Measure of variability (p. 334) A value that describes how data is spread out is called a **measure of variability.**

Medida de variabilidad (p. 334) Un valor que describe la dispersión de los datos se llama **medida de variabilidad.**

The range is a measure of variability.

Median (p. 315) The median of a data set is the middle value when the data are arranged in numerical order. When there is an even number of data values, the median is the mean of the two middle values.

Mediana (p. 315) La mediana de un conjunto de datos es el valor del medio cuando los datos están organizados en orden numérico. Cuando hay un número par de valores de datos, la mediana es la media de los dos valores del medio.

Five temperatures (°F) arranged in order are 44, 48, 52, 55, and 58. The median temperature is 52°F, because it is the middle number in the set of data.

Mode (p. 316) The mode of a data set is the item that occurs most often.

Moda (p. 316) La moda de un conjunto de datos es el dato que sucede con mayor frecuencia.

The mode of the set of prices \$2.50, \$2.75, \$3.60, \$2.75, and \$3.70 is \$2.75.

Multiple (p. 103) A multiple of a number is the product of the number and any nonzero whole number.

Múltiplo (p. 103) Un múltiplo de un número es el producto de ese número y cualquier número entero diferente de cero.

The number 39 is a multiple of 13.

EXAMPLES

Multiplication Property of Equality (p. 73) The Multiplication Property of Equality states that if each side of an equation is multiplied by the same number, the results arc equal.

Propiedad multiplicativa de la igualdad (p. 73) La propiedad multiplicativa de la igualdad establece que si cada lado de una ecuación se multiplica por el mismo número, los resultados son iguales.

Since $\frac{12}{2} = 6$, $\frac{12}{2} \cdot 2 = 6 \cdot 2$. If $a = b$, then $a \cdot c = b \cdot c$.

Net (p. 292) A net is a pattern that can be folded to form a three-dimensional figure.

Plantilla (p. 292) Una plantilla es un patrón bidimensional que se puede doblar para formar una figura tridimensional.

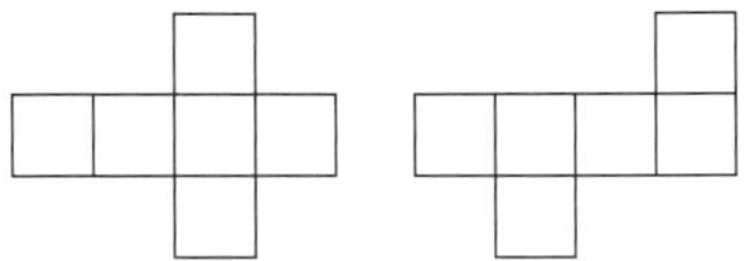

These are nets for a cube.

Numerical expression (p. 47) A numerical expression is a mathematical phrase with only numbers and operation symbols.

Expresión numérica (p. 47) Una expresión numérica es una expresión que tiene sólo números y símbolos de operaciones.

$2(5 + 7) - 14$ is a numerical expression.

Odd number (p. 87) An odd number is a whole number that ends with a 1, 3, 5, 7, or 9.

Número impar (p. 87) Un número impar es un número entero que termina en 1, 3, 5, 7 o 9.

43 and 687 are odd numbers.

Open sentence (p. 59) An open sentence is an equation with one or more variables.

Proposición abierta (p. 59) Una proposición abierta es una ecuación con una o más variables.

$b - 7 = 12$

Opposites (p. 206) Opposites are two numbers that are the same distance from 0 on a number line, but in opposite directions.

Opuestos (p. 206) Opuestos son dos números que están a la misma distancia del 0 en una recta numérica, pero en direcciones opuestas.

17 and −17 are opposites.

Ordered pair (p. 241) An ordered pair is a pair of numbers that describes the location of a point in a coordinate plane.

Par ordenado (p. 241) Un par ordenado identifica la ubicación de un punto. La coordenada x muestra la posición de un punto a la izquierda o derecha del eje de y. La coordenada y muestra la posición de un punto arriba o abajo del eje de x.

$(-2, 1)$ y O x

The x-coordinate of the point $(-2, 1)$ is -2, and the y-coordinate is 1.

EXAMPLES

Order of operations (pp. 8, 91)
1. Work inside grouping symbols.
2. Do all work with exponents.
3. Multiply and divide in order from left to right.
4. Add and subtract in order from left to right.

$2^3(7 - 4) = 2^3 \cdot 3 = 8 \cdot 3 = 24$

Orden de las operaciones (pp. 8, 91)
1. Trabaja dentro de los signos de agrupación.
2. Trabaja con los exponentes.
3. Multiplica y divide en orden de izquierda a derecha.
4. Suma y resta en orden de izquierda a derecha.

Origin (p. 241) The origin is the point on a coordinate plane where two number lines intersect.

Origen (p. 241) El origen es el punto de intersección de los ejes de x y de y en un plano de coordenadas.

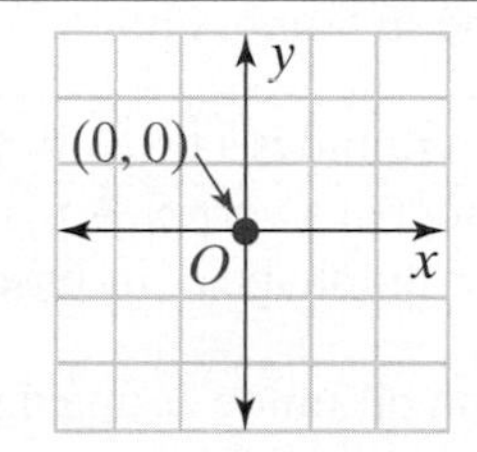

The ordered pair that describes the origin is (0, 0).

Outlier (p. 312) An outlier is a data item that is much greater or less than the other items in a data set.

Valor extremo (p. 312) Un valor extremo es un dato que es mucho más alto o más bajo que los demás datos de un conjunto de datos.

The outlier in the data set 6, 7, 9, 10, 11, 12, 14, and 52 is 52.

Parallelogram (p. 275) A parallelogram is a quadrilateral with both pairs of opposite sides parallel.

Paralelogramo (p. 275) Un paralelogramo es un cuadrilátero cuyos pares de lados opuestos son paralelos.

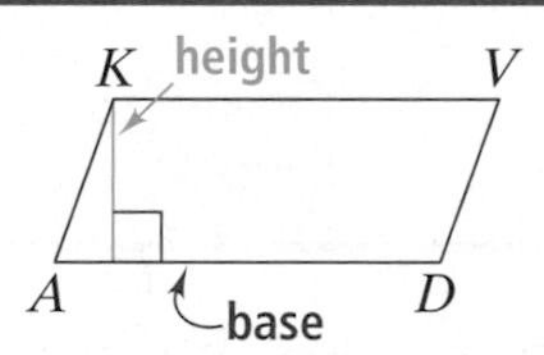

$\overline{KV}$ is parallel to $\overline{AD}$ and $\overline{AK}$ is parallel to $\overline{DV}$, so $KVDA$ is a parallelogram.

Percent (p. 179) A percent is a ratio that compares a number to 100.

Porcentaje (p. 179) Un porcentaje es una razón que compara un número con 100.

$\frac{25}{100} = 25\%$

Power (p. 90) A power is a number that can be expressed using an exponent.

Potencia (p. 90) Una potencia es un número que se puede expresar usando un exponente.

3^4, 5^2, and 2^{10} are powers.

Prime factorization (p. 95) Writing a composite number as the product of prime numbers is the prime factorization of the number.

Factorización en primos (p. 95) Escribir un número compuesto como el producto de sus factores primos es la factorización en primos del número.

The prime factorization of 12 is $2 \cdot 2 \cdot 3$, or $2^2 \cdot 3$.

EXAMPLES

Prime number (p. 94) A prime number is a whole number with exactly two factors, 1 and the number itself.

13 is a prime number, because its only factors are 1 and 13.

Número primo (p. 94) Un número primo es un entero que tiene exactamente dos factores, 1 y el mismo número.

Prism (p. 286) A prism is a three-dimensional figure with two parallel and congruent faces that are polygons. These faces are called bases. A prism is named after the shape of its base.

Prisma (p. 286) Un prisma es una figura tridimensional que tiene dos caras paralelas y congruentes que son polígonos. Estas caras se llaman bases. Un prisma recibe su nombre por la forma de su base.

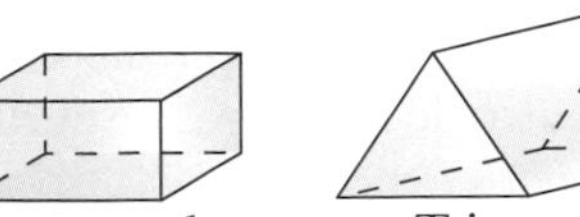

Rectangular Prism   Triangular Prism

Pyramid (p. 287) A pyramid is a three-dimensional figure with triangular faces that meet at a vertex. A pyramid's base is a polygon. A pyramid is named after the shape of its base.

Pirámide (p. 287) Una pirámide es una figura tridimensional que tiene caras triangulares que coinciden en un vértice. Su base es un polígono. Una pirámide recibe su nombre por la forma de su base.

Triangular Pyramid

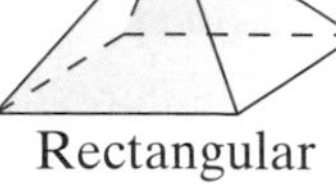

Rectangular Pyramid

Quadrants (p. 241) The x- and y-axes divide the coordinate plane is divided into four regions called quadrants.

Cuadrantes (p. 241) Los ejes de x y de y dividen el plano de coordenadas en cuatro regiones llamadas cuadrantes.

The quadrants are labeled I, II, III, and IV.

Range (p. 320) The range of a data set is the difference between the greatest and the least values.

Data set: 62, 109, 234, 35, 96, 49, 201
Range: $201 - 35 = 166$

Rango (p. 320) El rango de un conjunto de datos es la diferencia entre los valores mayor y menor.

Rate (p. 166) A rate is a ratio that compares two quantities measured in different units.

Suppose you read 116 words in 1 minute.

Your reading rate is $\frac{116 \text{ words}}{1 \text{ minute}}$.

Tasa (p. 166) Una tasa es una razón que compara dos cantidades medidas en diferentes unidades.

Ratio (p. 160) A ratio is a comparison of two quantities by division.

There are three ways to write a ratio: 9 to 10, $9 : 10$, and $\frac{9}{10}$.

Razón (p. 160) Una razón es una comparación de dos cantidades mediante la división.

	EXAMPLES
Rational number (p. 213) A rational number is any number that can be written as a quotient of two integers in which the denominator is not 0. **Número racional (p. 213)** Un número racional es cualquier número que puede ser escrito como cociente de dos enteros, donde el denominador es diferente de 0.	$\frac{1}{3}, -5, 6.4, 0.666\ldots, -2\frac{4}{5}, 0,$ and $\frac{7}{3}$ are rational numbers.
Reciprocal (p. 136) Two numbers are reciprocals if their product is 1. **Recíproco (p. 136)** Dos números son recíprocos si su producto es 1.	The numbers $\frac{4}{9}$ and $\frac{9}{4}$ are reciprocals.
Reflection (p. 245) A reflection, or flip, is a transformation that flips a figure over a line of reflection. **Refleción (p. 245)** Una refleción es una transformación que voltea una figura sobre un eje de reflexión.	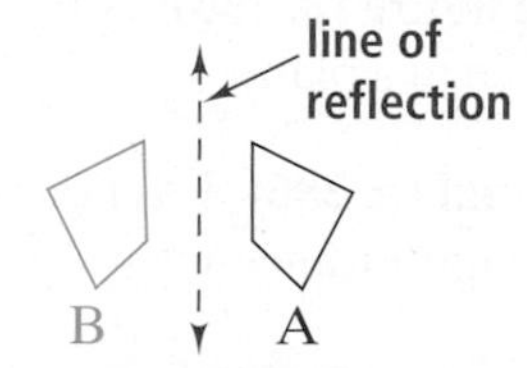 Figure B is a reflection of Figure A.

Solution (pp. 59, 224) A solution is any value or values that makes an equation or inequality true. **Solución (pp. 59, 224)** Una solución es cualquier valor o valores que hacen que una ecuación o una desigualdad sea verdadera.	4 is the solution of $x + 5 = 9$. 7 is a solution of $x < 15$.
Sphere (p. 287) A sphere is a three-dimensional figure that has no base. **Esfera (p. 287)** Una esfera es el conjunto de todos los puntos en el espacio que están a la misma distancia de un punto central.	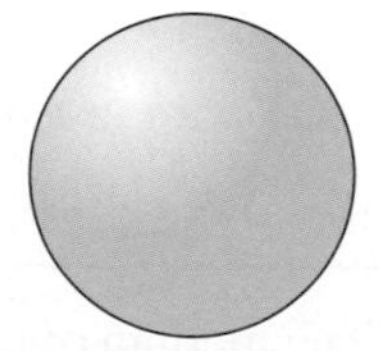
Statistical question (p. 345) A statistical question is one for which you expect to get a varity of different answers. **Pregunta estadística (p. 345)** Una pregunta estadística es una para la se pueden obtener una gran variedad de respuestas diferentes.	"What is your favorite color?" is a statistical question.
Subtraction Property of Equality (p. 65) The Subtraction Property of Equality states that if the same number is subtracted from each side of an equation, the results are equal. **Propiedad sustractiva de la igualdad (p. 65)** La propiedad sustractiva de la igualdad establece que si se resta el mismo número a cada lado de una ecuación, los resultados son iguales.	Since $\frac{20}{2} = 10$, $\frac{20}{2} - 3 = 10 - 3$. If $a = b$, then $a - c = b - c$.
Surface area of a three-dimensional figure (p. 293) The surface area of a three-dimensional figure is the sum of the areas of all the surfaces. **Área total de una figura tridimensional (p. 293)** El área total de una figura tridimensional es la suma de las áreas de todas sus superficies.	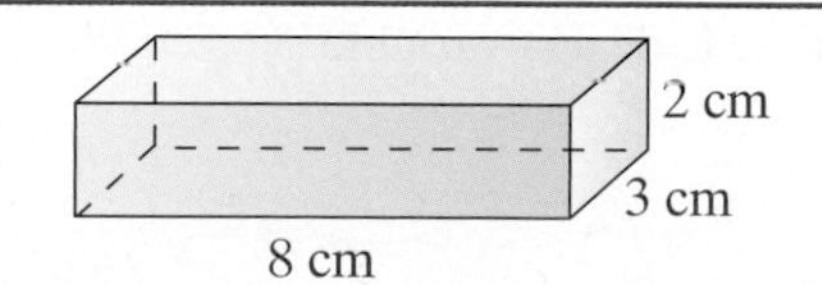

English/Spanish Glossary

T

EXAMPLES

Tape diagram (p. 161) A tape diagram uses length to show how two different quantities are related.

Diagrama con tiras (p. 161) En un diagrama con tiras se usa la longitud para mostrar la relación entre dos cantidades diferentes.

Ducks

Geese

Term (p. 113) A term is a number in a pattern.

Término (p. 113) Un término es un número en un patrón.

6, 12, 24, 48, . . . The third term in this pattern is 24.

Three-dimensional figure (p. 286) A three-dimensional figure is a figure that does not lie in a plane.

Figura tridemensional (p. 286) Las figuras tridimensionales son figuras que tienen longitud, anchura y altura.

face

edge

U

Unit cost (p. 167) A unit cost is a unit rate that gives the cost of one item.

Costo unitario (p. 167) Un costo unitario es una tasa unitaria que da el costo de un artículo.

$\frac{\$5.98}{10.2 \text{ fluid ounces}} = \$.59/\text{fluid ounce}$

Unit rate (p. 166) The rate for one unit of a given quantity is called the unit rate.

Tasa unitaria (p. 166) La tasa para una unidad de una cantidad dada se llama tasa unitaria.

If you drive 130 miles in 2 hours, your unit rate is $\frac{65 \text{ miles}}{1 \text{ hour}}$ or 65 mi/h.

Upper quartile (p. 323) The median of the upper half of a data set is the upper quartile.

Cuartil superior (p. 323) El cuartil superior es la mediana de la mitad superior de un conjunto de datos.

The upper quartile is 12 for the data below:
2, 3, 6, 9, 10, 12, 20

V

Variable (p. 47) A variable is a letter that stands for a number. The value of an algebraic expression varies, or changes, depending upon the value given to the variable.

Variable (p. 47) Una variable es una letra que representa un número. El valor de una expresión algebraica varía, o cambia, dependiendo del valor que se le dé a la variable.

x is a variable in the equation $9 + x = 7$.

EXAMPLES

Vertex of an angle (p. 286) The vertex of an angle is the point of intersection of two sides of an angle or figure.

Vértice de un ángulo (p. 286) El vértice de un ángulo es el punto de intersección de dos lados de un ángulo o figura.

vertex

Vertical line (p. 246) A vertical line is a straight line that extends up and down.

Recta vertical (p. 246) Una recta vertical es una recta que se extiende hacia arriba y hacia abajo.

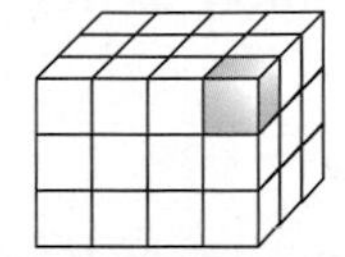

Volume (p. 299) The volume of a three-dimensional figure is the number of cubic units needed to fill the space inside the figure.

Volumen (p. 299) El volumen de una figura tridimensional es el número de unidades cúbicas que se necesitan para llenar el espacio dentro de la figura.

The volume of the rectangular prism is 36 cubic units.

Answers to Instant Check System™

Chapter 1

Check Your Readiness — p. 2

1. 310 **2.** 7,530 **3.** 40 **4.** 60 **5.** 700 **6.** 1,990 **7.** 175 **8.** 145 **9.** 14,192 **10.** 3,027 **11.** 10,000 **12.** 1,392 **13.** 747 **14.** 4,544 **15.** 43,700 **16.** 462 **17.** 5 **18.** 17 **19.** 32 **20.** 72

Lesson 1-1 — pp. 4–5

Check Skills You'll Need **1.** addition **2.** 150 **3.** 90 **4.** 350

Quick Check **1.** 95 **2.** 600

Lesson 1-2 — pp. 8–12

Check Skills You'll Need **1.** Comm. Prop. of Add. **2.** 57 **3.** 30 **4.** 175

Quick Check **1a.** 27 **b.** 16 **2.** $43

Checkpoint Quiz 1 **1.** 57 **2.** 38 **3.** 1,000 **4.** 68 **5.** 1,400 **6.** 4,300 **7.** 16 **8.** 0 **9.** 70 **10.** $70 **11.** 9 **12.** 11 **13.** 64 **14.** subtraction, division, addition

Lesson 1-3 — pp. 14–15

Check Skills You'll Need **1.** 1,321 **2.** twenty-eight **3.** eight thousand, six hundred seventy-two **4.** six hundred twelve thousand, nine hundred eighty **5.** fifty-eight thousand, twenty-six

Quick Check **1a.** sixty-seven and three tenths **b.** six and seven hundred thirty-four thousandths **c.** sixty-seven hundredths **2.** 0.15; 0.1 + 0.05 **3a.** 2.34 **b.** 0.1735 **c.** 9.1

Lesson 1-4 — pp. 19–20

Check Skills You'll Need **1.** Rounding **2.** 70 **3.** 110 **4.** 100 **5.** 3,200

Quick Check **1.** about 6; 6.16 **2.** about $22 **3.** 2.72 m

Lesson 1-5 — pp. 25–30

Check Skills You'll Need **1.** Yes; 130 is easy to divide by 5 mentally. **2.** about 600 **3.** about 180 **4.** about 100 **5.** about 10

Quick Check **1a.** 0.78 **b.** 21.85 **2a.** 0.06 **b.** 10.108 **c.** 0.126 **3.** $3.55

Checkpoint Quiz 2 **1.** twelve and thirty-five thousandths **2.** 7.32 **3.** 8.26 **4.** $5.24 **5.** 1.42 **6.** 13.86 **7.** 34.3 **8.** 0.984 **9.** 5.2312 **10.** 1.65 lb

Lesson 1-6 — pp. 31–33

Check Skills You'll Need **1.** A dividend is the number being divided. A divisor is the number that divides. **2.** 187 **3.** 37 **4.** 53

Quick Check **1a.** 372 **b.** 31 **2a.** 48.2 **b.** 1.52 **3.** 11 trading cards

Chapter 2

Check Your Readiness — p. 44

1. 29 **2.** 39 **3.** 18 **4.** 30 **5.** about 42; 42.15 **6.** about 9; 9.5 **7.** about 5; 5.1 **8.** about 2; 2.16 **9.** about 2; 2.27 **10.** about 15; 14.36 **11.** 18.95 **12.** 19.456 **13.** 310.27 **14.** 3.3 **15.** 170 **16.** 0.71

Lesson 2-1 — pp. 47–48

Check Skills You'll Need **1.** A mathematical expression is a phrase containing numbers and operation symbols. **2.** 32 **3.** 19 **4.** 441

Quick Check **1.** 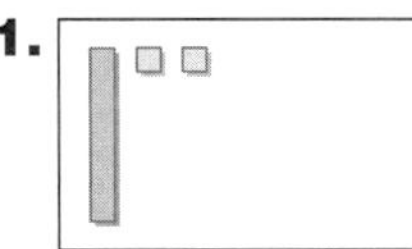 **2a.** 36 **b.** 5 **c.** 28 **3.** $255

Lesson 2-2 — pp. 52–57

Check Skills You'll Need **1.** To evaluate an expression means to replace a variable with a number and simplify it. **2.** 10 **3.** 30 **4.** 48 **5.** 11

Quick Check **1.** $x + 2$ **2.** Let b = Brandon's age; $b + 28$ **3.** $n + 4$

Checkpoint Quiz 1 **1.** 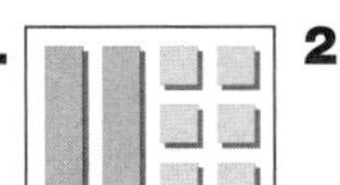 **2.** 

3. 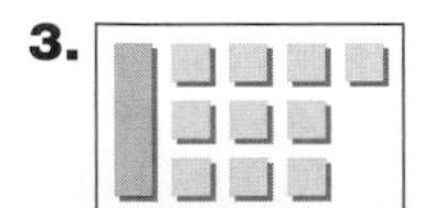 **4.** 56 **5.** 9 **6.** 70

7.

x	$\frac{x}{5}$
15	3
70	14
125	25

8.

x	$3x + 1$
4	13
10	31
22	67

9. $17 - d$ **10.** ae **11.** $14 \div q$

12.

n	$6n$
3	18
12	72
100	600

13.

n	$n + 4$
16	20
51	55
129	133

Lesson 2-3	pp. 58–59

Check Skills You'll Need **1.** Add the whole dollars first and then estimate when adding the cents. **2.** about 6; 6.37 **3.** about 4; 3.7 **4.** about 2; 1.7

Quick Check **1a.** true **b.** false **c.** false **2a.** 9 **b.** 80 **c.** 1.2 **3.** 43

Lesson 2-4	pp. 64–65

Check Skills You'll Need **1.** It has one or more variables. **2.** 1 **3.** 70 **4.** 14

Quick Check **1.** 4.8 **2.** w = the cat's weight last year; $1.8 + w = 11.6$; 9.8 lb

Lesson 2-5	pp. 68–71

Check Skills You'll Need **1.** It makes the equation true. **2.** 14 **3.** 11 **4.** 10

Quick Check **1a.** 81 **b.** 55 **2.** Let t = temperature at 7 P.M.; $t - 9 = 54$; $t = 63$.

Checkpoint Quiz 2 **1.** 60 **2.** 18.2 **3.** 2.2 **4.** 7.6 **5.** 10.8 **6.** 26.6 **7.** 7 **8.** 38.4 **9.** x = change received; $x + 5.73 = 10.00$; $x = \$4.27$

Lesson 2-6	pp. 72–74

Check Skills You'll Need **1.** Answers may vary. Sample: Equations contain equal signs, and expressions do not. **2.** 9 **3.** 2 **4.** 9 **5.** 3

Quick Check **1.** 40 **2.** 865 cards **3.** 15

Chapter 3

Check Your Readiness	p. 84

1. 50 **2.** 18 **3.** 15 **4.** 12 **5.** 117 **6.** 5 **7.** 9 **8.** 12 **9.** 86 **10.** 8 **11.** 43 **12.** 38 **13.** 13 **14.** 93 **15.** 118 **16.** 48

Lesson 3-1	pp. 86–87

Check Skills You'll Need **1.** division **2.** 49 **3.** 41 **4.** 50

Quick Check **1a.** no **b.** yes **2a.** divisible by 2, 3, 5, and 10 **b.** divisible by none of these **c.** divisible by 2 and 3 **3.** yes

Lesson 3-2	pp. 90–91

Check Skills You'll Need **1.** expression **2.** 25 **3.** 0 **4.** 2

Quick Check **1a.** 3.94^2; 3.94; 2 **b.** 7^4; 7; 4 **c.** x^3; x; 3 **2.** 27 **3a.** 6 **b.** 14

Lesson 3-3	pp. 94–98

Check Skills You'll Need **1.** No; 25 is divisible by 5 but not divisible by 10. **2.** 2, 3, 5, 9, 10 **3.** divisible by none of these **4.** 2, 5, and 10 **5.** 2, 5, and 10

Quick Check **1.** $1 \times 24, 2 \times 12, 3 \times 8, 4 \times 6$ **2a.** composite; $39 = 3 \times 13$ **b.** Prime; it has only two factors, 1 and 47. **c.** composite; $63 = 3 \times 21$ or $63 = 7 \times 9$ **3.** 3^3

Checkpoint Quiz 1 **1.** 3, 5 **2.** 2 **3.** 2, 3, 5, 10 **4.** 64 **5.** 10 **6.** 3,125 **7.** 64 **8.** $2^3 \times 5$ **9.** $2^4 \times 5$ **10.** $2^3 \times 5^3$ **11.** $1 \times 105, 3 \times 35, 5 \times 21, 7 \times 15$

Lesson 3-4	pp. 99–100

Check Skills You'll Need **1.** Answers may vary. Sample: Multiply two factors together to find the product. **2.** $3^2 \times 5$ **3.** 3×7 **4.** $3^2 \times 11$

Quick Check **1a.** factors of 6: 1, 2, 3, 6; factors of 21: 1, 3, 7, 21; GCF of 6 and 21: 3 **b.** factors of 18: 1, 2, 3, 6, 9, 18; factors of 49: 1, 7, 49; GCF of 18 and 49: 1 **c.** factors of 14: 1, 2, 7, 14; factors of 28: 1, 2, 4, 7, 14, 28; GCF of 14 and 28: 14 **2.** 6 in. **3a.** GCF = 16 **b.** GCF = 12

Lesson 3-5	pp. 103–112

Check Skills You'll Need **1.** A factor tree helps you write a number as a product of prime factors. **2.** $2^4 \times 5$ **3.** 2^5 **4.** $2^4 \times 13$ **5.** $2^2 \times 5^3$

Quick Check **1a.** 60 **b.** 70 **2.** 24

Lesson 3-6	pp. 107–112

Check Skills You'll Need **1.** An algebraic expression is a mathematical phrase that uses variables, numbers, and operation symbols. **2.** 22 **3.** 1 **4.** 9

Quick Check **1a.** $12n + 24$ **b.** $56 - 24m + 32p$ **c.** $24a + 36b - 60$ **2a.** $6(3 + 4)$ **b.** $7(8 + 7)$ **c.** $12(7 + 5)$ **3a.** $3(n + 7)$ **b.** $8(9 + 2h)$ **c.** $16(3y + 5z + 4)$ **4.** \$14.00

Checkpoint Quiz 2 **1.** 5 **2.** 24 **3.** 3 **4.** 6 **5.** 45 **6.** 36 **7.** 24 **8.** 150 **9.** $30x - 8$ **10.** $42 + 18c$ **11.** $72r - 80$ **12.** $10a - 60b + 25$ **13.** $8(x + 3)$ **14.** $5(5x + 3)$ **15.** $2(32x - 7y + 15)$ **16.** $10(4p + 9)$

Lesson 3-7	pp. 113–114

Check Skills You'll Need **1.** They have the same value **2.** 6 **3.** 195 **4.** 8

Quick Check **1a.** $9b$ **b.** $6c + 5$ **2.** $4a$

Chapter 4

Check Your Readiness p. 124

1.

18	
f	9

2.

12	
h	4

3.

14	
7	k

4.

18	
16	r

5.

14	
11	q

6.

20	
15	z

7. 4 **8.** 5 **9.** 12 **10.** 112 **11.** 100 **12.** 0.6 **13.** 12 **14.** 7 **15.** 3 **16.** 20 **17.** 6 **18.** 21

Lesson 4-1 pp. 127–129

Check Skills You'll Need **1.** Sample answer: List the multiples of each number. Circle the common multiples. The lowest common multiple is the least common multiple. **2.** 9 **3.** 24 **4.** 60 **5.** 200

Quick Check **1a.** $\frac{3}{20}$ **b.** $\frac{10}{63}$ **2.** 10 ft **3a.** $28\frac{3}{16}$ **b.** $27\frac{1}{2}$ **4.** $2\frac{5}{8}$mi

Lesson 4-2 pp. 132–134

Check Skills You'll Need **1.** Multiplication Property of Equality **2.** 30 **3.** 36 **4.** 8,750 **5.** 0.72

Quick Check

1.

32; $8 \div \frac{1}{4} = 32$

2.

1													
1/8	1/8	1/8	1/8	1/8	1/8	1/8	1/8	1/8	1/8	1/8	1/8	1/8	1/8

14; $1\frac{3}{4} \div \frac{1}{8} = 14$

Lesson 4-3 pp. 136–137

Check Skills You'll Need **1.** List the factors of 4 and 15. Choose the largest number that is a factor of both 4 and 15. **2.** 6 **3.** $\frac{1}{5}$ **4.** $\frac{1}{7}$ **5.** $\frac{4}{11}$

Quick Check **1a.** $\frac{4}{3}$ or $1\frac{1}{3}$ **b.** $\frac{1}{7}$ **2a.** $\frac{3}{4}$ **b.** $2\frac{2}{5}$ **3.** $\frac{1}{6}$ yard

Lesson 4-4 pp. 140–145

Check Skills You'll Need **1.** The product of the fractions is not 1 **2.** 28 **3.** $\frac{7}{24}$ **4.** $\frac{1}{6}$ **5.** $2\frac{8}{11}$

Quick Check **1a.** about 7 **b.** about 5 **2.** $1\frac{1}{4}$ cups **3a.** 6 **b.** $2\frac{1}{20}$

Checkpoint Quiz 1 **1.** 15 **2.** $23\frac{5}{8}$ **3.** 64 **4.** $\frac{1}{6}$ **5.** $1\frac{11}{21}$ **6.** $\frac{3}{5}$ **7.** $16\frac{1}{3}$ **8.** $2\frac{7}{30}$ **9.** 34 **10.** $4\frac{1}{2}$ **11.** $2\frac{1}{5}$ **12.** $15\frac{1}{2}$ **13.** 39 ft **14.** 24 cookies **15.** about 12

Lesson 4-5 p. 146–148

Check Skills You'll Need **1.** subtraction **2.** 26 **3.** 3.8 **4.** 18.9

Quick Check **1a.** $2\frac{3}{4}$ **b.** $11\frac{1}{4}$ **c.** $3\frac{2}{3}$ **2a.** $\frac{7}{12}$ **b.** $\frac{1}{4}$ **3a.** 30 **b.** 72 **4.** 48 **5.** 20 flags

Chapter 5

Check Your Readiness p. 158

1. 48 **2.** 42 **3.** 24 **4.** 9 **5.** 9 **6.** 16 **7.** 36 **8.** 100 **9.** 2 **10.** 16 **11.** 5 **12.** 25 **13.** $\frac{8}{21}$ **14.** $\frac{1}{2}$ **15.** $3\frac{8}{9}$ **16.** $4\frac{1}{8}$

Lesson 5-1 pp. 160–161

Check Skills You'll Need **1.** The numerator represents the number of parts considered, and the denominator represents the total number of parts. **2.** $\frac{5}{8}$ **3.** $\frac{6}{6}$

Quick Check **1a.** 2 to 4, 2 : 4, $\frac{2}{4}$ **b.** 2 to 6, 2 : 6, $\frac{2}{6}$ **2.** For every 3 dollars earned, 1 dollar is saved. **3.** The ratio of seconds to meters is 2 : 5. Every 2 seconds, Emma ran 5 meters.

Lesson 5-2 pp. 166–167

Check Skills You'll Need **1.** division **2.** 4 **3.** 4 **4.** 5 **5.** 6

Quick Check **1.** 79 cents per pound **2.** 11¢ per ounce; 9¢ per ounce; the 32 ounce container **3a.** $25 **b.** 250 words

Lesson 5-3 pp. 170–172

Check Skills You'll Need **1.** A ratio is a comparison of two numbers by division. **2.** 4 to 12 and 4 : 12 **3.** $\frac{6}{10}$ and 6 : 10 **4.** $\frac{12}{17}$ and 12 to 17 **5.** $\frac{8}{3}$ and 8 : 3

Quick Check **1.** Possible answers: 4 to 6 and 6 to 9 **2.** 9 pages **3.** 25 nickels

Lesson 5-4 pp. 174–175

Check Skills You'll Need **1.** 4 and 6 **2.** 5 **3.** 1 **4.** 4 **5.** 15

Quick Check **1.** 6 feet **2.** 2.5 kilograms **3.** 18 days

Checkpoint Quiz 1 **1.** 18 to 40 and $\frac{18}{40}$ **2.** $2.85 **3.** $45 **4.** Possible answers: 8 to 16 and 12 to 24 **5.** Possible answers: $\frac{4}{6}$ and $\frac{6}{9}$ **6.** Possible answers: 14 to 20 and 21 to 30 **7.** Possible answers: 18 to 10 and 27 to 15 **8.** 6 quarts **9.** 5,000 milligrams **10.** 360 meters

Lesson 5-5 pp. 179–180

Check Skills You'll Need **1.** Equivalent ratios have the same value. **2.** $\frac{4}{10}, \frac{6}{15}$ **3.** $\frac{26}{100}, \frac{39}{150}$ **4.** $\frac{6}{50}, \frac{9}{75}$ **5.** $\frac{2}{20}, \frac{3}{30}$

Quick Check **1.** $\frac{54}{100}$, 54% **2.**

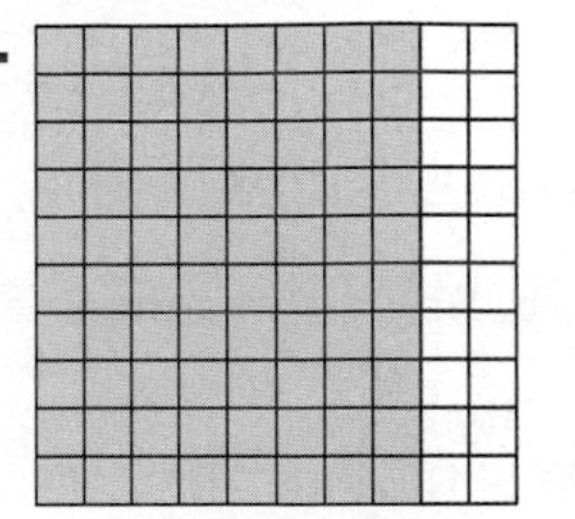

3a. $\frac{3}{4}$; 75% **b.** $\frac{1}{2}$; 50% **c.** $\frac{7}{10}$; 70% **4.** 80%

Lesson 5-6 pp. 184–185

Check Skills You'll Need **1.** 24 hundredths **2.** 0.55

Quick Check **1a.** $\frac{11}{20}$ **b.** $\frac{1}{25}$ **2a.** 0.25 **b.** 0.02 **3a.** 52% **b.** 5% **c.** 50% **4.** 5%

Lesson 5-7 pp. 188–192

Check Skills You'll Need **1.** Write the percent as a fraction with a denominator of 100. Then write the fraction as a decimal. **2.** $\frac{1}{2}$ **3.** $\frac{7}{20}$ **4.** $\frac{12}{25}$ **5.** $\frac{33}{50}$

Quick Check **1a.** $8 **b.** $30 **2a.** 10.92 **b.** 21.78 **3.** 9

Checkpoint Quiz 2 **1.** 35 : 100; 35% **2.** 2 : 5; 40% **3.** 0.74, $\frac{37}{50}$ **4.** 0.06, $\frac{3}{50}$ **5.** 0.6, $\frac{3}{5}$ **6.** 84% **7.** 70% **8.** 5% **9.** 34 questions **10.** $6.30

Lesson 5-8 pp. 193–195

Check Skills You'll Need **1.** percent **2.** $\frac{1}{5}$ **3.** $\frac{1}{20}$ **4.** $\frac{1}{4}$ **5.** $\frac{3}{5}$

Quick Check **1.** 50 games **2.** 30 miles **3.** 24 students

Chapter 6

Check Your Readiness p. 204

1. 79 **2.** 31 **3.** 39 **4.** 31 **5.** 0.6 **6.** 66 **7.** 41 **8.** 72 **9.** 15 **10.** 252 **11.** 12 **12.** 63 **13.** 16 **14.** 24 **15.** 20 **16.** 40

Lesson 6-1 pp. 206–207

Check Skills You'll Need **1.** The Identity Property of Addition states that the sum of any number and 0 is that number. The Identity Property of Multiplication states that the product of any number and 1 is that number. **2.** 9 **3.** 10 **4.** 0

Quick Check **1.** −8; sea level **2.** 5 **3a.** −12 **b.** the distance traveled by the bird

Lesson 6-2 pp. 210–211

Check Skills You'll Need **1.** Two numbers that are opposites are the same distance from zero on a number line, but in opposite directions. **2.** C **3.** D **4.** B **5.** A

Quick Check **1a.** > **b.** < **2.** −50, −25, 75, 100

Lesson 6-3 pp. 213–217

Check Skills You'll Need **1.** Integers are the set of positive whole numbers, their opposites, and zero. **2.** −4 **3.** +10 **4.** −8 **5.** −25

Quick Check **1a.** $\frac{-64}{10}$ **b.** $\frac{9}{1}$ **c.** $\frac{-5}{7}$ **d.** $\frac{-75}{100}$

2a.

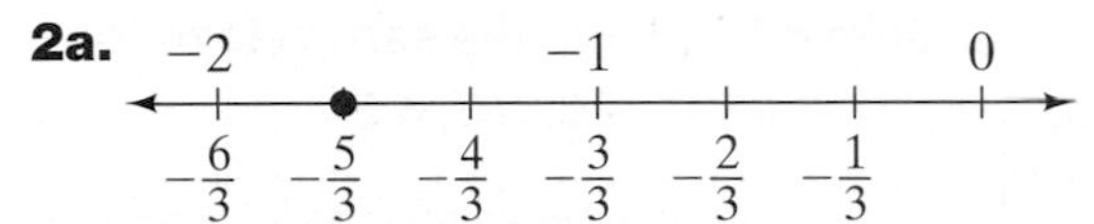

b. 0 1
$-\frac{1}{8}$ 0 $\frac{1}{8}$ $\frac{2}{8}$ $\frac{3}{8}$ $\frac{4}{8}$ $\frac{5}{8}$ $\frac{6}{8}$ $\frac{7}{8}$ $\frac{8}{8}$

c.

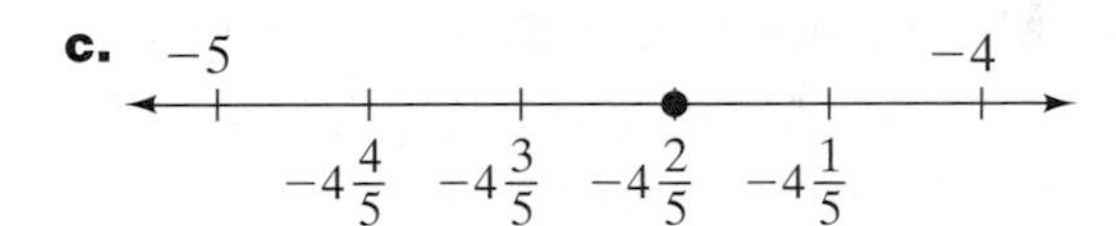

3a.

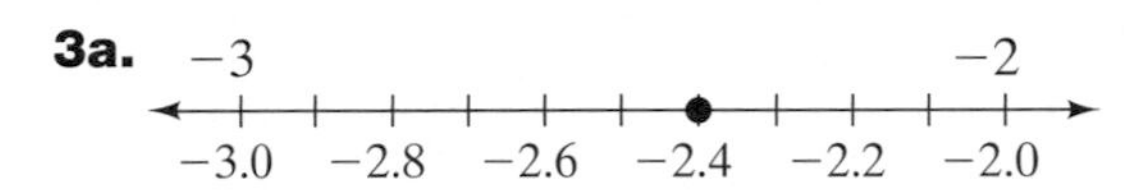

b.

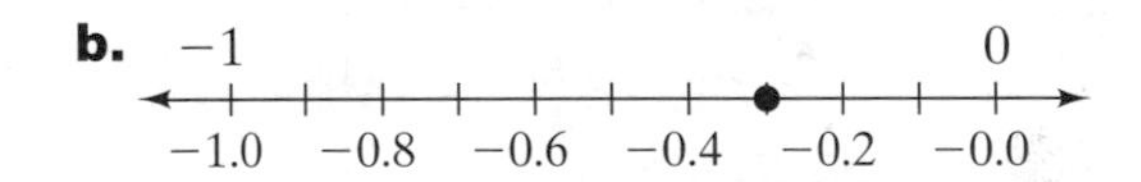

c. 1.5 1.6
1.50 1.52 1.54 1.56 1.58 1.60

4a. **b.** **c.**

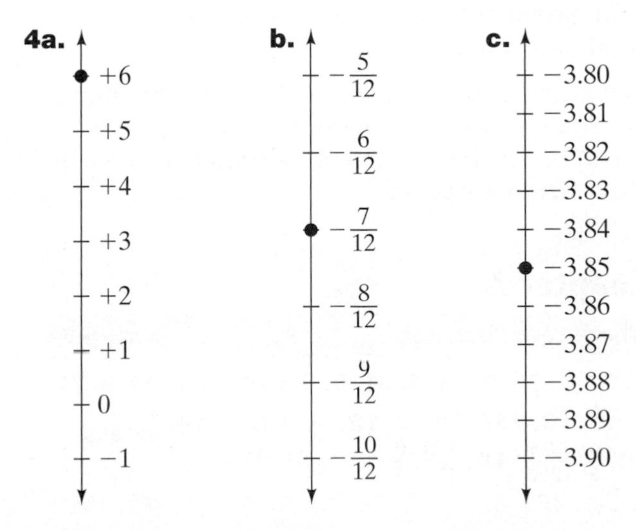

Checkpoint Quiz 1 **1.** 13 **2.** 64 **3.** $\frac{64}{100}$ **4.** $\frac{-43}{9}$

5. 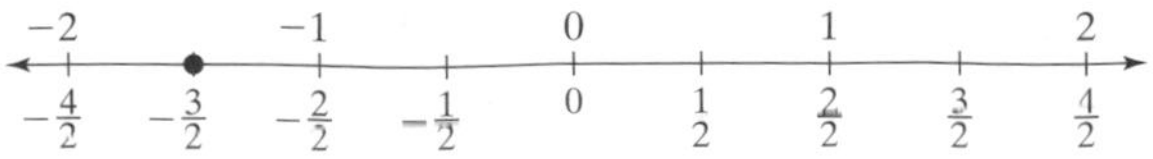

6. −32 **7.** −17, −15, −14, 16, 18
8. 6

Lesson 6-4 pp. 218–220

Check Skills You'll Need **1.** A rational number is any number that can be written as a quotient of two integers where the denominator is not zero.
2. $\frac{6}{1}$ **3.** $\frac{75}{100}$ **4.** $\frac{-4}{10}$ **5.** $\frac{-9}{4}$ **6.** $\frac{-5}{8}$ **7.** $\frac{635}{100}$

Quick Check **1a.** > **b.** < **2a.** < **b.** >
3a. City C **b.** Both cities have the same elevation.
4. $-6\frac{3}{4}$°C, $-6\frac{1}{2}$°, −6.45°C, −6.3°C, 6.2°C

Lesson 6-5 pp. 223–227

Check Skills You'll Need **1.** A number line shows integers from least to greatest. A number to the left of another number on a number line is less than the other number. **2.** > **3.** > **4.** < **5.** <

Quick Check **1.** Let *a* represent the altitude from which most skydivers jump. $a \leq 14{,}500$
2. Let *t* represent the number of hours you spend studying. $t \geq 2$. 

3. no

Checkpoint Quiz 2 **1.** > **2.** < **3.** > **4.** >
5. −4.2°F, $-4\frac{1}{2}$°F, −4.7°F, $-5\frac{1}{4}$°F, −5.5°F
6. $x > -2$ **7.** $d \leq 55$ **8.** $h \geq 48$

Lesson 6-6 pp. 228–229

Check Skills You'll Need **1.** An inequality is a mathematical sentence that contains <, >, ≤, ≥, or ≠. **2.** $x < 5$ **3.** $x \geq 12$

Quick Check **1.** $u \leq 9$ **2.** $z > 9$ **3.** Let p = the number of additional people the restaurant can serve; $p + 97 \leq 115, p \leq 18$; the restaurant can serve at most 18 more people.

Chapter 7

Check Your Readiness p. 238

1. 79 **2.** 31 **3.** 39 **4.** 31 **5.** 0.6 **6.** 66 **7.** 41 **8.** 72
9. 15 **10.** 252 **11.** < **12.** > **13.** = **14.** $\frac{1}{12}, \frac{1}{8}, \frac{1}{3}$
15. $\frac{4}{9}, \frac{7}{12}, \frac{5}{6}$ **16.** $\frac{1}{4}, \frac{1}{2}, \frac{6}{7}$

Lesson 7-1 pp. 241–242

Check Skills You'll Need **1.** 0
2. 

3. 

4. 

5. 

Quick Check **1a.** $B(-3, 2)$ **b.** $D(-2, -3)$ **c.** $E(2, -2)$

2a.-c. See the graph

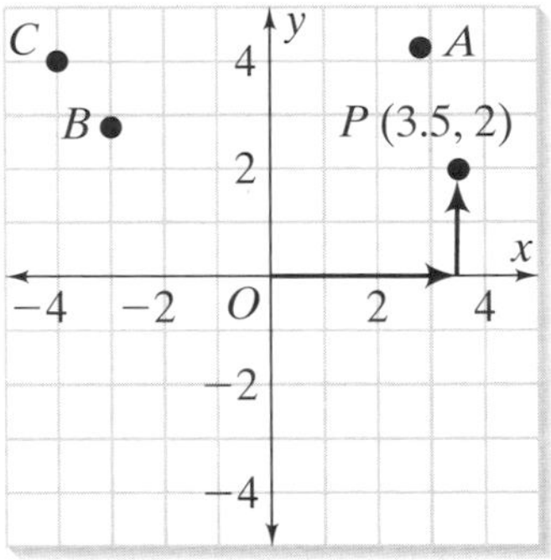

3a. City Hall
b. (3, −1)

Lesson 7-2 pp. 246–250

Check Skills You'll Need **1.** Integers are the set of positive whole numbers, their opposites, and zero. **2.** +50 **3.** −8 **4.** +600 **5.** −10

Quick Check **1a.** 4 **b.** 6 **c.** 3 **2.** 8 m **3.** reflected over the *x*-axis

Checkpoint Quiz 1 **1.** (1.5, 1.5) **2.** (−2, −1.5)
3. (−3.5, 2) **4.** (0.5, 2) **5.** 7 **6.** 3 **7.** 1 **8.** 8
9. 12 feet **10a.** (−4, −1) **b.** (4, 1)

Lesson 7-3 pp. 251–252

Check Skills You'll Need **1.** An expression does not have an equal sign. **2.** 11 **3.** 6 **4.** 12 **5.** 18

Quick Check

1a.

Input	Output
16	4
−24	−6
36	9

b.

Input	Output
−6	−14
−1	−9
4	−4

2. The time spent studying is the independent variable, and the test score is the dependent variable. **3.** $y = 20x$

Lesson 7-4 pp. 255–260

Check Skills You'll Need **1.** The coordinate plane is a surface formed by the intersection of two number lines. **2.** (2, 3) **3.** (−2, 1) **4.** (1, −5) **5.** (−3, 0)

Quick Check

1. not linear; see graph

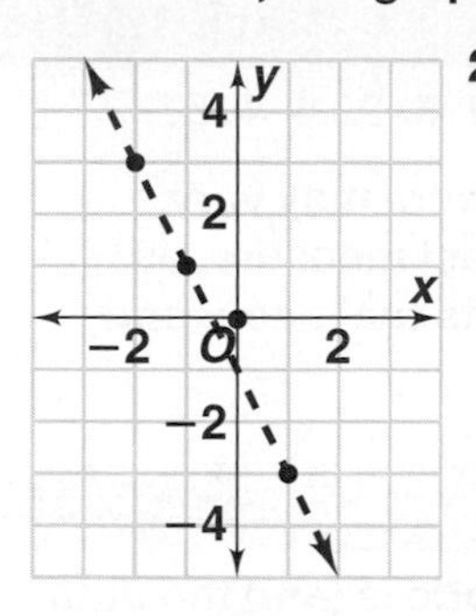

2.

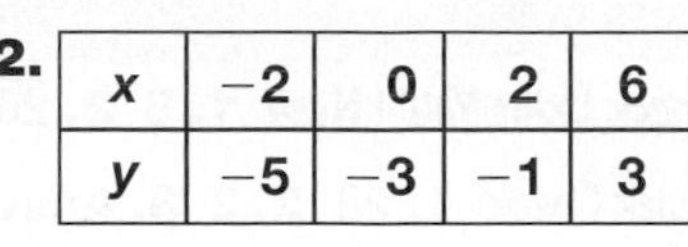

x	−2	0	2	6
y	−5	−3	−1	3

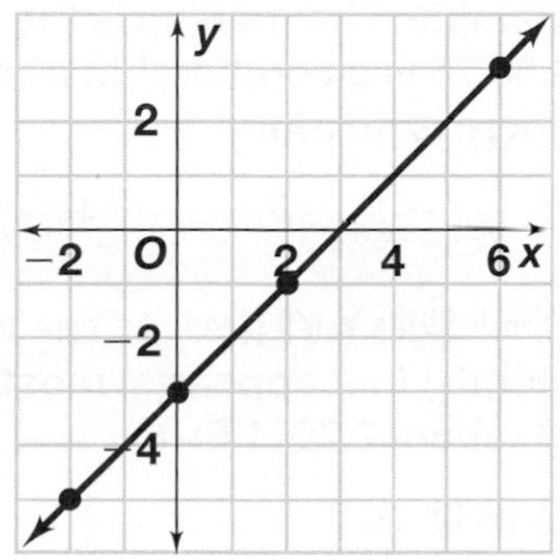

3.

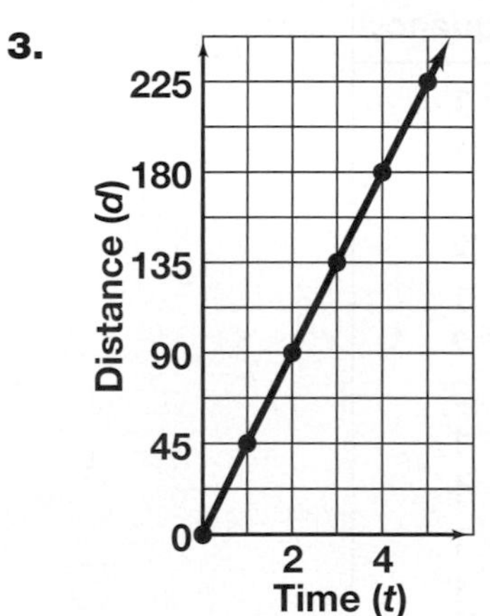

t	d
0	0
1	45
2	90
3	135
4	180
5	225

Checkpoint Quiz 2

1.

Input	Output
12	−24
36	−72
50	−100
105	−210

2.

Input	Output
64	49
78	63
99	84
120	105

3.

Input	Output
−9	−3
3	1
24	8
30	10

4.

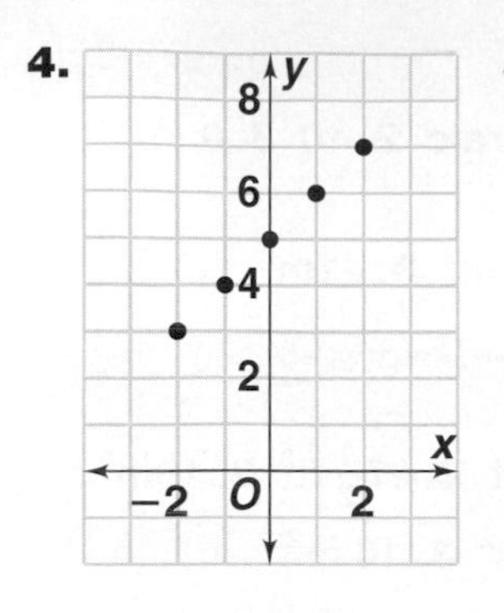

5.

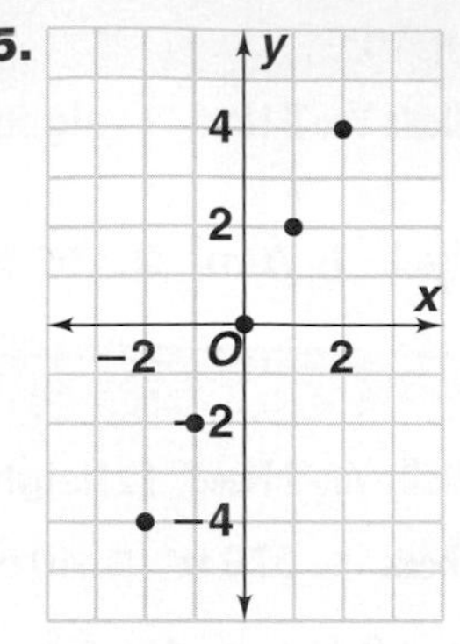

6.

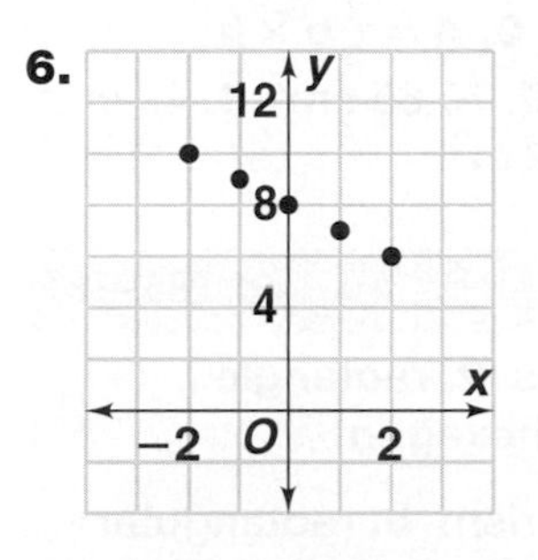

7.

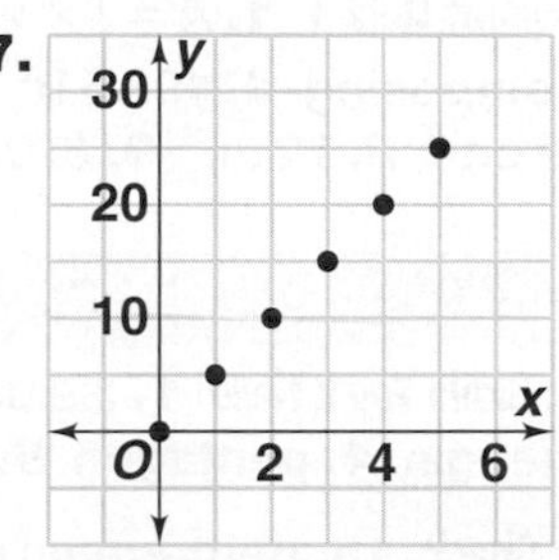

Lesson 7-5 pp. 261–262

Check Skills You'll Need **1.** a mathematical phrase with numbers, variables, and operation symbols **2.** $n + 6$ **3.** $3n$ **4.** $2n - 4$ **5.** $n \div 12$ or $\frac{n}{12}$

Quick Check **1.** $480; Students' tables will vary. See sample table.

Number of Hours	Dollars Earned
8	96
15	180
20	240
40	480

2. 165 miles: Students' graphs will vary. See sample graph.

3. $y = 4x$; $35.00

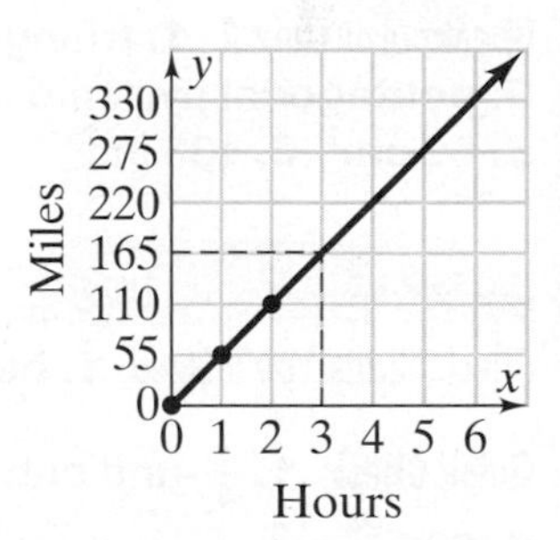

Chapter 8

Check Your Readiness p. 272

1. 0.56 **2.** 10.4 **3.** 8.75 **4.** 48 **5.** 13 **6.** 3.2 **7.** 4.1 **8.** $\frac{1}{5}$ **9.** $\frac{15}{2}$, or $7\frac{1}{2}$ **10.** $\frac{5}{36}$ **11.** $\frac{49}{4}$, or $12\frac{1}{4}$ **12.** $\frac{385}{8}$, or $48\frac{1}{8}$ **13.** $\frac{304}{15}$, or $20\frac{4}{15}$

Lesson 8-1 — pp. 275–276

Check Skills You'll Need **1.** algebraic **2.** 10 **3.** 6 **4.** 5 **5.** 12

Quick Check **1.** $70 m^2$ **2.** $259.5 m^2$ **3.** $41 m^2$

Lesson 8-2 — pp. 280–284

Check Skills You'll Need **1.** height **2.** $27\frac{1}{2} ft^3$ **3.** $18 m^3$

Quick Check **1.** $370 ft^2$ **2.** $40 m^2$ **3.** $16 m^2$

Checkpoint Quiz 1 **1.** $A = l \times w$ **2.** $A = \frac{1}{2}b \times h$ **3.** Composing **4.** $193.6 ft^2$ **5.** $70.65 cm^2$ **6.** $49 cm^2$ **7.** $89 cm^2$ **8.** $72 in.^2$ **9.** $629.2 m^2$

Lesson 8-3 — pp. 286–287

Check Skills You'll Need **1.** 3 sides **2.** rectangle **3.** triangle **4.** pentagon **5.** hexagon

Quick Check **1a.** pentagonal prism **b.** rectangular prism **c.** triangular prism **2.** rectangular prism

Lesson 8-4 — pp. 292–296

Check Skills You'll Need **1.** The area of a piece of paper is the two-dimensional space a rectangle of the same dimensions as the paper encloses. **2.** $21 m^2$ **3.** $60 m^2$

Quick Check **1.** Answers may vary. Sample:

2. $1,728 m^2$
3. $340 ft^2$

Checkpoint Quiz 2 **1.** triangular pyramid **2.** cone **3.** pentagonal pyramid **4.** hexagonal prism **5.** $62 cm^2$ **6.** $133 in.^2$

Lesson 8-5 — pp. 299–300

Check Skills You'll Need **1.** base **2.** 110.5 **3.** 2.7

Quick Check **1.** $\frac{1}{4}$-unit cube; $\frac{5}{16}$ cubic unit **2.** $596\frac{24}{25} m^3$

Chapter 9

Check Your Readiness — p. 308

1. 18 **2.** 40 **3.** 63.1 **4.** 423.9 **5.** 105.82 **6.** 25.87 **7.** 20.21 **8.** 1.06 **9.** 1.8 **10.** 14.203 **11.** 22.6 **12.** 4.03

Lesson 9-1 — pp. 311–312

Check Skills You'll Need **1.** quotient **2.** 27.5 **3.** 42.75 **4.** 59.35

Quick Check **1.** 4 **2.** 20 **3.** The outlier increases the value of the mean.

Lesson 9-2 — pp. 315–316

Check Skills You'll Need **1.** 5 **2.** 20 **3.** 22.4 **4.** 57

Quick Check **1.** 28 **2.** 2 **3.** Answers may vary. Sample: The median is the best measure, as 288.75 is an outlier that affects the mean, and there is no mode.

Lesson 9-3 — pp. 319–320

Check Skills You'll Need **1.** The mode is (are) the data item(s) that appear(s) most often. **2.** 5.25; 5; 4 **3.** about 2.29; 1.5; 0

Quick Check

1.

Initial	Tally	Frequency
A	I	1
B	I	1
C	I	1
D	II	2
J	I	1
K	II	2
L	III	3
P	I	1
S	I	1
T	I	1
V	I	1

The mode is L.

2. Number of Sales Calls

```
  X
  X                 X
  X X               X
  X X             X X
X X X X       X X X X
-------------------
0 1 2 3 4 5 6 7 8 9
     Sales Calls
```

3. 32

Lesson 9-4 pp. 323–327

Check Skills You'll Need **1.** median **2.** Most of the students are 11 or 12 years old.

Quick Check **1.** Least value: 7, lower quartile: 17, median: 22, upper quartile: 33.5 **2.** minutes; about three fourths

Checkpoint Quiz 1 **1.** about 20.6, 20, 19 **2.** 6 **3.** No; there are no data values that vary greatly from the rest. **4.** The mean or the median; the mode is too low to represent the data.

5.

Breakfast Cereals	
Fat (g)	Frequency
0	8
1	8
2	5
3	3

6. 3.5; 6 **7.** about half **8.** No; the median is 4.5 and the number of events makes sense for whole numbers only.

Lesson 9-5 pp. 328–329

Check Skills You'll Need **1.** frequency table **2.** 6 **3.** 2.25

Quick Check **1a.** 20–29 minutes **b.** less than 30 minutes **2.** A

Lesson 9-6 pp. 334–336

Check Skills You'll Need **1.** upper quartile **2.** 39 **3.** 15.6 **4.** 3

Quick Check **1a.** 5.5 **b.** There is less variability because the average distance is closer to the mean. This makes sense because 22 is closer to 24 than 17. **2a.** 7.5 **b.** The smaller IQR means that there is less variability in the new set of data.

Lesson 9-7 pp. 339–344

Check Skills You'll Need **1.** mean absolute deviation **2.** 20, 36, 38 **3.** 12, 17, 22.5 **4.** 4, 5, 6

Quick Check **1a.** y; z **1b.** There would be a gap between 4 and 6. **2a.** They are both symmetric, but this distribution has gaps in the data between 23 and 25 and between 25 and 27. This has 3 peaks, 22, 25, and 28. This is more spread out. **b.** Since the values are more spread out, it is obvious that there is more variability and the interquartile range will be greater. Since it is still symmetrical and has one peak at the center, it will have equal mean, median, and mode. **c.** It would still be symmetrical with gaps and have 3 peaks and equal mean and median, but it would have 2 modes at peaks 21 and 29.

Checkpoint Quiz 2 **1.** 33

2.

Interval	Tally	Frequency
60–69	||	2
70–79	|	1
80–89	卌 ||	7
90–99	||||	4

3.

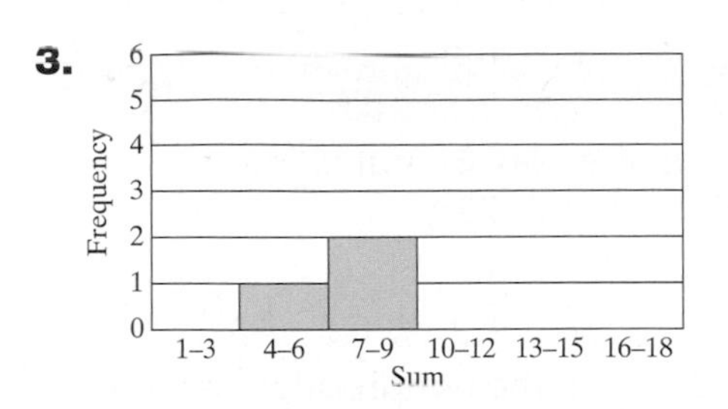

4. mammals: 24.25; amphibians: 4 **5.** mammals: 36.5; amphibians: 6.5 **6.** The mammal lifespans have far greater variability. **7.** The box for the amphibian data is more compact because the data cluster near 20 years.

Lesson 9-8 pp. 344–345

Check Skills You'll Need **1.** variability **2.** 2 **3.** 370 **4.** 8

Quick Check **1a.** No; there is only one possible answer. **b.** yes; possible answers include whole or mixed numbers involving one half. Answers may also vary because a person can wear different sizes for different types of shoe. **2a.** Biased; The words "delicious," "sweet," and "bitter" make the question biased. Rewrite as: Do you prefer grapes or strawberries? **b.** Biased: The question forces people to use fast service as the criterion. People may also consider price, reputation, and other factors. Rewrite as: Which internet service in your area do you prefer?

Selected Answers

Chapter 1

Lesson 1-1 — pp. 4–5

EXERCISES **1.** Comm. Prop. of Add. **5.** 50 **7.** 61 **9.** 66 **17.** 470 **19.** 1,300 **27.** Associative Property of Addition **33.** $360

Lesson 1-2 — pp. 8–9

EXERCISES **1.** expression **3.** multiplication **7.** 6 **15.** 68 **29.** $162 **33.** 76 g

Lesson 1-3 — pp. 14–15

EXERCISES **1.** 5; it is in the hundredths place. 7 is in the thousandths place. **3.** 3 tenths **5.** 3 thousandths **7.** 1 + 0.2 **9.** 7 + 0.5 + 0.02 **11.** two and three tenths **13.** six thousandths **21.** 40.009; 40 + 0.009 **23.** 0.700; 0.7 **27.** 2.7 **29.** 10.96 **35.** B: $0.9 million; $900,000 C: $1.6 million; $1,600,000 **37.** 4 tenths, or 0.4 **38.** 4 tens, or 40 **49.** 70

Lesson 1-4 — pp. 19–20

EXERCISES **1.** The decimal points were not lined up before subtracting. 5.8 − 2 = 3.8 **3.** 1.38 **5.** $9 **9.** about 6; 6.644 **11.** about 21; 21.516 **15.** about $15 **17.** about $48 **19.** about 3; 2.83 **21.** about 3; 3.05 **27.** $47.99 **29.** < **31.** > **33.** 1.26 million **41.** 800 **43.** 1,400

Lesson 1-5 — pp. 25–26

EXERCISES **1.** 7; there are 3 decimal places in the first number and 4 decimal places in the second number. So 3 + 4 = 7. **7.** 262.0 **9.** 56.414 **11.** 17.1 **13.** 2.34 **19.** 0.32 **21.** 0.63 **37.** 40; Methods may vary. Sample: paper and pencil **41.** 483.48 million mi **47.** 11.61

Lesson 1-6 — pp. 31–32

EXERCISES **1.** quotient

3. 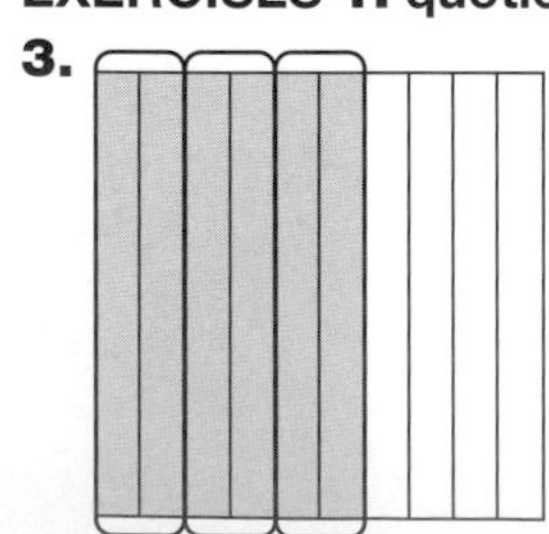

5. about 10 **6.** about 300 **15.** 7.2 **17.** 0.315 **28.** $7.75 **31.** $5.97 **36.** 20.30 **37.** 8.03, 8.035, 8.3, 8.308 **39.** 33.16

Chapter Review — pp. 40–41

1. Ident. Prop. of Add. **2.** expanded form **3.** order of operations **4.** expression **5.** Assoc. Prop. of Add **6.** 350 **7.** 20 **8.** 101 **9.** 130 **10.** 690 **11.** 4,300 **12.** 37 **13.** 0 **14.** 42 **15.** five hundred twenty-five and five tenths **16.** five thousand, two hundred fifty-five ten-thousandths **17.** five and twenty-five thousandths **18.** fifty and twenty-five ten-thousandths **19.** 45.2 **20.** 98.6 **21.** 5.13 **22.** 1.25 **23.** 0.27, 0.20 + 0.07 **24.** 42.6, 40 + 2 + 0.6 **25–30.** Answers may vary. Samples are given. **25.** about 357; 357.48 **26.** about 1; 0.931 **27.** about 3; 3.4 **28.** about 2; 1.7 **29.** about 4; 3.867 **30.** about 7; 7.4 **31.** 35.4 **32.** 9.18 **33.** 31.458 **34.** 10.4 **35.** $66.69 **36.** 2.02 **37.** 480 **38.** 6.94 **39.** 170 **40.** 0.16

Chapter 2

Lesson 2-1 — pp. 47–48

EXERCISES **1.** Answers may vary. Sample: A numerical expression is a mathematical phrase with only numbers and operation symbols. An algebraic expression is a mathematical expression with one or more variables. **3.** 20 **5.** 16 **7.** 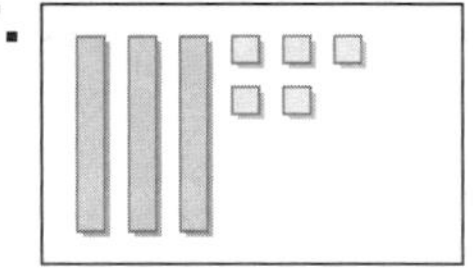 **9.** [figure]

15. 8 **17.** 193

21.

x	$x + 6$
1	7
4	10
7	13

25. 75 **27.** 4,620 bricks **29.** 10 hits; 15 misses **33.** 29.16

Lesson 2-2 — pp. 52–53

EXERCISES **1.** Answers may vary. Sample: Your grandfather is 50 years older than you. The expression $y + 50$ relates his age to yours. **3.** $m + 4$ **5.** $6 \times z$ **7.** $k - 34$ **9.** $50 + d$ **17.** $n - 3$ **19.** $n + 2$ **25.** $m \div n - 5$ **27.** $h + 2$ **29.** $(20 + 0.75n)t$ **33.** 14.505

Lesson 2-3 — pp. 58–59

EXERCISES **1.** The value(s) of the variable(s) that make(s) the equation true is (are) unknown. **3.** 15 **5.** 3 **7.** false **9.** true **11.** false **13.** true **15.** 2 **17.** 4.3 **29.** 3.3 lb

Lesson 2-4	pp. 64–65

EXERCISES 1. Subtracting 6 **3.** 18 **5.** 2.7 **7.** 48 **9.** 39
19. y = the year Mozart was born; $y + 6 = 1762$; $y = 1756$
21. m = number of minutes of music before adding song; $m + 4 = 120$; $m = 116$
23. 10 minutes **25.** 8.2 **27.** 0.29 **29.** 5.5 **33.** 16

Lesson 2-5	pp. 68–69

EXERCISES 1. She subtracted 4 from each side instead of adding 4 to each side. **3.** C **5.** B **7.** 42 **9.** 108 **21.** 12 **25.** 0

Lesson 2-6	pp. 72–73

EXERCISES 1. The Multiplication Property of Equality states that you can multiply each side of an equation by the same nonzero number and the equation will be the same. The Division Property states the same is true for division. **3.** B **5.** A **7.** 14 **9.** 9.5 **11.** 18 **19.** 441 **21.** 51,772 **29.** about 8.25 feet **31.** 0.2 **33.** 3.42 **40.** Six and Seven hundredths

Chapter Review	pp. 00–00

1. evaluate **2.** algebraic expression **3.** solution **4.** variable **5.** equation **6.** 8. **7.** 49. **8.** 42 **9.** $x \div 12$ **10.** $2b$ **11.** $h + k$ **12.** $n + 8$ **13.** $7n$ **14.** $n \div 3$ **15.** false **16.** true **17.** false **18.** 5 **19.** 8 **20.** 8 **21.** 5,640 **22.** 7 **23.** 1.4 **24.** 6.06 **25.** 129.7 lb **26.** 40 **27.** 56 **28.** 128 **29.** 2.5 **30.** 10.8 **31.** 60.8 **32.** 0.9 **33.** $16.68 **34.** 102

Chapter 3

Lesson 3-1	pp. 86–87

EXERCISES 1. If the number is divisible by 2, then the number is even; otherwise, the number is odd. **3.** C **5.** A **7.** no **11.** 3 and 5 **13.** 2 and 3 **23.** no **27.** 4 **29.** 4 **31.** Yes; $5 + 6 + 6 + 1 = 18$ and 18 is divisible by 9, so 5661 or $56.61, is divisible by 9. **33.** $1.00 **39.** 36

Lesson 3-2	pp. 90–91

EXERCISES 1. The exponent tells how many times the base is used as a factor. **3.** 3^2 **5.** 9^3 **7.** 2, 2, 2 **9.** 29^1; 29; 1 **11.** 25^3; 25; 3 **19.** 64 **21.** 25 **29.** 64 **31.** 40 **33.** 2^8 cells **35.** 5 and 6 **37.** H **39.** true

Lesson 3-3	pp. 94–95

EXERCISES 1. A prime number has exactly two factors and a composite number has more than two factors. **3.** 7; 7 has just two factors, 1 and 7. **5.** 1, 2, 4, 7, 14, 28 **7.** 1, 17 **15.** Prime; the only factors are 1 and 67. **19.** $2 \times 3 \times 7$ **21.** $2^4 \times 5^2$ **27.** 1,001 **29.** 9 rows **32.** 1×116; 2×58; 4×29 **33.** 3, 5; 5, 7; 11, 13; 17, 19; 29, 31; 41, 43; 59, 61; 71, 73 **37.** >

Lesson 3-4	pp. 99–100

EXERCISES 1. When two numbers have 1 as their only common factor, then the GCF = 1. **3.** B **5.** A **7.** factors of 24: 1, 2, 3, 4, 6, 8, 12, 24; factors of 45: 1, 3, 5, 9, 15, 45; GCF of 24 and 45: 3 **9.** factors of 30: 1, 2, 3, 5, 6, 10, 15, 30; factors of 35: 1, 5, 7, 35; GCF of 30 and 35: 5

13.
2) 24 60 GCF = 12
2) 12 30
3) 6 15
2 5

15.
3) 27 30 GCF = 3
9 10

19.

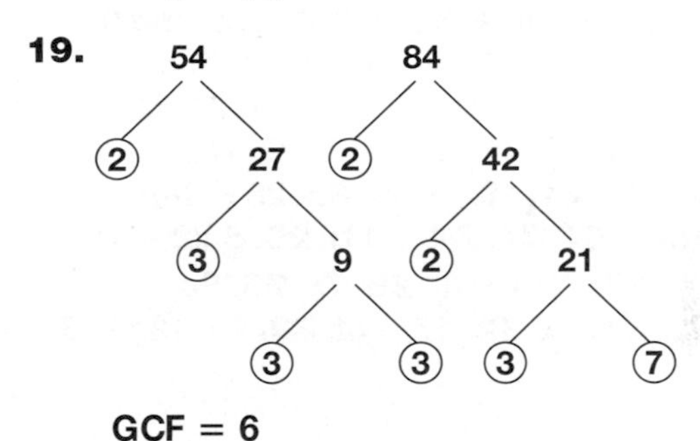

GCF = 6

21.

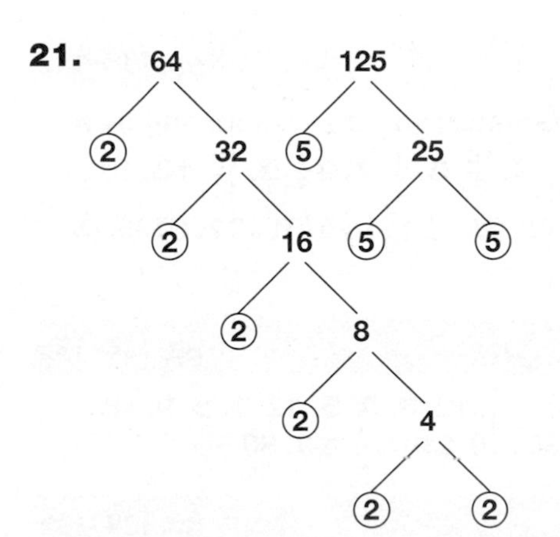

25. $9 **27.** 140 **31.** 7 groups; 2 counselors; 11 campers **33.** 2

Lesson 3-5 pp. 103–104

EXERCISES 1. Answers may vary. Sample: One number has many multiples. **3.** 16, 24, 32, 40 **5.** 48 **7.** 30 **9.** 80 **19.** 72 **21.** 56 **29.** 120th customer **31.** 48 **33a.** 2, 4, 5 **b.** 40 **35.** $2x$ **37.** $200xy$ **41.** $0.5 + 0.01$

Lesson 3-6 pp. 107–108

1. $3x + 15$ **6.** $40d - 150$ **8.** $18y - 36z + 72$ **10.** $4(3 + 4)$ **12.** $22(3 + 2)$ **19.** $3(3x + 4)$ **28.** \$27.00 **30.** $10(8p + 3q + r)$ **33.** 265 miles **38.** 216 trees **42.** G **44.** Estimate: 8, 8.28

Lesson 3-7 pp. 113–114

1. $9b$ **3.** $5x$ **8.** $10 - 3w$ **9.** $14x + 24y$ **11.** $4s + 3t$ **15.** Answers may vary. Sample: You can use the Commutative Property to change the order in which you add or multiply and you can use the Associative Property to change the way you group the numbers you are adding or multiplying. **17.** $256 - 36x$ **19.** H **21.** 34 **24.** 5.8

Chapter Review pp. 120–121

1. equivalent fractions **2.** common factor **3.** prime factorization **4.** 3 and 9 **5.** 3, 5, and 9 **6.** 2, 3, and 9 **7.** 2, 3, 5, 9, and 10 **8.** 17 **9.** 5 **10.** $2^2 \times 7$ **11.** 3×17 **12.** $2^2 \times 5^2$ **13.** 2×5^3 **14.** 2 **15.** 2 **16.** 5 **17.** 8 **18.** 132 **19.** 140 **20.** $2x - 6y + 14$ **21.** $10x + 30$ **22.** $28 + 14n$ **23.** $24x + 16y - 64$ **24.** $2(4 + 11)$ **25.** $50(2 + 1)$ **26.** $9(2x + 7)$ **27.** $8(7n + 6)$ **28.** $7x$ **29.** 9c **30.** $21b + 2c$ **31.** $7x$ **32.** $17 - 6t$ **33.** $f + 12g - 3$

Chapter 4

Lesson 4-1 pp. 130–131

EXERCISES 1. Greater; you are multiplying by a greater number. **3.** $\frac{10}{3}$ **5.** $\frac{1}{2}$ **7.** $3\frac{1}{8}$ **9.** $\frac{10}{11}$ **13.** $10\frac{1}{2}$ **17.** \$1,017 **21.** 48 **25 a.** $1\frac{5}{6}$ **b.** $5\frac{1}{2}$ ft **27.** \$195.75 **29.** $5\frac{1}{4}$ **33.** 64

Lesson 4-2 pp. 134–135

EXERCISES 1. $3 \div \frac{1}{4}$; 12 **3.** A **5.** 12 **7.** 8 **9.** 48 **15.** 20 **17.** 12 **25.** 10 **29.** $5\frac{1}{2}$ **33.** 80

Lesson 4-3 pp. 138–139

EXERCISES 1. 1 **5.** 2 **7.** 7 **9.** $\frac{3}{5}$ **11.** $11\frac{2}{3}$ **15.** $2\frac{2}{3}$ **17.** $7\frac{1}{3}$ **23.** $\frac{1}{9}$ yard

25. 24;

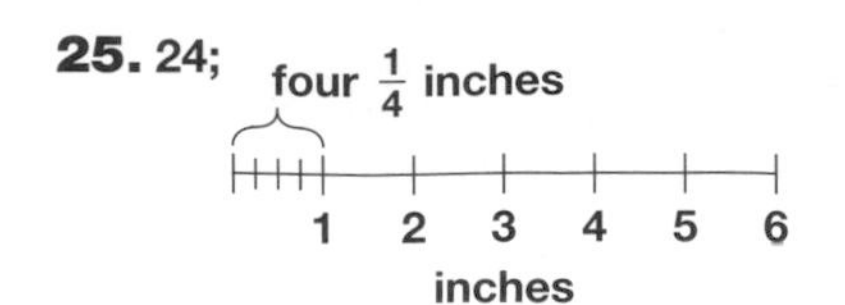

27. 2 **31.** about $1\frac{3}{10}$ times more **33.** 4 **37.** 2, 3

Lesson 4-4 pp. 142–143

EXERCISES 1. about 3 **3.** Annie; Jocelyn incorrectly renamed $4\frac{1}{2}$ as $\frac{8}{2}$. **5.** about 7 **7.** about 2 inches per hour **9.** $1\frac{7}{12}$ **11.** $\frac{2}{9}$ **13.** 4 **19.** $1\frac{1}{25}$ **23.** \$4.55 **25.** 30 books **31.** 2×7^2

Lesson 4-5 pp. 149–150

EXERCISES 1. Answers may vary. Sample: Let $b = 8$. Since $\frac{8}{4} = 2$, b must be greater than 8. **3.** $\frac{5}{2}$ **5.** 44 **7.** 10 **9.** $\frac{13}{45}$ **11.** $\frac{1}{8}$ **13.** $1\frac{1}{9}$ **20.** \$24 **23.** $4\frac{1}{6}$ **27.** $\frac{d}{12} = 14\frac{1}{2}$; 174 mi **29.** 4 **33.** $16\frac{1}{3}$

Chapter Review pp. 154–155

1. 12 **2.** 12 **3.** 80 **4.** 84 **5.** $\frac{3}{10}$ **6.** $\frac{2}{39}$ **7.** $17\frac{1}{2}$ **8.** $3\frac{7}{8}$ **9.** $6\frac{14}{15}$ **10.** $20\frac{15}{22}$ **11.** $\frac{1}{3}c$ **12.** 12 **13.** 8 **14.** 3 **15.** No; Sample answer: Marcus can only make 2 shelves. **16.** 3 **17.** 4 **18.** 6 **19.** $\frac{5}{36}$ **20.** 16 **21.** $5\frac{2}{3}$ **22.** $\frac{5}{11}$ **23.** $\frac{8}{9}$ **24.** $1\frac{3}{7}$ **25.** $\frac{2}{25}$ **26.** $4\frac{17}{52}$ **27.** $12\frac{3}{7}$ **28.** 20 buckets **29.** 1; $\frac{33}{35}$ **30.** 3; $2\frac{76}{105}$ **31.** 3; $3\frac{51}{112}$ **32.** 2; $1\frac{11}{13}$ **33.** about 19 appointments **34.** $\frac{1}{4}$ **35.** $\frac{7}{24}$ **36.** $3\frac{17}{25}$ **37.** $3\frac{13}{18}$ **38.** 96 **39.** 25 **40.** 2 **41.** $\frac{3}{4}$

Chapter 5

Lesson 5-1 pp. 162–163

EXERCISES 1. $\frac{9}{5}$ is a comparison of two numbers by division; $1\frac{4}{5}$ is not. **3.** B **5.** A **7.** 24 to 11, 24 : 11, $\frac{24}{11}$ **9.** The ratio of boys to girls is 4 to 5, because for every 4 boys there are 5 girls. **13.** Yes. Since there is an equal number of red and white roses, then for every red rose there is 1 white rose, so the ratio is 1 to 1. **21.** $\frac{15}{32}$

Lesson 5-2 pp. 168–169

EXERCISES 1. 40 miles in 1 hour; a unit rate gives the speed per 1 unit of a quantity, which in this case is hours, or 1 hour. **3.** C **5.** D **7.** 23 desks per classroom **11.** \$.15 per oz; \$.16 per oz; 16 oz for \$2.39 **15.** 45 ft **19.** 208 words in 8 min **23.** About 28.6 miles per gallon; answers may vary. Sample: I divided 279.9 by 9.8. **25.** 0.15 mi/s **29.** $2\frac{1}{2}$

Lesson 5-3 pp. 172–173

EXERCISES **1.** Answers will vary. Possible answer: 1 : 2 and 2 : 4 **3.** 10 girls **5.** Possible answers: 10 to 8, 15 to 12, 20 to 16, 25 to 20 **9.** Possible answers: 16:14, 24:21, 32:28, 40:35 **11.** 12 inches **15.** 15 tulips **19.** Yes. Possible explanation: 4 cups of flour will be enough to make 6 dozen cookies which is 72 cookies. **23.** $6 **27.** $\frac{1}{6}$

Lesson 5-4 pp. 176–177

EXERCISES **1.** 100 g is not equal to 1 kg. 1,000 g is equal to 1 kg. **3.** 3 pounds **5.** 4 feet **7.** 12 cups **9.** 1.55 kilometers **13.** 6 minutes **15.** 396,000 yards **21.** You need to know how many kilograms equal 1 pound. **25.** 20 to 17, 20 : 17, $\frac{20}{17}$

Lesson 5-5 pp. 181–182

EXERCISES **1.** $\frac{32}{100}$; 32% **3.** 67% **5.** 90% **7.** $\frac{64}{100}$; 64%

11. 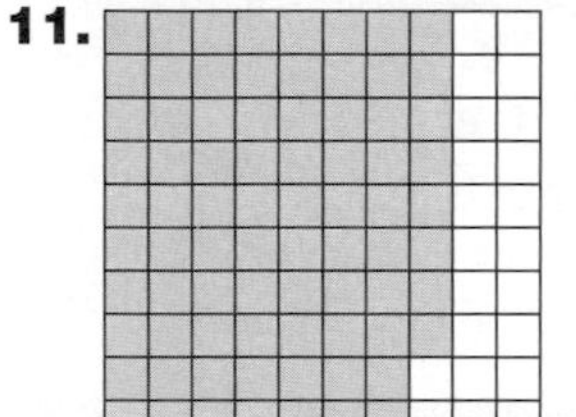 **13.** 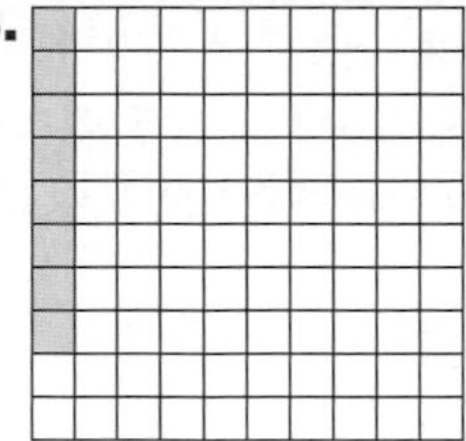

15. $\frac{4}{5}$; 80% **21.** 60% **23.** 84% **27.** 70% **29.** 52% **31.** about 19% **39.** 125

Lesson 5-6 pp. 185–187

EXERCISES **1.** The ratio does not compare a number to 100. **5.** $\frac{7}{10}$ **7.** $\frac{1}{20}$ **15.** 0.15 **17.** 0.82 **25.** 0.06 **27.** 8% **29.** 22% **31.** 95% **33.** 25% **39.** C **43.** $\frac{1}{5}$, 22%, 0.24, $\frac{1}{4}$ **49.** 75% **51.** 25% **55.** 12

Lesson 5-7 pp. 190–191

EXERCISES **1.** 5 **3.** 3 **5.** 30 **7.** 126 **9.** 616 **18.** $16 **19.** 36 **22.** 90 dancers **25.** 6 **27.** 152 **29.** No; 50% off is half the price. The 10%-off coupon is applied to a price that is less than $60. **33.** $270 **35.** Store B has a better rate; $\frac{2}{3}$ is equal to $66\frac{2}{3}$%, which is greater than 60%. **39.** $\frac{2}{5}$

Lesson 5-8 pp. 195–196

EXERCISES **1.** 90 **3.** $10; check student diagrams. **5.** 250 **7.** 250 **9.** 5 **11.** 50 **13.** 48 **17.** $1.36 **19.** 6 games **23.** $525 **27.** 5 quarts **29.** 2.65 km

Chapter Review pp. 200–201

EXERCISES **1.** D **2.** A **3.** B **4.** C **5.** 15 to 23, 15 : 23, $\frac{15}{23}$ **6.** 15 to 8, 15 : 8, $\frac{15}{8}$ **7.** 23 to 8, 23 : 8, $\frac{23}{8}$ **8.** 15 to 46, 15 : 46, $\frac{15}{46}$ **9.** The ratio of lemons to oranges is 5 : 3 because for every 5 lemons there are 3 oranges. **10.** 40 minutes **11.** $12.50 **12.** $1.40 for 24 ounces

13.

2	4	6	8
3	6	9	12

14.

5	10	20	25
6	12	24	30

15. 8 cups **16.** 2.3 meters **17.** 17,952 feet **18.** 330 yards **19.** $\frac{1}{4}$, 25% **20.** $\frac{1}{2}$, 50% **21.** $\frac{3}{5}$, 60% **22.** 80% **23.** 75% **24.** 90% **25.** 30% **26.** $\frac{2}{5}$, 0.40 **27.** $\frac{1}{4}$, 0.25 **28.** $\frac{14}{25}$, 0.56 **29.** $\frac{3}{25}$, 0.12 **30.** 19% **31.** 16% **32.** 4% **33.** 70% **34.** 9.6 **35.** $1.20 **36.** 21.6 **37.** 2 **38.** 64 **39.** 65 **40.** 2,000 **41.** 450 **42.** $20.00

Chapter 6

Lesson 6-1 pp. 207–209

EXERCISES **1.** Answers may vary. Sample: Some integers are −1, 0, 1, 2, and 3; −5.7, 0.3, 2.92, and 10.5 are not integers. **3.** *M* **5.** *P* **7.** 100 **9.** −12 **13.** 10 **15.** −14 **17.** 8 **19.** 38 **21.** 9 **23.** −8 **27.** Janet **29.** −6 **33.** −3; 3 **37.** negative **39.** 7; $-|-7| = -7$; The opposite of −7 is 7. **43.** $8\frac{3}{4}$ cups

Lesson 6-2 pp. 211–212

EXERCISES **1.** C **3.** Answers may vary. Sample: On a number line, numbers increase from left to right. Since negative numbers are less than 0, they are on the left. Positive numbers are greater than 0 and on the right, so $a < b$. **5.** $<$ **7.** $<$ **9.** $>$ **11.** $>$ **17.** −5, −2, 0, 2, 5 **19.** −33, −28, −16, −13 **23.** 9 **25.** $<, >$ **29.** 40 **31.** 12

Lesson 6-3 pp. 215–216

EXERCISES **1.** Answers will vary. Samples: 14, −3, 2.8, −0.42, $\frac{1}{2}$, $-\frac{5}{8}$, $1\frac{3}{4}$, $-12\frac{1}{10}$ **3.** *Q* **5.** *P* **7.** Zero is a rational number. It can be expressed as the quotient of two integers in which the denominator is not zero, such as $\frac{0}{1}$ or $\frac{0}{2}$. **9.** $\frac{-7}{4}$ **11.** $\frac{24}{10}$

13. 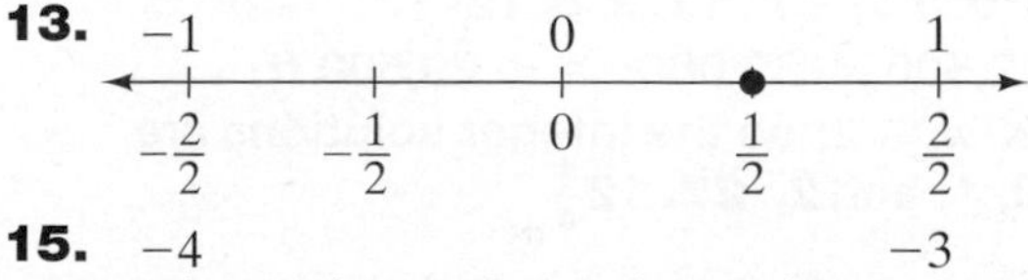

15. 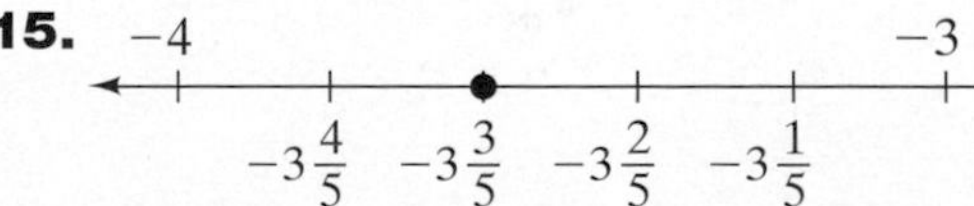

Selected Answers

17.

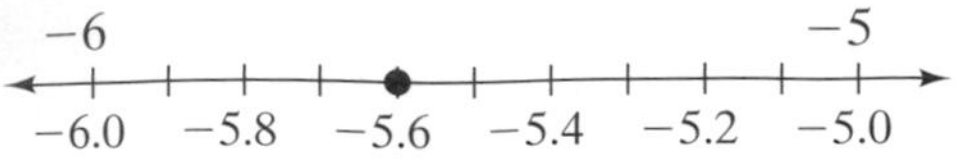

21.

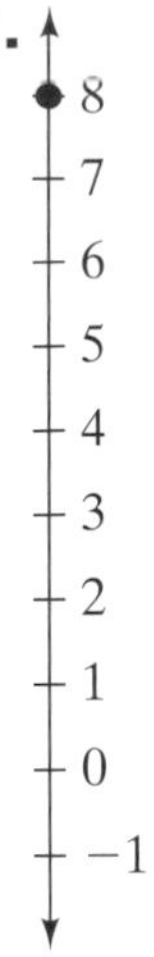

25. 0.276 can be written as the quotient of two integers with 1000 as the denominator: 0.276 = 276/1000. **27.** −0.16 **31.** true; Samples: $3 = \frac{3}{1}$, $-5 = -\frac{5}{1}$ **33.** true; Samples: $-5.7 = -\frac{57}{10}$, $-6\frac{1}{7} = -\frac{43}{7}$

35.

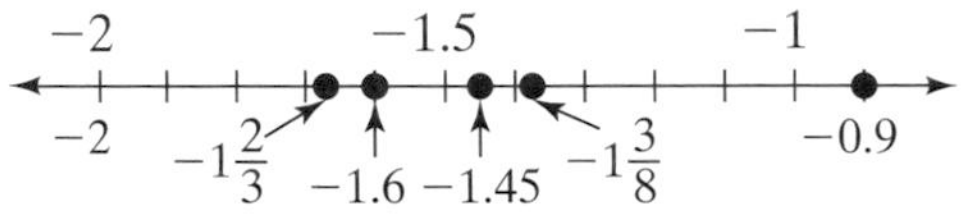

37. $1.50 per square foot

Lesson 6-4 pp. 220–222

EXERCISES **1.** Sample answer: If I plot the numbers on a number line, $-\frac{3}{5}$ is closer to 0 than $-\frac{4}{5}$. **3.** > **5.** $-5\frac{7}{8}$, −5.19, 5.4 **7.** > **9.** > **11.** < **13.** < **15.** $-2.8 < -2\frac{3}{4}$; the water was lower in Week 1. **17.** $-8\frac{6}{20}$, −8.2, $\frac{32}{4}$ **27.** 18.7

Lesson 6-5 pp. 225–226

EXERCISES **1.** solutions **3.** $x < -1$ **5.** $l > 15$

7. $p \leq 4$

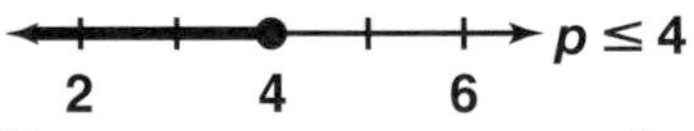

9. $d \geq \$20$

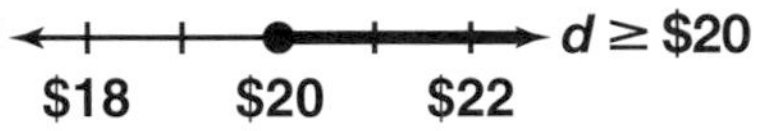

11. a. $x < -25$, **b.** $x > 25$ **13.** true **17.** Answers may vary. Sample: Use an open circle at −20, and shade to the left of the open circle to show numbers less than −20.

19.

Lesson 6-6 pp. 229–230

EXERCISES **1.** addition **3.** subtraction **5.** $c \leq 10$ **7.** $z < 5$ **9.** $j > -7$ **11.** $s \leq 12$ **21.** $a + 2{,}500 < 32{,}000$; $a < 29{,}500$ ft **23.** $-3 < x \leq 2$; so the integer solutions are −2, −1, 0, 1, and 2. **27.** $12\frac{1}{4}$

Chapter Review pp. 234–235

EXERCISES **1.** inequality **2.** rational numbers **3.** opposites **4.** absolute value **5.** −14 **6.** 6 **7.** 4 **8.** −5 **9.** 33 **10.** −20 **11.** 9 **12.** < **13.** < **14.** < **15.** > **16.** −2, −1, 1, 2 **17.** −6, −4, 0, 5 **18.** −7, −3, 5, 9 **19.** $\frac{21}{1}$ **20.** $\frac{31}{10}$ **21.** $\frac{14}{9}$ **22.** $-\frac{7}{1}$

23.

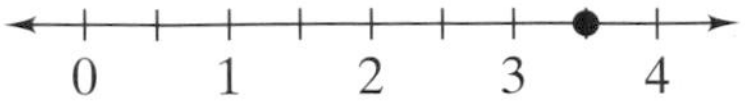

24.

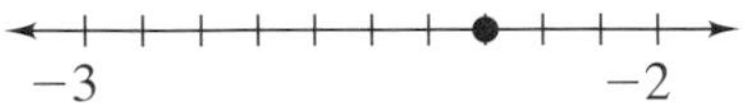

25.

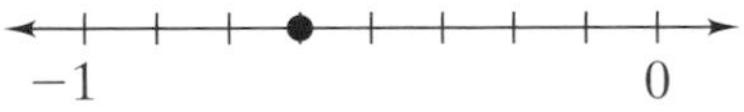

26.

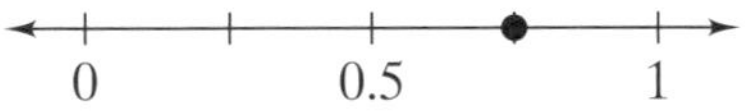

27. < **28.** > **29.** < **30.** > **31.** $-4\frac{1}{4}$°C, −4.3°C, $-4\frac{1}{2}$°C, −4.9°C, −5°C **32.** false **33.** true **34.** false **35.** true

36.

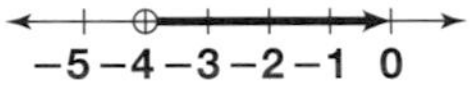

37.

38.

39.

40. $q < 3$ **41.** $t < 5$ **42.** $v > 16$ **43.** $y \geq -20$ **44.** $16 + p \geq 50$; $p \leq 34$; at least 34 more pages

Chapter 7

Lesson 7-1 pp. 243–244

EXERCISES **1.** Answers may vary. Sample: The first coordinate tells how far to move left or right. The second coordinate tells how far to move up or down. **3.** B **5.** (−1, 1) **9.** *P*

12–17.

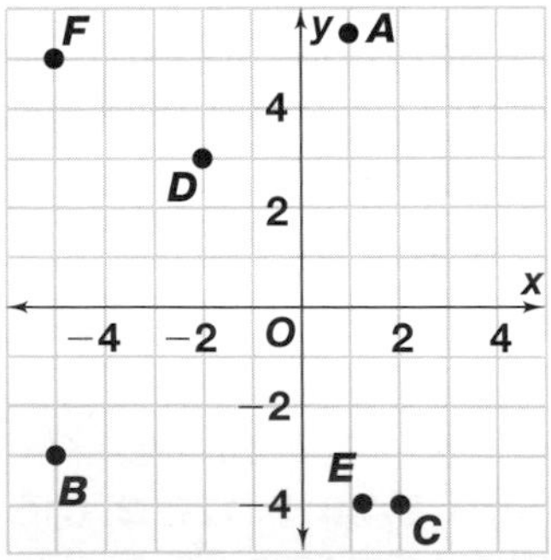

19. (2, −1) **23.** III **27.** *x*-axis **33a.** Africa, **b.** Europe **35.** (−1, 2), (7, 2), (5, 8) **39.** $-4 \leq r$

Lesson 7-2 pp. 248–249

EXERCISES **1.** A horizontal line extends left and right. A vertical line extends up and down. **3.** (7, 2) **5.** 8 units **7.** 12 units **15.** 24 units **17.** 40 units **19.** *x*-axis **23.** *x*-axis **29.** Either (−10, 13) and (4, 13) or (−10, −3) and (4, −3) **31.** −5 **37.** −1.2, −1, −0.12, $1\frac{1}{2}$, 2

Lesson 7-3 pp. 253–254

EXERCISES **1.** The dependent variable's value depends on the independent variable's value.
3. -4 **5.** $y = 15x$ **7.** $-6, 1, 10$ **9.** The independent variable is number of years, and the dependent variable is the height of the tree. **11.** $y = \frac{x}{12}$
13. $y = x - 1$
19. $y = 8n + 5$

Sample Table:

Number of Hours	Earnings ($)
1	13
2	21
3	29
n	$8n + 5$

22. $264 = 3n, n = 88$ books

Lesson 7-4 pp. 258–259

EXERCISES **1.** It is a straight line. **3.** $-1, 0, 1, 2$
5. $-3, 0, 3$

7.

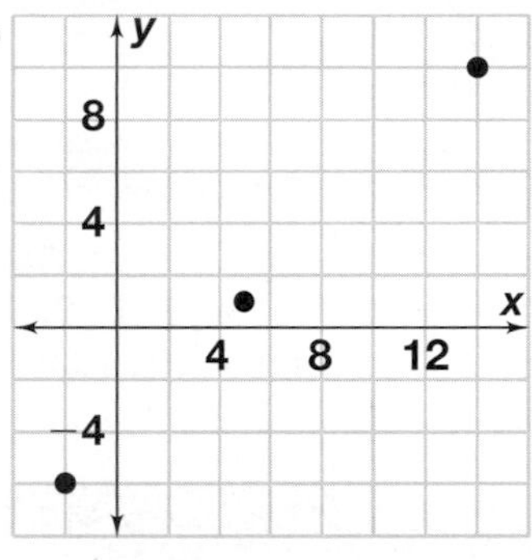

linear

9.

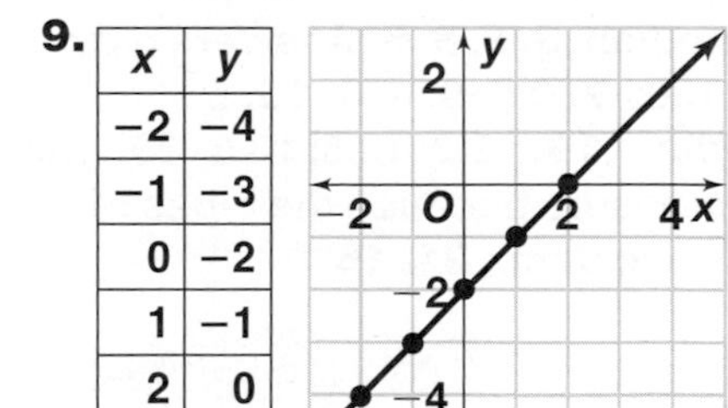

x	y
–2	–4
–1	–3
0	–2
1	–1
2	0

17. 8, 9, add 2 **21.** Not linear; the graph is not a line.

23.

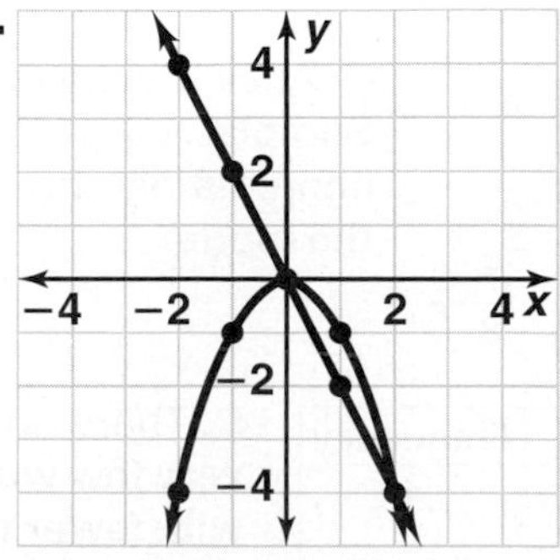

(0, 0), (2, -4); answers may vary. Sample: The graph of $y = -2x$ is a straight line. The graph of $y = -x^2$ is a curve. The graph of $y = -x^2$ is symmetric with respect to the y-axis, but $y = -2x$ is not.

26. $5, 2, 0, -1, -4$

Lesson 7-5 pp. 263–264

EXERCISES **1.** make a table of values, make a graph, or write an equation **3.** 54 books
5. 6 hours **7.** $32.50 **11.** $3\frac{1}{2}$ hours **13.** $5.25
17. Answers will vary. Sample: I can solve the equation for x equals 4. I can complete the pattern in the table to find the y value when x is 4 hours. Or, I can find the point on the graph where $x = 4$, and find the y value for that point.
19. I can look at a given number of hours for each boat and see which has traveled more miles. Students' graphs will vary. See sample in margin.

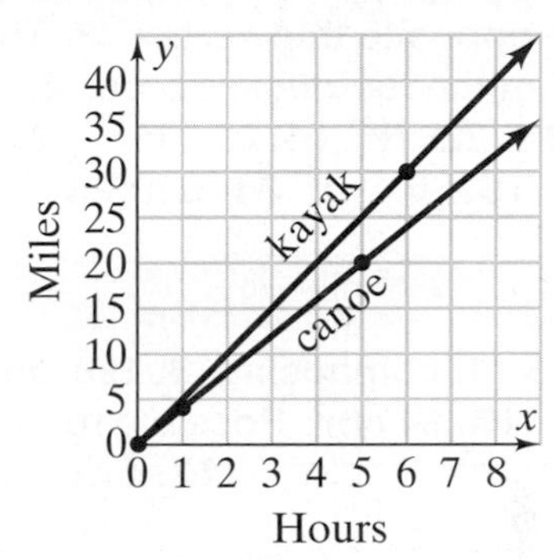

Chapter Review pp. 268–269

EXERCISES **1.** function **2.** vertical line
3. quadrants **4.** origin **5.** $-2, 1\frac{1}{2}$ **6.** $0.5, -3$ **7.** $-1, 3\frac{1}{4}$ **8.** $4.75, 4$ **9.** 5 **10.** 2 **11.** 26 yards **12 a.** 3, 2 **b.** $-3, -2$ **13.** $25, -15, 22$ **14.** $36, 3, -12$, **15.** The independent variable is the time you spend running. The dependent variable is how far you run.

16.

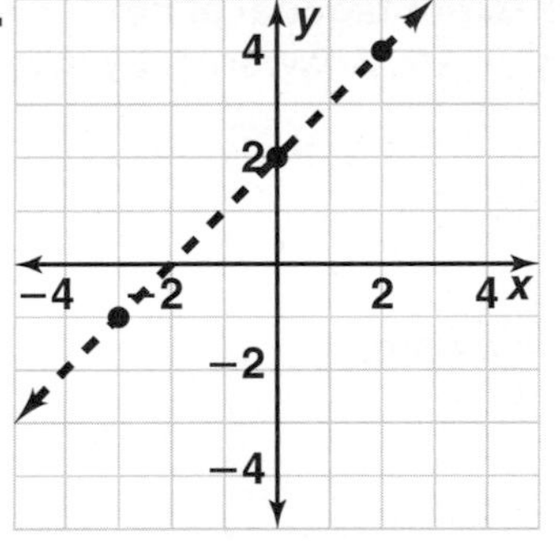

not linear

17.

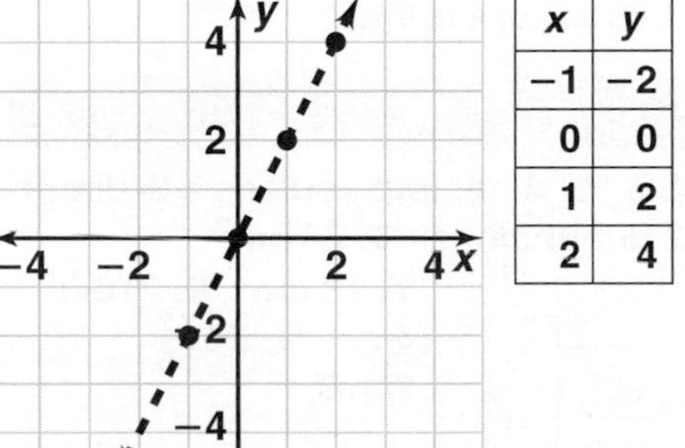

x	y
–1	–2
0	0
1	2
2	4

Selected Answers

18. 35 miles; Students' tables will vary. See sample below.

Hours	Miles
0	0
1	7
3	21
5	35

19. \$18: Students' graphs will vary. **20.** $y = 5x$; \$17.50

Chapter 8

Lesson 8-1 pp. 277–278

EXERCISES **1.** The height of a triangle is the length of the perpendicular segment from a vertex to the base opposite that vertex. **3.** The triangle's area is half of the rectangle's area. **5.** 16 m^2 **9.** 99 yd^2 **11.** 228 ft^2 **14.** 25.2 $in.^2$ **15.** $33\frac{3}{16}$ ft^2, or 33.1875 ft^2 **16.** 86.4 m^2 **21.** 6 ft **25.** 246

Lesson 8-2 pp. 282–283

EXERCISES **1.** composing **3.** 198 cm^2 **7.** 78 cm^2 **11.** 245 m^2 **15.** 84 cm^2; Possible rectangle shown.

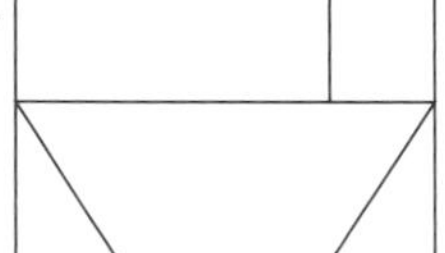

17. 4 m **21.** 9

Lesson 8-3 pp. 288–289

EXERCISES **1.** Answers may vary. Sample: They are both three-dimensional shapes. A prism has two parallel and congruent bases, but a pyramid has only one base. **3.** cone **5.** cylinder **7.** hexagonal prism **9.** pentagonal prism **13.** pyramid **15.** cone **19.** Answers may vary. Sample:

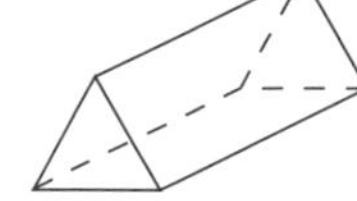

21. Answers may vary. Sample:

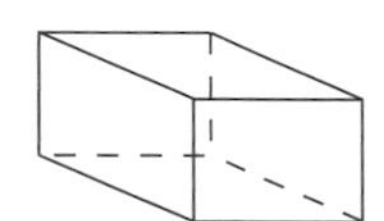

24. $x + 13.79 \leq 25; x \leq 11.21$

Lesson 8-4 pp. 294–295

EXERCISES **1.** A net lets you see a 3-dimensional object in 2 dimensions. **3.** 24 cm^2

5.

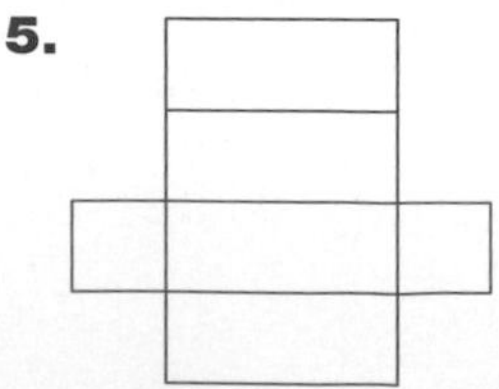

7. 78 cm^2 **9.** 216 ft^2 **17.** $2xy$ **21.** $\frac{2}{3}$ **23.** 6

Lesson 8-5 pp. 301–302

EXERCISES **1.** Volume is the measure of an object's capacity. Area is the measure of the number of square units on the surface of the figure. **3.** $\frac{1}{125}$ cm^3 **5.** 57 ft^3 **7.** $\frac{1}{2}$ unit cubes; $17\frac{1}{2}$ cubic units **11.** $5{,}925\frac{6}{25}$ m^3 **12.** $48\frac{7}{16}$ yd^3 **15.** 72 yd^3 **19.** 15 ft^3 **21.** Answers may vary. Sample: $1\frac{2}{3}$ yd by $1\frac{1}{3}$ yd by $1\frac{3}{3}$ yd **23.** the trailer that is 20 ft by $8\frac{1}{2}$ ft by $7\frac{1}{2}$ ft; 357 ft^3 **27.** 63 ft^2

Chapter Review pp. 304–305

EXERCISES **1.** faces **2.** pyramid or cone **3.** net **4.** parallelogram **5.** volume **6.** 48 ft^2 **7.** 187.72 m^2 **8.** 210 $in.^2$ **9.** 168 ft^3 **10.** 648 m^3 **11.** triangular prism **12.** rectangular pyramid **13.** cylinder **14.** 40 $in.^2$ **15.** 122 m^2 **16.** 1,224 ft^2 **17.** $1\frac{67}{125}$ m^3 **18.** $6{,}303\frac{1}{3}$ ft^3 **19.** $795\frac{1}{5}$ $in.^3$ **20.** $15\frac{5}{8}$ ft^3

Chapter 9

Lesson 9-1 pp. 313–314

EXERCISES **1.** Answers may vary. Sample: Add the data and divide the sum by 5. **3.** 6 **5.** 5 **9.** 105 **13.** 43.75 minutes **15.** 50; increases **19.** 10.2 **29.** 19.341

Lesson 9-2 pp. 317–318

EXERCISES **1.** median **3.** 8; 8 **5.** Answers may vary. Sample: 60, 100. **7.** 0.5 **9.** 475 **13.** 8 **15.** none **17.** median **19.** 13.2; 13.5; 13.5 **23.** The mode is the best measure because the types of shoes are not numeric data. **31.** 15

Lesson 9-3 pp. 321–322

EXERCISES **1.** Answers may vary. Sample: Both the dot plot and frequency table show the data grouped in an easy-to-read way.

3.

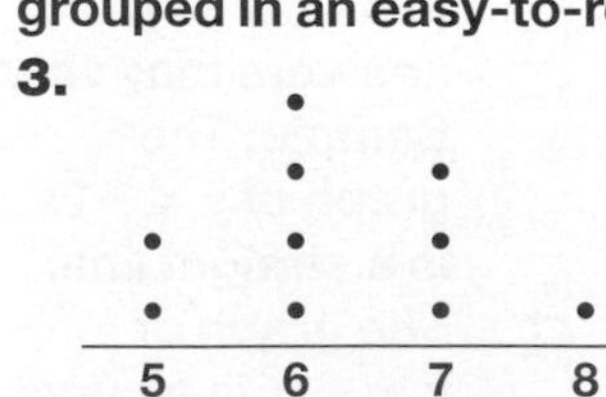

5. Answers may vary. Sample: A dot plot immediately shows the mode.

7.

Type of Car	Tally	Frequency
Compact	IIII	4
Mid-size	III	3
SUV	II	2
Wagon	I	1
Pick-up	II	2

9. There are very few words with fewer than 3 letters.

11. 1.7 m **15.** the number of organisms in a sample **19.** Check students' work. **23.** 60

Lesson 9-4 pp. 325–326

EXERCISES **1.** the median of the upper half of the data **3.** one quarter

5. 14

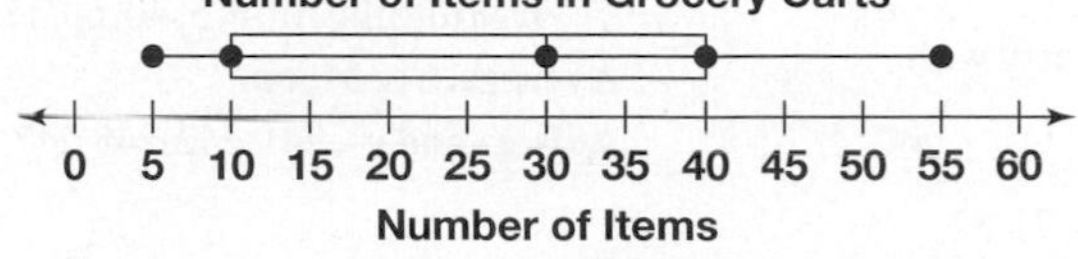

7 a. about three fourths **b.** number of ice cream flavors **13.** Answers may vary. Sample: 1, 2, 3, 4, 5, 6, 7, 8—the mean is 4.5, the lower quartile is 2.5, and the upper quartile is 6.5; each of these is the mean of two different data values.

15.

Minutes	Tally	Frequency
20	I	1
25	III	3
35	II	2
45	III	3
60	I	1

Lesson 9-5 pp. 329–331

EXERCISES **1.** frequency **3.** 25

5.

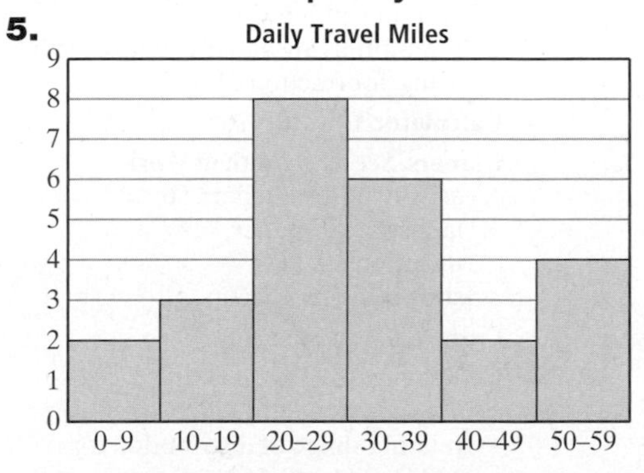

7. 32 **9.** Answers may vary. Sample: The greatest number of cars were washed between 3 P.M. and 4:59 P.M. **13.** Sample: List the frequencies from least to greatest. The median is the middle number. **15.** \$400; \$479.94; Multiply the lower bound (or upper bound) for each interval by the frequency and then add all the results. **17.** 3.5

Lesson 9-6 pp. 336–338

EXERCISES **1.** The range is the difference between the highest and lowest value, so it describes variability in the whole data set. The IQR is the difference between the lower quartile and the upper quartile, so it describes the variability in the middle range of the data values. **3a.** 3 **b.** The range of the middle half of the rainfall values is 3. **5.** Comparing MAD, 7 > 3, so there is more variability in the range of rainfall in July. The average distance to the mean is greater **7.** 2.3 **9.** 6.3 **11.** 9.5 **19.** It increases the MAD; the 0 is an outlier and it pulls the mean down, which increases the MAD. **21.** 0; 0

26.

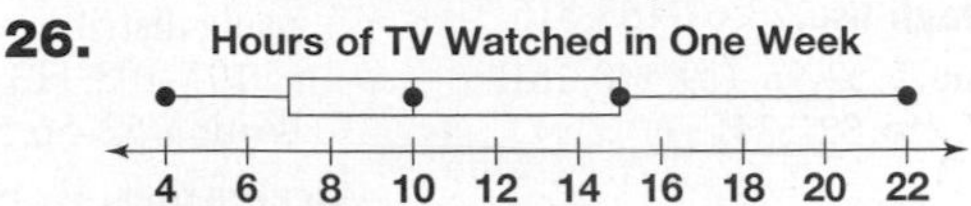

Lesson 9-7 pp. 341–343

EXERCISES **1.** symmetry **3.** No peaks, no symmetry; clusters around $\frac{1}{2}$–1 and 3–3$\frac{1}{2}$. Gap between 1 and 3. **13.** Check students' answers.

Lesson 9-8 pp. 346–348

EXERCISES **1.** not **3 a.** Yes **b.** No **5.** Yes; likely answers include numbers greater than or equal to zero. **7.** No; there is just one answer. **11.** not biased **13.** not biased **19.** Bar graph; the data is categorical so a histogram would not be appropriate.

Chapter Review pp. 350–351

EXERCISES **1.** C **2.** A **3.** G **4.** E **5.** B **6.** mean: 45, median: 49, mode: 50 **7.** mean: 6, median: 7, mode: 9

8.

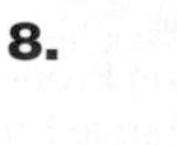

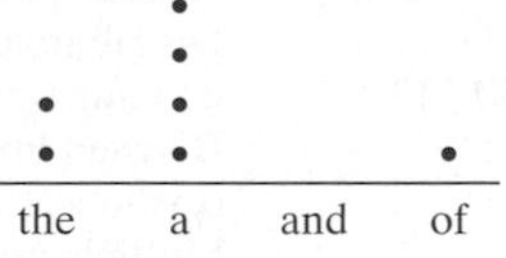

9.

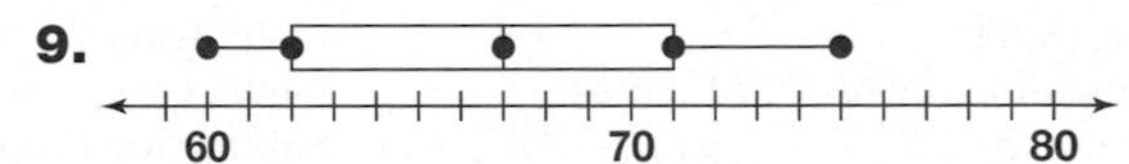

10.

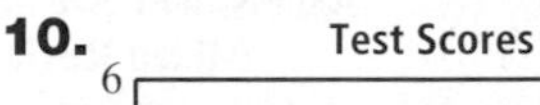

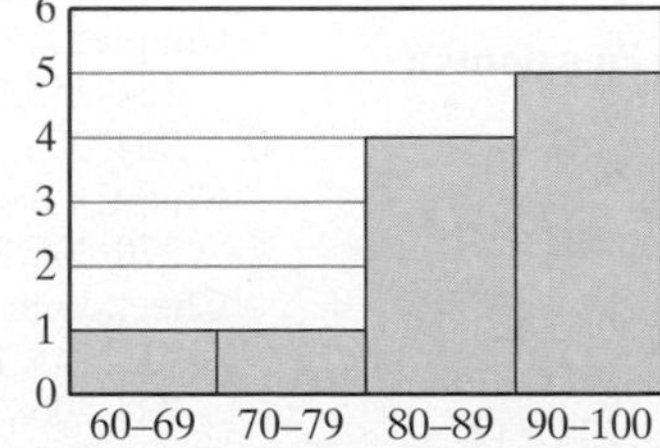

11. MAD: about 1.06, IQR: 2 **12.** the data have symmetry and cluster around 11; the fact that the data is clustered means that the data does not vary greatly **13.** no; there is only one answer **14.** biased; the words greasy and fresh could influence the answers

Index

Index

F

G

H

I

K

L

M

N

O

Index

S

X

Y

Z

Acknowledgments

Staff Credits

The people who make up the Prentice Hall Math team—representing design services, editorial, editorial services, educational technology, marketing, market research, photo research and art development, production services, publishing processes, and rights & permissions—are listed below. Bold type denotes core team members.

Dan Anderson, Carolyn Artin, Nick Blake, **Stephanie Bradley,** Kyla Brown, Patrick Culleton, Katherine J. Dempsey, **Frederick Fellows, Suzanne Finn,** Paul Frisoli, Ellen Granter, **Richard Heater,** Betsey Krieble, Lisa La Vallee, Christine Lee, Kendra Lee, Cheryl Mahan, **Carolyn McGuire,** Eve Melnechuk, Terri Mitchell, Jeffrey Paulhus, Mark Roop-Kharasch, Marcy Rose, Rashid Ross, Irene Rubin, Siri Schwartzman, Vicky Shen, **Dennis Slattery,** Elaine Soares, Dan Tanguay, Tiffany Taylor, Mark Tricca, Paula Vergith, Kristin Winters, Helen Young

Additional Credits

Paul Astwood, Sarah J. Aubry, Jonathan Ashford, Peter Chapman, Patty Fagan, Tom Greene, Kevin Keane, Mary Landry, Jon Kier, Dan Pritchard, Sara Shelton, Jewel Simmons, Ted Smykal, Steve Thomas, Michael Torocsik, Maria Torti

TE Design

Susan Gerould/Perspectives

Illustration Credits

Kenneth Batelman: 129
Joel Dubin: 160
Trevor Johnston: 130
XNR Productions: 150

Additional Artwork:

Rich McMahon; Ted Smykal

Photography

Front Cover: Wolfgang Kaehler/CORBIS
Back Cover: Ian Cartwright/Getty Images

Front Matter: Page xi, David Young-Wolff/PhotoEdit, Inc.; **xii,** STUDIO CARLO DANI/Animals Animals; xiii, Tony Freeman/PhotoEdit; **xiv,** Faidley/Agliolo/SuperStock; **xv,** Theo Allofs/Corbis; **xvi,** Pearson Education; **xvii,** AP Photo/The Grand Rapids Press, Lance Wynn; **xx,** 2004 Jay Wade www.JayWade.com; **xxi,** AFP Photo/Don Emmert/Corbis.

Chapter 1: Page 3, Andrew Leyerle/Dorling Kindersley; **4,** Mitch Kezar/Getty Images, Inc.; **7,** Jonathan Nourok/PhotoEdit Inc.; **8,** Lori Adamski Peek/Getty Images, Inc.; **10,** John Moore; **11,** Nathan Benn/Corbis; **13,** Richard Haynes; **14,** © Syracuse Newspapers/Dick Blume/The Image Works; **15,** AP Photo/Tom Gannam; **18,** Richard Haynes; **19,** David Young-Wolff/PhotoEdit Inc.; **19 bl,** PictureQuest; **20,** Bob Daemmrich/The Image Works; **21,** Royalty-Free/Corbis; **23,** Richard Hayes; **24,** Tony Freeman/PhotoEdit; **25,** Marc Romanelli/Alamy; 26tl, Richard Haynes; **29,** David Young-Wolff/PhotoEdit; **31,** Chad Slatter/Getty Images, Inc.; **31,** Courtesy of Glenda Powers/Fotolia LLC.; **33,** John Moore; **35,** Toyofumi Mori/Getty Images;

Chapter 2: Page 45, Vanessa Vick/Photo Researchers, Inc.; **46,** Richard Haynes; **47,** Tom Prettyman/PhotoEdit; **48,** Index Stock Imagery, Inc.; **50,** ThinkStock/SuperStock; **52,** Getty Images; **54 tl,** Richard Haynes; **54 mr,** Richard Haynes; **56,** NASA; **57,** Monkey Business/Fotolia LLC.; **58,** Peter Beck/Corbis; **59,** Russ Lappa; **62,** Richard Haynes; **63,** Richard Haynes; **65,** Image Source/Superstock, Inc.; **65 bl,** Richard Haynes; **67,** National Geographic Society; **68,** David Young-Wolff/Photo Edit; **71,** Richard Haynes; **72,** Digital Vision/Getty Images; **75,** RubberBall Productions/Index Stock; **76,** Dianna Blell/Peter Arnold, Inc.

Chapter 3 Page 85, Blair Seitz/Photo Researchers, Inc.; **86,** Scott Payne/FoodPix; **87 bl,** Wally McNamee/Corbis; 87 tl, Richard Haynes; **88,** Prentice Hall; **89,** Bob Daemmrich/Photo Edit, **90,** Frank Zullo/Photo Researchers; **91,** Richard Haynes; **92,** Terry W. Eggers; **93,** Prof. G. Schatten/Science Photo Library/Photo Researchers, Inc.; **94,** Tom Carter/PhotoEdit; **97,** Jeremy Horner/Corbis; **98,** Richard Haynes; **99,** Osterreichische Post AG; **100,** Rhoda Sidney/PhotoEdit; **101,** Steve Cole/Getty Images; **102,** Jeff Greenberg/PhotoEdit; **103,** Tom Stewart/Corbis; **104 mr,** Richard Haynes; **104 ml,** Russ Lappa; **106,** Tony Freeman/PhotoEdit; **107,** Spencer Grant/Photo Edit; **108,** Richard Haynes; **112,** Richard Haynes; **117,** Dario/Fotolia;

Chapter 4: Page 125, Courtesy of Felix Pergande/Fotolia LLC; **126,** Richard Haynes; **127,** age footstock/SuperStock; **128,** Silver Burdett & Ginn/Pearson Education; **131,** John Moore; **132,** Courtesy of karandaev/Fotolia; **133,** Richard Haynes; **134,** Richard Haynes; **136,** Dan McCoy/Rainbow; **136 bl,** Richard Haynes; **137,** Alan Linda Detrick/Grant Heilman Photography, Inc.; **139,** Prentice Hall; **141 tl,** Russ Lappa; **141 bl,** Richard Haynes; **143,** Ariel Skelley/Corbis; **145,** Richard Haynes; **146,** Adam Smith/Getty Images, Inc.; **149,** Joseph Nettis/Photo Researchers, Inc.

Chapter 5: Page 159, Courtesy of maigi/Fotolia LLC; **160 bl,** Richard Haynes; **162,** Russ Lappa; **163,** LWA-Dann Tardif/CORBIS; **164 tr,** Richard Haynes; **165 tr,** Richard Haynes; **166,** Michael Newman/PhotoEdit; **169,** AP Photo/The Grand Rapids Press, Lance Wynn; **170,** Courtesy of LituFalco/Fotolia LLC; **171,** Richard Haynes; **174,** Courtesy of Anastasia Tsarskaya/Fotolia LLC; **175,** , Richard Haynes; **181,** © Jupiterimages/Thinkstock; **183 tr,** Richard Haynes; **185,** David Hanover/Getty Images, Inc.; **187,** The Academy of Natural Science/Corbis; **188,** Dennis MacDonald/PhotoEdit; **192,** Superstock, Inc.; **193,** Richard Haynes.

Chapter 6: Page 205, Frank Siteman/IndexStock; **206,** Neal Preston/Corbis; **208,** Rene Frederick/Getty Images; **209,** Corbis; **210,** Tom Carter/PhotoEdit; **213,** Courtesy of Morten Heiselberg/Fotolia LLC; **217,** Richard Haynes; **218 ml,** Courtesy of Jérôme SALORT/Fotolia LLC; **218 mr,** Courtesy of Serenityphoto/Fotolia LLC; **223,** 1986 James Mayo/Chicago Tribune; **224,** Tony Freeman/PhotoEdit; **226,** Mike Dobel/Masterfile; **228,** AFP Photo/Don Emmert/Corbis.

Chapter 7: Page 239, Science VU/Visuals Unlimited; **242,** Myrleen Ferguson Cate/PhotoEdit; **247,** Courtesy of auremar/ Fotolia LLC; **250,** Jack Kurtz/The Image Works; **257 tl & br,** Richard Haynes; **259,** Sally & Derk Kuper.

Chapter 8: Page 273, Jeff Greenberg/Peter Arnold, Inc.; **274,** Richard Haynes; **275,** Tim Thompson/Getty Images, Inc.; **278,** Tony Hopewell/Getty Images, Inc.; **279,** Richard Haynes; **280,** AP/Wide World Photos; **284,** Stephen Simpson/Getty Images, Inc.; **285,** ml, mm, mr, & tr, Russ Lappa; **286,** Royalty Free/ Corbis; **287,** Courtesy of Tetra Images/Alamy; **288 ml,** Tony Freeman/PhotoEdit; **288 mr,** R.M. Arakaki/International Stock; **288 br;** Courtesy of Claudio Colombo/Fotolia LLC; **288 bl,** John Elk III/Stock Boston; **292,** Courtesy of Amir Kaljikovic/Fotolia LLC; **297,** Richard Haynes; **299,** Zigmund Leszcynski/Animals Animals.

Chapter 9: Page 309, Mark Newman/Alamy; **310,** Richard Haynes; **311,** Bob Daemmrich/Stock Boston; **312,** STUDIO CARLO DANI/Animals Animals; **314,** Gary Braasch/Getty Images, Inc.; **315,** Richard Haynes; **316,** Dick Blume/Syracuse Newspaper/The Image Works; **317,** Richard Haynes; **319,** Photo Courtesy of Adidas America, Public Relations Office; **321,** Craig Lovell/Corbis; **323,** Nancy Sheehan/PhotoEdit; **324,** Courtesy of Lorraine Swanson/Fotolia LLC; **328,** Jeff Greenberg/The Image Works; **329,** Courtesy of Maximus/Fotolia LLC; **340,** Courtesy of corepics/Fotolia LLC; **342,** Richard Haynes; **346,** Courtesy of Dmitry Naumov/Fotolia LLC.

Additional Credits:

Chapter 1: Whole chapter taken from Chapter 1 of *Prentice Hall Mathematics Course 1,* Global Edition.
Chapter 2: Whole chapter taken from Chapter 3 of *Prentice Hall Mathematics Course 1,* Global Edition.
Chapter 3: Lessons 1, 2, 3, 4, and 5 taken from Chapter 4 of *Prentice Hall Mathematics Course 1,* Global Edition. Lessons 6 and 7 taken from *Prentice Hall Mathematics Course 1,* Common Core Edition.
Chapter 4: Whole chapter taken from Chapter 6 of *Prentice Hall Mathematics Course 1,* Global Edition.
Chapter 5: Lessons 1, 2, 6, and 7 taken from Chapter 7 of *Prentice Hall Mathematics Course 1,* Global Edition. Lesson 5 taken from Chapter 6 of *Prentice Hall Mathematics Course 2,* Global Edition. Lessons 3, 4, and 8 taken from *Prentice Hall Mathematics Course 1,* Common Core Edition.
Chapter 6: Lessons 1 and 2 taken from Chapter 11 of *Prentice Hall Mathematics Course 1,* Global Edition. Lessons 3, 5, and 6 taken from Chapter 12 of *Prentice Hall Mathematics Course 1,* Global Edition.
Chapter 7: Lessons 1, 2, 3, and 5 taken from *Prentice Hall Mathematics Course 1,* Common Core Edition. Lesson 4 taken from Chapter 11 of *Prentice Hall Mathematics Course 1,* Global Edition.
Chapter 8: Whole chapter taken from Chapter 9 of *Prentice Hall Mathematics Course 2,* Global Edition.
Chapter 9: Lessons 1, 2, and 3 taken from Chapter 2 of *Prentice Hall Mathematics Course 2,* Global Edition. Lessons 4, 5, 6, 7, and 8 taken from *Prentice Hall Mathematics Course 1,* Common Core Edition.